The Bacteria

VOLUME II: METABOLISM

THE BACTERIA

A TREATISE

Volume I: Structure
Volume II: Metabolism
Volume III: Biosynthesis
Volume IV: Growth
Volume V: Heredity

The Bacteria

A TREATISE ON STRUCTURE AND FUNCTION

edited by

I. C. Gunsalus

Department of Chemistry
University of Illinois
Urbana, Illinois

Roger Y. Stanier

Department of Bacteriology
University of California
Berkeley, California

VOLUME II: METABOLISM

1961

ACADEMIC PRESS • *NEW YORK AND LONDON*

ACADEMIC PRESS INC.

111 FIFTH AVENUE
NEW YORK 3, N. Y.

United Kingdom Edition
Published by
ACADEMIC PRESS INC. (LONDON) LTD.

17 OLD QUEEN STREET, LONDON, S.W. 1

Library of Congress Catalog Card Number 59-13831

PRINTED IN THE UNITED STATES OF AMERICA

CONTRIBUTORS TO VOLUME II

H. A. BARKER, *Department of Biochemistry, University of California, Berkeley, California*

M. I. DOLIN, *Biology Division, Oak Ridge National Laboratory, Oak Ridge, Tennessee*

DAVID M. GELLER, *Department of Pharmacology, Washington University School of Medicine, St. Louis, Missouri*

I. C. GUNSALUS, *Department of Chemistry, University of Illinois, Urbana, Illinois*

MARTIN D. KAMEN, *Graduate Department of Biochemistry, Brandeis University, Waltham, Massachusetts*

L. O. KRAMPITZ, *Department of Microbiology, School of Medicine, Western Reserve University, Cleveland, Ohio*

W. D. MCELROY, *Department of Biology, Johns Hopkins University, Baltimore, Maryland*

JACK W. NEWTON, *Pioneering Laboratory for Microbial Chemistry, Northern Utilization Research and Development Division, Agricultural Research Service, U. S. Department of Agriculture, Peoria, Illinois*

H. J. ROGERS, *National Institute for Medical Research, Mill Hill, London, England*

C. W. SHUSTER, *Department of Bacteriology, University of California, Berkeley, California*

LUCILE SMITH, *Department of Biochemistry, Dartmouth Medical School, Hanover, New Hampshire*

W. A. WOOD, *Department of Agricultural Chemistry, Michigan State University, East Lansing, Michigan*

PREFACE

The gross metabolism of microorganisms in energy liberating reactions and pathways has for the most part followed upon the analogous studies of mammalian tissues and of yeast cells. Such studies have been made possible by the abundance of the latter materials and the inclination and affiliation of early enzymologists. In many instances the record of compounds and pathways among the vast array of microorganisms is far from complete. Nevertheless the presently available data show with abundant clarity the occurrence of fundamental differences in catalysts, pathways, and energy coupling steps among the bacteria and between these organisms and mammalian and yeast cells. If the present volume makes evident the gaps and incongruities in knowledge which helps to foster clarification of the actual properties of the individual types of bacteria, the impetus for the present "source book" aspect of this volume will fulfill the objective of the authors and editors.

The variation in pathways among the bacteria and the quantitative preponderance of these pathways under different conditions has in many cases served as a refined tool for the recognition and clarification of processes relatively minor in other cells. One may hope that a view of current understanding, usually of a role in energy supply pathways frequently resulting from enrichment methods of isolation, can be useful to mature investigators and to the growing body of students whose education and research is fostered by the ready availability of such information.

An informed concept of energy liberating patterns is important to a critical appraisal of the biosynthetic pathways and growth phenomena in bacteria now assembled in volumes 3 and 4 of this series. This is true in the sense of reaction types, the raw materials furnishing the monomers for cell structure, and as a basis for an understanding of the limiting factors in various aspects of growth. The rapid rate at which information accumulates in this area should not outdate present viewpoints if the generally held concept of the state of completeness of the data and the validity of the ideas of basic principles considered to prevail in metabolism as related to cell behavior are at all accurate. Thus with the main emphasis shifted to investigations of other aspects of cellular behavior, one may expect for energy metabolism that gaps in knowledge will eliminate gradually, and some hypotheses altered, but the bases for reasoning will, in the main, be sustained.

The editors are appreciative of this opportunity to thank the authors of this volume for their cooperation and patience in the removal of partial overlap among the chapters and with the difference in rate in which some of the chapters became available. Again we have refrained from suggesting style or choice of material to the authors on the thesis that the selection of material and the freshness of viewpoint of each author is of far greater value than any loss from lack of uniformity. We also wish to express at this time our appreciation to the publishers and to the members of their staff for constant help and encouragement in the many tasks accompanying the assemblage and preparation of this volume.

I. C. Gunsalus
R. Y. Stanier

February 1961

CONTENTS OF VOLUME II

5. The Dissimilation of High Molecular Weight Substances 257

H. J. Rogers

6. Survey of Microbial Electron Transport Mechanisms 319

M. I. Dolin

7. Cytochrome Systems in Aerobic Electron Transport 365

Lucile Smith

The Bacteria

A TREATISE ON STRUCTURE AND FUNCTION

VOLUME I: STRUCTURE

VOLUME III: BIOSYNTHESIS

VOLUME IV: GROWTH

CHAPTER 1

Energy-Yielding Metabolism in Bacteria

I. C. GUNSALUS AND C. W. SHUSTER

I. Metabolism and the Cell*

Fermentation, oxidation, and photosynthesis (light-driven reactions) compose the quantitatively major portion of cellular metabolism. They are also the principal sources of cellular energy supply. The presence in cells of large amounts of catalysts and intermediates of these pathways has simplified both the recognition of the major energy-mobilizing reactions and formulation of the main pathways of carbon and energy flow. Participation of the microbe as experimental material in this advance has permitted a par-

* Abbreviations used in this chapter: DPN, DPNH—Diphosphopyridine nucleotide, reduced; TPN, TPNH—Triphosphopyridine nucleotide, reduced; ADP, ATP—Adenosine diphosphate, Adenosine triphosphate; IDP, ITP—Inosine diphosphate, Inosine triphosphate; DPT—Diphosphothiamine; CoA—Coenzyme A; PEP—Phosphoenolpyruvate; KDPG—2-Keto-3-deoxy-6-phosphogluconate; FP, $FP_{red.}$—Flavoprotein, reduced; fH_4—Tetrahydrofolic acid; N^{10}-formyl-fH_4—N^{10}-Formyltetrahydrofolic acid; N^5,N^{10}-methenyl-fH_4—N^5,N^{10}-Methenyl tetrahydrofolic acid; N^5,N^{10}-methylene-fH_4—N^5,N^{10}-Methylene tetrahydrofolic acid; RNA—Ribonucleic acid; DNA—Deoxyribonucleic acid; Pi—Inorganic (ortho) phosphate; HMG-CoA—Hydroxymethylglutaryl CoA; Glucose-U-C^{14}—Uniformly labeled glucose-C^{14}.

tial visualization of the energy-yielding and material flow machinery serving each of a wide variety of microorganisms. While not complete, this knowledge is sufficiently advanced to provide a chemical basis for comprehending the properties and behavior of specific microbial species. The unity of material and processes[1] in living cells has been most useful in guiding initial studies of little known organisms. Also, the elucidation of new reactions and pathways becomes easier as the recorded cases of systems nature has found workable (thermodynamically probable), both for making energy available biologically and for making essential metabolites, are extended.

Fortunately, the principles and reaction types found in elucidating the energy-furnishing pathways have proved useful in guiding the study of biosynthetic reactions and whole cell investigations of active transport, adaptation, growth and its control, and to a more limited extent, in understanding the chemical changes which accompany modification of genetic characteristics by mutation, transformation, etc. The plan of Volumes II, III, and IV of the present sequence follows the chronology of knowledge accumulation and the context of its application to biological problems. This places the quantitatively major energy transformations in Volume II, the chemistry of the biogenesis of cellular components in Volume III, and the biology and chemistry of growth and general physiology—the coupling of the energy metabolism and biosynthetic reactions and adding of the restrictions of biological behavior—in Volume IV. Volume V, dealing with heredity, will employ the principles and data of Volumes II to IV to an extent dictated by the moderate penetration of molecular understanding into the information and code systems of biology.

The function of the present chapter is to consider problems of energy metabolism which apply to all cells and to ask how far we have progressed, and can progress, in relating this information to the problems of the individual cell—bacteria being, in the main, unicellular organisms. The viewpoint is one of optimism that energy (equilibria), specificity and molecular interactions can tell more of cellular behavior and its control than is now understood. The principal questions concern the quantitative relationships of biologically available energy released by glycolysis, oxidation, and light to chemical bond transformation to whole cell requirements. These questions are actually asked of the data presented in subsequent chapters of this volume.

Undoubtedly the present chapter will raise more questions than it will answer, for the properties which suit the microbe to the solving of pertinent biological problems ask questions in many areas and call for an excellence in many disciplines, not all of which have become the common property of all investigators of the many microorganisms in nature. Bacteria show an increasing ability to attract investigators from a broad area of physical and biological sciences; the knowledge and skills thus acquired greatly enrich the science of microbiology and the life of the microbiologist, student and investigator. It is with the objective of contributing to the ease of communication and more effective cooperation of multiple attacks on biological and chemical questions with which the microbe can deal that this attempt at an orderly relating of development and status is made.

A. PROGRESS AND PROBLEMS

Excellent reviews, both critical and authoritative, concerning recent progress in understanding the energy metabolism of bacteria are available; reference to these is made both in this chapter and in the following chapters. In addition, the following chapters present the data in the perspective of their growth and relationship to the microbic processes in recapitulation and evaluation as a basis for further study. Some subjects are, for the moment, relatively complete; a few are changing rapidly; and others, e.g., oxidative energy coupling, barely opened at the chemical level. The specialist can expect to find little beyond a current summary in the area of his immediate interest. It is for the microbiologist with pressing preoccupation in other areas of the subject, the nonmicrobiologist seeking a convenient tool to explore and/or analyze a biological or chemical question, the students, young and old, that the statement of progress and problems is intended.

In biology, the *concept of unity* and the *principle of variety* in relation to structure and function have provided a viewpoint with which to evaluate, explore, and experiment. Kluyver and van Niel,[2] in 1956, attributed to the microbe a major role in extending our insight into the essence of metabolism ". . . owing mainly to its impressive metabolic diversity." Thus Kluyver voiced, near the end of his career, his belief in the *principle of variety* as a biological factor among organisms affording a tool to solve problems.

Thirty years earlier, the *concept of unity* arose from Kluyver's recognition as an underlying principle, in the apparent confusion of biological oxidation, of the uniformity among organisms of the mechanisms of hydrogen transport which, by a series of single-step reactions, accomplish biological energy release. Based on a common material substrate, a common reaction sequence was seen to occur in all cells. With this insight, Kluyver had founded comparative biochemistry.[1] These two principles, *unity* and *variety*, underlie the utility of the microbe as a tool for chemical and biological investigation. On their validity rest the general principles elaborated via study of microbial systems. (An excellent account of Kluyver's contributions written by van Niel may be found in the recounting of Kluyver's life.[4])

With respect to comparative biochemistry, it might be appropriate here to urge the student to consider now the variety, perhaps the "uncomparative," of biochemistry—those details of fine structure wherein reside specificity, uniqueness, and the genetic differences which underlie the metabolic differences. Today, comparative biochemistry is as valid as the day Kluyver conceived this generalization; the only change has been the documentation of the hypothesis as a working principle in nature. Knowledge of many an obscure organism became possible because Kluyver had suggested borrowing data from the better documented cases in order to make a start. The need to teach these principles on which to build will continue. The counsel to look for variety is the urge to seek still other hypotheses to guide future investigations and to uncover the next valid and useful generalizations.

Many of the reactions and routes of supply for biologically available energy are known, and an estimate of the magnitude of the remaining problem is possible. The pattern needs to be completed and further analysis made of the mechanisms of action of catalysts as reactants and of "concerted reaction mechanisms," along with other problems. More pressing now, perhaps, are the problems applied to the cell: a reappraisal of the knowledge and its application to metabolism at a cellular level. Among these definable cellular problems are: (1) the availability of substances as substrates based on catalysts for their uptake and turnover at rates compatible with cellular needs, (2) equilibria of sufficient driving force to release free energy for cellular function, (3) coupling mechanisms to convert the available energy to the manifold work functions of the organism, and (4) the control of coupling, rates, and specificity to reproduce the cell and/or perform its work and maintenance functions.

B. Fitness of the Microbe

As an investigative tool, the microbe may well be judged by its contributions made to metabolism; as such, the record is impressive. Yeasts contributed through the battles of Pasteur and Liebig; they have continued to serve modern biochemistry. Highly remembered, as described in the first chapter of Harden, "Alcoholic Fermentation,"[5] are demonstration of cell-free glycolysis in yeast pressed juice (enzyme extracts) (Buchner[6]), discovery of coenzymes, coenzyme I [diphosphopyridine nucleotide (DPN)], yeast carboxylase acting on pyruvate with diphosphothiamine (DPT) as coenzyme,[7] and the identification of the phosphorylated intermediates of glycolysis, hexosediphosphate, and hexosemonophosphate (see Meyerhof[8]).

An equal or even more impressive list derives from the bacteria. *Pseudomonas saccharophila*, via Doudoroff, contributed sucrose phosphorylase,[9] glucosyl transfer, and the formation of multiple disaccharides.[10] Later, 2-keto-3-deoxy-6-phosphogluconic acid and its aldolase,[11] and a direct route (carbon chain intact) from pentose to ketoglutarate were shown.[12, 12a]

β-Glucose-1-phosphate as a biological intermediate of maltose phosphorolysis and as a step in the formation of α-glucosido-xylose was later added by *Neisseria*.[13] The propionic acid bacteria contributed CO_2 as a heterotrophic metabolite in net fixation (Wood and Werkman[14]), which opened a new era of intermediary metabolism. Recently, their use has shown the second function of B_{12}-coenzyme in carbon chain rearrangement; the movement of the coenzyme A (CoA)-bound carboxyl in the succinyl-methylmalonyl-coenzyme A isomerase;[15] and the role of biotin in transcarboxylation to form propionate in a cyclic nonenergy-requiring system.[16] The clostridia, principally through the efforts of Barker,[17] served to clarify the role of coenzyme A esters in fatty acid oxidation[18] and the function of vitamin B_{12} in coenzyme form[19] as catalyst of carbon chain transfer, from glutamate to β-methyl aspartate.[20] Clostridia also contributed the role of tetrahydrofolic acid (fH_4) in formimino[21] as well as formyl transfer in the generation of phosphate anhydrides.[22] The lactic acid bacteria contributed active acetyl (acetyl phosphate),[23] induced (adaptive) enzyme formation,[24] the existence of lipoic acid,[25] and its role in acyl generation[26] from keto acids, which also opened new approaches to keto acid metabolism.[27] In vitamin B_6 metabolism, these bacteria gave a clue to its active form,[28] coenzyme form,[29] and metabolic role.[30, 31] As auxotrophs resembling mammals in their nutritive requirements, the lactic acid bacteria[32] led to a demonstration of the general synonymy of bacterial growth factors and vitamins (further example of comparative biochemistry) which fostered rapid multiple vitamin assays[33] and the discovery, isolation, and relation to metabolism of a series of vitamin-cofactor prosthetic group substances (see reference 34). *Escherichia coli* contributed extensively to current views of induced enzyme formation,[35] initiated microbial genetics as a study,[36] placed virus studies on a quantitative basis;[37] the related salmonella coupled virus infection and genetic information transfer.[38] Understanding of the role of deoxyribonucleic acid (DNA) in transformation of pneumococci[39] opened the way to new genetic concepts and their chemical implications. Genetic-chemical progress in biological polymer formation has been supported heavily by the microbes: ribonucleic acid (RNA) reactions (RNA-nucleotide diphosphate) by *Azotobacter vinelandii*,[40] DNA in enzyme induction,[41] DNA formation (DNA-nucleoside triphosphate),[42] protein biogenesis by staphylococci[43] and *E. coli*,[44] and amino acid activation by *E. coli*.[45]

This representative but not inclusive list illustrates the extent and scope of indebtedness to microbes for metabolic data and raises the question of the sources of this effectiveness. The answer is not far to seek. It includes (1) speed, (2) variety, (3) adaptability, (4) specificity, and (5) ecological diversity, to list five worthy of brief amplification.

1. Speed and Yield

The high metabolic rate of microbes can be illustrated at many levels; let us take but two examples, growth rate and enzymic activity in extracts. Generation time (time to double protoplasm) approaches 15 minutes in several heterotrophic bacteria, e.g., *E. coli*,[46] *Clostridium welchii*,[47] and *Streptococcus faecalis*.[48] The doubling time for mammalian cells in tissue culture approaches one day (24 hours), thus, a rate advantage of about 100-fold favoring the microbe, i.e., 24 hr. $\times$ 60'/15' = 96. The cause is not clear, although one could cite correlations of growth rate with size,[49] surface/volume ratio, and ratio of genetic material to cytoplasm.

A comparison of metabolic rates of *whole cells* (dry weight) yields similar figures for both respiration and glycolysis (see Table I). The values correlate inversely with the size relationships[49] as do all the above characteristics (bacteria/muscle cell = 10^2; bacteria/yeast = 10^1). A similar rate advantage is observed with *soluble enzymes* and *enzyme systems*, expressed as activity per unit weight or amount of protein (see Table II). In the latter case, one could attribute the higher specific activity to smaller enzyme (lower molecular weight per active site), higher turnover number (TON) (higher catalytic activity per active site or more active sites per enzyme), fewer enzymes per cell (higher per cent of protein in each, or given enzymes), or less padding with unessential material. The source of higher activity in two cases of energy pathway enzymes is attributable to more enzyme per cell: β-galactosidase,[50] 6 % of soluble cell protein, and formyl kinase[51] crystalline enzyme after 10-fold purification from cell extract.

TABLE I

RELATIVE SIZE AND METABOLIC QUOTIENTS

Organism or tissue	Cell volume, cm.^{3}	$Q_{O_2}{}^a$	Reference	$Q_G{}^b$	Reference
Rat liver	—	9	228	0.15	228
Rat brain	—	14	228	0.9	228
Saccharomyces cerevisiae	10^{-10}	40–80 (glucose)	228	3.0	229
Escherichia coli	10^{-12}	800 (acetate)	230	19	231
Azotobacter vinelandii	10^{-12}	4200 (acetate)	232	c	—
Streptococcus faecalis	10^{-12}	186 (pyruvate)	233	13	225

^{a} Q_{O_2} = μl./mg. dry wt./hr.

^{b} Q_G = μmoles glucose utilized/mg. dry wt./hr.

^{c} Anaerobic, no glycolysis.

TABLE II

RELATIVE ENZYME ACTIVITIES OF BACTERIAL AND TISSUE EXTRACTS

Enzyme or system	Bacteria	Specific activity[a]	Reference	Tissue	Specific activity	Reference	Ratio
Pyruvic oxidation	Escherichia coli	0.7	234	Pig heart	0.31	235	2.2
Pyruvic oxidation	Proteus vulgaris	2.9	236	Pigeon breast muscle[b]	0.1	237	29
α-Ketoglutarate oxidation	Escherichia coli	0.62	234	Pig heart[b]	0.23	238	2.7
					0.003	239	207
Succinic thiokinase	Escherichia coli	3.0	240	Spinach	0.013	242	230
	(succinate-adapted)	58	241	Spinach	0.013	242	4460
Amino acid incorporation (leucine)	Escherichia coli	0.03	44	Liver	0.0016	243	19
Butyryl-CoA dehydrogenase	Clostridium kluyveri	0.4	17	Liver	0.001	244	400

[a] Specific activity = μmoles/mg. protein/hr.
[b] Extract of acetone powder.

2. VARIETY AND SPECIFIC SELECTION

The variety of compounds which serve as carbon and energy sources for some microbes is almost without limit[52] (see Chapter 5, p. 258). The working hypothesis of the general microbiologist, experimentally applied in the enrichment, or elective culture, method of Beijerinck, has an excellent record of accomplishment. The proposition as usually stated is: any compound which can react with a negative free energy change ($-\Delta F$) is a potential energy source for some organism, or as frequently stated in more restricted form: any organic compound in nature is broken down by some organism with the return of carbon to the atmosphere. Thus organisms can be isolated by selective enrichment on diverse carbon sources (Chapter 5, p. 260). The metabolic rates on these sources will be high in consequence of their function in the energy release routes. Examples of the use of carefully selected enrichments to solve important metabolic problems, frequently by enhanced enzyme abundance, are well represented among Barker's contributions to microbiology and biochemistry.[17] To list a few: both purines and glycine led to folic acid-mediated energy release systems in Clostridium acidi-urici,[21] and Clostridium cylindrosporum;[22] glutamic acid fermentation led to the role of B_{12}[19] (see Chapter 3), and ethanol-acetate to fatty acid oxidation. The oxidation of aromatic compounds provides an excellent example of the use of unique carbon compounds which permit the recognition of induced enzymes independently of enzymes which are always present to transfer essential metabolites; see Stanier,[53] Evans,[54] or the review of Elsden and Peel.[55] Further specific examples of selection for specific activities and variability of pattern can be found in any general microbiology text,[56] publications of the Delft school of microbiology,[57] or survey of microbic activities.[17, 52]

3. Adaptability

With a given strain selected for its metabolic potential, catalytic activity can be increased many fold by added substrates for enzyme induction by physiological conditions of culture.[58-60] Vitamin level,[61] conditions of pH,[62] and aerobiosis,[63] to mention a few of the latter, are also determinative. Examples could be extended; they will not be cited here, but are discussed where pertinent in other parts of this chapter. As pointed out by Monod,[64] in reference to bacterial growth, these are not subjects of study but the tools of the science.

4. Specificity

At the enzyme level, present data do not indicate the superiority of one organism over another in substrate range or specificity of the enzymes formed. In contrast, at the cellular level, the specific activity, and therefore relatively lower level of side reactions, can be greatly altered through both selection (Section I, B, 2), and adaptation (Section I, B, 3). These changes have been most helpful in tracing pathways and in the further purification of enzymes, i.e., the purification is simplified because of high enough protein[50, 51] (or system[65]) concentration for their physical properties to exert an effect. Also, purification can be accomplished with smaller, and thus manageable, amounts of material. Enhanced enzyme stability not directly attributable to this cause has been observed in several instances. The overlap in methodology to gain the advantages indicated under headings 2, 3, and 4 is apparent.

5. Carbon vs. Energy Economy of Cells

The Doudoroff hypothesis[66] concerns the limiting factor in natural ecological conditions for aerobic and for anaerobic organisms, or conditions of growth. In this view, the limitation during anaerobic growth is energy; during aerobic growth, carbon. Complicated as are the metabolic interactions in whole cells, two primary causes would seem to account in large measure for these conditions: (1) in glycolysis, a low energy yield per substrate mole is caused by incomplete breakdown, i.e., limited electron acceptors; (2) in respiration, excess oxygen as electron acceptor, the competition of many microorganisms, in both number and kind, transforms the carbon to CO_2 by both useful (generating biologically available energy) and uncontrolled oxidation. Furthermore, respiration is generally considered to occur at maximal rate at a lower substrate concentration (principally carbon and phosphate) than does fermentation.[67]

The energy yields of various dismutative (glycolytic) and oxidative reactions are considered in detail in Chapters 2, 3, and 4, and are collected in Section II and in Tables IV and VI of this chapter. One could further argue from the endogenous respiration rates of washed anaerobic and aerobic cells in this same direction; i.e., assimilation of carbon is low in glycolytically produced cells and relatively high in aerobic cells even though grown with limited substrate.[68]

With a given function in mind, one can frequently, almost always, with a little thought and effort, grow and harvest cells for enhanced capacity for one's purpose.

C. PICKUP AND REPLACEMENT

At the time the glycolytic scheme was nearing completion as a sequence of single-step reactions, it was stated that energy-mobilizing and energy-using reactions are linked by a common intermediate.[69] This intermediate was identified as a compound of phosphorus, namely, adenosine triphosphate (ATP).[69]

For a reaction sequence, e.g., glycolysis, to serve as a biologically useful energy source, another requisite was recognized, i.e., the system must operate with a net gain in utilizable energy; some step must pick up a new component. In line with ATP serving as the couple, inorganic (ortho) phosphate was recognized as that compound. The Neuberg (see Chapter 2) methylglyoxal fermentation schemes were recognized to lack, among other qualifications, these energy-coupling steps. If one prefers to consider the thiolesters as intermediates in metabolism, transferring as they do the coupled energy via phosphate incorporation and transfer to form ATP, this is still an accurate statement of the acquisition of energy in biologically available form and its use. These are also the bases of argument in constructing energy balances for microbial fermentations.

Applied to the multiple pathways of microbial *glycolysis*, only two sorts of reactions have been shown to meet these requirements: (1) the dehydrogenation of triosephosphate and (2) oxidative reactions with diphosphothiamine (DPT). The latter concerns two substrates, ketose sugars and

α-keto acids—in glycolysis only pyruvate. With *noncarbohydrate* substrates, two other reactions, those yielding formyl and carbamyl, are considered potential microbial ATP generators. One paper has been published relating glutamyl (glutamine) to ATP generation[70] as a stoichiometrically important bacterial pathway. In actuality, both formyl and carbamyl are carboxyl-generating systems, as are all but one of the substrate-coupled energy-generating reactions; this is an enol phosphate generation by dehydration.

Formyl, as N^{10}-formyl tetrahydrofolic acid (N^{10}-formyl-fH_4), is formed by formimino transfer or hydroxymethyl transfer, followed by oxidation to the formyl derivative; carbamyl is formed from the ureido group of citrulline or of creatinine (*N*-methyl hydantoin).[71] These reactions will be recognized as part of the amino acid and purine fermentation systems; both are discussed by Barker (Chapter 3) and their possible relationship to growth is summarized in Section III of this chapter.

These four reaction types—triosephosphate, DPT-keto oxidation, formyl tetrahydrofolic, and carbamyl—generate ATP by pickup and transfer of inorganic phosphate via carboxyl or potential carboxyl group in one or more bacterial species. Each appears to be an important, or sole, source of ATP energy for the endergonic reactions of biosynthesis and growth. They meet the criteria of pickup and replacement reactions for phosphate and phosphate anhydrides. The stoichiometry of formation and use is considered subsequently.

All cells meet a second type of replacement problem: the maintenance of the compounds in cycles performing metabolic work against a diversion to cellular components by biosynthetic pathways and loss through chemical and enzymic instability. The latter include, for example, the chemical instability of β-keto acids, SH groups, and enzymic hydrolysis of phosphate anhydrides and esters by ATPases, etc. Only quantitative differences exist between the problems of replacement of essential metabolites used for cellular synthesis and as components of cycles liberating energy for cell work—the latter being quantitatively larger.

The calculation of carbon balances for the products of glycolysis usually suffers little from removal of intermediates for cell formation, due to the limited cell formation as a consequence of low energy yield in glycolysis[72] (see also Section III, B). Aerobic, i.e., respiration-powered, growth, energy-rich and carbon-poor, suffers more from need for replacement of cycle components due to enhanced synthesis amounting to 40 % of the carbon turned over in optimum cases (Section IV).[41] Assimilation of carbon into carbohydrate (glycogen) or other storage compounds, not protoplasm, is also quantitatively significant, especially in nitrogen limited growth. This problem is also considered in Section IV of this chapter.

D. Crosspoints and Cycling

Departure from quantitatively important pathways of carbon flow and energy generation occurs in a number of bacteria; the causes for the most part discernible from recurring patterns permitting, in some cases, prediction of behavior. These include:

1. *Multiple patterns* (alternate routes) at essential sites for energy, and biosynthetic intermediate generation such as reactions of hexosemonophosphates, triosephosphates, and pyruvate. Hexosemonophosphate can, in most organisms, lead to oxidation, dehydration, cleavage, or phosphorylation. In each case a sequence is initiated which can lead to triosephosphate, whose oxidation makes energy available as ATP, and carbon skeletons usable as synthetic intermediates. Triosephosphate may become oxidized or reduced or enter a half-dozen sorts of condensation reactions. Pyruvate may be reduced, carboxylated, oxidized, or cleaved, yielding acyl by several routes. Each of these reactions permits initiation of one of several pathways, i.e., the availability of alternative routes.

In case of limitation of some component in a reaction pathway, or cycle, many organisms exhibit bypasses through which energy coupling is not obligatory, thus permitting turnover; for example, inorganic phosphate level for oxidation[73] is insured by phosphatase action.

2. *The absence of a key enzyme*, or limiting amount of one enzyme for substrate turnover to serve in the cellular energy supply system, may shunt substrate to one of the alternate pathways less favorable energetically or for biosynthesis of intermediates. The prime example in carbohydrate fermentation is the loss of fructosediphosphate aldolase leading to initiation of several alternate oxidation and transfer cycles with reduced energy yield per mole of substrate transformed. Product labeling from uniquely labeled substrates, in both products and cell components, will usually divulge the functional pathways.

3. *Secondary enzyme induction*, in the case of accumulation of intermediates due to blocked pathways, or the absence of key substrates blocking feedback, will frequently circumvent situations in which usual intermediates are not available. These cases include response in carbohydrate fermentation to chain length and configuration with alteration in carbohydrate flow patterns and appearance of more complicated product-labeling patterns. Simple cases are the build-up of pyruvate before a metabolic lesion in the energy-coupled pathways of its oxidation with the induction of a bypass oxidase yielding the normal products without energetic coupling,[74] and the

glyoxalate bypass supporting cellular synthesis with two carbon substrates.[75]

4. *Reactions thermodynamically unfavorable to reversal.* Numerous cases are recorded of reversible reactions whose equilibria so strongly favor products that they seem not to serve a quantitatively important role for microbial growth and synthesis in the reverse direction. A frequently quoted example is the lack of evidence for the reversal of kinases in phosphorylation of primary alcohols, i.e., regeneration of hexose carbon skeleton by hydrolysis rather than by transphosphorylation to adenosine diphosphate (ADP), regeneration of phosphoenol pyruvate via oxalacetate or malic enzyme rather than by ATP phosphorylation of pyruvate. The action of phosphatase for carbohydrate esters can be classed under point 3 of this list.

5. *Additional oxidation of pyruvate* leads to more reduced products than triose (lactate and ethanol-CO_2 are triose level), i.e., formation of propionic acid, glycerol, or molecular hydrogen (H_2). Cellular growth yields (see Section III) constitute a practical demonstration of enhanced energy yield.

6. *Tendency to cycle.* Biological catalysis is often viewed as a continuous flow process transforming substrate to products of lower energy content plus cellular material. The compounds formed in the cells may be of either higher or lower energy content per carbon than the substrate. These compounds are also almost certain to have participated in energy-requiring transport reactions. More closely viewed, however, the flow routes comprise a continuous series of interacting cycles of both substrates and cofactors. The cycles of the cofactors are frequently two-step, although three or more steps are not uncommon. Representative of two-step cycles are the oxidation-reduction of electron transport catalysts, and phosphorylation and dephosphorylation between ADP and ATP. Among the catalysts undergoing three or more step cycles are lipoic acid (oxidized, reduced, and acylated), biotin (unsubstituted, carboxylated, and activated—biotin activation requires ATP, but an intermediate has not been identified), and folic acid, which undergoes an even larger number of steps in one-carbon transformation cycles.

The loss of cycle intermediates by side reactions and by cellular synthesis, while not on the main line of energy generation or essential metabolite formation, may be difficult to distinguish from these for reasons of ubiquitous occurrence and essentiality. Specific examples are loss of CO_2 from carbon cycles with at least three known mechanisms for its return to products functional in known cycles, and oxalacetate and ketoglutarate as amino acid precursors.

Detailed documentation of cyclic mechanisms in glycolysis is given in Chapter 2, of respiration in Chapter 4; the energy-liberating cycles are discussed in the following section of this chapter.

II. Energy-Yielding Reactions

A. Carbohydrate Cleavage and Oxidation

Detailed studies of bacterial fermentations during the past ten years have revealed several new routes, as summarized in recent reviews[55, 76, 77] and in Chapter 2 of this volume. Well-known fermentations whose detailed pathways are incompletely understood, and preliminary evidence on more recently recognized ones, suggest the existence of still other mechanisms, e.g., pathways from glucose to propionate,[16, 78] arabinose to α-ketoglutarate,[12] and the fermentation of galactose by lactic acid bacteria.[79] The pathway of breakdown of some carbohydrates and of their formation for cellular constituents, i.e., rhamnose of Gram-positive cell walls,[3] is obscure. Still, it seems not too early to attempt some recognition of optimum routes for cellular energy release and biosynthetic precursor formation. Fermentation of uniquely labeled substrates and quantitative measurements of growth have, in fact, already furnished some clues to unexplained routes and new energy-coupling reactions[55, 108, 109] which require explanation and encourage attempts to construct tentative schemes.

Documentation of the products and mechanisms of bacterial carbohydrate fermentation is available from Chapter 2 of Wood; we shall consider here only the reactions and mechanisms concerned in inorganic phosphate pickup, phosphate anhydride formation transferable to ATP, and the quantitative aspects of growth. In glycolysis, net ATP generation is dependent on inorganic phosphate uptake plus the return of any anhydride phosphate used in priming the carbohydrates to ATP. The ATP used in cell work functions releases ortho- or pyrophosphate,[80] necessitating a net gain by glycolysis.

The over-all ATP yield in a fermentation will depend on the reaction steps, the potential of the oxidation reduction reactions, and the energy required to prepare the ultimate electron acceptors.

The maximal energy yield, i.e., of orthophosphate esterified, per unit substrate seems to occur in systems which cleave ketose prior to oxidation.[55] Two cleavage mechanisms generating 2 ATP per ketose are known, namely, the fructose-1,6-diphosphate aldolase characteristic of the Embden-Meyerhof pathway, reaction (1):

$$\text{glucose} \xrightarrow{\text{2 ATP}} \text{fructose-1,6-diP} \xrightarrow{\text{aldolase}} \begin{array}{c} \text{dihydroxy-acetone-P} \\ + \\ \text{glyceraldehyde-3-P} \end{array} \qquad (1)$$

and the phosphoketolase cleavage of xylulose-5-P:

$$\text{pentose} \xrightarrow{\text{ATP}} \text{xylulose-5-P} \xrightarrow{\text{Pi}} \text{acetyl-P} + \text{glyceraldehyde-3-P} \qquad (2)$$

These reactions will be considered in terms of the mechanism of phosphate anhydride formation and nature of hydrogen acceptors.

The Embden-Meyerhof pathway[8] operates with a net energy gain of 2 ATP, as summarized by:

$$2 \text{ glucose} + 2 \text{ Pi} + 2 \text{ ADP} \rightarrow 2 \text{ lactate} + 2 \text{ ATP} \qquad (3)$$

This yield, via fructosediphosphate aldolase and 2 moles of triosephosphate, occurs because each triose esterifies 1 orthophosphate on oxidation and returns, via enolase[81] with phosphoenol pyruvate formation, the ATP required to initiate the fermentation of glucose.[8]

Triosephosphate oxidation, an important model for substrate level oxidation with generation of high energy phosphate, is visualized in Scheme I.[82-85]

(a)

$$
\begin{array}{ccc}
\text{CHO} & & \text{OH} \\
| & & | \\
\text{CHOH} & + \text{RSH} \rightarrow & \text{R—S—CH} \\
| & & | \\
\text{CH}_2\text{OP} & & \text{CH}_2\text{OH} \\
& & | \\
& & \text{CH}_2\text{OP}
\end{array}
$$

(b)

$$
\begin{array}{ccc}
\text{OH} & & \text{R—S—C=O} \\
| & & | \\
\text{R—S—CH} & + \text{DPN} \rightarrow & \text{CHOH} \quad + \text{DPNH} + \text{H}^+ \\
| & & | \\
\text{CHOH} & & \text{CH}_2\text{OP} \\
| & & \\
\text{CH}_2\text{OP} & &
\end{array}
$$

(c)

$$
\begin{array}{ccc}
\text{R—S—C=O} & & \text{OPO}_3^- \\
| & & | \\
\text{CHOH} & + \text{HPO}_4^- \rightarrow \text{RSH} + & \text{C=O} \\
| & & | \\
\text{CH}_2\text{OP} & & \text{CHOH} \\
& & | \\
& & \text{CH}_2\text{OP}
\end{array}
$$

SCHEME I

This sequence, as formulated by Racker,[85] is now taken as a classical example of a mechanism of thiol addition, dehydrogenation, and phosphorolysis of thiolester with retention of energy in acyl phosphate bond. The acyl-phosphate-ATP transfer (1,3-diphosphoglycerate to ADP) has a favorable equilibrium toward ATP[86]: $\Delta F = -4000$ calories.

Other organisms are presumed to ferment triosephosphate in a similar manner: muscle and yeast triosephosphate dehydrogenases,[87] but not the bacterial enzymes, have been examined. The amount of triosephosphate formed is thus a determining factor in the total energy yield. The energy yield of 2 ATP per glucose, reaction (3), considers no ATP generation below pyruvate, i.e., for lactic- and alcoholic-CO_2 fermentations. Pyruvate reactions with ATP generation will be considered in Section II, B.

Pentose fermentation, with uptake of 2 phosphates and generation of 2 ATP per mole, became apparent with the discovery of phosphoketolase.[88] This enzyme forms 1 mole each of acetylphosphate and triosephosphate from xylulose-5-phosphate, reaction (2). The generation of acetylphosphate in the initial cleavage without priming via ATP compensates for the formation of but 1 triosephosphate. This is energetically equivalent to the Embden-Meyerhof fermentation of hexose. Net yield:

$$\text{pentose} + 2 \text{ Pi} + 2 \text{ ADP} \longrightarrow \text{acetate} + \text{lactate} + 2 \text{ ATP} \qquad (4)$$

An analogous phosphoketolase cleavage of fructose-6-phosphate has been reported by Racker and co-workers[89, 90] for the aerobic bacterium, *Acetobacter xylinum*, as in reaction (5):

$$\text{fructose-6-P} + 2 \text{ Pi} \longrightarrow \text{aceytl-P} + \text{eyrthrose-4-P} \qquad (5)$$

The net inorganic phosphate uptake and ATP gain depend on subsequent reactions of the tetrosephosphate[90] which replaces the triosephosphate of the pentulose cleavage, reaction (2).

The pertinent observations on acetylphosphate generation via phosphoketolase[88-93] are: adaptive fermentation of pentose by lactobacilli (*Lactobacillus pentosus*,[93a] *L. arabinosus*,[94] *L. plantarum*[88]) yielding in fermentation 1 mole each of acetate and lactate.[93a, 94] Acetate is formed exclusively from pentose carbons 1 and 2, which are converted quantitatively to the acetate methyl and carboxyl, respectively. Extracts from pentose-induced cells cleave xylulose-5-P to acetylphosphate and triose-P.[88, 92] An enzyme fraction purified 45-fold over the extract shows a requirement for DPT, Mg^{++}, a thiol, and stoichiometric amounts of inorganic phosphate.[92, 93] Surprisingly, although similar to transketolase in the requirement for DPT,[95] both acetylphosphate and triosephosphate are reported not to exchange with xylulose-5-P either in the presence or absence of inorganic phosphate (Pi).[77] Acetylphosphate does not arsenolyze and presumably does not exchange phosphate with Pi. Arsenate will replace Pi in the cleavage of xylulose-5-P to form acetate in place of acetyl-P. These data clearly indicate an irreversible step in the early phases of acetyl-P generation; this observation strongly suggests a difference between the initial reactions of xylulose-5-P with phosphoketolase and with transketolase.[77] These data led Breslow[96] to formulate a mechanism for the acetyl-P generating reaction with an early irreversible dehydration of a glycolaldehyde-DPT complex. Need for further extension of this aspect of the problem is clearly indicated.

The fructose-6-P phosphoketolase, reaction (5), requires further comment.[89, 90] This enzyme has not so far been reported in anaerobic, glycolytic organisms, although both ketopentose and ketohexose are cleaved by the *A. xylinum* phosphoketolase in sonic extracts. The pentulose phosphoketolase is present in anaerobically grown cells, i.e., lactic acid bacteria induced with pentose[88] and in *Leuconostoc mesenteroides*,[97] which ferments hexose via a pentose pathway. *A. xylinum* may very well form 3 moles of acetate from fructose via a series of phosphoketolase cleavages accompanied by cycling of the carbon skeleton through transaldolase + transketolase.[90, 98] As indicated earlier, the ATP yield from fructose-6-P will depend on the subsequent reactions of erythrose-4-P. The latter could regenerate fructose-6-P and two more moles of acetylphosphate, as outlined in Scheme II.[90] These reactions represent a nonoxidative pathway which could generate 2 ATP per mole of fructose. Although 3 phosphoketolase reactions generate 3 ATP, 1 phosphate ester is presumably returned to Pi by a phosphatase reaction forming fructose-6-phosphate from fructose-1,6-diphosphate (Scheme II). If the 2 triosephosphate molecules formed were fermented through the usual triosephosphate dehydrogenase reaction, 4 additional moles of ATP would be generated, or a net gain of 2 beyond those required to prime the 2 moles of fructose. The over-all fermentation, which utilizes both phosphoketolase and triosephosphate oxidation mechanisms for phosphate pickup, could yield 5 ATP per 2 fructose, 2.5 ATP per hexose. This yield assumes freedom from electron acceptor restrictions, i.e., is not a completely fermentative mechanism. The possibility of 3 substrate level phosphorylations per hexose is of interest, however, for the previous limit by Embden-Meyerhof fermentation was considered to be two. The possibility of an isomerase for tetrose-4-P to tetrulose-4-P, followed by a second phosphoketolase, should not be eliminated; the energy yield would in this case also be two, plus any phosphorylation derived from the final dispensation of the remaining two carbons, presumably free glycolaldehyde. Present evidence encourages the consideration of recycling in tetrosephosphate metabolism.

Oxidation of hexose, or hexosephosphate, prior to cleavage occurs in both aerobic and anaerobic bacteria. Such reactions, pyridine nucleotide- or flavoprotein-mediated, presumably lead to the formation of acyl lactones.[99] The latter appear to open hydrolytically, thus without energy coupling, i.e., acyl phosphate formation,[82, 101, 103] reactions (6) and (6a).

$$\text{glucose} + \text{DPN (or FP)} \rightarrow \text{glucono-}\gamma\text{-lactone} \xrightarrow{\text{HOH}} \text{gluconate} \qquad (6)$$

$$\text{glucose-6-P} + \text{TPN} \rightarrow \text{6-P-glucono-}\gamma\text{-lactone} \xrightarrow{\text{HOH}} \text{6-P-gluconate} \qquad (6a)$$

Degradation from gluconic acid may occur by either of two pathways; in all cases, via the phosphorylated derivative 6-P-gluconic acid:

1. *Entner-Doudoroff* pathway, initiated by 6-P-gluconate dehydration

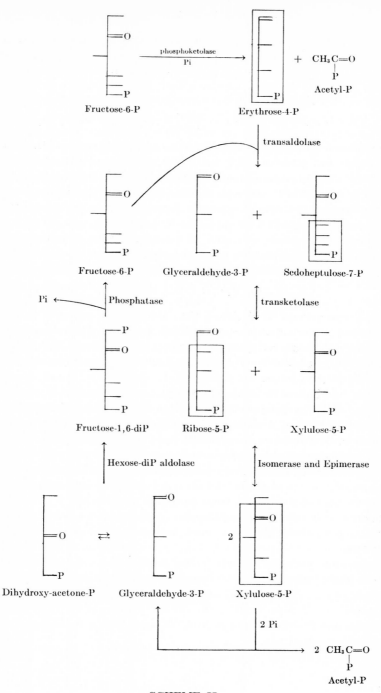

Fructose-6-P   phosphoketolase / Pi   Erythrose-4-P   + $CH_3C{=}O$ | P   Acetyl-P

transaldolase

Fructose-6-P   Glyceraldehyde-3-P   +   Sedoheptulose-7-P

Pi ←   Phosphatase   transketolase

Fructose-1,6-diP   Ribose-5-P   +   Xylulose-5-P

Hexose-diP aldolase   Isomerase and Epimerase

Dihydroxy-acetone-P   ⇄   Glyceraldehyde-3-P   2   Xylulose-5-P

2 Pi

2   $CH_3C{=}O$ | P   Acetyl-P

SCHEME II

17

and aldol cleavage of the product.[11] The reactions catalyzed by these two specific enzymes, a dehydrase and an aldolase, plus the structure of the intermediate are indicated in reactions (7) and (8).[11]

$$\text{6-P-gluconate} \xrightarrow{-\text{HOH}} \text{2-keto-3-deoxy-6-P-gluconate} \tag{7}$$

$$\text{2-keto-3-deoxy-6-P-gluconate} \xrightarrow[\text{aldolase}]{\text{KDPG-}} \text{pyruvate} + \text{triosephosphate} \tag{8}$$

The primary oxidation is not coupled to phosphate uptake, thus the system yields but one net ATP via triosephosphate dehydrogenase unless pyruvate is further oxidized. (The other aspects of these reactions are discussed in appropriate connotation, see Chapter 2.) Of importance here is the requirement, in anaerobic glucose fermentation, of an acceptor for one electron pair provided by the products of reaction (8).

2. *Pentose Phosphate Pathway.* The pathway from glucose to pentose phosphate via 6-P-gluconate is represented by reaction (6) then phosphorylation, or, phosphorylation then reaction (6a) plus reaction (9)[103, 104]:

$$\text{6-P-gluconate} + \text{TPN} \rightarrow CO_2 + \text{ribulose-5-P} + \text{TPNH} \tag{9}$$

The epimerization of ribulose-5-P to xylulose-5-P prepares the product of reaction (9) for subsequent phosphoketolase cleavage, reaction (2).

The Entner-Doudoroff and pentose phosphate pathways have been found in a variety of aerobic[105, 106] and anaerobic[107-109] organisms since their first discovery in the former.

These two hexose monophosphate systems are similar in energy yield but give different product labeling from uniquely labeled glucose. The labeling of each is also different from labeling by Embden-Meyerhof fermentation. The three pathways each yield triose phosphate from carbons 4 to 6, with aldehyde group from carbon 4. Thus the difference in product labeling occurs from the first three carbons. The *Pseudomonas lindneri* fermentation is an alcoholic (yeast type) bacterial fermentation.[107] The organism possesses a yeast type pyruvate carboxylase.[107] The Entner-Doudoroff and the Embden-Meyerhof pathways each yield 2 moles of pyruvate per hexose; thus the stoichiometry does not distinguish between these two.

The pentose pathway, shown to yield alcohol and CO_2 from carbons 1 to 3[109] via phosphoketolase,[97] with *Leuconostoc* could, in the presence of pyruvate carboxylase, equally well account for the products. The two points of difference among these three pathways are: (1) the position of labeling in products, and (2) the difference in ATP yield. These are shown in Tables III and IV respectively.

The prime difference in labeling for alcoholic fermentation by the three pathways is the source of the methyl group of ethanol, Table III. These are: carbon 1 for Embden-Meyerhof, carbon 2 for pentose phosphate path-

TABLE III

GLUCOSE FERMENTATION: LABELING PATTERNS

Glucose carbon	Alcoholic or alcohol-lactic			Lactic		
	E.M.[a]	P.P.[b]	E.D.[c]	E.M.[a]	P.P.[b]	E.D.[c]
1	CH_3	CO_2	CO_2	CH_3	CO_2	COOH
2	CH_2OH	CH_3	CH_2OH	CHOH	CH_3	CHOH
3	CO_2	CH_2OH	CH_3	COOH	CH_2OH	CH_3

[a] E. M.: Embden-Meyerhof pathway.
[b] P. P.: Pentosephosphate pathway (via phosphoketolase).
[c] E. D.: Entner-Doudoroff pathway.

TABLE IV

CARBOHYDRATE CLEAVAGE MECHANISMS AND ATP YIELDS

Substrate	Cleavage type	End products	Triose-P, moles	Calcu-lated yield (ATP)
Hexose	FDP-aldolase[a]	2 Lactate	2	2
Hexose	Phosphoketolase	1 Lactate, 1 acetate, 1 CO_2	1	1
Pentose	Phosphoketolase	2 Lactate, 1 acetate	1	2
Hexose	KDPG-aldolase[b]	2 Ethanol, 2 CO_2	1	1
Aldonic acid	FDP-aldolase + KDPG-aldolase	1.83 Lactate (?),[c] 0.5 CO_2	1	1.33[c]

[a] FDP-aldolase: fructose-1,6-diphosphate aldolase.
[b] KDPG-aldolase: 2-keto-3-deoxy-6-phosphogluconate aldolase.
[c] High lactate yields >1.75 mole/glucose in presence 0.001 M arsenite. Resting cells $\simeq$ 1.5 lactate, 0.5 + CO_2, 0.5 $C_2(O/R = 0)$ missing (calculated as acetate via phosphoketolase $\simeq$ 1.67 ATP).

way, and carbon 3 for Entner-Doudoroff. The CO_2 is formed from carbon 1 in both hexosemonophosphate pathways and from carbon 3 in the Embden-Meyerhof (HDP) pattern. These data leave the source of the ethanol carbinol as carbon 3 in pentose phosphate and carbon 2 in both Entner-Doudoroff and Embden-Meyerhof pathways. The labeling data of Gibbs and DeMoss[107] for the *Pseudomonas lindneri* fermentation conform to the Entner-Doudoroff hexosemonophosphate cleavage to pyruvate, followed by decarboxylation to acetaldehyde and reduction to ethanol.

In contrast to the net 2 moles ATP per pentose fermented by the phosphoketolase reaction, hexose fermentation yields only 1 ATP. This results from acetylphosphate reduction to ethanol by the two electron pairs generated in oxidation of glucose-6-P to CO_2 and pentulose-5-P via 6-P-gluconate [reactions (6a) and (9)]. The decreased energy yield can be viewed as the energy required to prepare an electron acceptor. The reduction of acetyl to acetaldehyde occurs in the energy-rich form as either phosphate or the coenzyme A derivative.

The isotopic data indicate a pentosephosphate pathway in the leuconostoc (heterolactic) fermentation of glucose.[109, 110] Phosphoketolase has also been reported in these cells, even when glucose-grown.[97] For balance data, see Chapter 2, Table XX.

Aldonic acid fermentation occurs as an inducible system in lactic acid bacteria.[108, 113] This substrate, oxidation state intermediate between hexose and pentose, appears from both labeling and induced enzyme data to combine the Entner-Doudoroff and pentose cleavage pathways.

Hexonic acids appear not to be reduced, i.e., gluconolactone hydrolysis to gluconic acid, reaction (6a), is not reversible; thus the initial cleavage of the carbon chain is not likely to be of the Embden-Meyerhof type. *S. faecalis* is homofermentative on glucose and yields two lactate with labeling as in the Embden-Meyerhof pathway.[111, 112] From gluconate, the principal products are lactate and CO_2[108] with —CO_2 from gluconate carbon 1. Either hexosemonophosphate cleavage will furnish this label. The whole cell fermentation has been reported by Sokatch and Gunsalus to form about 1.5 lactate and slightly more than 0.5 CO_2 per gluconate and to lack for balance about 0.5 mole of C_2 at the oxidation level of acetate. In the presence of 10^{-3} molar arsenite, the CO_2 yield is almost exactly 0.5 mole and the lactate increases to above 1.75 mole. These data lead to the suggestion of the limiting case-0.5 CO_2 + 1.83 lactate as the sole products, reaction (10):

$$6 \text{ gluconate} + 8 \text{ ADP} \xrightarrow{8 \text{ Pi}} 11 \text{ lactate} + 3 \text{ CO}_2 + 8 \text{ ATP} \tag{10}$$

Both isotopic and enzymic data are compatible with fermentation by the complementary function of the two hexosemonpohosphate pathways (Entner-Doudoroff and pentosephosphate).[108, 113] Gluconate-1-C^{14} fermentation yields $C^{14}O_2$ at the same specific activity as carbon 1 of the substrate. Gluconate-2-C^{14} labels lactate in all positions, with carbon 2 containing 40 to 60 % of the label. The enzyme complement of gluconate-adapted cells includes fructose-1,6-diphosphate aldolase, 2-keto-3-deoxy-6-phosphogluconate (KDPG) aldolase, transketolase, and transaldolase.

Calculations of net energy gain by the combination of Entner-Doudoroff and pentosephosphate pathways for the anaerobic fermentation of gluconic acid by reaction (10) is 1.33 ATP per gluconate;[55] the energy calculations from growth data do not confirm the calculated 1.33 ATP per mole, but indicate the somewhat higher value of about 1.7 to 1.8 (see Section III, B and Table VIII).

For each type of fermentation, certain "indicator enzymes" help predict the pathway, or combinations of pathways, functioning in monosaccharide degradation. Buyze *et al.*[114] studied the distribution of enzymes among the lactobacilli and found hexosediphosphate aldolase present only in the homofermentative strains. All heterofermentative strains contained glucose-6-P and 6-P-gluconate dehydrogenases, a finding compatible with the pentosephosphate cleavage mechanisms. It would be desirable to know if the Entner-Doudoroff enzymes (6-phosphogluconic dehydrase and KDPG aldolase) and pentose pathway enzymes (phosphoketolase and acetokinase[142]) are present.

This brief discourse on the data concerning probable reaction routes and their alternatives from the study of labeling, indicator enzymes, and product yields is intended to direct attention to the coupling reactions and their influence on energy yields. The fermentation data (Chapter 2) can be evaluated in this way to extend knowledge of mechanisms.

B. PYRUVATE OXIDATION AND ELECTRON ACCEPTORS

In numerous carbohydrate fermentations generating pyruvate via triosephosphate oxidation, pyruvate is further oxidized. Electron acceptors are thus required, not only for the reduced pyridine nucleotide formed during triosephosphate oxidation, but for an additional pair of electrons generated by pyruvate oxidation. The nature of the electron acceptors and the oxidation mechanism determines the energy gain from pyruvate cleavage. Many normally fermentative organisms can use oxygen as an electron acceptor for both pairs of electrons.[115] Access to oxygen permits an estimation of the energy gain by substrate oxidation independent of the reactions required for anaerobic formation of acceptors. Enzymic studies provide a more complete picture of the mechanisms but should be guided by net energy approximations to differentiate between alternate routes of acceptor synthesis.

Pyruvate is generated in the fermentation of several organic acids without prior oxidation steps, thereby relieving the requirement for additional electron acceptors; three examples will be considered:

1. *Citrate fermentation* by lactic acid bacteria,[116, 117, 118, 119] and *Aerobacter aerogenes*[119, 120] through a retrograde aldol reaction yields oxalacetate and acetate.[122] Subsequent decarboxylation of oxalacetate forms pyruvate, 1 mole per citrate.[123]

2. *Glutamate fermentation* by *Clostridium tetanomorphum* yields pyruvate, acetate, and ammonia by a similar aldol cleavage mechanism. The reaction sequence includes rearrangement of glutamate to β-methylasparate, then deamination and hydration with formation of citramalate.[124] Aldol cleavage of citramalate (citramalase) gives rise to pyruvate and acetate by aldol cleavage.[125]

3. *Glycine fermentation* by *Diplococcus glycinophilus* occurs through serine. This intermediate arises by the transfer of the glycine carbon-2 from one molecule to another in a reaction sequence mediated by tetrahydrofolic acid.[126, 127] Serine is deaminated to pyruvate.[127a] The transfer of the glycine carbon-2 leaves a C-1 at the oxidation level of formate; since this carboxyl ultimately appears as CO_2, an acceptor must be provided for two electrons. These electrons may ultimately appear as molecular hydrogen[128] or may reduce CO_2 to acetate by an undisclosed reaction sequence.

Although the mechanism and complexity of reaction sequences differ in these cases, they have in common the formation of pyruvate without prior oxidation steps. These reactions occur in bacterial fermentations described in Chapters 2, 3, and 4. Serine fermentation (Chapter 3, Table VI) also forms pyruvate without electron liberation. The energy available for biological work depends on the electron and acyl acceptors and the reaction mechanisms by which electrons reach the final acceptor, i.e., whether the potential difference between the electron donor and acceptor provides sufficient energy to couple electron transport with phosphate uptake and whether acyl generation from the substrate is coupled to ATP formation.[129]

1. PYRUVATE OXIDATION SYSTEMS

The oxidation of pyruvate occurs by one of a series of alternate mechanisms, as shown in Table V. At least three distinct energy-coupled mechanisms have been found in bacteria:

(1) *Lipoic acid-linked*,[26, 27, 130, 131] with the disulfide form of the coenzyme

TABLE V

PYRUVATE OXIDATION PATHWAYS

Type or organism	Electron acceptors	Acyl acceptors	Products
Streptococcus faecalis and *Escherichia coli*	Lipoic, FP,[a] DPN	Lipoic, CoA	Acetyl-CoA, CO_2, DPNH
Lactobacillus delbrueckii	FP	HPO_4^-	Acetyl-P, CO_2, $FP_{red.}$
Clostridium[b]	H^+, (FP)	CoA, HPO_4^-	Acetyl-P, CO_2, H_2
Escherichia coli "clastic"[c]	Formate	CoA, HPO_4^-	Acetyl-P, formate
Proteus vulgaris and *Escherichia coli* "aerobic"	FP	(OH^-)	Acetate, CO_2, $FP_{red.}$

[a] FP: Flavoprotein.

[b] These systems also exchange CO_2 rapidly with pyruvate and appear to require biotinyl—as "CO_2" acceptor.

[c] Exchanges formate rapidly.

considered to act as both acyl and electron acceptor. The route of electrons from the reduced coenzyme passes through a flavoprotein of sufficiently low potential to reduce pyridine nucleotide.[132-136]

(2) *Flavoprotein-linked*, as in *Lactobacillus delbrueckii*,[137] with phosphate as obligatory acyl acceptor. The flavoprotein will transfer electrons to riboflavin or to a number of dyes. Under anaerobic conditions, a second molecule of pyruvate is reduced via a flavoprotein lactic dehydrogenase.

(3) *"Clastic" cleavage*,[138-141] yielding acetylphosphate coupled to ATP through acetokinase.[142] The immediate electron acceptor, the carriers and the mechanism are still obscure. In *Clostridium sticklandii*, folic acid has been shown to be a specific electron acceptor.[143, 144] The transfer of electrons may result in the evolution of molecular hydrogen either with or without formate as a formal intermediate. Biotin[145] and folic acid[146] have recently been implicated in these mechanisms and may lead to clarification.

An additional "noncoupled" acetate generating pyruvic oxidase (Table V), usually termed the "Proteus" type, regardless of source, is known to operate aerobically[74, 147-149] via flavoprotein[150] and cytochrome b.[148] Recent evidence suggests the induction of this system after pyruvate accumulation in the final phases of growth.[150] Organisms shown to contain the "Proteus" enzyme also contain the lipoic-type oxidase.[27] Whether the "Proteus" system is present or functions in glycolytic (anaerobic) metabolism is unclear; the system is included in Table V for completeness, without prejudice to interpretation when the data are available.

2. HYDROGEN ACCEPTORS

The reduced products formed by the electrons from pyruvate oxidation will determine the net ATP equivalents in a given fermentation. The yields estimated from present knowledge of the mechanism and stoichiometry of anaerobic pyruvate fermentation as found in various bacteria are tabulated in Table VI. The values in the table represent product ratios and ATP yields for fermentation of pyruvate or pyruvate + 2 electrons, i.e., carbohydrate fermentation with 1 mole DPNH formed per mole of pyruvate. In each case, the balances assume no external hydrogen acceptors and only one fermentation pathway, i.e., no mixed product yields. In this sense they are idealized values; the actual yields in fermentation usually digress somewhat from the values presented in the table (see footnotes).

Pyruvate generates electrons of sufficiently low potential to reduce hydrogen ion to molecular hydrogen (H_2). With hydrogen evolution, pyruvate yields 1 mole each of CO_2, H_2 and acyl, with the energy of the latter convertible to ATP.[138, 139] In contrast, triosephosphate oxidation has not been shown to yield H_2; thus the stoichiometry requires additional acceptors of higher potential. In other terms, triosephosphate fermentation has not

TABLE VI

EFFECT OF ELECTRON ACCEPTORS ON ATP YIELD OF PYRUVATE FERMENTATIONS

System	Pyruvate		Pyruvate + 2 e	
	Product ratio	ATP yield	Product ratio	ATP yield
Coliform[a]	1 Formate 1 Acetate	1.0	0.5 Lactate 0.5 Formate 0.5 Acetate	0.5
Clostridial[b]	1 Acetate, 1 CO_2, 1 H_2	1.0	0.5 Butyrate 1 CO_2, 1 H_2	0.5
Clostridial[c]	0.5 Ethanol, 0.5 acetate, 1 CO_2	0.5	1 Ethanol 1 CO_2	0
Clostridial[b]	0.5 Butyrate 1 CO_2	0.5	0.5 Butanol 1 CO_2	0
Propionic[d]	0.33 Propionate 0.66 Acetate 0.66 CO_2	0.66	0.66 Propionate 0.33 Acetate 0.33 CO_2	0.33

[a] Wood, Chapter 2, Table IX.
[b] Wood, Chapter 2, Table V.
[c] Barker, Chapter 3, Table VI.
[d] Wood, Chapter 2, Table XIV.

been shown to yield acetate, CO_2, and 2 H_2.[17] The formation of formate and acetylphosphate provides a similar electron acceptor ratio to $CO_2 + H_2$ with the same energy yield of 1 ATP per pyruvate.[141] This stoichiometry appears in coliform bacteria[140, 141] and in some lactic acid bacteria,[117] especially those from alkaline medium.

The CO_2 formed by pyruvate oxidation remains as a product in most fermentations but does undergo reduction to acetate[151, 152] or methane[17] by clostridia and methane bacteria. To a lesser extent, CO_2 is incorporated into reduced products in the *E. coli* and lactic fermentations;[153] these reactions are usually stoichiometrically unimportant. The data are not clear on the route of CO_2 reduction to acetate and methane. The formation of 3 moles of acetate as the sole product of glucose fermentation occurs with equilibration of acetate and CO_2;[17, 152] the stoichiometry would be compatible with a high energy yield. The energy requirement for CO_2 activation prior to reduction is unknown; thus, a prediction of the net energy yield must await elucidation of the enzymic steps. It seems probable that growth data with clostridia of different product patterns might furnish a basis for predicting ATP yields and deciding among possible mechanisms.

Acetyl can serve as an electron acceptor to form ethanol or, after condensation to acetoacetyl, to form butyrate.[17] Two pairs of electrons are required per acetyl in ethanol formation and two pairs for each two acetyl in butyrate formation; both reductions permit the oxidation of 2 moles of pyruvate. Since 1 acyl disappears in the reduction to ethanol and at least 1 in butyrate formation, these reactions yield no more than 1 ATP per 2 pyruvate. Reduction of 1 pyruvate to lactate is an energetically equivalent mechanism. The butyrate-forming system yields 1 ATP per 2 pyruvate only if condensation proceeds by the thiolase reaction. If this condensation should require an activated CO_2 similar to the yeast and animal systems for fatty acid synthesis,[155-157] butyrate formation would occur without ATP gain. Butyryl reduction to butanol also occurs in some organisms, permitting further pyruvate oxidation;[158] as with acetyl reduction to ethanol, the carboxyl appears to undergo reduction in the acyl form[159] (butyryl CoA) with the disappearance of 1 acyl per 2 pairs of electrons. Therefore, butanol formation would permit the oxidation of 2 moles of pyruvate with the acyl derived from one oxidation lost in the reductive process. Viewing butanol formation from the standpoint of triosephosphate fermentation, an increase in net yield acyl (ATP generation) would occur only if molecular hydrogen is produced as an accessory reduced product.

The reduction of 1 mole pyruvate to propionate permits oxidation of 2 moles pyruvate for a net gain of 2 acyl per 3 pyruvate fermented, i.e., 2 acyl per propionate formed (Table VI). The actual acceptor steps in this sequence are the reduction of oxalacetate to malate, and fumarate to succinate. According to Swick and Wood,[16] the reduction occurs without net energy change while providing an acceptor for the oxidation of pyruvate to acetate and CO_2. With triose phosphate from carbohydrate fermentation, only 1 pyruvate oxidation step is possible per 2 propionate, or one acyl convertible to ATP per 3 triose—half the yield from pyruvate (Table VI). The exact reaction sequence in carbohydrate fermentation to propionic acid is not in complete form.[78] The growth yield coefficients for propionic acid bacteria and *Micrococcus lactolyticus* (Elsden[160]) indicate more net energy gain in the over-all process than predicted by any of the currently proposed mechanisms. A further discussion of mechanisms is given in Section III.

The currently available data, in many cases suggestive, are discussed briefly to illustrate the problems. Solutions clarifying these concepts may well be developed from growth and other whole organism studies, leading ultimately to clarification of enzymic steps and reaction pathways.

C. FORMATE AND CO_2 PRODUCTION

ATP is generated from the fermentation of several substrates by steps other than triosephosphate or pyruvate oxidation. Enrichment cultures have yielded bacterial strains which grow at the expense of substrates that undergo cleavage without oxidative energy coupling in initial reactions. Instead, CO_2 or formate may appear in the products by coupled, nonoxidative reactions. The pathways serving for C-1 cleavage, transfer, and release with coupled ATP formation may actually include the formal intermediates which serve in the biosynthetic incorporation of the same C-1 unit.

1. FORMATE

The fermentation of purines by *Clostridium cylindrosporum* is illustrative of ATP-coupled formate release. With guanine as substrate, the principal products are equivalent amounts of glycine and formic acid plus larger amounts of CO_2 and ammonia and traces of acetate.[22] Cell extracts ferment xanthine to formiminoglycine by noncoupled hydrolytic reactions.[17] Further degradation of this intermediate requires the presence of substrate amounts of ADP and Pi. The coupled cleavage of formiminoglycine yields glycine, formate, and ammonia with a net energy gain of one ATP, according to the stoichiometry in reaction (11).

$$\text{formiminoglycine} + \text{ADP} + \text{Pi} \rightarrow \text{formate} + \text{NH}_3 + \text{glycine} + \text{ATP} \quad (11)$$

The over-all reaction proceeds by discrete steps, first transferring the formimino moiety to tetrahydrofolic acid (fH_4). Ammonia elimination occurs either by hydrolysis of the formimino tetrahydrofolate compound or by ring closure to the methenyl derivative, reaction (12).[161,162]

$$\text{formiminoglycine} + fH_4 \rightarrow \text{glycine} + \text{ammonia} + N^5,N^{10}\text{-methenyl-}fH_4 \quad (12)$$

Phosphate pickup and ATP formation occur by coupled cleavage of formyl tetrahydrofolic acid via formylase,[163] reaction (13).

$$N^{10}\text{-formyl-}fH_4 + \text{ADP} + \text{Pi} \rightarrow \text{formate} + \text{ATP} + fH_4 \quad (13)$$

The enzyme catalyzing the latter step has been prepared in crystalline form from *C. cylindrosporum* after only 10-fold purification.[51]

The energy metabolism takes a different route in a similar purine fermentation by *Clostridium acidi-urici*. Instead of glycine and formate, only acetate and CO_2 are found as products of uric acid fermentation (see Barker, Chapter 3, p. 183). In this case, the formyl moiety is recycled by reduction to hydroxymethyl tetrahydrofolate and transfer to the C-2 of glycine, forming serine.[21] Serine is deaminated to pyruvate which serves, via oxidation, as the substrate for the sole energy-yielding reaction. The electron pair donated in pyruvate oxidation presumably is utilized via pyridine nucleotide in the reduction of methenyl tetrahydrofolate to methylene tetrahydrofolate, i.e., no accessory electron acceptor is required, reaction (14).

$$\text{pyruvate} + N^5,N^{10}\text{-methenyl-}fH_4 \rightarrow \text{acetyl-P} + CO_2 + N^5,N^{10}\text{-methylene-}fH_4 \quad (14)$$

Formate and formate derivatives are also products of the biological degradation of histidine. An energy-coupling mechanism equivalent to that found in the purine fermentation could be expected. The initial deamination and hydrolytic steps form formiminoglutamic, considered to be a common intermediate in all systems studied, but this is apparently the extent of the similarities. Extracts of pseudomonads[164] further degrade formiminoglutamic to formate, ammonia, and glutamic acid, while formamide and glutamic acid are formed from the same intermediate by the fermentations of *C. tetanomorphum*[165] and *A. aerogenes*.[166] There has, as yet, been no implication of tetrahydrofolic acid involvement in these reactions, and it has been assumed that the energy metabolism is centered in the further degradation of glutamic acid (see Barker, Chapter 3, p. 173). Coupled reactions in the splitting of formiminoglutamate are indicated, however, by the studies with liver extracts which catalyze a transfer of the formimino group to tetrahydrofolic acid.[167] Tetrahydrofolic acid-mediated reactions could be operative in the histidine fermentation by *Micrococcus aerogenes*[168] in which the products do not include appreciable quantities of either formate or formamide. Apparently the C-1 residue is recycled into the other fermentation products, acetate or lactate. These interpretations suffer from the lack of enzymic data.

2. CO_2 VIA CARBAMYLPHOSPHATE

Release of CO_2 from several carbon-nitrogen bond systems yields energy convertible to ATP by substrate level phosphate pickup reactions. Phosphorolytic cleavage of ureido compounds produces carbamylphosphate, from which the phosphate is transferred to ADP. Carbamylphosphate is formed biosynthetically from CO_2 + NH_3 at the expense of 2 moles of ATP, 1 each for the activation of CO_2 and ammonia.[169, 170] In contrast to the synthetic route, the degradative reaction seems to yield only 1 ATP per mole.[171, 172] Two examples of the role of carbamylphosphate in anaerobic fermentations are presented.

Arginine is fermented by certain lactic acid bacteria[173-175] and by *Clostridium perfringens*.[176] The fermentation products are ornithine, CO_2, and 2 moles of ammonia, with an energy yield apparent from growth and enzymic observations. Although arginine alone will not support growth of lactic acid bacteria, an additional energy yield can be demonstrated by the growth increment due to added arginine in cultures metabolizing glucose under substrate-limited conditions[55] (see Section III). The energy-coupled step, as indicated by enzymic studies, is the phosphorolysis of citrulline, forming ornithine and carbamylphosphate,[172] reaction (15).

$$\text{citrulline} + \text{Pi} \rightarrow \text{carbamylphosphate} + \text{ornithine} \qquad (15)$$

Citrulline arises from arginine via a noncoupled (hydrolytic) deamination.

Carbamylphosphate is also implicated as an intermediate in creatinine degradation. Sarcosine, ammonia, and CO_2 are the sole products of an anaerobic, growth-supporting fermentation of creatinine by an organism identified as *Eubacter sarcosinogenum*.[71] As with arginine fermentation, the initial step is a deamination of creatinine, forming N-methyl hydantoin.[177] The role of carbamylphosphate in the further degradation of N-methyl hydantoin was demonstrated by coupling with the citrulline-ornithine system[71] according to the stoichiometry in reaction (16):

$$\text{creatinine} + \text{ornithine} \rightarrow \text{citrulline} + NH_3 + \text{sarcosine} \qquad (16)$$

In the absence of the carbamyl acceptor, the fermentation is coupled with Pi uptake. In this organism, the acyl phosphate is converted into inorganic polyphosphates liberating $CO_2 + NH_3$,[178] reactions (17) and (18).

$$\text{creatinine} + \text{Pi} \rightarrow NH_3 + \text{sarcosine} + \text{carbamylphosphate} \qquad (17)$$

$$\text{carbamylphosphate} + \text{ADP} \rightarrow CO_2 + NH_3 + \text{ATP} + (\text{Pi})_n \rightleftharpoons \text{ADP} + (\text{Pi})_{n+1} \qquad (18)$$

The mechanism of cleavage of the N-methyl hydantoin ring and of carbamylphosphate formation awaits clarification.

D. Electron Transfer

Dolin (Chapter 6), Newton and Kamen (Chapter 8), and Geller (Chapter 10), have illustrated in detail patterns of electron flow for biologically useful energy development. These patterns ultimately supply useful chemical bond energy by generation of ATP or its equivalent. The systems are: (1) electron donor-acceptor couples with either organic or inorganic electron donors and acceptors, and (2) electron donor-acceptor systems in which light furnishes the energy potential.

According to present concepts, light quanta are capable of moving electrons to a higher energy (excited) state through proper interactions with pigments, i.e., chlorophyll.[179] Such electrons may return to a more stable (ground) state or, alternatively, may leave the molecular complex as reducing agents; the photocatalyst itself may then be an acceptor for an electron at the ground state energy level. Thus the photocatalysts are presumed to feed electrons to an independent electron transport system which generates ATP equivalents in a way considered not unlike, and perhaps identical to, the organic and inorganic electron donor-acceptor reactions considered in case (1).

The electron donor-acceptor systems are known by their potential differences to permit energy units of size 7000 to 8000 calories to be stored in the ATP bond. It seems probable that the number of sites for coupling permitted by the pathway of a system is of greater importance than the total free energy change. This may also be the limiting factor in either photosynthetic or solely chemical oxidative mechanisms. The problem which hinders a clear definition of the extent to which electron transport serves as a driving force for microbial biosynthetic and growth reactions is the very sketchy state of knowledge of the mechanisms, and even the catalysts, through which the electron flow is mediated. In contrast to mammalian tissue, in which P/O ratios of 3 for donor systems via pyridine nucleotide to oxygen are not uncommon,[180] experimental values with microbial systems characteristically run below 1,[181, 182] approaching those of mammalian systems only in rare cases.[183,184]

In mammalian systems with one couple between pyridine nucleotide and flavoprotein, a P/O ratio of 2 is found between flavoprotein and oxygen. With microbial systems, the differences between P/O ratios of pyridine nucleotide and flavoprotein-linked oxidations are slight and provide no evidence for an additional couple to bring the P/O ratio above 2. The evidence which is available, rather quaintly, comes from anaerobic systems, namely, growth-driving systems such as that in *Clostridium kluyveri*,[17] which cannot otherwise be explained with net energy gain and accommodate the observed reaction stoichiometry. Barker[17] has discussed the energetics of the *C. kluyveri* fermentation and shown that the potential difference in electron transfer via flavoprotein between reduced pyridine nucleotides and olefinic thioesters is sufficient to permit coupled ATP synthesis by "oxidative phosphorylation." An initial report of success in coupling the oxidation of molecular hydrogen by crotonyl-CoA, yielding butyryl-CoA with an efficiency of 1 ATP per mole in fresh extracts, has not been extended;[185] other attempts to repeat these observations have not met with success.[186] Attempts to fractionate the extracts gave only partial steps in the over-all activity without energy coupling; in fact, seven flavoproteins have been recognized in column separation; the substrates for several have been identified. The difficulties in demonstrating coupling seem likely to prove experimental; thus, further work is required. A careful examination of the energy available from the clostridial-type fermentation of carbohydrates forming fatty acids would seem to offer an additional opportunity for understanding these mechanisms.

There are a few recorded instances of energy gain by substrate level oxidations upon admission of electron acceptors which merely permit oxidation of more moles of substrate rather than gain in ATP from the electron transport system per se.[180]

With mammalian and plant systems, keto acid oxidation shows P/O ratios of 4 by the addition of a substrate level couple to the P/O ratio of 3 for pyridine nucleotide oxidation.[180] The microbial systems, from the oxidative viewpoint, appear also to contain coupled substrate oxidation mechanisms in most instances.[129] Evidence is accumulating that microorganisms have inducible respiration systems[74, 157] which bypass the phosphorylative mechanisms and thus appear to be merely heat-generating. Efforts to demonstrate phosphorylation in extracts may suffer from the presence of active noncoupled oxidative catalysts.

The two microbial systems offering promise for the evaluation of electron transport-coupling are: (1) the *Alcaligenes faecalis* system developed by Pinchot,[181] which contains a particulate electron transport chain, a soluble protein component, and at least one heat-stable component, all of which are in the process of identification; and (2) the system from acid-fast bacteria with which Brodie[183, 184] and co-workers have obtained the highest P/O ratio reported for microbial systems, i.e., 1.8 with succinate as substrate. These workers have also made progress in the identification of biologically active quinoid compounds,[187, 188] and have evidence of their function in the phosphorylative coupling systems.[188-190] Coenzyme Q (ubiquinone) is widely distributed,[191] as is vitamin K.[192] Evidence for the function of these compounds in electron transport and a role in energy-coupling may be extended to microorganisms.

There is evidence of electron transport from whole cell and growth data which could prove fruitful in determining the amount of coupling in respiration;[192a, 193] this is discussed in Section III.

III. Energy Growth and Yield

A. GROWTH YIELD MEASUREMENTS

Microbial growth, as represented by the increase of cells in bacterial culture, is clearly described by Monod[64, 193] and by Novick.[194] The pertinent parameters for the culture are: (1) duration of the growth lag (L), (2) growth rate (R) expressed in time required for doubling of protoplasm (bacterial density), and (3) total growth (end point) of cells expressed as dry weight per unit volume.

In energy-limited synthesis, the end point of growth is the primary concern. Both Monod[64] and Novick[194] discuss the dependence of growth yield on energy source for both static and steady state growth conditions. Monod[193] showed the reproducibility of growth yield of *E. coli* in NH_4 salts medium with aeration and its dependence on the amount of carbohydrate added to the culture. In his terms, total growth (G) is related to energy source concentration (C) by:

$$K = \frac{G}{C} \qquad (19)$$

where K becomes the growth yield constant. The reciprocal, $1/K$, is the amount of substrate required to form a unit cell, defined as 1 cell or 1 μg.

dry weight of cells, depending on the units of G. C and G in μg./ml. give K the dimensions of μg./μg. Monod established the dimensions of K in cell dry weight per weight solid substrate, expressing G and C in mg./l, or μg./ml.

Bauchop and Elsden[72] have expressed growth (G) in the units used by Monod and substrate concentration (C) in μmoles, using μmoles/ml. instead of Monod's μg./ml. units. Their[72] molar yield coefficient, indicated by Y, assumes the dimensions of μg. dry weight cells formed per μmole substrate. Elsden suggests a subscript to indicate the substrate, i.e., Y_G for glucose, Y_{GAL} for galactose. The Y values relate to Monod's K values as:

$$Y = K \times \text{mol. wt.} \qquad (20)$$

The molar growth yield coefficient, Y, was selected in order to make comparison of cells per mole with ATP formed per mole to determine if a constant relating growth yield to energy could be found. An energy yield unit, Y_{ATP}, would be μgrams cells formed per μmole ATP generated in the metabolism of 1 μmole of substrate where the mechanism and the ATP yield are known. If Y_{ATP} were found to be a constant among different organisms, it could prove useful in predicting ATP yields in cases of unknown mechanisms. Thus, for glucose fermentation to lactate or alcohol-CO_2 via the Embden-Meyerhof glycolytic pathway, ATP yield per mole is 2. Thus:

$$\frac{Y_G}{Y_{ATP}} = 2; \qquad \frac{Y_G}{2} = Y_{ATP} \qquad (21)$$

The utility of the ATP yield calculation is dependent upon the experimental verification. Verification which is in part supplied by studies described below.

Growth in continuous flow systems can be used for growth yield measurements; in fact, they offer distinct advantages over the static methods. Novick[194] has summarized the theory and principles concerned in continuous growth studies. Novick and Szilard[195, 196] have described an apparatus, the "chemostat," which has proved highly effective and convenient for aerobic growth studies; Rosenberger and Elsden[197] have built a modified anaerobic "chemostat" for measuring fermentative growth yields. A second condition of continuous flow operation, the "turbidostat" can also be applied to measurement of yield coefficients. The "chemostat" and "turbidostat" differ only in the means of selecting the steady state population—in all other regards the controlling conditions are similar. With the chemostat, one selects a dilution rate, whereas with the turbidostat, one selects a population level and by means of a suitable device (usually a photoelectric cell) controls the dilution rate by changes in flow rate to hold the population (bacterial density) constant. Herbert et al.[197a] compare static and continuous growth cultures in reference to yield coefficients,[72] offer an alternate formulation of the Monod and Novick-Szilard continuous growth culture equations, and supply data for quantitative comparison with the results predicted by the theoretical formulation. They also point out errors in alternate formulations which have found their way into the literature since the Monod and Novick-Szilard treatments.

Novick's discussion of continuous flow systems considers two conditions of operation: in the first, the growth rate is limited by some unknown internal condition of the cell, not the concentration of a supplied nutrient. The growth rate is maximum, a characteristic of the cell; in the second, a condition of operation, one of external control, the growth rate is determined by the concentration of some limiting nutrient, i.e., the growth rate is below the maximum the cell can attain if the nutrient concentration is increased. The conditions of operation for both the turbidostat and the chemostat may be described as nutrient limited growth. The chemostat condition of operation, which can be most conveniently applied to the measurement of growth yields, is considered here (for full details and other conditions of operation, see Novick[194] or Herbert[197a]). In this case, the level of bacteria remains constant, i.e., $dN/dt = 0$ (N = number of cells per ml.; bacterial density in μg. cells per ml. is equally convenient). The growth rate (α), determined by the nutrient whose concentration (c) is limiting, becomes $\alpha(c)$. With the population stable, the growth rate on the limiting nutrient is equal to the dilution of the culture by new medium. Where w = flow rate, v = volume of culture, w/v is the dilution of the culture per unit time by new medium. Therefore:

$$\alpha(c) = \frac{w}{v} \tag{22}$$

If a = input concentration of limiting nutrient (reservoir medium), and (c), the concentration in the growth tube, Novick's equation 5, (see p. 101 in ref. 194) for the bacterial density maintained in the growth tube will be:

$$N = \frac{a - c}{Q}; \quad \text{if } c \ll a, N \approx \frac{a}{Q} \tag{23}$$

Since Novick defined Q as the amount of limiting factor required to form one cell, perhaps (q) would serve for 1 μg. cells. The amount of nutrient, Q, to form one cell is assumed to be independent of growth factor concentration (c); in general, (c) is small compared to (a), and a/Q set equal to N, is within experimental error. In Monod's units, equation (23) assumes the dimensions:

$$\frac{\mu g.}{ml.} \left(\begin{matrix} \text{bacterial} \\ \text{density} \end{matrix} \right) = \frac{\mu g./ml.}{\mu g.} \left(\frac{\text{nutrient concentration}}{\text{factor to form 1 } \mu g. \text{ cells}} \right) \tag{24}$$

In these units:

$$\frac{N_{(\mu g./ml.}}{(a - c)_{(\mu g./ml.)}} = \frac{1}{q} = \frac{G}{C} = K \tag{25}$$

Thus

$$\frac{1}{q} = K$$

and

$$\frac{1}{q} \times \text{mol. wt.} = Y_s \tag{26}$$

Cell number and bacterial density (μg. cells) can readily be related for any organism, thus equating Q and q (see Luria[49]). For *E. coli*, one cell equals ca. 1.1×10^{-12} g. wet weight, or at about 75% water, ca. 0.28×10^{-12} g. dry weight. Therefore, 1 μg. dry cells is equivalent to about 3.6×10^6 cells, or:

$$Q \approx \frac{q}{3.6 \times 10^6} \tag{27}$$

Similarly, K and Y can be related to cell number.

The advantage of the chemostat (continuous flow) over the growth tube (static) for measuring growth yield is illustrated by an experiment of Bauchap and Elsden[72] with *S. faecalis* in semi-synthetic medium using arginine as energy source, i.e.,

$$\text{citrulline} + \text{ADP} + \text{iP} \rightarrow \text{ornithine} + CO_2 + NH_3 + \text{ATP} \tag{28}$$

Static growth experiments gave erratic values. In the chemostat, reproducible values were obtained in line with the chemical and enzymic evidence of ATP yield and earlier static growth experiments in a yeast extract-tryptone medium. The correlation of motility and arginine breakdown in absence of oxygen by pseudomonads furnishes independent though qualitative evidence of energetic coupling[198a]—whether or not this observation can be quantitated remains to be seen.

All calculations of growth yield from total growth, by static or flow methods, carry the assumption of a single limiting factor for growth amount (end point). The realization of this condition is a problem in selection of growth conditions. To apply the principle of limiting factor to energy liberation by fermentation or oxidation of a carbon source which furnishes both energy and carbon, an additional restriction obtains: the formation of carbon skeletons for essential metabolites must be in excess of cell requirement; i.e., energy, not carbon, must be limiting (see refs. 179, 179a, 197b).

Experimental evidence of energy-limited growth is available along three lines (see Bauchop and Elsden[55, 72]). First, in the glycolytic experiments with *S. faecalis*, the energy substrate (glucose) furnishes less than 5% of the cell carbon (this requires less than 1% of the glucose fermented); second, cell carbon is furnished from compounds not participating in the energy release (i.e., amino acids, growth factors); and third, supplementation with arginine yields growth increments proportional to arginine added; arginine is degraded only as far as ornithine, the 5-carbon skeleton remaining intact, and thus does not participate significantly as a carbon source.

B. GROWTH MEASUREMENTS AND CALCULATED ENERGY YIELDS

Cell yields as a function of substrate concentration have been measured for both aerobic and anaerobic growth. Monod,[193] in systematic studies of aerobic growth, related bacterial dry weight, measured by optical density, to weight of substrate for three facultative bacteria, *Bacillus subtilis*, *Escherichia coli*, and *Salmonella typhimurium*. These data permitted a rational formulation of growth parameters which has been extended[64, 194] and has received increased use as a tool in physiological studies. Imperfect knowledge of reaction steps and of energy coupling in bacterial respiration restricts the usefulness of available data for present purposes, as does incomplete information of products, i.e., degree of oxidation of the substrates. Conversion of substrate carbon to cells in yields as high as 50 to 55% (see p. 613 in ref. 197a) and difficulties in measuring "effective protoplasm" further complicate the theoretical interpretation. In contrast, the more detailed knowledge of "anaerobic" fermentation mechanisms permits a more quantitative consideration of substrates, products, and energy linkages. Growth yield data are available for glucose fermentation to both lactic acid and alcohol + CO_2 by organisms known to employ the Embden-Meyerhof pathway. The pathway documentation comprises both labeling and enzymic data. The organisms used, *Streptococcus faecalis* and *Saccharomyces cerevisiae*, have widely different nutritive requirements and systematic properties. The experiments employed several media at several growth temperatures without materially altering cell yields. These data permit initial approximation of cell yield as a function of glucose concentration. As the data in Table VII show, *S. faecalis* growth yield in two media, measured by both static and continuous flow methods, is remarkably uniform. The growth yield coefficient for *S. cerevisiae* corresponds surprisingly well with the values found for *S. faecalis*. Thus, the values from Table VII, $Y_G = 20\pm$, are considered characteristic of cell yield from energy-limited growth via the Embden-Meyerhof fermentation with a calculated net yield of 2 ATP per glucose, the Y_{ATP} being equal to $10\pm$, equation (20). Clearly, one would prefer a broader selection of or-

TABLE VII

ANAEROBIC GROWTH YIELDS

Organism	Medium	Growth conditions	Energy source	Yield (Y)	Reference
Streptococcus fae- calis	Complex	Static	Glucose	20	72, Fig. 1
	Semi-synthetic	Static	Glucose	20	108
	Semi-synthetic	Static	Glucose	21	72, Fig. 2
	Semi-synthetic	Continuous	Glucose	21	72, Fig. 5
Saccharomyces cerevisae	Synthetic	Static	Glucose	20	72, Fig. 2
Streptococcus fae- calis	Complex	Static	Arginine	10	72, Fig. 1
	Semi-synthetic	Chemostat	Arginine	10.5	72, Fig. 6, Table 3

ganisms and conditions to establish a constant for evaluation of unknown cases. The present value can be adjusted, if necessary, when further data are available. In our opinion, the available data, tabulated in Table VII, are preferable to the average values used by Bauchop and Elsden[72] because of the assumptions required in the selection of non-Embden-Meyerhof values; the value for Y_G, indicated by Table VII, is somewhat lower than the unit selected by these workers. Two lines of evidence are available to test the validity of the calculated $Y_{ATP} = 10$. First, S. faecalis is known to degrade arginine to ornithine, as shown in equation (29):

$$\text{arginine} + H_2O + ADP + Pi \rightarrow 2\ NH_3 + CO_2 + \text{ornithine} \qquad (29)$$

The mechanism has been shown to occur by hydrolysis of arginine to citrulline[171] and the conversion of citrulline to ornithine, reaction (28). The mechanism of the latter occurs via phosphorolysis of citrulline to carbamyl plus ornithine; the carbamylphosphate reacts with ADP, generating $ATP + CO_2 + NH_3$.[198, 198a] Thus, arginine dihydrolase, via citrulline, yields 1 ATP per arginine, i.e., one would predict $Y_{Arg} \approx Y_{ATP} \approx 10$. The values in Table VII are Y_{Arg} of 10 and 10.5, one from static culture with a yeast extract-tryptone medium and the second in chemostat measurements with synthetic medium and arginine as an adjunct to glucose as second energy source. These Y_{Arg} values are in complete agreement with the Y_{ATP} value calculated from the glucose growth data.

Growth yields on several substrates with a variety of organisms are shown in Table VIII.[55, 72, 108, 109, 198] These include bacteria with known Embden-Meyerhof pathways in comparison to the growth of S. faecalis (the latter calibrated in absolute units, Table VII) and absolute growth yields for several organisms whose fermentation pathways are only par-

TABLE VIII
YIELD COEFFICIENTS OF ANAEROBIC FERMENTATIONS[a]

Organism	Medium	Energy source	Y	Y/Y_{ATP}	ATP/ mole calcu- lated	Reference
Streptococcus faecalis	Complex	Glucose	1.0^b	2.0	2.0	109
Lactobacillus delbrueckii	Complex	Glucose	0.98	1.96	2.0	109
Leuconostoc mesenteroides	Complex	Glucose	0.71	1.42	1.0	109
Leuconostoc mesenteroides	Complex	Arabi- nose	0.81	1.62	2.0	109
Streptococcus faecalis	Semi-synthetic	Glucose	20.0	1.9	2.0	108
Streptococcus faecalis	Semi-synthetic	Gluco- nate	17.6	1.6	$\begin{cases} 1.33^c \\ \text{or} \\ 1.67^d \end{cases}$	108
Streptococcus faecalis	Complex	Ribose	21.0	2.0	2.0	198
Pseudomonas lindneri	Complex	Glucose	8.3	0.8	1.0	72
Propionibacterium pentosaceum	Semi-synthetic	Glucose	37.5	3.5	—	72
Propionibacterium pentosaceum	Semi-synthetic	Glycerol	20.0	1.9	—	72
Propionibacterium pentosaceum	Semi-synthetic	Lactate	7.6	0.72	—	72
Micrococcus lactolyticus	—	Lactate	10.1	1.0	—	160

[a] End point measured in static growth under N_2.
[b] Y values relative to *S. faecalis* = 1.
[c] Equimolar Entner-Doudoroff and pentosephosphate pathways.
[d] Equimolar Entner-Doudoroff and phosphoketolase pathways.

tially known. In Table VIII, upper part, the growth yield for *Lactobacillus delbrueckii*, a homofermentative lactic organism, compares favorably with *S. faecalis*, i.e., OD*/mole respectively 73 and 75; or relative yield, 0.98 for *delbrueckii*, which is excellent agreement.[109] The data with *Leuconostoc mesenteroides*, a heterofermentative lactic organism, compare with *S. faecalis*, 55/75 = 0.71; with 2 ATP per glucose for *S. faecalis*, the leuconostoc value calculates at 1.42 ATP per glucose.[109] Calculations for the leuconostoc pathway via pentose and phosphoketolase, with reduction of acetylphosphate to ethanol, indicate an ATP yield of 1. The value of 1.42 obtained from the growth data would lead one to conclude an error in measurement or that the pathway does not proceed as calculated. The growth yield experiments should be repeated with careful attention to the products. For example, if accessory electron acceptors lead to acetylphos-

---

* OD/mole: increase in optical density on a molar basis, in a standardized system in which cell weight corresponds to a linear increase in optical density.[109]

phate formation, the acetate could appear as a product with a decrease in ethanol, permitting formation of 1 ATP from acetylphosphate per each two electron pairs diverted. If further careful growth experiments and product analyses confirm the fermentation, i.e., glucose transformed to 1 mole each of ethanol, CO_2, and lactate, with growth yields indicating ATP yields appreciably higher than one, the possibility of other energy-yielding reactions in the fermentation should be considered.

The leuconostoc fermentation of arabinose (Table VIII), indicates molar growth yields of 0.81 compared to glucose, or 1.62 ATP equivalents per arabinose. The calculated ATP yield via phosphoketolase is 2 [reaction (4)]. As suggested for the glucose growth yield with this leuconostoc, further measurements should be made with arabinose and other pentoses, including ribose. One would predict an ATP yield of 2 with ribose, both from the product and enzymic data.[93a, 94, 97, 109] If arabinose is metabolized by an alternate route, the 1.6 ATP per mole may occur, and further enzymic studies would be indicated.

Similarly, from Table VIII, the observed growth yields during gluconate fermentation indicate an ATP yield of 1.8, or considerably in excess of the 1.33 value calculated from combined Entner-Doudoroff and pentose pathways to lactate and CO_2 as sole products [reaction (10)]. Reference to the original paper[108] shows lactate yield of 1.5 with CO_2 slightly above 0.5, indicating 0.5 molecules of C_2 compound at the oxidation level of acetate unaccounted for. If this product occurs and is formed via phosphoketolase, the ATP yield would calculate at 1.67, i.e., considerably closer to the measured than the 1.3 value calculated for the stoichiometry found in resting cells, as indicated in reaction (10).

Gluconate fermentation balance 1.8^+ lactate and 0.5 CO_2 was extrapolated from resting cell fermentation in the presence of 0.001 M arsenite in which lactate yield was above 1.75 and CO_2 yield was almost exactly 0.5. The presence of transaldolase and transketolase in gluconate-adapted, but not glucose-grown, cells of $S.$ $faecalis$, supported the suggestion of pentose cycling and fermentation by Embden-Meyerhof pathway.[76, 108] An assay of gluconate-grown cells for phosphoketolase and acetokinase[92] is indicated. In addition to enzyme experiments, further growth yield measurements with lactic bacteria on a variety of substrates, including those more oxidized and more reduced than hexose, should prove useful.

Propionibacterium pentosaceum growth yield data (Table VIII), warrant special attention, particularly the implication of an ATP yield of 3.5 or more. Glucose fermentation, reaction (30), proceeds, at least in part, to the level of pyruvate by the Embden-Meyerhof pathway.[78] Propionate formation is considered to occur stoichiometrically by reduction of two pyruvate to propionate with oxidation of a third mole to acetate and CO_2.

$$1.5 \text{ glucose} \rightarrow 2 \text{ propionate} + 1 \text{ acetate} + 1 \text{ CO}_2 \tag{30}$$

From the standpoint of energetics, the route of the fermentation is important. According to current concepts, the pathway includes fermentation to pyruvate via an Embden-Meyerhof pattern, carboxylation of pyruvate to oxalacetate followed by reduction to succinate.[78] Succinate is presumed to be transformed to a coenzyme A ester and isomerized to methylmalonyl-CoA.[15] Two alternate routes have been suggested at the methylmalonyl-CoA level: (1) decarboxylation by the reversal of reaction (31), as described by Flavin and Ochoa:[199]

$$ATP + CO_2 + \text{propionyl-CoA} \rightarrow \text{methylmalonyl-CoA} + Pi + ADP \qquad (31)$$

The decarboxylation reaction might provide an extra high energy bond. Alternatively, Swick and Wood[16] have proposed a mechanism of oxalacetate formation by transcarboxylation between methylmalonyl-CoA and pyruvate by a biotin-enzyme transcarboxylase, Scheme III. If this transcarboxylation reaction is coupled with the isomerization [reaction (4), Scheme III], the over-all transformation would be balanced energetically without net ATP synthesis from the pyruvate to propionate reaction; 1 ATP would be generated in the oxidation of pyruvate to acetate, which occurs once for each 1.5 glucose, i.e., yield 2.66 ATP per glucose.

$$\text{pyruvate} + \text{methylmalonyl-CoA} \xrightarrow{\text{Biot E}} \text{oxalacetate} + \text{propionyl-CoA} \qquad (1)$$

$$\text{oxalacetate} + 4\ e \rightarrow \text{succinate} \qquad (2)$$

$$\text{succinate} + \text{propionyl-CoA} \rightarrow \text{succinyl-CoA} + \text{propionate} \qquad (3)$$

$$\text{succinyl-CoA} \rightarrow \text{methylmalonyl-CoA} \qquad (4)$$

$$\text{Sum: pyruvate} + 4\ e \rightarrow \text{propionate} \qquad (5)$$

SCHEME III

An alternate mechanism of oxalacetate formation from phosphoenolpyruvate could, in theory, lead to the higher energy yield indicated by the growth experiments. By coupling the mechanism described by Utter and Kurahashi,[200] [reaction (1), Scheme IV], with the isomerase and decarboxylase reactions, one can visualize the sequence outlined in Scheme IV.

$$PEP + IDP + CO_2 \rightarrow \text{oxalacetate} + ITP \qquad (1)$$

$$\text{oxalacetate} + 4\ e \rightarrow \text{succinate} \qquad (2)$$

$$\text{succinate} + \text{propionyl-CoA} \rightarrow \text{succinyl-CoA} + \text{propionate} \qquad (3)$$

$$\text{succinyl-CoA} \rightarrow \text{methylmalonyl-CoA} \qquad (4)$$

$$\text{methylmalonyl-CoA} + ADP + iP \rightarrow CO_2 + ATP + \text{propionyl-CoA} \qquad (5)$$

$$\text{Sum: PEP} + iP + ADP + IDP \rightarrow \text{propionate} + ATP + ITP \qquad (6)$$

SCHEME IV

The Utter-Kurahashi carboxylase has not been reported so far for bacteria.

The possibilities presented in Schemes III and IV offer different estimates of net ATP gain by the propionate fermentation. Although no energy yield is involved in propionate synthesis by the transcarboxylation mechanism (Scheme III), one pair of electrons is donated by pyruvate oxidation, presumably coupled to phosphate uptake. Accounting for the complete fermentation of glucose according to the balance in reaction (30), 1.5 glucose gives rise to 3 pyruvate, 2 of which are reduced to propionate and the third oxidized to acetate for an over-all yield of 4 ATP per 1.5 glucose or 2.66 ATP per glucose. The generation of propionate through phosphoenolpyruvate (Scheme IV) could provide for a net uptake of 2 iP per propionate formed, in addition to the 2 derived from pyruvate formation and oxidation, increasing the total yield to 4 ATP per glucose. A similar yield of 4 ATP per glucose could be realized by still a third pathway of C-4 formation, carboxylation of pyruvate by malic enzyme with propionyl-CoA formation through coupled decarboxylation.[200a] Elsden[200a] has also considered the possibility of electron transport coupled phosphate incorporation via the fumarate-succinate reduction based on potential differences and the difference in properties of the *Propionibacterium* and *Veillonella* succinic dehydrogenases from the mammalian enzyme as shown by Singer and coworkers.

The aerobic growth experiments of Monod with *E. coli*, if evaluated on the assumptions of energy limitation and carbon excess and if the anaerobic growth yield of 10 μg. cells per ATP formed is used, indicate that the cells would give relatively low net energy yields, as shown in Table IX. The only marked difference in the K values, efficiency of conversion of carbon to cells, among the carbohydrates tested, is the lower value for rhamnose. With Monod's values, recalculation on a molar basis places the pentoses at about ⅚ of hexose with the rhamnose considerably lower, about ⅔. The equivalence hexose:pentose appears to be per carbon, perhaps indicating a consideration of the degree of oxidation rather than molar equivalence. For the

TABLE IX
AEROBIC GROWTH YIELDS OF *Escherichia coli*

Substrate	K^a	Y^b	Yield $(Y/Y_{ATP})^c$
Glucose	0.24	43.2	4.1
Fructose	0.22	40.4	3.9
Xylose	0.21	31.5	3.0
Arabinose	0.24	36.0	3.4
Rhamnose	0.16	26.4	2.5

[a] Data of Monod.[193]

[b] $Y = K \times$ molecular weight of substrate.

[c] $Y_{ATP} = 10.5$.[72]

study of aerobic energy supply it seems likely that one should devise a unit to express the amount of oxidation possible in addition to the molar yields. i.e., based on energy released by electron transport as ratio cells formed per O_2 taken up. Synthesis of cell components from glucose plus ammonium ion presents a further energetic problem in the form of the energy expenditure for monomer syntheses (see Section III, D). Diversion of carbon (energy) substrate to cells in an amount up to 25 to 55% of that used requires energy calculations to be based on the fraction of the substrate oxidized. Both of these factors will require further data and theoretical development. A consideration of the data of Storck and Stanier[201] and Morris[201a] can at best be considered as a "game" to direct attention to the nature of essential evidence required. If one assumes complete utilization of substrate to cells [i.e., no carbon residue less oxidized than CO_2 accumulates in the medium and conversion of $\frac{1}{5}$ (Monod[193] value) or $\frac{1}{2}$ (Morris[201a] and Herbert[197a] values] the growth per mole of substrate approximates, at 10 μg. cells/ATP, a 5 ATP yield per glucose at 20% glucose conversion to cells and a yield of 12 to 14 ATP at 50 to 55% conversion to cells. It seems possible these experiments represent energy-limited growth with complete substrate oxidation; if so, the efficiency of oxidative energy coupling is low, or the energy requirement for the manufacture of essential metabolites from glucose and ammonia (monomer formation) may be high. Presumably monomer formation would be the main difference between this aerobic carbon-ammonia growth and the assimilation of amino acids and cofactors with more than 95% of the carbon transformed to products through the energy-liberating systems of the anaerobic cell. Further consideration of the behavior of aerobic growth yields under different conditions of growth is clearly indicated. It seems particularly desirable to measure growth yields in the chemostat with vitamin and amino acids to determine if assimilation of noncarbohydrate carbon into cells will decrease appreciably in conversion of carbohydrate to cells.

Storck and Stanier[201] measured a few aerobic growth yields with *Pseudomonas fluorescens*, A3.12, on citric acid cycle intermediates and a series of aromatic compounds. Although the data are brief and in comparative units (turbidity), several interesting relationships appear (Table X). The figures given are averages from two or more measurements at different substrate concentrations; variations of molar yield were less than 5% for the values given.

The growth yields on citric cycle compounds really show three difference values: citrate-ketoglutarate, ketoglutarate-succinate, and succinate-fumarate. If one starts with the latter, 22 units of growth difference, with a difference of one pair of hydrogens presumed to pass from flavoprotein to oxygen, one can assume as unit either 2 ATP, as for mammalian tissue, or

TABLE X

MOLAR GROWTH YIELDS OF *Pseudomonas fluorescens* A3.12[a]

Substrate	Molar growth yield[b]	Δ	Δ
Citrate	206		—
α-Ketoglutarate	192	14	—
Succinate	151	41	—
Fumarate	129	22	
Mandelate	255		
Phenyl glyoxalate	252	3⎱	
Benzoate	211	41⎰	44
p-Hydroxy benzoate	206	5	—

NOTE: Molar yield = 0.01 mole/liter = 209; 11 μmole/ml. = 209.

[a] Arbitrary turbidity units.

[b] Data of Storck and Stanier.[201]

half this if the bacterial P/O ratio is 1. Any estimates can be adjusted at a later date when the turbidity values are available in bacterial dry weight units and more internal comparisons can be made; corrections for measurement of effective protoplasm, presumably based on nitrogen, also can be made. If one assumes 2 ATP for the succinate-fumarate difference, the ketoglutarate-succinate difference would be 4. Perhaps in comparison to mammalian tissue, a substrate phosphorylation occurs, with a second phosphorylation also between pyridine nucleotide and flavin. It would be well to know if the ketoglutarate oxidation of this organism generates acyl by substrate-level coupling. In these units, the citrate-ketoglutarate difference would appear closer to 1 assumed ATP unit than 2. If the pathway is through isocitrate, with a TPN-linked dehydrogenase, the electrons may not be available for energy couple, or they may be diverted to the reduction of substrates to cellular material. Certainly this increment does not represent a value greater than the succinate-fumarate difference; one would predict a higher value in DPN-mediated electron-transport coupled energy below flavoprotein. The pathway from citrate may be via an isocitritase with succinate and glyoxalate as oxidizable substrates; if so, the growth yield should represent succinate[151] plus any utility of glyoxalate oxidation. Clearly, molar growth yields on malate, pyruvate, acetate, and glyoxalate, perhaps also ethanol, glycolate, and tartrate, would be most useful. It would be beneficial also to have values for isocitrate and *cis*-aconitate to check the assumption of their equivalence to citrate. One might expect a pyruvate-acetate difference equal to the ketoglutarate-succinate difference, i.e. about 41.

If one could arrive at suitable values for acetate and oxalacetate, one could assume they would approximate citrate, less 1 ATP for the citrogenase (condensing enzyme) reaction. A continuation of the reasoning above, i.e., 22–33 units for a pyridine nucleotide-linked hydrogen oxidation, 44 for α-keto acid to the next lower fatty acid, assuming fumarate and malate equal (a hydration), it would become clear that our selection of 11Δ units for ATP is too optimistic, i.e., fumarate $129 - (22 + 41) = 66$ as predicted value for acetate oxidation, $+$ oxalacetate, 96, $= 162$. Compared to 206 for citrate, even without subtracting 1 ATP to drive the reaction, or with this subtraction, 150, i.e., more numbers are needed to play this game and to find if aerobic growth yields can help to determine efficiency of coupling in bacterial respiration.

If the numbers are accepted at face value, the aromatic oxidation series, mandelate to p-hydroxybenzoate (Table X), contains three interesting bits of information.

(1) Mandelate and phenyl glyoxalate, which differ by one hydrogen pair, show the same growth yield, i.e., no energy couple. Unpublished work by Shuster,[202] undertaken to determine the hydrogen transport catalyst for mandelate oxidation, revealed an E_0' for the mandelate-phenylglyoxalate of about $+.1$ volts, i.e., above the succinate-fumarate potential; perhaps too high for an ATP couple.

(2) Phenyl glyoxalate-benzoate oxidation, 2 electrons, gave the same difference value as ketoglutarate-succinate. Enzymic studies of this sequence in mandelate-adapted cells revealed a soluble yeast-type carboxylase for phenylglyoxalate to benzaldehyde and both TPN- and DPN-linked benzaldehyde dehydrogenases.[203] Assuming these enzymes are the main pathway in intact cells, one is faced with a reinterpretation of the probable ATP equivalence and mechanism of the ketoglutarate-succinate sequence, i.e., perhaps a P/O ratio of 1 from flavoprotein (succinate) and 2 for pyridine nucleotide-ketoglutarate would re-evaluate these increments as 1 and 2 ATP with the suggestion of 2 for the benzaldehyde-benzoate oxidation, i.e., pyridine nucleotide oxidation. Clearly, more data are needed to reason fruitfully. Continuing to other studies of side chain oxidation preceding ring cleavage, the Storck and Stanier data indicate the energetic utility of the oxidations, at least the phenylglyoxalate (benzaldehyde)-benzoate reaction.

(3) A third interesting value, benzoate-hydroxybenzoate oxidation, does not serve an energetically useful function. Current knowledge of aromatic ring hydroxylation implicates molecular oxygen[55] without energy couple. The present values are in keeping with this mechanism.

C. RESTRICTIONS ON MEASUREMENTS

The accumulated experience of microbial physiology has defined, in practical terms, the conditions of organism, medium, pH, temperature, aerobiosis, and age to meet particular experimental needs. Restrictions on interpretation of growth yield measurements are similarly defined in the statement of the problem (Section I, A of this chapter), and in the reviews by Monod,[64] Novick,[194] Rosenberger and Elsden,[197] and Herbert et al.[197a] It seems desirable, nevertheless, to list here briefly a few of the quantitatively more important experimental restrictions.

(1) One must know the quantity of energy-yielding substrate used, the products formed, and their amount. The phrases "substrate added" and "products from resting cell fermentation" do not sufficiently define the stoichiometry of a cellular process in growth, unless one demonstrates that all the added substrate is metabolized to the indicated products under the experimental conditions.

(2) Diversion of substrate to cellular material—either effective proto-plasm or stored "assimilated" substances (glycogen, lipid, or polypeptide)—must be known. This is troublesome in aerobic systems where the diversion of substrate to cellular material is quantitatively significant and where there exists an almost complete lack of knowledge of reaction route, mechanisms, and energy liberation and expenditure. For those cases in which 20 to 50 % of the substrate carbon is incorporated in cellular material, further experimental data will be required.

In anaerobic growth experiments, conditions can frequently be arranged to render the conversion of substrate to cellular material less than the experimental errors of measurement. The excellent experiment of Bauchop and Elsden[72] with defined medium demonstrated diversion of less than 1 % of isotopically labeled glucose to TCA-precipitable components. These data are deemed worth citing as an example. The cells were grown with 0.1 % (1 mg./ml.) glucose-U-C[14] in a semi-synthetic medium containing 1 % (10 mg./ml.) hydrolyzed casein supplemented with appropriate levels of the remaining amino acids (cysteine, tryptophan, and asparagine), growth factors, and salts. One hundred and fifty milliliters of medium containing 150 mg. glucose yielded, after washing with 5 % TCA and 0.5 % sodium lactate to remove adsorbed C[14] compounds, 27.8 mg. of cells containing 1156 c.p.m. from a total of 1357×10^2 added as glucose. This corresponds to 0.92 % of the glucose carbon; assuming the cells are 50 % carbon on a dry weight basis, the substrate furnished 4 % of the total cell carbon. These values concern only the acid-insoluble fraction of the cell, since the 5 % TCA would liberate the phosphorylated sugars, and the organic and amino acids of the metabolic pool. The pool usually amounts to less than 10 % of the organic carbon of the cell but can be relatively rich in carbohydrates. Thus, an insignificant amount, not much more than 1 % of the glucose carbon, was diverted from fermentation products. From the viewpoint of cells, the nitrogenous constituents (amino acids and growth factors) supplied over 95 % of the new cellular material. The conditions of item (1) above, namely, measurement of lactic acid recovery on the basis of glucose used, was not reported in this experiment. With the low carbohydrate level employed, energy derived from transfer of electrons to external acceptors could have occurred, but is presumed not to have been appreciable since the growth yields are similar to other measured values. It would nevertheless be useful to have such data.

(3) Energy-liberating processes other than the ones defined by the substrate metabolized frequently occur in growth experiments. There are two sorts, those arising from external electron acceptors, e.g., incomplete anaerobiosis, with oxygen serving as electron acceptor, or the presence in the nutritive medium of components which the organism is able to reduce with substrate hydrogen. Second, the presence of oxidizable substrates whose metabolism leads to ATP generation (e.g., fermentation or dismutation of amino acids, see Chapter 3). With anaerobic growth, the principal evidence of these reactions is the growth of the organism on the medium without the addition of energy-yielding substrate (base medium) or a larger than proportional growth increment for the first addition of substrate. If measurement of growth increment is constant over a 5- to 10-fold range of substrate concentration, one usually assumes an adequate control. One should not, however, overlook possible interaction of energy substrate with enzyme formation for alternate substrates, or pathways, nor the quantitative importance of the conversion of substrates other than the assumed energy source (e.g., when the energy source comprises 0.1 % glucose in the presence of 1 % hydrolyzed casein plus other nutrients).

(4) Nutrient limitation without decrease in metabolic rate of cells. Since the obligatory coupling of glycolysis, or respiration, and cell growth is not universal, care must be exercised to make measurements only when the energy source is limiting. The procedures described by Novick[194] and by Monod[64] can be applied to control the majority of these cases. In some instances, oxidative or fermentative reactions in nutrient-limited media have resulted in alteration of cell composition "assimilation" of nonprotoplasmic material without detection.

Senez and co-workers (see LeGall[204] and Pichinoty[205]) discuss an interesting instance from both the practical and theoretical viewpoint. In these experiments, the type of nitrogen source was altered rather than its quantity. In two instances, one an anaerobic vibrio, the second an aerobically grown aerobacter, the rate-limiting factor appeared to be the type of nitrogen source (N_2 or NO_3^-) with the rate-limiting step being the reduction to ammonia. These workers concluded that the metabolic rate of the cells proceeds undiminished, whereas the growth rate halves, thus cutting the efficiency of cellular synthesis per unit carbon to about 50 %. The importance of the type of nitrogen source as a growth-limiting condition would not be detected by alterations in the level of the energy-furnishing substrate. It would be interesting to determine if nutrients, particularly growth factors, would alter the growth rate on limiting type of nitrogen source. For example, Carnahan and Castle[206] observed an increased biotin requirement for clostridia growing on N_2, as compared to NH_3, and Nason et al.[207] observed an increased flavin requirement for growth with nitrate reduction. These data impinge on the mechanism and constancy of degree of coupling between energy-liberating reaction and formation of new protoplasmic material.

D. CELLULAR ENERGY REQUIREMENTS

The extent of understanding of the relationship between energy metabolism and cellular function may be defined by four questions: (1) What are the energy-yielding reactions? (2) What are the energy-requiring work functions and how much energy do they require? (3) What is the behavior of energy metabolism in environments of limiting growth and new synthesis? (4) How much can available methods tell the investigator of factors governing growth, biosynthetic, and assimilation rates? Large gaps in our understanding, especially in the areas defined by questions (2) and (3), severely limit an over-all evaluation.

One point of reference is suggested by the Y_{ATP} values found in quantitative anaerobic growth experiments. Aside from their value in the empirical comparison of the energy yields of different fermentations, these values should suggest the energy requirements for the formation of the bacterial cell. A comparison between the observed and predicted yields from 1 mole of ATP can be made within the restrictions discussed in the preceding Sections III, B and C. Bauchap and Elsden[72] cultivated anaerobic organisms in media presumed to contain a full complement of building blocks for cellular synthesis; under such conditions the major portion of the energy required could be assumed to serve for polymerization reactions forming proteins, nucleic acids, lipids, and polysaccharides. This assumption ignores the energy for active transport, physical work of motility, etc., which will fall into the residue of energy once approximations are made for the cellular polymerization. From the known ratios of cellular components (see Luria[49]), the energy cost of polymer synthesis can be approximated by assuming any predictable number of molecules of ATP involved in each condensation reaction. A sample calculation of this type is presented in Table XI. The basic assumptions used in predicting the energy costs of monomer incorporation are as follows: (1) Amino acids are incorporated into protein at the expense of a pyrophosphorylitic cleavage of XTP (two high-energy bonds) plus a third high-energy bond spent between soluble RNA and protein, or a total of three high-energy phosphates per residue polymerized. (2) Nucleic

TABLE XI
Energy Expenditure for Polymer Synthesis[a]

Substance	Dry weight (%)	Monomer units		ATP Equivalents for polymerization	
		Average mol. wt.	μmoles/ 100 mg. cells	per monomer	μmoles per 100 mg cells
Protein	60	110	545.0	3	1635
Nucleic Acid	20	300	66.6	5	333
Lipid[c]	10	60	303	3	909
Polysaccharide	10	166	60	2	120
					2997

[a] One hundred milligrams dry weight of cells.
[b] Generalized values (see Luria, Vol. 1, Chapter 1).
[c] Calculated as fatty acid.

acid formation per monomer can be approximated as requiring 5 energy-rich phosphates per residue—3 for formation of nucleotide from base plus 1-pyrophosphoryl-pentose-5-phosphate and 2 in pyrophosphate elimination for polymerization (if RNA formation proves to be via orthophosphate elimination, the calculated value should be lowered by $\frac{1}{5}$ of the RNA content). (3) Pyrophosphate, once formed via activation reactions, is not recovered, i.e., it is removed by hydrolysis. (4) Lipid (fatty acid) synthesis occurs, at the cost of 3 ATP per acetate incorporated, by activation of acetate by pyrophosphorolysis of ATP and a subsequent carboxylation forming malonyl-CoA, the substrate for condensation. (5) Polysaccharide synthesis proceeds through uridinediphospho intermediates at the cost of 2 ATP per monomer. The summation, about 3,000 μmoles of ATP, represents the calculated expenditure for the synthesis of 100 mg. of polymeric material from preformed building blocks, i.e., each micromole of ATP has the potentiality of forming about 33.3 μgm. of cellular substance. The difference between the observed cellular yields (10 μgm. per μmole ATP) under the conditions imposed, indicates that the listed reactions account for only about 30% of the energy actually expended. There are, of course, many variables of the energy requirement neglected in the approximation for polymerization. Actually, the considerable amount of energy devoted to lipid synthesis may be misleading since under anaerobic conditions each monomer incorporated will provide an electron acceptor for two pairs of electrons, allowing extra energy-coupled oxidations. One could add to these values an estimate for transport across cell membranes, for mobility, etc. One can visualize the energy requirement of the cell as serving three roles: (1) monomer formation, (2) polymerization, and (3) movement, including mechanical motion of flagellar origin, transport of metabolites across membrane and other boundaries, and deformations in cell growth, etc. The energy cost of active transport could be approximated only with multiple assumptions; motility could be circumvented by using nonflagellated types, as in the growth experiments with lactic bacteria. Possibly the energy dissipated by ATPase mechanisms is large. If so, considerable variations in this activity would be necessary to shift the observed growth yield appreciably. Although the cellular yields are in direct proportion to available ATP under energy-limited conditions, the relationship between cell synthesis and energy metabolism remains empirical.

IV. Energy Excess: Nutrient Limitations

Cessation of growth in a bacterial culture in the presence of energy source, with some other factor limiting, raises the question of the constancy or tightness of coupling between energy-liberating reactions and cell growth. The behavior of the cells and the fate of carbon during glycolysis or respiration by cell suspensions become the limiting case. The intermediate conditions, nutrients present but growth limited without substrate exhaustion, result from an unknown factor limiting the growth, i.e., unfavorable physical or chemical environment (pH, toxic chemicals accumulated) or the end point reached when a single limiting chemical, not energy substrate, is exhausted. The latter case is used in growth factor assay. The behavior of the culture and its cells has been studied to a limited extent (McIlwain[208]).

In the case of limiting factor other than energy source, the substrate may continue to be degraded either at full or reduced rate. In these cases, the available energy cannot be used for growth and must be dissipated in some other fashion. The condition of energy release without coupled growth must be understood if variables in growth yield and substrate carbon use for non-energy functions are to be understood. As part of the larger problem of uncoupling in the presence of limiting factors, three mechanisms of energy dissimilation other than the formation of new protoplasm will be briefly discussed. They are: (1) accumulation of polymeric products, either in storage form or as unusable waste; (2) dissipation as heat by "ATPase mechanisms"; and (3) activation of shunt mechanisms bypassing energy-yielding reactions or requiring a greater expenditure of energy for priming.

A. ASSIMILATION: POLYMER FORMATION

The relationship between energy metabolism and carbon assimilation in washed cell suspensions (resting cells) has long been associated with the incorporation of a fraction of the substrate carbon into cells. During respiration, the "oxidative assimilation" can use a large fraction of the substrate; during glycolysis, "fermentative assimilation," the amount is smaller. Barker[209] established the oxidative assimilation of more than half the carbon from organic acids during oxidation by resting cells of the colorless alga, *Prototheca zopfii*. Since then the occurrence of massive accumulation has been observed in many organisms with a wide variety of substrates.[68] Anaerobic "fermentative assimilation" was established by van Niel and Anderson[210] with suspensions of both resting and growing yeast. The products of anaerobic glucose fermentation accounted for only 70% of the carbohydrate utilized, with the remainder presumably incorporated into "cellular material." Under nutrient-limited conditions, the assimilated carbon is not incorporated into new protoplasm but is found to be in accessory polymeric (storage or waste) products, e.g., capsular slime (3), polypeptides,[211] glycogen[212] or lipids of the poly-β-hydroxybutyrate type.[212a] Not all compounds degraded result in polymer accumulation; formate oxidation by suspensions of *E. coli* proceeds to completion without measurable accumulation of new cellular or polymeric material.[213] Only those compounds yielding "useful" energy to the cell promote assimilation.

Carbohydrate polymers, internal or external, are among the principal products of substrate "assimilation" during nutrient-limited substrate turnover. Cellulose synthesis provides the most striking example of polysaccharide synthesis. Both *A. xylinum*[214] and *A. acetigenum*[215] accumulate up to one-quarter of the glucose metabolized as extracellular cellulose. Each hexose unit converted to cellulose requires one ATP for activation; the polymerization occurs via uridine-diphosphoglucose catalyzed by particle-bound enzymes associated with the cell membrane.[216] The other principal form of extracellular polysaccharides is capsular material.[217]

Internal storage, usually analyzed as glycogen, is common in bacteria. Dagley and Dawes,[212] for example, observed glycogen accumulation after growth had ceased in cultures due to limitations other than depletion of energy source. Palmstierna and co-workers[217-219] found glycogen accumulation to be maximum in continuous cultures in nitrogen-limited medium. Glycogen synthesis was much greater after nitrogen exhaustion with either glucose or lactate as energy source. The maximal amounts of glycogen stored internally accounted for 20% of the dry weight.

Among the compounds, in addition to carbohydrate, which are found frequently in the cytoplasm of bacterial cells are polyphosphates, usually as granules. Such granules accumulate in both aerobic and anaerobic bacteria and appear to react directly with ATP by transphosphorylation, reaction (32).

$$ATP + (PO_3)_n \rightarrow ADP + (PO_3)_{n+1} \qquad (32)$$

An enzyme catalyzing this reaction has been purified from extracts of *E. coli*, but the cultural conditions leading to polyphosphate formation have not been established.

B. ATPase: Direct and Indirect

The role of limiting metabolite levels in the control of metabolism has been considered in many cases since cell-free yeast glycolysis was found to be phosphate limited and Harden and Young found fructosediphosphate to be the product of bound phosphate and missing carbon.[5] A clue in the initial experiments was the shift in stoichiometry from 2 moles of alcohol per glucose to 1 mole per glucose on change from whole cell suspensions to extracts. The mechanism of this apparent return of phosphate to the inorganic level in the intact cell, but not the extract, engaged Meyerhof's curiosity as late as 1949.[227] One could envision the return of ATP phosphorus to the inorganic level in growing cultures through the work functions of cellular transport, biosynthesis of intermediates, polymerization—but the continued fermentation by suspensions, without apparent work functions, remained obscure. Meyerhof convinced himself that in the yeast cell the cause is the occurrence of a very unstable phosphatase which does not withstand drying or prolonged storage in yeast extracts. In very careful and systematic studies, Meyerhof examined the level of phosphatase, its disappearance from dry cells and extracts, and re-established the normal alcoholic fermentation balance by the addition of ATPases to yeast extracts.

Whether or not Meyerhof's "ATPase" of intact yeast fermentation is a direct hydrolytic enzyme or occurs by other mechanism, it appears to be the prototype for nonproliferating glycolysis or respiration, i.e., energy-linked system without apparent work function. The cell confined to glycolysis without growth must either regenerate orthophosphate and energy-rich phosphate acceptor (ADP or ATP) or transform metabolites by an alternate noncoupled mechanism. This problem is the more important from the need to understand the mechanisms of coupling or its lack in growing and nonproliferating cells.

Knowledge of glycolytic control in microbial cells is in a completely unsatisfactory state. Even a knowledge of the phosphatases which could perform either direct or indirect ATPase activity is fragmentary and in most cases completely lacking. It may be true that ATPase activities are entirely lacking in fermentative bacteria. If this is true, combined reactions which can lead to a net release of ATP might be sought; in fact, several reactions have been related to glycolytic rate. In lactic acid bacteria, glutamic-glutamine, and to a lesser extent ornithine-citrulline-arginine, have been implicated. Further, one can visualize organic acid mechanism such as coupled citrogenase (condensing enzyme)-citritase which would energetically equal an ATP hydrolysis.

The rate of glycolysis of washed streptococci in cell suspensions is markedly stimulated by addition of glutamic acid and ammonia, histidine and ammonia, or glutamine.[223] In some instances, the rate increase is as much as 5- to 8-fold. Gale[224] has demonstrated a glycolytic requirement for incorporation of glutamate by cell suspensions. McIlwain[225] has demonstrated a glucose dependency for the conversion of glutamine to glutamic plus NH_3 as well as for the reverse reaction. One can visualize the expenditure of at least one energy-rich phosphate bond in the glutamate permease reaction from the data of Gale. It is also possible to visualize an "ATPase"-type reaction by a coupled glutamine synthetase-glutaminase reaction. A severalfold stimulation of glycolytic rate in washed cell suspensions by chemical additions which could serve an ATPase function may, but by no means must, state their mode of action. McIlwain and co-workers[225] have observed, in common with Meyerhof's labile ATPase of yeast, a complete inability to prepare a glutaminase in extracts of streptococci, although in the same extracts they were able to obtain active arginine dihydrolase. The mechanisms of the glutamine hydrolysis in these organisms remains obscure.

The arginine dihydrolase reaction which occurs in two steps, hydrolytically from arginine to citrulline and phosphorolytically from citrulline to ornithine plus carbamyl phosphate, requires 2 moles ATP in the reverse (synthetic) direction. Thus, a repetition of the first step, hydrolysis of arginine to citrulline, return of citrulline to arginine via an ATP-dependent condensation with aspartate, would yield a net loss of high-energy phosphate.[171, 172] The primary question is: do these reactions constitute a mechanism permitting nonproliferating cell glycolysis, i.e., the regeneration of phosphate acceptors and orthophosphate?

Several reactions of organic acids, normally energy-linked oxidations, would appear to obviate the accumulation of phosphate anhydride energy. Three examples will be given. (1) The acetone-butanol fermentation of clostridia, (2) the acyloin fermentation of lactic acid bacteria and *Aerobacter*, and (3) the oxidative pyruvate-acetate bypass.

The clostridial butanol fermentation (Wood, Chapter 2, Table V), as distinguished from acetate or butyrate fermentation, occurs without net energy gain beyond the pyruvate stage (see Table VI, this chapter). By the thiolase condensation and Lynen cycle for acetoacetate generation from acetoacetyl-CoA, this product stoichiometry could account for the conversion of 2 moles of acetyl-CoA to acetone and CO_2 without net energy gain. Acetone arises via the decarboxylation of acetoacetate, Scheme V. The mechanism of the microbial acetoacetate-forming system has not been clarified. Scheme V is based on Lynen's recent data with mammalian tissue.[227]

$$2 \text{ acetyl-CoA} \rightarrow \text{acetoacetyl-CoA} + \text{CoA} \tag{33}$$

$$\text{acetoacetyl-CoA} + \text{Acetyl-CoA} \rightarrow \text{HMG-CoA} + \text{CoA} \tag{34}$$

$$\text{HMG-CoA} \rightarrow \text{acetoacetate} + \text{acetyl-CoA} \tag{35}$$

$$\text{acetoacetate} \rightarrow \text{acetone} + CO_2 \tag{36}$$

$$\text{Sum: } 2 \text{ acetyl-CoA} \rightarrow \text{acetone} + CO_2 + 2 \text{ CoA}$$

SCHEME V

A nonenergy-generating system from pyruvate yields 2 moles of CO_2 and 1 acyloin without acyl ($\sim$P generation[76]). One pair of electrons formed from glucose via triosephosphate could reduce acetoin to butyleneglycol, but one residual electron pair would remain for another acceptor.

It is not as yet clear whether glycolyzing cells form bypass systems which dissipate the energy of oxidation in heat without phosphorylative coupling; aerobic *E. coli* cells do form a phosphate-independent pyruvate oxidase.[74]

C. Uncoupling in Growth

Experiments of Senez *et al.* (see refs. 204 and 205) with nitrogen-limited growth (N_2 or NO_3^- in place of NH_3) showed a depressed growth rate without decreased substrate turnover—thus a metabolic rate independent of growth. This would be possible only if some mechanism either bypassing ATP generation or permitting its dissipation at a uniform rate is present in the cell. The principle illustrated here is the apparent lack of regulation by feedback or limiting level of essential cofactor or stoichiometric participation in nonproliferating cell fermentation and respiration. As indicated in earlier sections of this chapter, many questions are raised by the fundamental problems of energy metabolism and its relation to growth, biosynthesis, and control of cell functions.

Cell behavior in nutrient-limited growth is a prime example of an area in which much information is needed; it has implications of control of proliferation and energy turnover in organized biological forms, including mammals.

Acknowledgment

Dr. S. R. Elsden has made many helpful contributions of data prior to publication and critical discussions of this manuscript for which the authors wish to express their appreciation.

References

[1] A. J. Kluyver, "The Chemical Activities of Microorganisms." Univ. of London Press, London, 1931.

[2] A. J. Kluyver and C. B. van Niel, "The Microbe's Contribution to Biology." Harvard Univ. Press, Cambridge, Massachusetts, 1956.

[3] M. R. J. Salton, *in* "The Bacteria" (I. C. Gunsalus and R. Y. Stanier, eds.), Vol. I, p. 97. Academic Press, New York, 1960.

[4] A. F. Kamp, J. W. M. LaRiviére, and W. Verhoeven, eds., "Albert Jan Kluyver, His Life and Work." North-Holland Publ., Amsterdam, 1959.

[5] A. Harden, "Alcoholic Fermentation." Longmans, Green, London, 1923.

[6] E. Buchner, *Ber.* **30,** 117 (1897).

[7] K. Lohmann and P. Schuster, *Biochem. Z.* **294,** 188 (1937).

[8] O. Meyerhof, *in* "A Symposium on Respiratory Enzymes," p. 3. University of Wisconsin Press, Madison, Wisconsin, 1942.

[9] M. Doudoroff, N. Kaplan, and W. Z. Hassid, *J. Biol. Chem.* **148,** 67 (1943).

[10] M. Doudoroff, H. A. Barker, and W. Z. Hassid, *J. Biol. Chem.* **168,** 725 (1947).

[11] J. MacGee and M. Doudoroff, *J. Biol. Chem.* **210,** 617 (1954).

[12] R. Weimberg and M. Doudoroff, *J. Biol. Chem.* **217,** 607 (1955).

[12a] R. Weimberg, *J. Biol. Chem.* **234,** 727 (1959).

[13] C. Fitting and M. Doudoroff, *J. Biol. Chem.* **199,** 153 (1952).

[14] H. G. Wood and C. H. Werkman, *Biochem. J.* **30,** 48 (1936).

[15] E. R. Stadtman, P. Overath, H. Eggerer, and F. Lynen, *Biochem. Biophys. Research Communs.* **2,** 1 (1960).

[16] R. W. Swick and H. G. Wood, *Proc. Natl. Acad. Sci. U. S.* **46,** 28 (1960).

[17] H. A. Barker, "Bacterial Fermentations." Wiley, New York, 1956.

[18] H. A. Barker, *in* "Symposium on Phosphorus Metabolism," (W. D. McElroy and B. Glass, eds.) Vol. I, p. 204. Johns Hopkins Press, Baltimore, Maryland, 1951.

[19] H. A. Barker, R. D. Smyth, H. Weissbach, J. I. Toohey, J. N. Ladd, and B. E. Volcani, *J. Biol. Chem.* **235,** 480 (1960).

[20] H. A. Barker, R. D. Smyth, R. M. Wilson, and H. Weissbach, *J. Biol. Chem* **234,** 320 (1959).

[21] R. D. Sagers, J. V. Beck, W. Gruber, and I. C. Gunsalus, *J. Am. Chem. Soc.* **78,** 694 (1956).

[22] J. C. Rabinowitz and H. A. Barker, *J. Biol. Chem.* **218,** 147 (1956).

[23] F. Lipmann, *Cold Spring Harbor Symposia Quant. Biol.* **7,** 248 (1939).

[24] H. Karstrom, *Ergeb. Enzymforsch.* **7,** 350 (1938).

[25] D. J. O'Kane and I. C. Gunsalus, *J. Bacteriol.* **54,** 20 (1947).

[26] I. C. Gunsalus, *J. Cellular Comp. Physiol.* **41** Suppl. 1, 113 (1953).

[27] I. C. Gunsalus, *in* "Mechanism of Enzyme Action" (W. D. McElroy and B. Glass, eds.), p. 545. Johns Hopkins Press, Baltimore, Maryland, 1954.

[28] E. E. Snell, *J. Biol. Chem.* **154,** 313 (1944).

[29] I. C. Gunsalus, W. W. Umbreit, W. D. Bellamy, and C. E. Foust, *J. Biol. Chem.* **161,** 743 (1945).

[30] W. D. Bellamy and I. C. Gunsalus, *J. Bacteriol.* **48,** 191 (1944).

[31] F. Schlenk and E. E. Snell, *J. Biol. Chem.* **157,** 425 (1945).

[32] E. E. Snell and F. M. Strong, *Ind. Eng. Chem., Anal. Ed.* **11,** 346 (1939).

[33] E. E. Snell, *Physiol. Revs.* **28,** 255 (1948).

[34] E. E. Snell, *Ann. Rev. Microbiol.* **3,** 97 (1949).

[35] J. Monod and M. Cohn, *Advances in Enzymol.* **13,** 67 (1952).

[36] J. Lederberg and E. L. Tatum, *Cold Spring Harbor Symposia Quant. Biol.* **11,** 113 (1946).

[37] M. Delbrück, *Advances in Enzymol.* **2,** 1 (1942).

[38] N. D. Zinder and J. Lederberg, *J. Bacteriol.* **64,** 679 (1952).

[39] O. T. Avery, C. M. MacLeod, and M. McCarty, *J. Exptl. Med.* **79,** 137 (1944).

[40] M. Grunberg-Manago, P. J. Ortiz, and S. Ochoa, *Biochim. et Biophys. Acta* **20,** 269 (1956).

[41] S. E. Luria, *Ann. N. Y. Acad. Sci.* **71,** 1085 (1958).

[42] I. R. Lehman, M. J. Bessman, E. S. Simms, and A. Kornberg, *J. Biol. Chem.* **233,** 163 (1958).

[43] E. F. Gale and J. P. Folkes, *Biochem. J.* **53,** 483 (1953).
[44] S. Spiegelman, *in* "Recent Progress in Microbiology," Symposium 7th Intern. Congr. Microbiol., Stockholm, 1958 (G. Tunevall, ed.), p. 81. C. C Thomas, Springfield, Illinois, 1959.
[45] P. Berg, *Federation Proc.* **16,** 152 (1957).
[46] M. M. Mason, *J. Bacteriol.* **99,** 103 (1935).
[47] A. R. Fuchs and G. J. Bonde, *J. Gen. Microbiol.* **16,** 317 (1957).
[48] G. Toennies and G. D. Shockman, *Proc. 4th Intern. Congr. Biochem., Vienna, 1958,* p. 365 (1959).
[49] S. E. Luria, *in* "The Bacteria" (I. C. Gunsalus and R. Y. Stanier, eds.), Vol. I, p. 1. Academic Press, New York, 1960.
[50] K. Wallenfels and M. J. Zarnitz, *Angew. Chem.* **69,** 482 (1957).
[51] J. C. Rabinowitz and W. E. Pricer Jr., *Federation Proc.* **17,** 293 (1958).
[52] H. J. Rogers, *in* "The Bacteria" (I. C. Gunsalus and R. Y. Stanier eds.), Vol. II, p. 257. Academic Press, New York, 1960.
[53] R. Y. Stanier, *Bacteriol. Revs.* **14,** 179 (1950).
[54] W. C. Evans, *Ann. Repts. on Progr. Chem. (Chem. Soc. London),* **53,** 279 (1956).
[55] S. R. Elsden and J. L. Peel, *Ann. Rev. Microbiol.* **12,** 145 (1958).
[56] E. Adelberg, M. Doudoroff, and R. Y. Stanier, "General Microbiology" Prentice-Hall, New York, 1958.
[57] C. B. van Niel, *Bacteriol. Revs.* **13,** 161 (1949).
[58] M. Cohn, *Bacteriol. Revs.* **21,** 140 (1957).
[59] H. L. Kornberg, *Ann. Rev. Microbiol.* **13,** 49 (1959).
[60] I. C. Gunsalus, *Proc. 4th Intern. Congr. Biochem., Vienna, 1958,* p. 226 (1959).
[61] W. D. Bellamy and I. C. Gunsalus, *J. Bacteriol.* **50,** 95 (1945).
[62] E. F. Gale, *Bacteriol. Revs.* **7,** 139 (1943).
[63] M. Grunberg-Manago and I. C. Gunsalus, *Bacteriol. Proc.* 1953, 73.
[64] J. Monod, *Ann. Rev. Microbiol.* **3,** 371 (1949).
[65] L. J. Reed and M. Koike, *Federation Proc.* **19,** 36 (1960).
[66] M. Doudoroff, *in* "My Twenty-five Years with Saccharophila." In preparation.
[67] A. C. Aisenberg and V. R. Potter, *J. Biol. Chem.* **224,** 1115 (1957).
[68] C. E. Clifton, *Advances in Enzymol.* **6,** 269 (1946).
[69] F. Lipmann, *Advances in Enzymol.* **1,** 99 (1941).
[70] P. F. Smith, *J. Bacteriol.* **73,** 91 (1957).
[71] J. Szulmajster, in press.
[72] T. Bauchop and S. R. Elsden, in press.
[73] M. J. Johnson, *Science* **94,** 200 (1941).
[74] L. P. Hager, *J. Am. Chem. Soc.* **79,** 5575 (1957).
[75] H. L. Kornberg, *Proc. 4th Intern. Congr. Biochem., Vienna, 1958* p. 251 (1959).
[76] I. C. Gunsalus, B. L. Horecker, and W. A. Wood, *Bacteriol. Revs.* **19,** 79 (1955).
[77] B. L. Horecker, *J. Cellular Comp. Physiol.* **54,** Suppl. 1, 89 (1959).
[78] H. G. Wood, R. Stjernholm, and F. W. Leaver, *J. Bacteriol.* **72,** 142 (1956).
[79] A. G. C. White, R. H. Steele, and W. A. Pierce, Jr., *J. Bacteriol.* **70,** 82 (1955).
[80] A. Kornberg, *Advances in Enzymol.* **18,** 191 (1957).
[81] K. Lohmann and O. Meyerhof, *Biochem. Z.* **273,** 60 (1934).
[82] O. Warburg, W. Christian, and A. Griese, *Biochem. Z.* **282,** 157 (1935).
[83] T. Bücher, *Biochim. et Biophys. Acta* **1,** 292 (1947).
[84] E. Racker and I. Krimsky, *J. Biol. Chem.* **198,** 721 (1952).
[85] E. Racker, *in* "Mechanism of Enzyme Action" (W. D. McElroy and B. Glass, eds.), p. 464. Johns Hopkins Press, Baltimore, Maryland, 1954.

[86] H. A. Krebs and H. L. Kornberg, "Energy Transformations in Living Matter." Springer, Berlin, 1957.

[87] G. T. Cori, M. W. Slein, and C. F. Cori, *J. Biol. Chem.* **173,** 605 (1948).

[88] E. C. Heath, J. Hurwitz, and B. L. Horecker, *J. Am. Chem. Soc.* **78,** 5449 (1956).

[89] M. Schramm, V. Klybas, and E. Racker, *J. Biol. Chem.* **233,** 1283 (1958).

[90] M. Schramm and E. Racker, *Nature* **179,** 1349 (1957).

[91] B. L. Horecker, P. Z. Smyrniotis. and J. Hurwitz, *J. Biol. Chem.* **223,** 1009 (1956).

[92] B. L. Horecker, E. C. Heath, J. Hurwitz, and A. Ginsburg, *Federation Proc.* **16,** 198 (1957).

[93] E. C. Heath, J. Hurwitz, B. L. Horecker, and A. Ginsburg, *J. Biol. Chem.* **231,** 1009 (1958).

[93a] J. O. Lampen, H. Gest, and J. C. Sowden, *J. Bacteriol.* **61,** 97 (1951).

[94] D. A. Rappoport, H. A. Barker, and W. Z. Hassid, *Arch. Biochem. Biophys.* **31,** 326 (1951).

[95] E. Racker, G. De la Haba, and I. G. Leder, *J. Am. Chem. Soc.* **75,** 1010 (1953).

[96] R. Breslow, *J. Cellular Comp. Physiol.* **54** Suppl. 1, 100 (1959).

[97] J. Hurwitz, *Biochim. et Biophys. Acta* **28,** 599 (1958).

[98] M. Schramm, Z. Gromet, and S. Hestrin, *Nature* **179,** 28 (1957).

[99] H. J. Strecker and S. Korkes, *Nature* **168,** 913 (1951).

[100] W. A. Wood and R. F. Schwerdt, *J. Biol. Chem.* **201,** 501 (1953).

[101] O. Warburg and W. Christian, *Biochem. Z.* **242,** 206 (1931).

[102] E. Negelein and W. Gerischer, *Biochem. Z.* **284,** 289 (1936).

[103] B. L. Horecker and P. Z. Smyrniotis, *Arch. Biochem.* **29,** 232 (1950).

[104] B. L. Horecker, P. Z. Smyrniotis, and J. E. Seegmiller, *J. Biol. Chem.* **193,** 383 (1951).

[105] R. Kovachevich and W. A. Wood, *J. Biol. Chem.* **213,** 757 (1955).

[106] N. Entner and M. Doudoroff, *J. Biol. Chem.* **196,** 853 (1952).

[107] M. Gibbs and R. D. DeMoss, *J. Biol. Chem.* **207,** 689 (1954).

[108] J. T. Sokatch and I. C. Gunsalus, *J. Bacteriol.* **73,** 452 (1957).

[109] R. D. DeMoss, R. C. Bard, and I. C. Gunsalus, *J. Bacteriol.* **62,** 499 (1951).

[110] I. C. Gunsalus and M. Gibbs, *J. Biol. Chem.* **194,** 871 (1952).

[111] M. Gibbs, R. Dumrose, F. A. Bennett, and M. R. Bubeck, *J. Biol. Chem.* **184,** 545 (1950).

[112] M. Gibbs, J. T. Sokatch, and I. C. Gunsalus, *J. Bacteriol.* **70,** 572 (1955).

[113] J. T. Sokatch, A. P. Prieto, and I. C. Gunsalus, *Bacteriol. Proc.*, **1956,** 112.

[114] G. Buyze, J. A. van den Hamer, and P. G. de Haan, *Antonie van Leeuwenhoek, J. Microbiol. Serol.* **23,** 345 (1957).

[115] M. I. Dolin, *Arch. Biochem. Biophys.* **55,** 415 (1955).

[116] C. R. Brewer and C. H. Werkman, *Enzymologia,* **6,** 273 (1939).

[117] J. J. R. Campbell and I. C. Gunsalus, *J. Bacteriol.* **48,** 71 (1944).

[118] J. J. R. Campbell, W. D. Bellamy, and I. C. Gunsalus, *J. Bacteriol.* **46,** 573 (1943).

[119] S. Dagley and E. A. Dawes, *J. Bacteriol.* **66,** 259 (1953).

[120] M. Deffner, *Ann.* **536,** 44 (1938).

[121] M. Deffner and W. Franke, *Ann.* **541,** 85 (1939).

[122] D. C. Gillespie and I. C. Gunsalus, *Bacteriol. Proc.* **1953,** 80.

[123] C. R. Brewer and C. H. Werkman, *Antonie van Leeuwenhoek, J. Microbiol. Serol.* **6,** 110 (1940).

[124] J. T. Wachsman and H. A. Barker, *J. Biol. Chem.* **217,** 695 (1955).

[125] H. A. Barker, R. M. Wilson, and A. Munch-Peterson, *Federation Proc.* **16,** 151 (1957).

[126] H. A. Barker, B. E. Volcani, and B. P. Cardon, *J. Biol. Chem.* **173,** 803 (1948).

[127] R. D. Sagers and I. C. Gunsalus, *Bacteriol. Proc. (Soc. Am. Bacteriologists)* p. 119 (1958).

[127a] M. Benziman, R. D. Sagers, and I. C. Gunsalus, *J. Bacteriol.* **79**, 474 (1959).

[128] B. P. Cardon and H. A. Barker, *Arch. Biochem. Biophys.* **12**, 165 (1947).

[129] I. C. Gunsalus and R. A. Smith, *in* "Proceedings of the International Symposium on Enzyme Chemistry, Tokyo-Kyoto (1957)" (K. Ichihara, ed.), p. 77. Academic Press, New York, (1958).

[130] L. P. Hager, J. Fortney, and I. C. Gunsalus, *Federation Proc.* **12**, 213 (1953).

[131] I. C. Gunsalus, L. Barton, and W. Gruber, *J. Am. Chem. Soc.* **78**, 1763 (1956).

[132] V. Massey, *Biochim. et Biophys. Acta* **30**, 205 (1958).

[132a] V. Massey, Q. H. Gibson, and C. Veeger, *Biochem J.* **77**, 341 (1960).

[133] V. Massey, *Biochim. et Biophys. Acta* **32**, 286 (1959).

[134] R. L. Searls and D. R. Sanadi, *Biochem. Biophys. Research Communs.* **2**, 189 (1960).

[135] R. L. Searls and D. R. Sanadi, *Biochem. Biophys. Research Communs.* **2**, 226 (1960).

[136] A. Brodie, unpublished observations (1954).

[136a] G. W. Notani and I. C. Gunsalus, *Federation Proc.* **18**, 295 (1959).

[137] L. P. Hager, D. M. Geller, and F. Lipmann, *Federation Proc.* **13**, 734 (1954).

[138] H. J. Koepsell and M. J. Johnson, *J. Biol. Chem.* **145**, 379 (1942).

[139] R. S. Wolfe and D. J. O'Kane, *J. Biol. Chem.* **205**, 755 (1953).

[140] H. Chantrenne and F. Lipmann, *J. Biol. Chem.* **187**, 757 (1950).

[141] H. J. Strecker, H. G. Wood, and L. O. Krampitz, *J. Biol. Chem.* **182**, 525 (1950).

[142] I. A. Rose, M. Grunberg-Manago, S. R. Korey, and S. Ochoa, *J. Biol. Chem.* **211**, 737 (1954).

[143] B. E. Wright and M. L. Anderson, *Biochim. et Biophys. Acta* **28**, 370 (1958).

[144] B. E. Wright and M. L. Anderson, *J. Am. Chem. Soc.* **79**, 2027 (1957).

[145] C. W. Shuster and F. Lynen, *Biochem. Biophys. Research Communs.* **3**, 350 (1960).

[146] C. Delavier-Klutchko, *Compt. rend. acad. sci.* **249**, 2418 (1959).

[147] H. S. Moyed and D. J. O'Kane, *Arch. Biochem. Biophys.* **39**, 457 (1952).

[148] H. S. Moyed and D. J. O'Kane, *J. Biol. Chem.* **195**, 375 (1952).

[149] D. J. O'Kane, *Federation Proc.* **13**, 739 (1954).

[150] L. P. Hager, *J. Biol. Chem.* **229**, 251 (1957).

[151] H. A. Barker and M. D. Kamen, *Proc. Natl. Acad. Sci. U. S.* **31**, 219 (1945).

[152] H. G. Wood, *J. Biol. Chem.* **194**, 905 (1952).

[153] T. B. Platt and E. M. Foster, *J. Bacteriol.* **75**, 453 (1958).

[154] D. S. Goldman, *J. Biol. Chem.* **208**, 345 (1954).

[155] S. J. Wakil, *J. Am. Chem. Soc.* **80**, 6465 (1958).

[156] S. J. Wakil, E. B. Titchener, and D. M. Gibson, *Biochim. et Biophys. Acta* **29**, 225 (1958).

[157] F. Lynen, *J. Cellular Comp. Physiol.* **54**, Suppl. 1, 33 (1959).

[158] H. G. Wood, R. W. Brown, and C. H. Werkman, *Arch. Biochem.* **6**, 243 (1945).

[159] R. M. Burton and E. R. Stadtman, *J. Biol. Chem.* **202**, 873 (1953).

[160] S. R. Elsden, personal communication (1960).

[161] J. C. Rabinowitz and W. E. Pricer, Jr., *J. Biol. Chem.* **222**, 537 (1956).

[162] R. D. Sagers and I. C. Gunsalus, *Bacteriol. Proc.* **1958**, 119.

[163] J. C. Rabinowitz and W. E. Pricer, Jr., *J. Am. Chem. Soc.* **78**, 1513 (1956).

[164] H. Tabor and A. H. Mehler, *J. Biol. Chem.* **210**, 559 (1954).

[165] J. T. Wachsman and H. A. Barker, *J. Bacteriol.* **69**, 83 (1955).

[166] B. Magasanik and H. R. Bowser, *J. Biol. Chem.* **213**, 571 (1955).

[167] H. Tabor and J. C. Rabinowitz, *J. Am. Chem. Soc.* **78**, 5705 (1956).

[168] H. R. Whiteley, *J. Bacteriol.* **74**, 324 (1957).

[169] M. E. Jones, L. Spector, and F. Lipmann, *J. Am. Chem. Soc.* **77**, 819 (1955).

[170] M. E. Jones, L. Spector, and F. Lipmann, *Proc. Intern. Congr. Biochem 3rd., Congr., Brussels, 1955*, p. 278 (1956).

[171] H. D. Slade, C. C. Doughty, and W. C. Slamp, *Arch. Biochem. Biophys.* **48**, 338 (1954).

[172] V. A. Knivett, *Biochem. J.* **56**, 602 (1954).

[173] H. D. Slade, *Arch. Biochem. Biophys.* **42**, 204 (1953).

[174] M. Korzenovsky and C. H. Werkman, *Arch. Biochem. Biophys.* **46**, 174 (1953).

[175] G. M. Hills, *Biochem. J.* **34**, 1057 (1940).

[176] G. C. Schmidt, M. A. Logan, and A. A. Tytell, *J. Biol. Chem.* **198**, 771 (1952).

[177] J. Szulmajster, *Biochim. et Biophys. Acta* **30**, 154 (1958).

[178] J. Szulmajster and R. C. Gardiner, *Biochim. et Biophys. Acta* **39**, 165 (1960).

[179] A. T. Jagendorf, *Federation Proc.* **18**, 974 (1959).

[180] J. B. Neilands, *Ann. Rev. Biochem.* **27**, 455 (1958).

[181] G. B. Pinchot, *J. Biol. Chem.* **229**, 1 (1957).

[182] P. E. Hartman, A. F. Brodie, and C. T. Gray, *J. Bacteriol.* **74**, 319 (1957).

[183] A. F. Brodie and C. T. Gray, *J. Biol. Chem.* **219**, 853 (1956).

[184] A. F. Brodie, *J. Biol. Chem.* **234**, 398 (1959).

[185] C. W. Shuster and I. C. Gunsalus, *Federation Proc.* **17**, 310 (1958).

[186] Brown and E. R. Stadtman, unpublished observations.

[187] A. F. Brodie and J. Ballantine, *J. Biol. Chem.* **235**, 232 (1960).

[188] A. F. Brodie and J. Ballantine, *J. Biol. Chem.* **235**, 226 (1960).

[189] A. F. Brodie, M. M. Weber, and C. T. Gray, *Biochim. et Biophys. Acta* **25**, 448 (1957).

[190] M. M. Weber and A. F. Brodie, *Biochim. et Biophys. Acta* **25**, 447 (1957).

[191] B. O. Linn, N. R. Trenner, C. H. Shunk, and K. Folkers, *J. Am. Chem. Soc.* **81**, 1263 (1959).

[192] C. Martius, *Chem. Weekblad* **53**, 196 (1957).

[192a] S. R. Elsden, in Press.

[193] J. Monod, "Recherches sur la croissance des cultures bacteriennes" (Librairie scientifique), 210 pp. Hermann, Paris, 1942.

[194] A Novick, *Ann. Rev. Microbiol.* **9**, 97 (1955).

[195] A. Novick and L. Szilard, *Proc. Natl. Acad. Sci. U. S.* **36**, 708 (1950).

[196] A. Novick and L. Szilard, *Science* **112**, 715 (1950).

[197] R. F. Rosenberger and S. R. Elsden, *J. Gen. Microbiol.* **22**, 726 (1960).

[197a] D. Herbert, R. Elsworth, and R. C. Telling, *J. Gen. Microbiol.* **14**, 601 (1956).

[197b] D. Herbert, *in* "Recent Progress in Microbiology," Symposium, 7th Intern. Congr. Microbiol., Stockholm, 1958 (G. Tuneval, ed.) p. 381. C. C Thomas, Springfield, Illinois, 1959.

[198] T. Bauchop, *J. Gen. Microbiol.* **18**, vii (1958).

[198a] N. W. Preston, J. C. Sherris, and J. G. Shoesmith, *J. Gen. Micobiol.* **15**, vii (1956).

[198b] E. L. Oginsky, M. Korzenovsky, and H. D. Slade, *in* "A Symposium on Amino Acid Metabolism" (W. D. McElroy and B. Glass, eds.), pp. 300, 309, 321. Johns Hopkins Press, Baltimore, Maryland, 1955.

[199] M. Flavin and S. Ochoa, *J. Biol. Chem.* **229**, 965 (1957).

[200] M. F. Utter and K. Kurahashi, *J. Biol. Chem.* **207**, 821 (1954).

[200a] S. R. Elsden, personal communication (1960).

[201] R. Storck and R. Y. Stanier, unpublished observations (1956).

[201a] J. G. Morris, *J. Gen. Microbiol.* **22,** 564 (1960).

[202] C. W. Shuster, unpublished observations (1959).

[203] C. F. Gunsalus, R. Y. Stanier, and I. C. Gunsalus, *J. Bacteriol.* **66,** 548 (1953).

[204] J. Le Gall and J. C. Senez, *Compt. rend. acad. sci.* **250,** 404 (1960).

[205] F. Pichinoty, 1960.

[206] J. E. Carnahan and J. E. Castle, *J. Bacteriol.* **75,** 121 (1958).

[207] A. Nason, *in* "Symposium on Inorganic Nitrogen Metabolism" (W. D. McElroy and B. Glass, eds.), p. 109. Johns Hopkins Press, Baltimore, Maryland, 1956.

[208] H. McIlwain, D. A. Stanley, and D. E. Hughes, *Biochem. J.* **44,** 153 (1949).

[209] H. A. Barker, *J. Cellular Comp. Physiol.* **8,** 231 (1936).

[210] C. B. van Niel and E. H. Anderson, *J. Cellular Comp. Physiol.* **17,** 49 (1941).

[211] C. B. Thorne, *Symposium Soc. Gen. Microbiol.* **6,** 68 (1956).

[212] S. Dagley and E. A. Dawes, *Biochem. J.* **45,** 331 (1949).

[212a] R. Y. Stanier and M. Doudoroff, *Proc. Natl. Acad. Sci. U. S.* **45,** 1246 (1959).

[213] R. P. Cook and M. Stephenson, *Biochem. J.* **22,** 1368 (1928).

[214] S. Hestrin and M. Schramm, *Biochem. J.* **58,** 345 (1954).

[215] T. K. Walker and H. B. Wright, *Arch. Biochem. Biophys.* **69,** 362 (1957).

[216] L. Glaser, *Biochim. et Biophys. Acta* **25,** 436 (1957).

[217] H. Palmstierna and R. Stjernholm, *Acta Chem. Scand.* **11,** 900 (1957).

[218] T. Holme, *Acta Chem. Scand.* **11,** 763 (1957).

[219] T. Holme, T. Laurent, and H. Palmstierna, *Acta Chem. Scand.* **11,** 757 (1957).

[220] S. R. Kornberg, *Biochim. et Biophys. Acta* **26,** 294 (1957).

[221] J. M. Wiame, *J. Am. Chem. Soc.* **69,** 3146 (1947).

[222] O. Meyerhof, *J. Biol. Chem.* **180,** 575 (1949).

[223] C. E. Foust, Ph.D. Thesis, Cornell University, Ithaca, New York (1947).

[224] E. F. Gale, *J. Gen. Microbiol.* **1,** 53 (1947).

[225] H. McIlwain, J. A. Roper, and D. E. Hughes, *Biochem. J.* **42,** 492 (1948).

[226] R. Davies, *Biochem. J.* **37,** 230 (1943).

[227] F. Lynen, *Proc. 4th Intern. Congr. Biochem., Vienna, 1958* **13,** p. 267 (1959).

[228] J. S. Fruton and S. Simmonds, "General Biochemistry," 2nd ed. Wiley, New York, 1958.

[229] F. Lynen, G. Hartmann, J. Netter, and A. Schuegraf, *in* "Regulation of Cell Metabolism" (Ciba Foundation Symposium), p. 256. London, 1959.

[230] L. O. Krampitz, *in* "The Bacteria" (I. C. Gunsalus and R. Y. Stanier, eds.), Vol. II, p. 209. Academic Press, New York, 1960.

[231] C. B. Fowler, *Compt. rend. acad. sci.* **231,** 1348 (1950).

[232] R. W. Stone and P. W. Wilson, *J. Bacteriol.* **63,** 605 (1952).

[233] I. C. Gunsalus, M. I. Dolin, and L. Struglia, *J. Biol. Chem.* **194,** 849 (1952).

[234] L. P. Hager and H. L. Kornberg, *Biochem. J.* **78,** 194 (1961).

[235] S. Korkes, A. del Campillo, and S. Ochoa, *J. Biol. Chem.* **195,** 541 (1952).

[236] P. K. Stumpf, *J. Biol. Chem.* **159,** 529 (1945).

[237] V. Jagannathan and R. S. Schweet, *J. Biol. Chem.* **196,** 551 (1952).

[238] D. R. Sanadi, J. W. Littlefield, and R. M. Bock, *J. Biol. Chem.* **197,** 851 (1952).

[239] S. Kaufman, C. Gilvarg, O. Cori, and S. Ochoa, *J. Biol. Chem.* **203,** 869 (1953).
[240] R. A. Smith, unpublished observations (1958).
[241] E. Knight and J. Grunau, unpublished observations (1960).
[242] S. Kaufman and S. G. A. Alivisatos, *Federation Proc.* **13,** 239 (1954).
[243] H. Sachs, *J. Biol. Chem.* **228,** 23 (1957).
[244] H. R. Mahler, S. J. Wakil, and R. M. Bock, *J. Biol. Chem.* **204,** 453 (1953).
[245] M. G. P. J. Warringa, O. H. Smith, A. Guiditta, and T. P. Singer, *J. Biol. Chem.* **230,** 97 (1958).
[246] C. B. van Niel, *J. Gen. Microbiol.* **16,** 499 (1957).

Chapter 2

Fermentation of Carbohydrates and Related Compounds

W. A. Wood

I. Introduction

Fermentation was one of the first biological phenomena to stimulate the curiosity of natural philosophers and inquisitive observers and thus to become the object of intensive investigations. In the past half-century, studies have been made on nearly every conceivable phase of Pasteur's *"La vie sans air."* These explorations, aided by a wide spectrum of organisms, substrates, culture conditions, and recently by advanced analytical methods, have revealed an equally broad spectrum of products formed in greatly varying yields. The results, in most cases, can now be interpreted in terms of a unified concept of reaction patterns providing energy and material for vital processes of living cells. Although the information available is comprehensive and detailed, it will become evident as this presentation develops that many details, and probably new principles, remain to be elucidated.

The fundamental characteristics of the fermentation processes which will be discussed in detail are: (a) the pathways of carbon, (b) the derivation and role of hydrogen acceptors in permitting fermentation to proceed and in determining its products, (c) the influence of substrate (oxidation-reduction state, chain length, etc.) on process and products, and (d) the site and yield of energy in the several patterns. Exposition and understanding of present knowledge requires that the details of the organisms, substrate(s) conditions, products, and yields be given attention. Often the reasons will be given why a unique metabolic pattern—a genetic heritage—particularly fits a selected organism for the elucidation of a general principle.

The magnitude of the material presented on microbial fermentation products, pathways, and mechanisms does not reflect a universal inherent merit but the fact that a sourcebook may well have reference value which permits contemporary investigators to review, refine, and explain phenomena passed over briefly in the course of the growth of microbiology as a science. As opposed to this, the outline is meant to reflect what appears at present to be the general principles and the primary types of microbial fermentations in terms of products and the effects of substrates and conditions on their yield as well as the best explanation which this author can deduce as to their mechanism and biological meaning in terms of energy metabolism. An attempt is made, in addition, to indicate those areas in which information is fragmentary and the conclusions are based on untested inference.

A. PATHWAYS OF CARBON

To evaluate the type of energy generating system in a given fermentation, one must consider the routes for carbon atoms during the process. As recently discussed by Elsden,[1] the several primary pathways of fermentation deliver characteristic amounts of energy utilizable for biological work including biosynthesis. The energy-mobilizing steps and the products may or may not vary with the process. Therefore, energy yield alone, where measured or measurable, may not reveal carbon flow patterns. The most useful tool for formulation of pathways is the accurate quantitative evaluation of isotope distribution in the products from a uniquely labeled substrate. In most cases, this alone is insufficient and must, as illustrated by examples in the text, be followed by evidence of enzyme type and abundance.

B. HYDROGEN ACCEPTOR

In fermentation, as in aerobic metabolism, energy mobilization derives ultimately from oxidation (dehydrogenation). Hence for fermentation proceeding in the absence of oxygen, the generation of the hydrogen acceptors is of primary consequence. A wide variety of hydrogen acceptors, including pyruvate, acetaldehyde, dihydroxyacetone phosphate, fructose, acetoin, and carbon dioxide, serve in this capacity. The corresponding reduced products, lactate, ethanol, glycerol (α-glycerophosphate), mannitol, 2,3-butanediol and methane, accumulate. The most common biological hydrogen acceptors are aldehydes and carboxylic acids, which yield primary alcohols upon reduction. The reduction of ketones and ethylenic double bonds to secondary alcohols and saturated carbon chains and the formation of molecular hydrogen also serve. However, organisms devoid of or limiting in these processes comprise the greater portion of known species.

C. EFFECT OF CHAIN LENGTH AND OXIDATION-REDUCTION STATE OF THE SUBSTRATE

Fundamental but predictable changes in the fermentation mechanism occur with substrates of different carbon chain lengths and degrees of oxidation with a resultant alteration of product distribution and energy yield. For C_3 substrates and its multiples (including hexose polymers) a common pathway exists, but for C_4, C_5, and C_7 sugars and polyols different sequences come into play. With polyols, two hydrogen atoms more reduced than the corresponding carbohydrates, there appears to be little change from the hexose fermentation route, the main difference being an increased yield of reduced products. In contrast, with substrates more oxidized than carbohydrates, i.e., hexonic acids, the carbon flow and fermentation mechanisms in some instances change drastically.

D. ENERGY YIELD

The data of several physiologists indicate for growing cultures under conditions of energy source limitation a constant relationship between the amount of energy source and cell yield.[1a] Such a relationship would imply a relatively tight, or at least a constant coupling between substrate turnover, energy yield, and biosynthesis (see Volume II, Chapter 1). Until recently, the generation and transfer of biochemically useful energy in fermentation processes was considered to be substrate coupled, i.e., transferred between chemical groups one of which was a substrate molecule. These groups, in the terminology of Lipmann,[1b] appear first as high energy phosphate or thiol ester bonds on intermediates derived from the substrate (substrate phosphorylation). Energy generation as phosphate anhydrides by electron transport (oxidative phosphorylation), as characteristically seen in aerobic metabolism, was considered to be absent from anaerobic metabolic processes. Although not demonstrated in all anaerobic processes, a form of oxidative phosphorylation appears to be present in certain instances.[1c, 1d] Whether or not electron transport energy is coupled to phosphate anhydrides, the level of energy available will depend on the availability of electron acceptors to permit further substrate oxidation, the amount of phosphate anhydride formed depending upon the number of energy-trapping events per electron pair transferred. The formation of reduced products is a requisite of enhanced energy yield. In the propionic and butyric acid fermentations, electron transport coupled to oxidative phosphorylation appears to account in part for the large growth yield reported in these fermentations (see Volume II, Chapter 1).

E. Substrates Fermented

A wide variety of substrates is fermented by relatively few distinct pathways. The ability to ferment sugars and related compounds of different configuration from glucose results from the cell's ability to convert substrates to intermediates common to the pathways for glucose fermentation, often a matter of induced formation of enzymes for a few additional reactions rather than the creation of new mechanisms. With changes in chain length or oxidation state an altered carbon flow pattern develops in which a pentose rather than a hexose pathway becomes the common sequence. Thus far three general patterns have been observed in microorganisms. Presumably, the genetic potential to shift adaptively from one pattern to another with changes in available substrate bestows in natural habitats survival value upon an organism.

F. Relationship of Fermentation Mechanism to Type of Organism

The energy-generating mechanism and the available systems for disposing of hydrogen atoms are fundamental characteristics of an organism and express themselves in the type of products formed, i.e., the fermentation characteristic of the organism. This relationship presumably underlies the importance of fermentation products and substrates in systematic bacteriology.

The fundamental importance of glucose metabolism requires detailed discussion of the major fermentation patterns. Thus the homolactic, heterolactic, ethanol, propionic, formic, acetone-butyl, and other well-known fermentations of glucose will be considered. Fermentations involving (a) other carbohydrates, although convertible to intermediates of known pathways, and (b) substrates of differing chain lengths and oxidation-reduction states will be treated in a second section. The fermentation of organic acids and the reduction of carbon dioxide that are related only to the final reactions of the carbohydrate fermentations are discussed in a third section.

II. Methodology

The classic procedures of microbiology provide rudimentary information on the fermentation pattern. Observations of acid production, (indicator added, change in pH), gas formation and rate and amount of growth furnish (a) a means of surveying the substrates fermented and comparing the range of substrate availability among strains, species, and genera, and (b) a guide to products formed.

A. FERMENTATION BALANCES

The stoichiometry of substrate conversion to products in a fermentation can be derived only from accurate quantitative determination of substrate used and products formed. Fermentations involve as over-all reactants only the substrate and water. It is therefore convenient to construct a balance to account for all of the carbon atoms in the substrate distributed among the products. The H and O atoms can be balanced only by comparing the ratio in the substrate and products with H_2O since a net uptake or loss of water may occur. Needless to say, useful information can be obtained only when a large proportion of the carbon, hydrogen, and oxygen can be accounted for, and very little is converted to cells.

Many of the classic fermentation balances were prepared two or more decades ago when accurate and specific methods for many products were lacking, or when not all products were quantitatively known or measured. For instance, CO_2 (frequently added as carbonate buffer) was considered to be metabolically inert and was not considered in balances prepared before the pioneering work of Wood and Werkman[1e] in 1936. In this instance and in numerous others, i.e., glycerol fermentation, balances constructed before this concept and observation require reconsideration. On the other hand, balances of Lavoisier[1f] as early as 1784 to 1789 were sufficiently accurate to formulate the stoichiometry of the alcoholic fermentation and are valid today.

In the absence of specific methods, reasonably specific procedures for separating related compounds were employed and resulted in many of the successful balances. Titration was a means of determining acid concentration. For instance, volatile and nonvolatile fractions were separated, followed by identification and quantitation of the volatile acids by such determinations as Ducleaux distillation constants, ether-water partition coefficients, or azeotropic distillations. There were, however, no rapid procedures for estimating ethanol and mixtures of glycerol and mannitol. It is not surprising, therefore, that some balances do not show a full carbon recovery or oxidation-reduction balances corresponding to the substrate.

The recent development of partition and ion exchange chromatography

TABLE I

CALCULATION OF FERMENTATION BALANCE OF *Lactobacillus lycopersici*[244]

	mMoles/ liter	mMoles/100 mmoles of C_6 (1)[a]	mMoles carbon (2)	O/R value (4)	Oxidized (5)	Reduced (5)	Calc. C_1 (7)
Glucose fermented	112.2	100.0	300.0	0	—	—	—
Products formed:							
Lactic acid	89.7	40.0	120.0	0	—	—	0
Acetic acid	19.7	8.7	17.4	0	—	—	8.7
Ethanol	78.9	35.2	70.4	−2	—	−70.4	35.2
Carbon dioxide	95.1	42.4	42.4	+2	+84.8	—	—
Glycerol	43.5	19.4	58.2	−1	—	−19.4	0
			308.4		+84.8	−89.8	43.9

[a] Numbers (1) to (7) refer to text.

NOTE: (3) Carbon recovered = 308.4/300 = 102.7%; (6) O/R balance = 84.8/89.8 = 0.943; (8) C_1 recovery = C_1 observed/C_1 calculated × 100 = 96.5%.

has made the identification and quantitative determination of fermentation acids simple and accurate. Similar techniques applied to glycerol, mannitol, and mixtures of carbohydrates allow separation and determination by nonspecific methods. Specific enzymic methods for succinate, acetate, ethanol, and glucose, and relatively specific colorimetric methods for lactate, pyruvate, and carbohydrates have greatly simplified the preparation of fermentation balances. A series of methods developed by Neish[2] and associates and published in monograph form is the best source of modern methods available.

As an aid to understanding the balances presented in subsequent sections, the fermentation balance and its preparation will be described briefly. The steps below, which have evolved from the procedures of Johnson *et al.*,[3] Erb *et al.*,[4] and Barker,[5] are generally applicable and may be followed in connection with Table I.

(1) Express the amount of substrate fermented and products formed in mmoles per 100 mmoles of substrate (C_6) utilized (mmoles product formed/mmoles substrate used × 100).

(2) Calculate the mmoles of carbon in the substrate and in each product by multiplying the mmoles per 100 mmoles of C_6 by the number of carbon atoms in each substrate and product molecule.

(3) Determine the percent of carbon recovered (mmoles of C in products/mmoles of C in substrate × 100).

(4) Determine the oxidation-reduction state of the substrate and prod-

ucts. One system is based upon a comparison of the ratio of hydrogen and oxygen atoms in the products with that in water. When this ratio is 2 or CH_2O, the O/R state is zero. Each 2H in excess of the above ratio is expressed as -1, whereas a decrease of each 2H is expressed as $+1$. Thus glucose, lactate, and acetate have an oxidation-reduction number of zero, whereas carbon dioxide is $+2$ and ethanol is -2.

(5) Multiply the "mmoles of product per 100 mmoles C_6 fermented" by the oxidation-reduction number. Place the plus values in one column, the minus values in another.

(6) Calculate the O/R balance (mmoles oxidized/mmoles reduced).

(7) Estimate the amount of C_1 expected from the number of mmoles of C_2 compound and substances derived from C_2 compounds.

(8) Express as the ratio (C_1 observed/ C_1 calculated). These may be CO_2, formate, etc.

The above steps were performed in the balance illustrated in Table I. The number in parentheses above each column indicates the step involved.

Errors result if (a) substrate carbon provides a major source of cell carbon; recoveries in the fermentation balance may be low to an extent of 20 %; (b) other ingredients of the medium also yield the same fermentation products; and (c) carbon dioxide fixation occurs.

Aside from allowing a formulation of the fermentation equation, balances also may yield information as to mechanisms involved. In such studies the effect of changes in pH (see Tables II and VIII), oxidation-reduction level of the substrate, and in time are observed. Most of the information so derived, however, relates to the terminal reactions of fermentation rather than to the major pathways involved.

B. USE OF RADIOISOTOPES

Whereas fermentation balances reflect the over-all result of a fermentation and allow certain inferences as to the mechanism, fermentation of substrates containing C^{14} in specific positions gives information of which atoms of the substrate appear in particular positions of the products. Since the mechanisms of intermediary metabolism of carbohydrates in plant, animal, and mammalian cells have become well-known, interpretation of the labeling patterns is facilitated. Thus, the yield of information concerning a fermentation mechanism is far greater than is inherent in the method. Gibbs and associates,[6] for instance, have found in the homolactic fermentation of glucose-3,4-C^{14} by *Lactobacillus casei* that only the carboxyl group of lactate was labeled with C^{14} and that the specific activity corresponded to that of carbon atoms 3 or 4 of the substrate. Similarly, with glucose-1-C^{14} the radioactivity was present in the methyl group of lactate at one-half the specific activity of carbon 1. Therefore, lactate must have been derived from 2 molecules of pyruvate whose carbon atoms arose from glu-

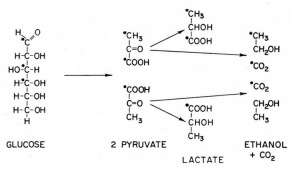

FIG. 1. Labeling pattern of Embden-Meyerhof pathway.

cose, as shown in Fig. 1. Similar tests with the ethanolic fermentation by yeasts have been performed by Koshland and Westheimer.[7] Since this pattern is in agreement with the way pyruvate is derived from glucose in the Embden-Meyerhof pathway of glycolysis and from no other known route, labeling data of this sort are taken as evidence that the Embden-Meyerhof pathway functions in that fermentation.

Other fermentative pathways give different labeling in the products. For instance, in the hexose monophosphate route, carbon atom 1 of hexose yields carbon dioxide or the carboxyl rather than the methyl group of pyruvate. Hence, in simple cases, the amount of radioactive carbon dioxide released in the fermentation of glucose-1-C^{14} is considered to indicate the amount of hexose monophosphate pathway which is functioning. A variation of this route, exemplified by the ethanolic fermentation of *Pseudomonas lindneri*,[8] yields 2 moles of pyruvate, as shown in Fig. 2. In this case carboxyl-labeled pyruvate is formed. If the pyruvate is then decarboxylated, labeled carbon dioxide is released as in the hexose monophosphate pathway. However, when substrates labeled in other positions, particularly glucose-3,4-C^{14}, are metabolized, it is possible to distinguish between these variations of the hexose monophosphate pathways (see Section III, B).

In simpler cases the use of isotopically labeled substrates allows verification of the postulated metabolic pathways under physiological conditions.

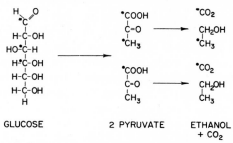

FIG. 2. Labeling pattern of Entner-Doudoroff pathway.

Conclusions derived from this type of experiment are not subject to the criticism leveled against biochemical studies that ascertain the presence of enzymes and intermediates of a given pathway by the use of broken cell preparations or inhibitors. In addition, unexpected labeling patterns are effective indicators of anomolous reactions or new pathways. A striking example is presented by the fermentation of glucose by *Leuconostoc mesenteroides*.[9, 10] In this case, instead of glucose-1-C^{14} yielding methyl-labeled ethanol or lactate as expected from an Embden-Meyerhof mechanism, the carbon dioxide was labeled. Further investigations of this anomolous result in conjunction with enzyme studies established a new pathway for ethanol formation. When detailed biochemical information is lacking, however, as in the *Propionibacterium arabinosum* fermentation,[11, 12] studies with radio-isotopes give clues as to which pathways would be possible, but this technique alone is not effective in establishing the details of the new process.

C. BIOCHEMICAL STUDIES

The following types of biochemical evidence have been sought in establishing pathways, particularly the Embden-Meyerhof glycolytic system: (a) isolation of intermediates which accumulated during glucose fermentation, (b) fermentation of intermediates to typical end products or to other intermediates of the postulated pathway, (c) demonstration of individual reactions and enzymes. With the exception of the phosphorus balance studies of O'Kane and Umbreit,[13] artificial and often drastic conditions were imposed. For example, sodium fluoride ($0.2M$ to $0.5 M$) has been widely used to cause the accumulation of phosphoglycerate during the fermentation of glucose.[14] Since phosphoglycerate is more oxidized than glucose, an external hydrogen acceptor such as acetaldehyde was supplied.

From a historical point of view, experiments utilizing these methods played an important role in establishing the Embden-Meyerhof system as the primary mechanism of fermentation. In the light of newer knowledge indicating that several other pathways also utilize the initial and final steps of the glycolytic system, it has become evident that only the central portion of the Embden-Meyerhof pathway, i.e., reactions between fructose-1,6-phosphate and glyceraldehyde-3-phosphate, is unique to that pathway.[15] All of the other intermediates are common to several routes. In spite of this, it is desirable in the appropriate sections to present salient information obtained with the above procedures.

III. Carbohydrate Fermentation Types

A. HEXOSE DIPHOSPHATE PATHWAY (EMBDEN-MEYERHOF GLYCOLYTIC SYSTEM)

The first fermentation pathway visualized in detailed steps, and perhaps the best documented today, is the Embden-Meyerhof scheme for fermentation of glucose. The initial data were well known and assembled principally from investigations of glucose conversion to lactate in muscle and to alcohol in yeast. Although its adequacy to explain the energetic and mechanistic requirements for muscle and yeast created the impression of its being the only pathway for glucose utilization, general acceptance of its function as an important, but not sole, route in microbial fermentations was long delayed. A clear statement and evaluation of the evidence up to 1950 has been presented by Elsden.[16]

Since 1950, two important developments in understanding glucose fermentation have occurred: (a) enzymic and isotopic studies have established the occurrence in microorganisms and in plant and animal tissue of patterns not explainable as part of the Embden-Meyerhof pathway and (b) a realization that the reactions of the Embden-Meyerhof (fructose-1,6-diphosphate) system serve also in other glycolytic and oxidative patterns. All of the "alternate" routes of hexose utilization, in fact, show the reactions from glyceraldehyde-3-phosphate to pyruvate.

The intermediates of the Embden-Meyerhof pathway are indicated in Fig. 3. Many detailed accounts of these reactions are available in texts[17, 18] and reviews.[15, 16] All of the known intermediates and dissociable coenzymes

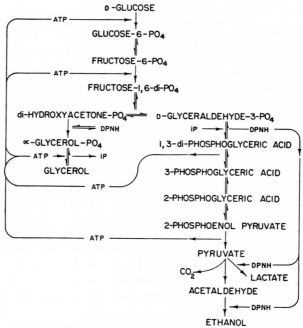

Fig. 3. Embden-Meyerhof-Parnas glycolytic scheme.

have been isolated and carefully characterized and most of the enzymes prepared in crystalline form from several cell types.

Concomitant with the understanding of the steps in carbohydrate breakdown has come an understanding of the mechanism of substrate-coupled energy generation involving the uptake of inorganic phosphate and the eventual formation of "high energy" (Lipmann,[1b]) mixed phosphoric-acyl anhydride and thiol ester bonds transferable to the nucleotide carrier systems for maintenance and growth (see Chapter 1).

1. YEAST ETHANOLIC FERMENTATION

The study of ethanol production in relation to wine and beer manufacture supplied in the late eighteenth and throughout the nineteenth century our earliest understanding of microorganisms as agents of fermentation. While this treatise is concerned with the bacteria, the background of investigation is so coupled with the yeasts that it is considered desirable to document the classical studies with yeast which have initiated the current concepts of fermentation. Lavoisier[1f] and Black[19] in the late eighteenth century, followed by Gay-Lussac[20] in 1815, made accurate determinations of fermentation products which led to the classical Gay-Lussac equation:

$$\text{glucose} \rightarrow 2 \text{ ethanol} + 2 \text{ } CO_2$$

Pasteur, in 1857,[19a] showed by more detailed measurements the formation of small amounts of glycerol and succinate and perhaps more important to the development of concepts of that day, showed that some of the sugar was incorporated into cellular material. (See Harden[20a] for discussion of early concepts of fermentation.) More recent investigations[21] with modern methods and automatic pH control have established the pattern of minor products (Table II), but have not altered the basic concept (see Section III, A, 1c).

The availability of large quantities of yeast as a by-product of beer manufacture was a major factor in the early development of knowledge of fermentation mechanisms. A major contribution by Buchner[22] in 1897 was the demonstration that a cell-free yeast juice converted carbohydrate to ethanol. This fundamental observation initiated research which developed steadily until, by the mid-1940's, the nature of the individual reactions, enzymes, metabolic intermediates, coenzymes, and energy relationships of the alcoholic fermentation had been established. Parallel studies on the mechanism of muscle glycolysis demonstrated a fact of greatest interest to comparative biochemistry, i.e., that most of the reactions of muscle glycolysis are identical to those of the yeast ethanolic fermentation. This unifying concept emerged in detailed form in the early 1940's as the Embden-Meyerhof glycolytic system. Further details of yeast glycolysis as

TABLE II
ETHANOL FERMENTATION BY YEAST[a]

Product	mMoles/100 mmoles of glucose fermented				
	pH 3.0	pH 6.0	pH 6.0[b]	pH 7.6	pH 7.6[b]
2,3-Butanediol	0.75	0.53	0.39	0.68	0.33
Acetoin	Nil	Nil	Nil	0.19	0.01
Ethanol	171.5	160.5	165.9	129.9	148.0
Glycerol	6.16	16.2	10.4	32.3	25.1
Butyric acid	0.13	0.36	0.39	0.21	0.35
Acetic acid	0.52	4.03	4.27	15.1	9.16
Formic acid	0.36	0.82	0.46	0.49	0.43
Succinic acid	0.53	0.49	1.14	0.68	0.43
Lactic acid	0.82	1.63	1.73	1.37	0.87
Carbon dioxide	180.8	177.0	178.0	148.5	167.8
Glucose carbon assimilated	12.4	12.4	—	—	—
Fermentation time, hr.	29.0	15.5	16.0	25.0	32.0
Glucose fermented, %	98.5	98.0	98.5	60.3	98.1
Carbon recovered, %	93.8	96.4	94.0	91.3	94.1
O/R balance	1.03	1.05	1.03	1.01	1.04

[a] Neish and Blackwood.[21]

[b] Automatic pH control using ammonium hydroxide or sodium hydroxide.

deduced from studies with enzyme preparations are contained in the chapter by Nord and Weiss in Cook's recent volume on the biology of the yeasts.[18] Tracer studies of flow patterns of glucose-C^{14} carbon in intact fungal cells have been published for *Saccharomyces cerevisiae*,[7] and *Fusarium lini*.[23] From the energetic viewpoint, the phosphate balance in both the ethanolic (yeast) and the lactic (muscle) glycolysis is 2 moles of inorganic phosphate consumed and two moles of adenosine triphosphate (ATP) formed:

$$\text{glucose} + 2 \text{ iP} + 2 \text{ ADP} \rightarrow 2 \text{ ethanol} + 2 \text{ CO}_2 + 2 \text{ ATP} + 2 \text{ H}_2\text{O}$$

The free energy of hydrolysis of the terminal pyrophosphate bond on adenosine triphosphate is currently estimated at 7.7 kilocalories per mole,[24] thus approximately 15.4 kilocalories of biologically useful energy are mobilized during the fermentation of 1 mole of glucose via either the ethanolic or the lactic (homolactic) versions of glycolysis.

a. First Form of Fermentation. The ethanol fermentation in yeast can be altered to yield glycerol as a major product. Carl Neuberg and his associates[25-28] investigated the yeast fermentation in detail just prior to 1920 and described three kinds on the basis of products formed. A fourth kind was added in the 1930's on the basis of products formed by dried cells.[37-41]

The "normal" alcoholic fermentation—glucose → 2 ethanol + 2 CO_2—is considered as the *first form.*

b. Second Form of Fermentation. This form occurs during glucose fermentation in the presence of sodium sulfite. The acetaldehyde formed from pyruvate by carboxylase is trapped as a bisulfite addition compound, and is thus unavailable to serve as a hydrogen acceptor.[25-30] Under these conditions, dihydroxyacetone phosphate replaces acetaldehyde as the oxidant for the reduced diphosphopyridine nucleotide, forming α-glycerol phosphate which is dephosphorylated to glycerol. Thus both glycerol and acetaldehyde accumulate (Table II). The triose phosphates and pyruvate do not form stable bisulfite addition compounds; other acetaldehyde fixatives, i.e., dimedon, thiosemicarbazide, and the hydrazines, have the same effect. The fermentation thus approaches:

$$\text{glucose} + HSO_3^- \rightarrow \text{glycerol} + \text{acetaldehyde} \cdot HSO_3 + CO_2$$

Ethanol formation is not completely suppressed because the presence of sufficient trapping agent to bind all of the acetaldehyde becomes toxic. Based upon the reduction of one mole of triose phosphate to glycerol per mole of glucose, there is no net energy yield in that portion of the fermentation shifted by sulfite. Evidently the unaffected portion of the fermentation supplies sufficient energy.

Neuberg's bisulfite fermentation was employed during World War I for the production of glycerol (the Constein-Lüdecke and the Cocking-Lilly industrial processes in Germany and England, respectively).[19]

c. Third Form of Fermentation. As indicated earlier, yeast fermentation in alkaline medium forms glycerol at the expense of ethanol. The reduction of dihydroxyacetone phosphate to glycerol leaves a deficiency in reducing power which results in acetaldehyde accumulation. The acetaldehyde undergoes dismutation to equal amounts of acetate and ethanol; thus acetate becomes a quantitatively significant product [21, 31-35] as follows:

$$2 \text{ glucose} \rightarrow 2 \text{ glycerol} + \text{acetic acid} + \text{ethanol} + 2 CO_2$$

This represents a balance among the following oxidations and reductions:

glyceraldehyde-3-phosphate + iP + DPN^+ →

$$1,3\text{-diphosphoglycerate} + DPNH + H^+$$

$$\text{acetaldehyde} + DPN^+ \rightarrow \text{acetic acid} + DPNH + H^+$$

$$\text{dihydroxyacetone phosphate} + DPNH + H^+ \rightarrow \alpha\text{-glycerophosphate} + DPN^+$$

$$\text{acetaldehyde} + DPNH + H^+ \rightarrow \text{ethanol} \rightarrow DPN^+$$

Since acetaldehyde oxidation in yeast produces acetate rather than acetyl SCoA, there is no net energy yield in this form of the yeast fermentation.

Neish and Blackwood,[21] in recent experiments with automatic pH control, observed rapid fermentation between pH 2.4 and 7.4; the rate was very slow at pH 2.0 and at 8.0. Glycerol yields as high as 29 % were obtained in the more alkaline region. Nickerson and Carroll[36] reported for one organism (*Zygosaccharomyces acidifaciens*) the third form of fermentation as the normal process, i.e., without pH control.

   d. Fourth Form of Fermentation. The fourth fermentation type, reported by Neuberg and Kobel around 1930[37-41] appears to result from the use of dried preparations or cell-free extracts. In this case pyruvate is not metabolized rapidly and ethanol and carbon dioxide are not found. Thus pyruvate and glycerol accumulate:

$$glucose \rightarrow pyruvate + glycerol$$

2. HOMOLACTIC FERMENTATION

Scheele (1780) isolated and identified the acid of sour milk as lactic acid. The identification and association of lactic acid-producing organisms with fermentation was established by Bondeau, by Pasteur and Schultze, and by Lister (see reference 19). Since the 1880's when the first commerical fermentations were initiated, the production of lactic acid by fermentation has become an important industry. All members of the genera *Streptococcus, Pediococcus, Microbacterium,* a large number of lactobacilli, certain bacilli, and *Rhizopus* species ferment glucose predominantly to lactic acid with formation of trace amounts of volatile acids, ethanol, fumarate and carbon dioxide (Table III). Kluyver and Donker[42] have applied the term "homofermentative" as contrasted with the "heterofermentative" type in which other products occur in major amount. Orla-Jensen[43] recognized the heterofermentative organisms among the lactic acid bacteria and applied the terms "*Betacoccus*" and "*Betabacterium*" to denote the heterofermentative cocci and rods respectively. Although the homofermentative streptococci yield from glucose only traces of products other than lactate in the usual growing or cell suspension fermentation, Gunsalus and Niven[44] showed that at alkaline pH the production of formate, acetate, and ethanol was increased at the expense of lactate to the extent of 25 to 40 % of the sugar utilized. The latter products appeared in the ratio of 2:1:1. In contrast to earlier studies, Platt and Foster[45] with more modern methods found small amounts of carbon dioxide, glycerol, diacetyl, acetoin, and 2,3-butanediol which in aggregate accounted for as much as 18 % of the glucose carbon (Table III). In addition, $C^{14}O_2$ was incorporated into lactate, acetate, and cell material. $C^{14}O_2$ incorporation was not obtained with *Lactobacillus casei,*[6] *Lactobacillus plantarum,* and *Streptococcus lactis*[46] in earlier studies. It would be interesting to investigate the route of $C^{14}O_2$ incorporation into acetate and lactate.

TABLE III

GLUCOSE FERMENTATION BY *Streptococcus faecalis* AND *Streptococcus liquefaciens*[45]

Product	μMoles/100 μmoles of glucose fermented						
	S. faecalis			S. liquefaciens			
	pH 5.0[a]	pH 7.0[a]	pH 9.0[a]	No pH control	pH 7.0	pH 7[b]	pH 7[c]
Lactic acid	174	146	122	175	173	183	185
Acetic acid	12.2	18.8	31.2	18.0	23.3	14.3	10.4
Formic acid	15.4	33.6	52.8	0.52	6.55	0.91	0.10
Carbon dioxide	—	—	—	6.00	6.61	6.00	5.44
Ethanol	7.0	14.6	22.4	4.45	2.00	4.00	5.53
Glycerol	—	—	—	2.67	14.1	0	0.07
Biacetyl	—	—	—	0	0	0.16	0.09
Acetoin	—	—	—	0.10	0.9	0.12	0.01
2,3-Butanediol	—	—	—	0	0	1.24	0
Carbon recovery, %	95.0	90.0	88.0	97.5	105.0	99.8	98.8
O/R Index	1.02	1.18	1.18	1.06	0.99	1.07	0.98

[a] Initial pH.
[b] Sparged with N_2.
[c] Deficient medium.

The mechanism of microbial lactic acid fermentation has, in anaology to muscle glycolysis, been considered as an Embden-Meyerhof glycolysis wherein pyruvic acid is reduced to lactic acid rather than being decarboxylated and reduced to ethanol as in the yeast fermentation. The earliest evidence of Embden-Meyerhof intermediates in lactic bacteria was that of Stone and Werkman,[14] who reported that *Lactobacillus plantarum* accumulates phosphoglyceric acid when glucose is fermented in the presence of fluoride and acetaldehyde or other hydrogen acceptors. Evidence for other Embden-Meyerhof intermediates was reported by O'Kane and Umbreit,[13] who observed that during glucose fermentation *Streptococcus faecalis* removed inorganic phosphate from the medium and accumulated organic phosphate compounds with the solubility characteristics of the hexose mono and diphosphates and the glyceric acids. A complete enzymic analysis of the lactic bacteria has not been made, but some scattered reports in connection with other studies do exist.[46a]

Evidence from biochemical studies supports the view that the homolactic fermentation utilizes the glycolytic system, whereas the heterolactic fermentation follows a hexose monophosphate pathway (Section III, B, 2). Since homolactic organisms form other products in major amounts under certain conditions and may contain enzymes of the hexose monophosphate pathways a more precise definition of "homolactic" has been sought. As a result of assays for aldolase and enzymes of the hexose monophosphate pathways, it has been proposed that "homolactic" refer to those lactic acid bacteria containing aldolase, but not phosphoketolase.[46b,c]

Gibbs and associates[6] have provided the most convincing evidence for Embden-Meyerhof glycolysis by showing that *L. casei*, *L. pentosus* (*plantarum*), and *S. faecalis* ferment glucose-1-C^{14} to methyl-labeled lactate with a 50 % dilution of the specific activity in the methyl group over that of carbon atom 1 of glucose. Similarly, the fermentation of glucose-3,4-C^{14} yielded carboxy-labeled lactate without dilution of the specific activity. Since these labeling patterns exclusively fit the distribution of carbon atoms expected from the Embden-Meyerhof pathway (Fig. 1), there is no doubt that the glycolytic pathway is the quantitatively significant mechanism functioning in the homolactic fermentation. The following equation is assumed to describe the chemical and energetic transformations involved.

$$\text{glucose} + 2 \text{ iP} + 2 \text{ ADP} \rightarrow 2 \text{ lactate} + 2 \text{ ATP} + 2 \text{ H}_2\text{O}$$

Based upon a net formation of 2 moles of ATP, an energy yield of 15.4 kilocalories[24] per mole of glucose fermented is realized. Therefore, the lactic and similar fermentations are distinctly inferior to other (aerobic) methods of energy generation. Nevertheless, this energy transfer allows rapid development of cultures in an otherwise complete medium to a point where growth in 16 hours or less is limited by the amount of acid accumulated.

Since *Streptococcus faecalis* can grow anaerobically on pyruvate[47] or citrate (which produces pyruvate, Section IV, A), and achieves greater growth on glucose under aerobic conditions,[48] it is likely that substrate level energy generation results from pyruvate dismutation or oxidation with accompanying formation of acetyl~SCoA. (See Gunsalus[48a] for review of reactions.)

The stereoconfiguration of the lactic acid produced varies with the genus or species involved. The literature on this point is confusing and citations as to the configuration of the lactate produced may be erroneous for the following reasons: (*a*) "dextro" and "dextrorotatory" are used interchangeably, but now have different meanings; (*b*) the relationship between configuration (D,L) and optical rotation (*d*,*l*) was established after some of the rotations were published; (*c*) previous to the publication of Bancroft and Davis[48b] the effect of ionization of the carboxyl group and of salt formation upon rotation was not appreciated; (*d*) the same culture may produce different forms of lactic acid depending upon conditions or the phase (rough or smooth) of the culture.[49] The available data as to the configuration produced is summarized in Table IV.

TABLE IV

CONFIGURATION OF LACTIC ACID PRODUCED BY VARIOUS MICROORGANISMS

Organism	Configuration
I. Homofermentative type	
Streptococcus sp.	L(+)[a][50]
Lactobacillus caucasicus, lactis,	D(−)[b]
Lactobacillus leichmanii	D(−)[50-52]
Lactobacillus helveticus, bifidis,	DL[c][243]
Lactobacillus plantarum	DL[243]
Lactobacillus thermophilis, delbrueckii	L(+)[51-53]
Lactobacillus bulgaricus	DL or D(−)[52]
Lactobacillus casei	L(+), L(+), and D(−)[53]
Pediococcus sp.	DL[54]
Bacillus sp.	L(+)[55]
Clostridium sp.	DL[100, 106]
Butyribacterium rettgeri	DL[89]
II. Heterofermentative type	
Lactobacillus brevis, buchneri pasteuria-nus, fermenti	DL[50]
Leuconostoc sp.	D(−)[50]
Microbacterium sp.	L(+)[43]
Rhizopus sp.	L(+)[52]
III. Mixed fermentations	
Serratia sp.	D(−)[196]

[a] L(+) Zinc salt·2 H_2O, $[\alpha]_D$ = −8.25° (4%, 25°C); H_2O = 12.89%.[56]
[b] D(−) Zinc salt·2 H_2O, $[\alpha]_D$ = +8.25° (4%, 25°C); H_2O = 12.89%.
[c] DL Zinc salt·3 H_2O, $[\alpha]_D$ = 0, H_2O = 18.18%.

Lactic acid of L-configuration (dextrorotatory-sarcolactate) is produced by streptococci, whereas the opposite configuration is produced by members of the genus *Leuconostoc*. The lactate-producing *Bacillus calidolactis*, *Bacillus coagulans*, and *Microbacterium* and *Rhizopus* species also form L (+)-lactate, whereas pediococci and heterolactobacilli produce mixtures of isomers. Among the homofermentative lactobacilli, great variation exists in the type of lactate produced.[50]

One determinent of lactic acid configuration is the stereospecificity of the lactic dehydrogenase involved. In *Lactobacillus plantarum (arabinosus)*, which produces DL-lactate, two lactic dehydrogenases are present, each specific for a different isomer of lactate.[57] The combined action of these dehydrogenases can racemize either isomer of lactate with pyruvate being the intermediate. Katagiri, Kitahara, and their associates claim that the combined action of a stereospecific lactic dehydrogenase forming D(−) lactate and a lactic acid racemase is more important in their strains of *L. plantarum*. In this system D-lactate is formed first, then racemized by a mechanism which is distinct from the combined function of the two stereo-specific dehydrogenases.[58-69] A similar racemase is secreted by *Clostridium acetobutylicum*,[70-73] which racemizes α-acetolactate stereoisomers as well as those of lactate. Racemizing enzymes are not unknown in nature. An α-hydroxy acid racemase has also been found in animal tissue.[74] In addition, there is evidence for an interconversion of phosphoglycerate isomers in *L. plantarum*.[62] Although these structural differences are of considerable usefulness in classification or identification, they do not reflect fundamental differences in fermentation mechanism or in energy yield.

In addition to glucose, other hexoses such as fructose, mannose, galactose, disaccharides including lactose, maltose, and sucrose, and starch and dextrin among the polysaccharides serve as substrates for the homolactic fermentation. It is presumed that these sugars are converted to intermediates of the glycolytic system by inducible enzymes. Galactose is conspicuous for a variation in its fermentation by hyaluronic acid-producing strains of *Streptococcus pyogenes*. Whereas glucose yields predominantly lactate in the usual manner, about 50 % of the galactose carbon appears as acetic and formic acids and ethanol in the ratio 2:1:1.[75-78] The ratio is strikingly similar to that obtained by Gunsalus and Niven[44] for the fermentation of glucose by *S. liquefaciens* at a high pH. Although the fermentation balances are imperfect, pH does not appear to be the sole factor responsible for diversion of the homolactic fermentation of galactose. The results may be explained by differences in the rate of pyruvate formation from the two hexoses, but the possibility of an independent pathway for galactose fermentation should serve to motivate further consideration of these observations. Use has been made of the inducible nature of the galactose fermentation system in *S. agalactae* (*mastiditis*) for the quantitative estimation of glucose and galactose in mixtures.[79]

3. Butyric Acid and Solvent-Producing Fermentations

Among the clostridia and certain bacilli, butyric acid and solvents such as *n*-butanol, acetone, and isopropanol are characteristic products of carbohydrate fermentation.

a. Fermentation Types. Three closely related types are recognized. The differences reside in the presence of additional terminal reactions superimposed upon the basic scheme.

The *butyric type* exemplified by *Clostridium butyricum*,[81] and also displayed by *C. tyrobutyricum*,[82] and *C. lacto-acetophilum*,[83] produces butyric and acetic acids, carbon dioxide, and hydrogen. *C. perfringens* (*welchii*)[84, 85] and *C. tetani*[86] produce, in addition, lactate, ethanol, and sometimes formate. According to the fermentation balances in Table V, the following equation approximately fits the data for *C. butyricum*:

TABLE V

FERMENTATION BALANCES FOR CLOSTRIDIA

Products	mMoles/100 mmoles glucose fermented						
	Clostridium butyricum[81]	Clostridium lacto-acetophilum[82]	Clostridium perfringens[84,85]		Clostridium acetobutylicum[93]	Clostridium butylicum[100]	Butyribacterium rettgeri[89]
Butyric acid	76	73	9[a]	34[b]	4.3	17.2	29
Acetic acid	42	28	15	60	14.2	17.2	88
Lactic acid	—	—	160	33	—	—	107
Carbon dioxide	188	190	24	176	221	203.5	48
Hydrogen	235	182	21	214	135	77.6	74
Ethanol	—	—	10	26	7.2	—	—
Butanol	—	—	—	—	56	58.6	—
Acetone	—	—	—	—	22.4	—	—
Acetoin	—	—	—	—	6.4	—	—
Isopropanol	—	—	—	—	—	12.1	—
Carbon recovered, %	96.0	91.0	98.3	97.1	99.6	96.2	110.0[c]
O/R balance	0.97	1.16	0.81	1.05	1.01	1.06	0.74

[a] Iron deficient.

[b] Iron sufficient.

[c] C_1/C_2 ratio = 0.33.

$$4 \text{ glucose} \rightarrow 2 \text{ acetate} + 3 \text{ butyrate} + 8 \text{ CO}_2 + 8 \text{ H}_2$$

If it is assumed that butyrate arises by condensation of 2 acetate units, the amount of carbon dioxide observed agrees with the amount expected. Further, a 1:1 ratio between hydrogen and carbon dioxide was observed.

Examination of fermentation balances in the literature reveals considerable fluctuation in the quantity of products. It is not possible to rationalize all of these reports with current concepts, however, often because of irregularities in the experimental procedures employed. For instance, high ethanol and low butyric acid yields have been observed with a mutant of C. tetani[86] and by resting cells of C. botulinum.[87] Also formate, not normally an end product in clostridial fermentations, has been reported as a major product for several species.[84,85] The c. tetani balance, the pH of fermentation, and the amount of carbohydrate fermented in the formate-producing experiments should be checked.

Although lactate is not fermented by C. butyricum, under ordinary conditions, Bhat and Barker found that a closely related organism, *C. lacto-acetophilum*, fermented lactate when acetate was added as the hydrogen acceptor.[83] More recently Bryant *et al.* have reported that *C. tyrobutyricum*, isolated from grass silages, and *C. butyricum* also ferment lactate under these conditions.[82] Hence, from the standpoint of fermentation mechanisms, the similarities among *C. butyricum*, *C. tyrobutyricum*, and *C. lacto-aceto-philum* appear to be greater than the differences.

Another type of butyric acid fermentation is displayed by *Butyribac-terium rettgeri*. The products formed from glucose, pyruvate, or lactate are DL-lactate (glucose-substrate), carbon dioxide, hydrogen, acetic, and butyric acids. Caproic acid also is formed in lesser amounts[88] (Table V). As observed with the clostridia,[85] the yield of lactate is increased with iron deficiency.[89] In contrast to *C. butylicum*, which produces more than one mole of carbon dioxide and not more than one mole of C_2 (acetic and bu-tyric acid $\times$ 2) per mole of triose, *Butyribacterium* produces 0.4 mole of car-bon dioxide and 1.2 moles of C_2 per triose. *Butyribacterium* resembles several of the clostridia in that $C^{14}O_2$ is fixed into both the carboxyl and methyl groups of acetate during fermentation.[90] Pine and Barker[91] have shown that this process does not involve carbon dioxide fixation into di-carboxylic acids or the glycine-serine interconversion, and is stimulated rather than inhibited by the lack of iron.[89] In addition, acetate was shown to be the precursor of butyrate.[90] During growth in a defined medium, with lactate as an energy source, there is an absolute requirement for lipoic acid. With glucose or pyruvate, however, lipoic acid is not required. Sev-eral lines of evidence indicate that lipoic acid does not function in pyru-vate metabolism by this organism. Hence, a role in lactate metabolism is indicated.[92]

The fermentation of glucose-1-C^{14} by *Butyribacterium rettgeri* produced predominantly methyl-labeled products.[89] Although the specific activity of the methyl group was less than 50 %, it appears that the Embden-Meyer-hof pathway is the main fermentation system involved.

The acetone-butyl fermentation by *C. acetobutylicum* results from addi-tional terminal reactions which utilize the butyric acid and the precursors between acetyl and butyrate acetic acid to produce butanol and acetone, re-spectively[93] (Table V). Many studies have established the time course of product development and the effect of conditions and nutrition upon the outcome of the fermentation.[94-95] Stiles *et al.*, for instance, observed that the acids appeared early in the fermentation and that the solvents were pro-duced later. Again formic acid was encountered and was metabolized when added. Acetoacetate was implicated as an important precursor of both butyrate and acetone.[96, 97] The decarboxylase responsible for conversion of acetoacetate to acetone has been purified from extracts.[96, 98, 99]

The *isopropyl fermentation* by *C. butylicum* closely resembles that of *C. acetobutylicum* except that isopropanol is produced at the expense of acetone.[100] Again alkali suppresses alcohol formation and increases the acid production.[101, 102] There can be little doubt that acetone is the precursor of isopropanol, because its addition enhances the production of isopropanol. Moreover, the addition of hydrogen acceptors increases the amount of isopropanol and acetone, and decreases the alcohols, presumably by competing for the hydrogen utilized in alcohol formation.[102] Added butyric acid is reduced to butanol and increases the yield of isopropanol by eliminating the demand for hydrogen atoms in butyric acid synthesis.[101]

b. *General Characteristics of Clostridial Fermentations.* It is of considerable interest to find that clostridia, which normally do not produce lactate, can carry out a homolactic fermentation under abnormal conditions. Kempner and Kubowitz[103, 104] showed with *C. butyricum* that carbon monoxide and cyanide diverted the fermentation to the homolactic type in a manner which could be reversed by light or by removal of the inhibitor. [103, 105] The effective level of carbon monoxide or cyanide was of the same order of magnitude required to inhibit respiration of aerobic cells. A similar sensitivity has not been found in other lactic and ethanolic fermentations. The lactate formed is DL with a slight excess of the L-component.[108]

Pappenheimer and Shaskan[85] produced a homolactic fermentation in *C. perfringens* by decreasing the iron content of the medium (Table V). With iron-deficient medium (0.04 μg. of iron per ml.) growth was decreased about 50 % and 1.7 moles of lactate per mole of glucose were produced. Addition of iron up to 0.64 μg. per ml. increased growth and decreased lactate production to typical levels. At suboptimal iron concentrations the iron was completely taken up by the cells. Similarly, the addition of iron to whey fermentation by *C. acetobutylicum* decreased the lactate, formate, and ethanol content, and increased the amount of hydrogen, carbon dioxide, acetone, acetoin, butyrate, and acetate. Also, cultures obtained by serial transfer in low iron medium produced a homolactic fermentation.[107]

The data on (a) shift to lactic fermentation by carbon monoxide, cyanide, and iron deficiency, (b) the reversal of the monoxide and cyanide effect by light, and (c) inhibition by the same concentrations needed to inhibit respiration parallel the behavior expected from iron porphyrin function in pyruvate dissimilation. However, no spectral evidence has been obtained for these respiratory catalysts in clostridia.[107a] Further, Lerner and Mueller [108] found that cells from an iron-deficient medium, which do not ferment glucose, could be activated by glutamine, thereby suggesting an indirect effect of iron.

The early fragmentary biochemical evidence on the mechanism of fermentation suggested a non-Embden-Meyerhof process (lack of fluoride inhi-

TABLE VI

DISTRIBUTION OF C^{14} IN THE PRODUCTS OF GLUCOSE-C^{14}
FERMENTATION BY *Clostridium perfringens*

Product	Relative specific activity[a]				
	Glucose-3,4-C^{14}	Glucose-1-C^{14}	Glucose-2-C^{14}		Glucose-6-C^{14}
Carbon dioxide	95.0[b]	0[b]	0[b]	0[c]	0[b]
Ethanol					
CH_3—	4.2	25.2	0.3	0	22.7
—CH_2OH	2.1	0.4	21.3	48.2	0.2
Acetic acid					
CH_3—	1.1	41.5	0.3	0	35.2
—COOH	—	0.2	46.8	47.0	0

[a] Specific activity of each labeled carbon atom of glucose = 100.
[b] From Paege and co-workers.[116]
[c] From Cynkin and Gibbs.[117]

bition,[14] methylglyoxal formation[100, 109]). More recent enzymic and isotopic evidence, although incomplete, clearly indicates the existence of the
classical fermentation route. An iron-requiring aldolase, triose phosphate
isomerase and glyceraldehyde-3-phosphate dehydrogenase, were reported
by Bard and Gunsalus.[114] Also, the reduction of diphosphopyridine nucleotide (DPN) by glucose, glucose-6-phosphate, fructose-6-phosphate, and
fructose diphosphate is interpreted as evidence for the hexose diphosphate
pathway.[115] Further evidence for operation of the hexose diphosphate
pathway was obtained from the fermentation of glucose-1-C^{14}, -2-C^{14},
-3,4-C^{14}, and -6-C^{14} by *C. perfringens*.[116] The labeling of products (Table
VI) was qualitatively that expected of the glycolytic system. However,
ethanol and acetic acid formed from glucose labeled in carbon atoms 2, 6,
or 3 and 4 were not similarly labeled as would be expected if these products
were derived from a common precursor and produced a greater than 50%
decrease in specific activity. More recently Cynkin and Gibbs[117] found
equal labeling in ethanol and acetate with the expected 50% decrease in
specific activity.

During glucose fermentation, a large number of added compounds are
converted to normal products. Pyruvate and acetate contribute to all of
the products[118] and butyrate, acetoacetate, acetone, acetaldehyde, and acetoin are precursors of butanol, acetone, isopropanol, ethanol, and 2,3-bu-
tanediol, respectively.[99, 101, 113, 118] A comprehensive survey of compounds
utilized in this manner has been reported by Davies[96] (Table VII).

Pyruvate fermentations vary from that of *C. acetobutylicum*[110] and *C.*

TABLE VII
COMPOUNDS CONVERTED TO NORMAL PRODUCTS DURING GLUCOSE FERMENTATION
BY *Clostridium butylicum*[101] AND *Clostridium acetobutylicum*[96, 113]

Utilized	Not utilized	
Butyric acid	Glyceraldehyde	β-Hydroxybutyric acid
Acetic acid	Phosphoglyceric acid	2-3-Dihydroxybutyric acid
Acetaldehyde	Hexose diphosphate	Glyoxylic acid
Acetone	Lactic acid	Tetronic acid
Pyruvic acid	Formic acid	Crotonic acid
Acetoacetic acid	Methyl glyoxal	Transhydroxycrotonic acid
Oxalacetic acid	Fumaric acid	Tetrolic acid
	α-Hydroxybutyric acid	Vinylacetic acid
		Acetopyruvic acid

butylicum producing a complete array of products to the simple conversion to acetate, CO_2, and H_2 by *C. butyricum*.[106] Koepsell *et al.* showed that cell-free extracts of *C. butylicum* (a) formed acetate, CO_2, and H_2 from pyruvate but did not utilize formate,[121] (b) required inorganic phosphate for pyruvate utilization,[121] and (c) produced acetyl phosphate.[122]

Isotopic carbon dioxide exchanges readily with the carboxyl groups of pyruvate,[46, 120, 127-131] whereas formate does not.[132] These observations indicate that the earlier reports of $C^{13}O_2$ incorporation into lactate by *C. welchii*,[46, 119] *C. butylicum*,[119, 120] and *C. acetobutylicum*[46, 119] result from the CO_2 exchange into pyruvate. Thus, in spite of the claims for formate production and utilization[84, 95, 96, 100] this product of the *Escherichia coli* clastic reaction is not an intermediate in carbon dioxide and hydrogen formation by clostridia. Only in the formation of acetyl phosphate does the pyruvate clastic[126a] reaction of clostridia resemble that of *E. coli*[123-125] and the pyruvate oxidase of *L. delbruckii*.[126] It is interesting to note in this connection that cell suspensions of *Bacillus macerans* exhibit a clastic system typical of *E. coli* in that formate is produced. In contrast, extracts of this organism resemble *C. butylicum* in that carbon dioxide exchanges with pyruvate, whereas formate does not.[133]

The current concept of the fermentation reactions is shown in Fig. 4. Much of our knowledge derives from the brilliant studies of Stadtman and Barker with *C. kluyveri* which are described in Section IV, B. The formation of acetyl coenzyme A from pyruvate or from acetate is of major importance in these schemes. Acetyl~SCoA then undergoes (1) condensation and conversion of butyryl~SCoA via CoA derivatives of acetoacetate and β-hydroxy butyrate, or (2) reduction to acetaldehyde and ethanol. In addition to these pathways, reduction of pyruvate to lactate and the formation of acetylmethylcarbinol may also occur. Hydrogenase functions in the formation of

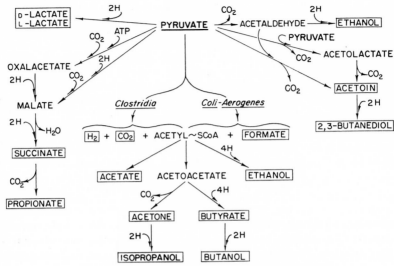

FIG. 4. Fermentation product formation from pyruvate.

hydrogen gas in common with the fermentations of *E. coli*, *Micrococcus lacti-lyticus* (*Veillonella gazogenes*), and methane bacteria.[131, 134-137]

The energy derived from these carbon skeleton interconversions does not exceed the two high energy phosphate bonds generated per mole of glucose fermented via the Embden-Meyerhof pathway. In view of the fact that a form of oxidative phosphorylation appears to occur in the *C. kluyveri* fermentation,[1] it is possible that a similar means of energy generation occurs in the transport of hydrogen from triose phosphate and pyruvate to acceptors which yield butyric acid, butanol, or isopropanol.

4. HOMOACETATE FERMENTATION

Clostridium thermoaceticum, isolated by Fontaine *et al.*,[138] ferments glucose, fructose, and galactose to yield 85 % of the carbon as acetate. By classical fermentation mechanisms (i.e., $C_6 \rightarrow 2\ C_3$) only 60 % of the carbon could appear in acetate. Wieringa[139, 140] showed that *C. aceticum* fermented hydrogen and carbon dioxide to acetate as the sole product, thereby demonstrating a net synthesis of acetate from CO_2 and suggesting the source of the third acetate in the *C. thermoaceticum* fermentation. Carbon dioxide fixation or exchange into acetate is now recognized in several other clostridia and anaerobes. Enrichments (but not pure cultures) of *C. lacto-acetophilum* incorporate $C^{14}O_2$ into acetate and butyrate[146] and carbon dioxide appears in both carbons of acetate during fermentation of: (*a*) hypoxanthine by *C. acidi-urici*,[147] glycine by *Diplococcus glycinophilis*,[148] and lactate by *Butyri-*

bacterium rettgeri.[90, 91] Thus, the reduction and condensation of CO_2 to acetate, like and reduction of CO_2 to methane, is a general problem involving CO_2 as a hydrogen acceptor, and presumably resulting in energy generation at substrate and possibly electron transport levels.

Evidence for the condensation of CO_2 to acetate in *C. thermoaceticum* is based on (*a*) conversion of xylose solely to acetate,[141] and (*b*) incorporation of $C^{14}O_2$ essentially equally into both carbon atoms of acetate during glucose fermentation.[142] In (*b*) the decrease in specific activity in acetate over that of the CO_2 added indicated that only one of the three moles of acetate came from carbon dioxide. In order to determine the amounts of doubly, singly, and nonlabeled acetate, Wood and co-workers[143-145] fermented glucose in the presence of $C^{13}O_2$ with *C. thermoaceticum*, converted the acetate to ethylene, and determined in the mass spectrometer the amounts of mass 30, 29, and 28 ethylene. It was established that about equal amounts of doubly, singly, and unlabeled acetates were produced. Only 2 to 5 % was singly labeled in the methyl group, however. About 55 % of the acetate carboxyl group equilibrated with the carbon dioxide pool, whereas about 14 % of the methyl group underwent exchange. Therefore, it was postulated that three processes were occurring simultaneously: (*a*) a synthesis of acetate without carbon dioxide fixation, (*b*) *de novo* synthesis of acetate with both carbon atoms derived from carbon dioxide, and (*c*) equilibration of the acetate carboxyl group with carbon dioxide. When glucose-1-C^{14} was fermented, the acetate was methyl-labeled. In the fermentation of glucose-3,4-C^{14}, the isotope did not enter the acetate directly. Thus, there is evidence that the Embden-Meyerhof pathway functions in producing two acetate molecules while the third is formed by carbon dioxide fixation.[144]

It was reported that formate is a better precursor of the methyl group whereas carbon dioxide is a better precursor of the carboxyl group. An enzymic basis for these reactions is currently not available. A pathway for incorporation into the carboxyl group can be envisaged but not for the methyl group.[145]

5. MIXED ACID FERMENTATION OF *Escherichia coli*

The fermentation displayed by facultative organisms, including the Enterobacteriaceae, bacilli, and others, yields a wide variety of products among which organic acids are the major component. Also characteristic of of this fermentation type is the prominance of the phosphorolytic cleavage of pyruvate to formate and acetate. Many of the fermentations have been investigated because of the potentiality of producing 2,3-butanediol by fermentation, whereas others, particularly the *E. coli* fermentation, have been studied from academic interest. The mixed acid-producing organisms can be divided into two groups; those organisms resembling *E. coli* in products (i.e., volatile acids, but no butanediol) and the second group which produces 2,3-butanediol as a major product (Section III, A, 6). Aside from this readily discernible distinction, considerable variation is displayed within each group. This results both from additional fundamental differences in genotype, and from the effect of conditions.

Harden[149] made the first relatively complete determination of the products of the *E. coli* fermentation and constructed a fairly accurate balance. The products found[150] are in essential agreement with the equation:

$$2 \text{ glucose} + H_2O \rightarrow 2 \text{ lactate} + \text{acetic acid} + \text{ethanol} + 2 CO_2 + 2 H_2$$

These studies were extended to other sugars and to substrates of higher and lower oxidation-reduction state by Kay,[151] Scheffer,[152] and others. Tikka[153] also showed that the pH of the medium shifted the fermentation with more lactic acid produced at a low pH and more formic acid at a higher pH. This phenomenon has since been encountered in many microorganisms of widely varying types.

The fermentation studies by Blackwood *et al.*,[154] carried out with automatic pH control and analyzed by modern methods, probably gives the most complete picture of the fermentation (Table VIII). An interesting contrast to many previous reports is the finding of butyric acid and glycerol among the products. In addition, a clear-cut effect of pH was observed. At pH 6.2, carbon dioxide and hydrogen were evolved, whereas at pH 7.8 gas evolution decreased markedly and an equivalent amount of formic acid was formed. Thus hydrogenlyase does not function at the higher pH. Fermentations by resting suspensions have been reported by Tikka[153] and more recently by Stokes.[150] Ethanol, and acetic, formic, lactic, and succinic acids were the major products. With resting cells an effect of pH was noted in phosphate buffer but not in bicarbonate buffer. Generally similar fermentations are found in *Photobacterium phosphoreum*,[155] in *Salmonella*[156] and *Proteus* species, *Vibrio comma*,[157] and in *Pseudomonas formicans*[158] (Table VIII).

Complete data derived from the fermentation of C^{14}-labeled glucoses are not available for this group of organisms. Preliminary information indicates that 85 % of the glucose utilized by *E. coli* follows the Embden-Meyerhof pathway while 15 % follows the hexosemonophosphate route.[159] However, a study of the metabolic pathways and enzymes in *E. coli* has produced considerable indirect evidence that the Embden-Meyerhof pathway is the major if not the sole route of fermentation.[160] Tikka[153] found, for instance, that cell extracts fermented glucose and hexose diphosphate to the same products and that the fermentation was influenced by pH in the same manner observed with cell suspensions. Also, most of the glycolytic enzymes have been found in *E. coli*.[15] Particularly important in establishing the ex-

TABLE VIII

MIXED ACID FERMENTATIONS

Products	mMoles per 100 mmoles glucose fermented				
	Escherichia coli[150, 154]			Photobacterium phosphoreum[155]	Pseudomonas formicans[158]
2,3-Butanediol	0.3[a]	0.26[b]	—[c]	0.004	—
Acetoin	0.059	0.190	—	Trace	—
Glycerol	1.42	0.32	—	—	—
Ethanol	49.8	50.5	77.0	80.7	64.0
Formic	2.43	86.0	121.0	95.5	105.0
Acetic	36.5	38.7	78.0	61.8	62.0
Lactic acid	79.5	70.0	20.0	68.2	43.0
Succinic acid	10.7	14.8	39.0	8.85	22.0
Carbon dioxide	88.0	1.75	—	73.5	—
Hydrogen	75.0	0.26	—	54.8	—
Carbon recovered, %	91.2	94.7	108.0	115.6	96.0
O/R balance	1.06	0.91	1.04	1.16	1.02

[a] pH 6.2.

[b] pH 7.8.

[c] Resting cells, grown aerobically.

istence of an Embden-Meyerhof scheme was the precise study by Utter and Werkman[161] of the "zymohexase," aldolase, and triosephosphate isomerase equilibria. Currently, however, it cannot be stated with certainty that other pathways do not also contribute to product formation.

As in the propionic and clostridial fermentations, the complexity of products and the diversions produced by alteration of conditions reflect variations in pyruvate metabolism. For example, in E. coli, (a) phosphorolytic cleavage of pyruvate to acetyl coenzyme A and formate; (b) reduction of acetyl phosphate to ethanol; (c) conversion of formate to hydrogen and carbon dioxide; and (d) the inability to form acetoin from pyruvate are characteristic. Conditions have a great influence, however, particularly upon the hydrogenlyase reaction (c above). In Aerobacter aerogenes the same pathways exist, but with diminished importance because the production of acetoin and 2,3-butanediol from pyruvate are of major importance and compete effectively for the pyruvate (see Section III, A, 6 and Fig. 4).

The cleavage and oxidation of pyruvate occurs in two similar systems: (a) in clostridia wherein acetyl coenzyme A (or acetyl phosphate), hydrogen, and carbon dioxide are produced and formate is not an intermediate, and (*b*) in the Enterobacteriaceae which form acetyl coenzyme A, or acetyl phosphate, and formate.[124] In these systems the acetyl coenzyme A generated is the source of acetate, ethanol, butyrate, and acetone. Each of these systems requires coenzyme A and diphosphothiamin.[15] The reversible nature of the clastic reaction has been demonstrated by showing an incorporation of labeled formate and carbon dioxide into the carboxyl group of pyruvate even when there was a net decrease in pyruvate.[162-166] Under the same conditions, however, acetyl phosphate does not exchange.

The energy available in the thiol ester bond of acetyl coenzyme A enters the high energy phosphate pool by means of phosphotransacetylase and acetokinase. Thus, an additional mole of ATP (7.7 kcal.) is generated for each mole of acetate formed.

Pakes and Jollyman[167] demonstrated that formate is converted to carbon dioxide and hydrogen by many microorganisms. Subsequent studies, including those by Quastel and Whetham,[168] and by Stephenson and Strickland,[169] revealed the association of formic dehydrogenase and hydrogenase with hydrogenlyase activity. Therefore, the idea was advanced that hydrogenlyase activity was due to the combined action of formic dehydrogenase and hydrogenase as follows:[170, 171]

$$HCOOH + A \xrightarrow{\text{formic dehydrogenase}} H_2A + CO_2$$

$$H_2A \xrightarrow{\text{hydrogenase}} H_2 + A$$

$$HCOOH \xrightarrow{\text{hydrogenlyase}} H_2 + CO_2$$

Hydrogenlyase is inducible;[156, 172] its formation is prevented by aerobiosis,[124, 156, 173] by the growth in a synthetic medium,[174, 175] by a high pH,[153, 154] and by the addition of nitrate.[173, 176] The function of formic dehydrogenase and hydrogenase as components of hydrogenlyase is not clearly understood, and is not generally accepted. Certain organisms such as *B. dispar*,[177] anaerogenic strains of *E. coli*,[178, 179] *Salmonella*,[156] *Eberthella*,[152] and *Shigella*[152] do not cleave formate to CO_2 and H_2. In several instances the organisms which lack the lyase contain ample formic dehydrogenase and hydrogenase.[156, 177] Thus, the hypothesis that these enzymes, functioning together, make up the lyase system is either false or requires modification to include a role of additional enzymes or factors.[156, 179-181] Since growth in iron-deficient media prevents lyase induction,[182] and α-α-bipyridyl inhibits lyase action,[183] it appears that a component of hydrogenlyase requires iron.

6. 2,3-BUTANEDIOL FERMENTATIONS

Several groups of organisms produce butanediol in fermentations which are otherwise of the mixed acid type. The process may be considered a composite of a series of subfermentations of glucose, two of which yield ethanol and lactate, and the remainder composed of one or more of the following butanediol fermentation types.[184]

"Diol hydrogen"

$$\text{glucose} \rightarrow 2,3\text{-butanediol} + 2 \ CO_2 + H_2 \tag{1}$$

"Diol-formic acid"

$$\text{glucose} \rightarrow 2,3\text{-butanediol} + \text{formate} + CO_2 \tag{2}$$

"Diol-glycerol"

$$3 \ \text{glucose} \rightarrow 2,3\text{-butanediol} + 2 \ \text{glycerol} + \ CO_2 \tag{3}$$

Further distinctions are based on the configuration of butanediol (D,L, or meso) produced.

a. Aerobacter aerogenes and Related Species. This fermentation was first recognized by Harden and Walpole[185] and some of the details have been recorded by Walpole,[186] Scheffer,[152] Werkman and associates,[192-194] and Harden and Norris.[187, 188] *Aerobacillus polymyxa,*[189] *Aeromonas (Pseudomonas) hydrophila,*[190] *Erwinia carotovora,*[197] and several species of *Aerobacter,*[191-195] *Serratia,*[196] and *Bacillus*[198-201] display variants of the same fermentation.

Due to the conversion of appreciable carbon to the neutral 2,3-butanediol (accompanied by increased CO_2 production), fewer acids are produced and small amounts of acetoin usually accumulate. These changes relative to the *E. coli* fermentation provide the basis for the methyl red test for acid production, the Voges-Proskauer test for acetoin, and the gas ratio test which are employed to differentiate the *Escherichia* and *Aerobacter* genera.

Altermatt *et al.*[202] has found that glucose and allose fermentations by *Aerobacter aerogenes* yielded the same products (Table IX). From hexose-1-C^{14}, the acetic acid, ethanol, lactic acid, and 2,3-butanediol were methyl-labeled, whereas with hexose-2-C^{14}, hydroxymethyl groups of 2,3-butanediol, lactate, and ethanol, and the carboxyl group of acetate were the only groups labeled. These results are in line with the pattern expected from utilization of methyl-labeled and carbonyl-labeled pyruvate (derived from hexose-1-C^{14} and hexose-2-C^{14}, respectively) exclusively via the Embden-Meyerhof pathway.

The interconversion of products during the fermentation and the effect of added hydrogen acceptors have been recorded by Werkman and associates.[192, 205-207] Under aerobic conditions, as would be anticipated, a greater proportion of acetoin accumulates.[194]

pH has a marked effect upon the 2,3-butanediol fermentation. Above pH 6.3, acetic and formic acids accumulates and the production of hydrogen, carbon dioxide, acetoin, and 2,3-butanediol is prevented. Below pH 6.3,

TABLE IX
Butanediol Fermentations

Products	mMoles/100 mmoles glucose fermented										
	Aerobacter aerogenes[202]	Aerobacter indologenes[193]		Serratia marcescens[203]		Serratia plymuthicum[203]	Serratia kielensis[203]	Erwinia carotovora[197]	Bacillus subtilis[198]	Aerobacillus polymyxa[189]	Aeromonas hydrophila[190]
2,3-Butanediol	19.2	58.0ᵃ	66.4ᵇ	64.0ᶜ	52.7ᵈ	46.5	Nil	15.0	54.60	65.1	54.7
Acetoin	—	2.0	0.0	1.87	7.99	3.56	1.69	—	1.56	2.8	1.7
Glycerol	4.2	—	—	1.28	1.29	1.70	1.72	—	56.80	—	—
Ethanol	51.5	70.5	69.5	46.0	29.6	50.5	46.2	66.2	7.65	66.2	52.0
Formic acid	68.4	54.4	17.0	48.2	3.32	3.32	2.13	134.0	1.32	—	—
Acetic acid	51.9	8.2	0.47	3.83	8.69	4.52	49.9	64.3	0.16	2.9	4.6
Lactic acid	10.1	6.4	2.9	10.12	20.9	33.9	103.9	23.1	17.61	—	23.3
Succinic acid	13.1	—	—	8.15	8.84	7.08	1.88	11.2	1.08	—	3.6
Carbon dioxide	79.6	140.5	172.0	116.8	158.9	145.2	99.8	13.2	117.8	199.6	166.2
Hydrogen	—ᶠ	11.6	35.4	Nil	0.22	58.7	91.1	—	0.16	70.9	57.5
% C recovered	95.3	102.0	100.3	102.5ᵉ	99.9	99.0	103.8	97.0	98.0	101.6	98.2
O/R balance	—ᶠ	1.01	0.99	1.02	—ᵈ	0.98	1.07	0.97	0.99	0.99	0.997

ᵃ Forty-seven hours.
ᵇ Two hundred and nine hours.
ᶜ Anaerobic.
ᵈ Aerobic.
ᵉ Including 26.8 mmoles of carbon in cells.
ᶠ Hydrogen not determined.

acetic acid is converted to acetoin and 2,3-butanediol, and hydrogen production is suppressed.[208] These data indicate that a gas ratio (H_2:CO_2) of 0.5, once considered to be characteristic of *Aerobacter*, is fortuitous. More recent studies by Neish and Ledingham,[184, 209] utilizing automatic pH control, revealed a broad maximum in rate of fermentation between pH 7.6 and pH 6.5 to 6.0 for both *A. aerogenes* and *Aerobacillus polymyxa*. *Serratia marcescens* and *B. subtilis* exhibit a much narrower range for maximum rate of 2,3-butanediol production centered at pH 6.2. At pH 6.2 to 6.3, both fermentation rate and butanediol production are at a maximum.

b. Serratia. Pederson and Breed[196] and later Sigurdsson and Wood[210] showed that *Serratia* resembled *A. aerogenes* in that a mixture of organic acids, acetoin, 2,3-butanediol, and ethanol are produced. Because of the possibility that organisms which produce butanediol, but not hydrogen, might be high producers of glycerol, Neish *et al.*[211] investigated four strains of *S. marcescens* which produce little hydrogen. However, 60% of the glucose utilized under anaerobic and aerobic conditions (Table IX) followed the "diol-formate" fermentation (Eq. 1) and the following oxidation:

$$\text{glucose} + \tfrac{1}{2}O_2 \rightarrow 2,3\text{-butanediol} + H_2O + 2\ CO_2 \tag{4}$$

The remainder of the glucose yielded L-lactate, ethanol, and a small amount of glycerol. Thus the lack of hydrogen production is due to the absence of hydrogenlyase rather than to glycerol formation. A formic dehydrogenase is present, however, as demonstrated by its oxidation in the aerobic fermentation.

In a further search for a butanediol-glycerol fermentation a survey of virtually all of the known *Serratia* species was made by Neish *et al.*[203] The fermentation balances (Table IX) permitted a division into three groups based upon differences in fermentation under anaerobic conditions. In the first group *S. marcescens*, *S. anolium*, and *S. indica* follow equations 1 and 4 for 2,3-butanediol formation. A second group containing *S. plymuthicum* and unnamed strains of *A. aerogenes* carries out the same process except that hydrogenlyase is not present. *S. kielensis*, however, does not produce butanediol, but resembles *E. coli* in that is produces acetate, CO_2, and H_2. The fermentation of the soft rot organism *Erwinia carotovora*[197] (Table IX) resembles that of *Serratia marcescens*.

c. Bacillus. *B. subtilis*,[184, 198, 199] *B. mesentericus*,[212] *B. anthracis*,[201] and *B. cereus*[201] ferment glucose to 2,3-butanediol, acetate, ethanol, glycerol, and carbon dioxide; in addition, traces of formate and succinate are formed (Table IX). The fermentation differs from the types displayed by *Serratia* and *Aerobacter* in that formate and hydrogen are essentially absent. Instead, the available hydrogen is utilized to form glycerol (Eq. 3). Under aerobic conditions glycerol formation is suppressed.[213]

In *B. subtilis* (both "Ford" and "Marburg" strains), thiamine promotes the formation of carbon dioxide and other products of pyruvate metabolism, whereas in its absence lactate becomes the major product. *B. subtilis* (Marburg), grown anaerobically on a complex medium, displays a homolactic fermentation; aerobically, acetate, acetoin, and carbon dioxide are formed.[214] Cells grown in synthetic medium also have lost fermentative capacity, but do oxidize glucose.[215]

The behavior of carbon dioxide, formate, and acetate during glucose fermentation by *B. subtilis* (Ford) has been studied by Neish.[204] As with *A. indologenes*, added acetate was readily metabolized with an increased yield of butanediol and ethanol and a marked decrease in glycerol production. Carboxyl-labeled acetate was readily converted to labeled ethanol, but not to 2,3-butanediol. Thus, the stimulatory effect of acetate upon butanediol production was an indirect result of its ability to act as a hydrogen acceptor, as shown for *Leuconostoc mesenteroides*.[216] Under the same conditions added formate was relatively inert, being recovered as such. In addition, C^{14}-formate did not yield labeled fermentation products. $C^{14}O_2$, on the other hand, was incorporated into succinic acid, the lactate carboxyl group, and formate at a slow rate (3%); much higher formate incorporation was observed with *S. marcescens* (38%) and *A. aerogenes* (54%).[204]

The effect of pH upon the fermentation resembles *S. marcescens* as described above. As in the case of *A. aerogenes*, Neish found that the fermentation of glucose-1-C^{14} yielded methyl-labeled 2,3-butanediol and lactate, and glycerol labeled in the primary alcohol groups; the carbon dioxide was not labeled. In line with the reasoning already presented for *A. aerogenes*, this labeling pattern constitutes evidence for the operation of the Embden-Meyerhof glycolytic system in *B. subtilis*.[204]

The relative amounts of the different fermentation types has been published by Ledingham and Neish[184] (Table X). For the purpose of comparison, all of the organisms were grown in the same medium containing calcium carbonate. Under other conditions a nearly pure fermentation type may be

TABLE X

RELATIVE IMPORTANCE OF THE VARIOUS FERMENTATION REACTIONS IN SPECIES OF BACTERIA PRODUCING 2,3-BUTANEDIOL[a]

Organism	Percentage of sugar dissimilated by fermentations producing				
	Diol-hydrogen	Diol-formic acid	Diol-glycerol	Ethanol	Lactic acid
Aerobacter aerogenes	52	2	—	23	2
Pseudomonas hydrophila	56	—	—	26	12
Bacillus polymyxa	68	—	—	33	—
Serratia plymuthicum	49	2	—	23	14
Serratia marcescens	1	55	1	27	6
Serratia indica	1	50	1	22	5
Serratia anolium	1	48	1	21	4
Bacillus subtilis (Ford type)	—	—	84	3	12

[a] Ledingham and Neish.[184]

TABLE XI

COMPARISON OF GENERA WHICH DISPLAY A 2,3-BUTANEDIOL FERMENTATION[a]

Organism	Aerobacter aerogenes	Aerobacillus polymyxa	Aeromonas hydrophila
Family	Enterobacteria-ceae	Bacillaceae	Pseudomonada-ceae
Morphology	Gram-negative rods, flagella peritrichous when present	Gram-negative spore-forming rods, flagella peritrichous	Gram-negative rods, flagella polar
Main products formed from glucose	2,3-Butanediol, ethanol, formic acid, lactic acid, carbon dioxide, hydrogen	2,3-Butanediol, ethanol, acetic acid, carbon dioxide, hydrogen	2,3-Butanediol, ethanol, acetic acid, lactic acid, carbon dioxide, hydrogen
Type of 2,3-butanediol	d-Meso mixture, $(\alpha)_D^{25} = +0.82$	Levo $(\alpha)_D^{25} = -13.19$	l-Meso mixture, $(\alpha)_D^{25} = -0.97$
Main products formed from pyruvic acid	2,3-Butanediol, acetic acid, carbon dioxide, hydrogen	Acetoin, acetic acid, carbon dioxide, hydrogen	Acetic acid, lactic acid, carbon dioxide, hydrogen

[a] Stanier and Adams.[190]

displayed. For instance, as high as 85% of the diol-glycerol fermentation has been obtained with *B. subtilis*, and *A. aerogenes* carries out a diol-hydrogen fermentation to the extent of 90%.[211] Doubtless these processes are not coupled as implied by the table but occur independently.

Stanier and Adams,[190] in a comparison of the butanediol fermentations have called attention, by the use of Table XI, to the comparative position of the several organisms from the standpoint of both classification and fermentation characteristics. The fermentations are similar although morphological characteristics vary widely. Yet there are distinct differences in the details of the fermentation. It is also known that organisms taxonomically related to those in the table display profoundly different fermentative patterns (*Pseudomonas lindneri*–ethanolic versus *Aeromonas* (*Pseudomonas*) *hydrophila*–butanediol). Stanier and Adams[190] state, "Thus the mechanism of carbohydrate metabolism cuts sharply across orthodox taxonomic divisions, a fact that suggests that a particular fermentative mechanism has developed independently in several branches of the bacterial kingdom during the course of evolution."

7. Synthesis of Acetoin and 2,3-Butanediol

Pyruvate, formed in glucose fermentation, is the precursor of acetoin and 2,3-butanediol. However, the details of the process are complex and have thus far eluded complete solution. This is due partly to a late recognition of the fact that several variations of the basic mechanism for acetoin synthesis exist individually in different organisms or together in the same organism. Nevertheless, it was recognized that pyruvate and/or acetaldehyde were precursors of acetoin in yeast and that the process was closely associated with pyruvate decarboxylation. The process has therefore been considered to occur in two steps, i.e., cleavage of pyruvate to form enzyme-acetaldehyde, and transfer to free acetaldehyde, forming acetoin. Thus the the roles of carboxylase and carboligase in acetoin synthesis were postulated and long debated.[217-221] It has since been shown that highly purified carboxylase fractions form acetoin from pyruvate in fixed proportion to the carboxylase activity.[222, 224] Hence, it is likely that these activities cannot be completely separated. Since acetaldehyde alone also yields traces of acetoin, [223-225] it is currently postulated that an aldehyde-diphosphothiamine compound is formed from pyruvate and also slowly from acetaldehyde.[15, 226, 227] Neuberg and associates[217-220] and others [228, 229] observed that the addition of various aldehydes with pyruvate yielded optically active acyloins. Therefore, aldehydes were considered to be the acceptor in a 2-carbon transfer reaction. Fractions have been obtained with greatly increased acetoin-forming ability relative to carboxylase. For instance, an acetoin-forming enzyme system has been separated from the yeast-type carboxylase of *P. lindneri*.[8] It therefore appears that these fractions should be assigned the aldehyde transfer function of carboligase.

Acetoin is produced from pyruvate by *B. subtilis*,[230] *A. aerogenes*,[231-233] *C. acetobutylicum*,[113] and other organisms as follows:

$$2 \text{ pyruvate} \rightarrow \text{acetoin} + 2 \text{ CO}_2$$

Since these microorganisms do not contain carboxylase or produce appreciable acetaldehyde, it is evident that a yeast-type carboxylase and carboligase reactions do not function. Also, enzyme preparations from *Aerobacter* species which produce acetoin do not utilize added acetaldehyde.[232] The bacterial process utilizes pyruvate as the aldehyde acceptor with a single enzyme presumably catalyzing the pyruvate decarboxylation and aldehyde transfer functions.[227] In this case as stable intermediate, $(+)$ α-acetolactate, is produced as follows:

$$2 \text{ pyruvate} \rightarrow (+) \ \alpha\text{-acetolactate} + \text{CO}_2$$

A stereospecific α-acetolactate decarboxylase then forms acetoin:

$$(+) \ \alpha\text{-acetolactate} \rightarrow (-) \text{ acetoin} + \text{CO}_2$$

TABLE XII

OPTICAL ROTATION OF 2,3-BUTANEDIOL PRODUCED BY VARIOUS BACTERIA[a]

Organism	Approximate composition of mixture	Reference
Aerobacter aerogenes	5–14% L(+), remainder meso	[185, 186]
Bacillus polymyxa	At least 98% D (−)	[235, 236, 237]
Pseudomonas hydrophila	About 8% D(−), remainder meso	[191]
Bacillus subtilis (Ford)	Up to 40% D(−), remainder meso	[198, 213]
Serratia marcescens	Predominantly meso	[211]
Serratia plymuthicum	Predominantly meso	[203]
Serratia anolium	Predominantly meso	[203]

[a] Ledingham and Neish.[184]

The first enzyme resembles carboxylase in that diphosphothiamine and manganous ions are required.[229] α-Acetolactate is inert in the yeast, animal, and plant acetoin-forming systems and thus does not appear to function in acetoin synthesis in these cells. The identity and characteristics of this pathway has been further established in *S. faecalis*[234] and in other organisms.[227]

2,3-Butanediol is produced by reduction of acetoin. In *Leuconostoc mesenteroides*, and doubtless in the butanediol-producing organisms, the reversible reaction is catalyzed by butanediol dehydrogenase with the equilibrium in the direction of reduction.[216]

$$\text{acetoin} + \text{DPNH} + \text{H}^+ \rightarrow \text{2,3-butanediol} + \text{DPN}^+$$

Hence, the balance between acetoin and 2,3-butanediol is determined by the amount of available hydrogen.

As shown in Table XII, the three possible stereoisomeric forms of butanediol are produced by bacteria, presumably but not necessarily, from (−) acetoin. It is likely that separate stereospecific dehydrogenases exist for all of these forms. Mixtures could arise through the simultaneous action of more than one butanediol dehydrogenase, or through the action of racemizing enzymes. The details of the stereospecificity remains to be elucidated, however.

B. HEXOSE MONOPHOSPHATE PATHWAYS

1. VIA PENTOSE PHOSPHATE TO HEXOSE PHOSPHATE

The so-called "hexose-monophosphate shunt," originally established as an oxidative mechanism alternate to glycolysis, is known to function in several variations in fermentation of hexoses, gluconic and 2-ketogluconic acids, and of pentoses.

The point of departure from the Embden-Meyerhof system for the alter-

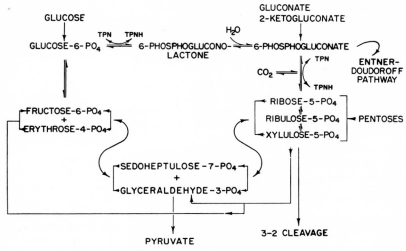

Fig. 5. Hexose monophosphate pathways.

nate routes is the oxidation of glucose-6-phosphate by a dehydrogenase originally named "zwischenferment" by Warburg and Christian.[238] In the late 1930's this shunt pathway, now known as the Warburg-Dickens-Horecker scheme, was thought to consist of successive oxidations and decarboxylations until the substrate was completely oxidized, or until a smaller intermediate enters the tricarboxylic acid cycle. Although such reactions do form pentose from hexose, the further degradation involves cleavage and transfer reactions for pentose phosphate of a type hitherto unknown in metabolism (see Fig. 5.) The transferring enzymes involved, transketolase and transaldolase, affect the synthesis of fructose-6-phosphate from pentose phosphate. The fructose-6-phosphate can then recycle through the hexose monophosphate pathway under aerobic conditions, or undergo fermentation via the glycolytic system (see Chapter 4).

2. Via 3–2 Cleavage of Pentose Phosphate

One major fermentation pattern follows the Warburg-Dickens-Horecker route except that pentose phosphate does not undergo transfer and cleavage reactions to form hexose phosphate esters, but is split into 3 and 2 carbon units (Fig. 11), yielding glyceraldehyde-3-phosphate and acetyl phosphate.[239] These are converted in fermentative organisms to lactate and ethanol, respectively.

a. Heterolactic Fermentation. Organisms isolated from a variety of sources, including wines, sauerkraut, silage, and spoiled tomato products, ferment hexoses with the production of ethanol, acetic acid, glycerol, man-

TABLE XIII

GLUCOSE AND FRUCTOSE FERMENTATIONS BY HETEROLACTIC ACID BACTERIA

Products	mMoles/100 mmoles of hexose fermented									
	Lactobacillus mannitopoeus[244]	*Lactobacillus lycopersici*[244]	*Leuconostoc mesenteroides*[a][216]		*Leuconostoc dextranicum*[246]		*Lactobacillus pentoaceticus*[242]		*Lactobacillus brevis*[246]	
Glucose fermented	+	+	+		+		+		+	
Fructose fermented				+		+		+		+
Lactic acid	83.1	94.2	102.0[b]	88.8[c]	83.5	53.4	90.6	44.0	83.1	33.1
Ethanol	66.6	59.4	112.0	95.6	81.2	51.2	61.2	12.0	74.1	0.8
Acetic acid	21.4	18.2	—	—	10.8	34.9	35.4	31.5	15.3	40.3
Carbon dioxide	90.5	74.6	96.0	103.8	86.5	77.5	86.1	58.0	81.0	44.7
Glycerol	42.9[d]	36.5[d]	—	—	24.0	2.1	—	—	32.6	3.8
Mannitol	—	—	—	—	—	29.8	—	47.3	—	62.3
Carbon recovery, %	107.4	103.5	104.0	93.6	98.9	99.1	92.0	93.5	101.1	101.9
O/R balance	1.02	0.97	0.86	1.08	0.95	1.15	1.41	1.63	0.9	1.32

[a] Resting cells.
[b] pH 4.5.
[c] pH 7.0.
[d] Glycerol calculated as acetate × 2.

nitol, and carbon dioxide in addition to lactic acid.[19] Gayon and Doubourg[240, 241] and others showed that organisms isolated from wine produced lactic and acetic acids, ethanol, carbon dioxide, and glycerol from hexoses, whereas the fermentation of fructose yielded the same products and mannitol. Studies of similar fermentations by Peterson and Fred,[242] Pederson,[243] and Nelson and Werkman[244, 245] with *Lactobacillus pentoaceticus*, *L. brevis*, *L. gayoni*, *L. mannitopoeus*, *Leuconostoc mesenteroides*, and *L. dextranicum* have served to establish the heterolactic fermentation in *Lactobacillus* and to differentiate sharply the lactobacilli into homo- and heterofermentative types with the above organisms belonging to the heterofermentative group. The *Betacoccus* of Orla-Jensen,[43] or genus *Leuconostoc*, resembles the heterolactobacilli.

The large number of fermentation balances published suggests that two separate patterns may be superimposed to varying degrees. In *Lactobacillus pentoaceticus*[242] and in nonproliferating *Leuconostoc mesenteroides*[216] only the basic fermentation (Table XIII) is displayed:

$$\text{glucose} \rightarrow \text{lactic acid} + \text{ethanol} + CO_2$$

In other organisms such as *Lactobacillus brevis*,[246] the second type,

$$\tfrac{3}{2} \text{ glucose} \rightarrow 2 \text{ glycerol} + \text{acetic acid} + CO_2$$

is present to the extent of 20 % to 30 % of the glucose utilized. Although glycerol was not determined by Peterson and Fred[242] or by Nelson and Werkman,[244] calculations based upon the assumption that glycerol = 2 acetate resulted in essentially complete carbon recovery.[244] Fructose fermentation by all of these organisms yields mannitol, lactic acid, acetic acid, carbon dioxide, and ethanol, the latter often is considerably decreased amounts (Table XIII).[242, 246, 247] The fermentation balances approximate the following equation:

$$3 \text{ fructose} \rightarrow 2 \text{ mannitol} + \text{lactic acid} + \text{acetic acid} + CO_2$$

The stoichiometry is adhered to in some cases (*L. brevis*), but in others (*L. pentoaceticus* and *Leuconostoc dextranicum*) less mannitol and acetic acid and more lactic acid and ethanol were found. Hence, it appears that there is a competition between the mannitol- and the ethanol-producing variations. The homolactobacillus, *Lactobacillus plantarum*,[243] produces only lactic acid under the same conditions. Thus, the heterolactic species utilize hydrogen acceptors other than pyruvate to regenerate diphosphopyridine nucleotide. In these cases acetyl phosphate and acetaldehyde, dihydroxyacetone phosphate, and fructose are reduced to ethanol, α-glycerol phosphate, and mannitol, respectively.

The mechanisms have been considered to involve extensions of the Embden-Meyerhof glycolytic system of the homolactic and yeast fermentations. Decarboxylation of pyruvate and reduction of acetaldehyde were thought to act in the route of ethanol formation. Also, the reduction of dihydroxyacetone phosphate to glycerol and fructose to mannitol were considered to be only minor variations in the same scheme.

The recent evidence establishes the fact that the heterolactic fermentation differs fundamentally from the homolactic type. Obviously, there is the greater array of products, and the different configuration of lactic acid produced (Table IV). In addition, with *Leuconostoc mesenteroides* the ratio of products cannot be varied by changing the pH of the culture as should result if a branched pathway produced these compounds.[242] Investigation of ethanol formation in *L. mesenteroides* by DeMoss, Bard, and Gunsalus[216] led to the discovery of a new pathway in this organism. Particularly significant were the findings that the energy yield as measured by growth was one-third lower per mole of glucose fermented than observed for homolactic organisms. In addition, aldolase and triose phosphate isomerase were not demonstrable. Subsequent studies by Gunsalus and Gibbs,[10] and by DeMoss[9] revealed that acetate-C^{14} was reduced to ethanol-C^{14} and that glu-

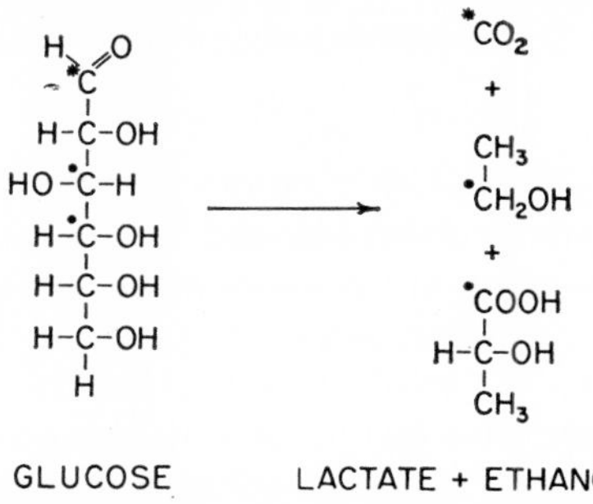

GLUCOSE LACTATE + ETHANOL + CO_2

FIG. 6. Labeling pattern of hexose monophosphate pathway.

cose-1-C^{14} and glucose 3,4-C^{14} were converted to products as shown in Fig. 6.

Extension of these procedures to heterolactobacilli by Gibbs et al.,[248] has shown that the release of carbon 1 of glucose as carbon dioxide is characteristic of glucose fermentations by all heterolactic organisms. This study is particularly valuable because the strains of *Leuconostoc mesenteroides*, *Lactobacillus fermenti*, and *L. pentoaceticus* employed were those studied earlier by Pederson,[243] Stiles et al.[249] and Peterson and Fred,[247] respectively. *Leuconostoc dextranicum* and a heterolactobacillus causing the greening of meat also performed in the same manner. The fermentation of glucosamine-C^{14} also produces the same labeling patterns in the products.[250]

All of these data indicate the existence of a new route for ethanol formation. Since carbon 1 of glucose yielded carbon dioxide as is characteristic of the hexose monophosphate pathway, this system was implicated in the heterolactic fermentation. Considerable evidence for the enzymes has been obtained by DeMoss[251-254] (Fig. 7). Of the glycolytic enzymes, hexokinase, phosphoglyceric transphosphorylase and dehydrogenases for D-glyceraldehyde-3-phosphate, D-lactic acid, ethanol, acetaldehyde, and acetoin have been demonstrated. Aldolase and triose phosphate isomerase were absent, however. Thus, the Embden-Meyerhof pathway cannot function in the heterolactic fermentation. In the hexose monophosphate pathway, a glucose-6-phosphate dehydrogenase utilizing either diphosphopyridine nucleotide or triphosphopyridine nucleotide is present. Recent studies indicate that 6-phosphogluconate is oxidized to pentose phosphate, presumably D-ribulose-5-phosphate. The missing step, a cleavage of D-xylulose-5-phosphate to yield acetyl phosphate and D-glyceraldehyde-3-phosphate, as first demonstrated in *Lactobacillus pentosus* by Heath et al.,[239] has recently been found in *Leuconostoc mesenteroides* also.[255] Thus, the oxidation of glucose-6-phosphate and 6-phosphogluconate can be linked to the reduction of acetyl phosphate and acetaldehyde with DPN serving as hydrogen carries. Glyceraldehyde-3-phosphate (G-3-P) yields D-lactic acid as in

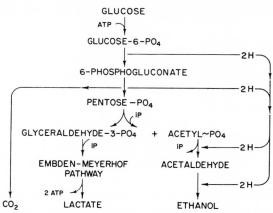

FIG. 7. Heterolactic fermentation (hexose monophosphate pathway) of *Leuconostic mesenteroides*.

glycolysis. Similar though less extensive evidence has been obtained for fructose fermentation by *Lactobacillus brevis*.[256]

The derivation of carbon atoms in the products fits the labeling data as follows: (*a*) carbon atom 1 of glucose is oxidized to carbon dioxide; (*b*) carbon atom 3 of glucose or carbon atom 2 of pentose becomes the carboxyl carbon of acetate; the carboxyl group of acetate upon reduction becomes the carbinol group of ethanol; (*c*) carbon atom 4, upon cleavage of pentose phosphate by phosphoketolase, becomes the aldehyde carbon of glyceraldehyde-3-phosphate. (*d*) Carbon atom 4 of hexose or the aldehyde carbon of glyceraldehyde-3-phosphate becomes a carboxyl group of lactate. The steps in the heterolactic fermentation are shown in Fig. 7. Since the products may be separated and degraded carbon by carbon, *Leuconostoc mesenteroides* fermentation has been utilized to determine the labeling patterns of glucose-C^{14}.[257] The technique has been useful in mammalian biochemistry, particularly in establishing the labeling patterns in glycogen and lactose.

An enzymic basis for separation of lactobacilli into hetero- and homofermentative groups, and the differentiation of the genus *Leuconostoc* from *Streptococcus* resides in abilities to produce the unique enzymes of the hexose monophosphate and hexose diphosphate pathways, respectively. Based upon enzyme assays, Buyze *et al.*[46b] concluded that three types of lactic acid bacteria exist: (*a*) obligate homofermenters with aldolase, but not dehydrogenases, for glucose-6-phosphate or 6-phosphogluconate, (*b*) obligate heterofermenters containing the above dehydrogenases and devoid of aldolase, and (*c*) facultative homofermenters containing the C_6-dehydrogenases, but fermenting via the Embden-Meyerhof system. The route of ribose synthesis in the obligate homofermenters thus becomes a pertinent question.

Only one mole of adenosine triphosphate is utilized in the initial phase of the hexose monophosphate pathway and two moles of adenosine triphosphate are generated in conversion of glyceraldehyde-3-phosphate to lactate. The energy contained in the carboxyl-phosphoryl linkage of acetyl phosphate presumably is lost in its reduction to ethanol. Thus, per mole of glucose fermented, the one mole of adenosine triphosphate synthesized is one-half that produced by glycolysis.

$$\text{glucose} + iP + ADP \rightarrow \text{lactate} + \text{ethanol} + CO_2 + ATP + H_2O$$

From this one would expect the growth yield per unit of carbohydrate utilized to be one-half that obtained with homofermentative organisms. However, the growth yield was only one-third less. An explanation for this inconsistency currently is not available.

Elsden[1] pointed out that the lower energy yield is characteristic of a pathway of dehydrogenation before cleavage and is partly the result of the exergonic hydrolysis of the lactone ring of 6-phospho-δ-gluconolactone without ATP formation.

3. VIA 2-KETO-3-DEOXY-6-PHOSPHOGLUCONATE

Another route thus far documented principally in pseudomonads, is called the Entner-Doudoroff pathway. The first step in this pathway is similar to the other hexose monophosphate system, i.e., glucose-6-phosphate is oxidized to 6-phosphogluconate. The route then diverges from the HMP pathway with the cleavage of 6-phosphogluconate to pyruvate and glyceraldehyde-3-phosphate via two reactions (Fig. 8). In succeeding steps the triose phosphate also yields pyruvate via the reactions of the Embden-Meyerhof route. Although most of the pseudomonads studied in connection with this pathway are aerobes, *Pseudomonas lindneri* illustrates the function of the Entner-Doudoroff route in fermentation (anaerobic glycolysis).

Pseudomonas lindneri, or *Termobacterium mobile*, the organism producing the fermentation of Mexican pulque, carries out an almost pure ethanolic fermentation, i.e., stoichiometry displayed by yeast. Kluyver and Hoppenbrouwers[258] reported that one mole of glucose yielded 1.8 moles each of carbon dioxide and ethanol and 0.2 moles of lactate. Gibbs and DeMoss[8, 259, 260] found by fermenting glucose-1-C^{14}, glucose 3,4-C^{14} and fructose 1,6-C^{14} that carbon atoms 1 and 4 yielded carbon dioxide as would be expected from a homoethanolic version of the heterolactic fermentation. The ethanol labeling, however, did not agree with the order predicted from the heterolactic fermentation as outlined in Section B, 2. With glucose-2-C^{14}, only the carbinol carbon of ethanol was labeled at one-half the specific activity of

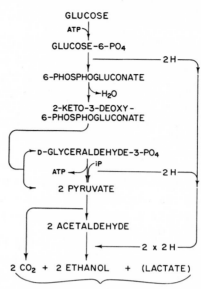

FIG. 8. Bacterial ethanolic fermentation (Entner-Doudoroff pathway) of *Pseudomonas lindneri*.

carbon atom 2 of glucose. With fructose-1,6-C^{14} the carbon dioxide and methyl carbon of ethanol were labeled. When considered in the light of an earlier observation that a yeast-type carboxylase and an ethanol dehydrogenase are present,[8] it was postulated that the ethanol is derived from pyruvate which arose from the glucose as shown in Fig. 2. This distribution of carbon atoms would be expected from the pathway of glucose utilization which has been found in *P. saccharophila*[261, 262] and *P. fluorescens*.[263, 264]

As in the heterolactic fermentation, the hydrogen atoms mobilized in the oxidation of glucose-6-phosphate and glyceraldehyde-3-phosphate reduce pyruvate and acetaldehyde. Thus, a yeast-type fermentation is accomplished by a completely different mechanism. Since one mole of pyruvate is produced without the intermediary oxidation of glyceraldehyde-3-phosphate, it appears that the energy yield would be one-half that obtained by yeasts for the same over-all conversion:

$$\text{glucose} + iP + ADP \rightarrow 2 \text{ ethanol} + 2\ CO_2 + ATP + H_2O$$

The fermentation by *P. lindneri* is the only known example of the function of the Entner-Doudoroff pathway in glucose fermentation. As described in Section III, E, 3, gluconic acid fermentation by *S. faecalis* also utilizes the same pathway in part.

5. CLEAVAGE OF FRUCTOSE-6-PHOSPHATE

It is theoretically possible for hexose fermentation to occur by the cleavage and transfer reactions of transaldolase and transketolase. Thus a reverse of the conversion of pentose phosphate to hexose monophosphate (Section III, D, 1, b; Fig. 5) and cleavage of pentose phosphate by phosphoketolase (Fig. 7) would yield G-3-P and acetyl phosphate as does the *L. mesenteroides* fermentation. However, the labeling pattern would be radically altered. A similar, but alternate, possibility is based upon the existence of fructose-6-phosphate phosphoketolase in *Acetobacter xylinum*.[264a] In conjunction with known enzymes, a fermentative sequence has been postulated[264a] which could be considered to yield acetate, or acetate and lactate as follows:

$$\text{fructose-6-P} + \text{iP} \rightarrow \text{erythrose-4-P} + \text{acetyl-P} + H_2O$$

$$\text{erythrose-4-P} + \text{fructose-6-P} \rightarrow \text{sedoheptulose-7-P} + \text{glyceraldehyde-3-P}$$

$$\text{sedoheptulose-7-P} + \text{glyceraldehyde-3-P} \rightarrow \text{ribose-5-P} + \text{xylulose-5-P}$$

$$\text{ribose-5-P} \rightarrow \text{xylulose-5-P}$$

$$2 \text{ xylulose-5-P} + 2 \text{ ip} \rightarrow 2 \text{ glyceraldehyde-3-P} + 2 \text{ acetyl-P} + 2 H_2O$$

$$3 \text{ acetyl-P} + 3 \text{ ADP} \rightarrow 3 \text{ ATP} + 3 \text{ acetate}$$

$$2 \text{ glyceraldehyde-3-P} \rightarrow \text{fructose-1,6-P} \rightarrow \text{fructose-6-P} + \text{iP}$$

or

$$2\text{-glyceraldehyde-3-P} + 2 \text{ iP} + 4 \text{ ADP} \rightarrow 4 \text{ ATP} + 2 \text{ lactate}$$

Sum for hexose fermentation:

$$\text{hexose} + 2 \text{ iP} + 2 \text{ ADP} \rightarrow 3 \text{ acetate} + 2 \text{ ATP} + 2 H_2O$$

or

$$2 \text{ hexose} + 5 \text{ iP} + 5 \text{ ADP} \rightarrow 3 \text{ acetate} + 2 \text{ lactate} + 5 \text{ ATP} + 5 H_2O$$

C. MULTIPLE PATHWAYS

1. PROPIONIC ACID FERMENTATION

Propionibacterium species, *Micrococcus lactilyticus* (*Veillonella gazogenes*), and *Clostridium propionicum* produce propionic acid, acetic acid, and carbon dioxide as major fermentative products. All except *Clostridium propionicum* form small amounts of succinic acid. Early studies by Fitz revealed that fermentation of lactate and malate yielded propionate, acetate and carbon dioxide. In 1878 he proposed the following fermentation equation:[265]

$$3 \text{ lactic acid} \rightarrow 2 \text{ propionic acid} + \text{acetic acid} + CO_2 + H_2O$$

The association of microorganisms producing propionic acid with the eyes in Emmenthaler cheese was studied by Orla-Jensen.[266] Von Freuden-reich and Orla-Jensen[267] succeeded in isolating pure cultures of propionic acid-producing organisms in 1906. Although the role of these organisms in Swiss cheese ripening and their classification has received much attention, the bulk of the fermentation data was obtained by Van Niel and somewhat later by Werkman and his associates. Representative balances appear in Table XIV.

Ideally, the stoichiometry for the better known fermentation types is represented by the following equations:

$$\tfrac{3}{2} \text{ glucose} \rightarrow 2 \text{ propionate} + \text{acetic acid} + CO_2 + H_2O$$

$$3 \text{ lactate} \rightarrow 2 \text{ propionate} + \text{acetic acid} + CO_2 + H_2O$$

$$3 \text{ pyruvate} + H_2O \rightarrow \text{propionate} + 2 \text{ acetate} + 2 CO_2$$

$$\text{glycerol} \rightarrow \text{propionate} + H_2O$$

The fermentation data indicate that these stoichiometries are achieved only in the roughest sense. The balances published by Wood and Werkman[272] and by Van Niel[273] for instance, showed the ratios of propionate to acetate to vary with *P. arabinosum* from 7.8 to 14.8, whereas the ratios with several other species was about 2.3. These calculations are made more approximate since succinate, present to varying degrees, was not considered in these calculations.

The propionibacteria ferment a wide variety of carbohydrates, polyols, and organic acids to the same products,[19, 274] although the proportions vary greatly. The substrates include lactose, sucrose, maltose, glucose, galactose, sorbitol, mannitol, glycerol, adonitol, pentoses, gluconate, 2-ketogluconate, erythritol, lactate, pyruvate, and malate.[275-277]

a. Fermentation Mechanism. The routes of pyruvate and propionate formation are by no means clearly understood. In addition, different routes from lactate to propionate appear to function in the propionibacteria and in *Clostridium propionicum.*

The evidence indicates that hexoses are converted to pyruvate at least to some extent by the Embden-Meyerhof pathway. Early studies by Virtanen[278-280] and by Pett and Wynne[281] with dried cells established the uptake of inorganic phosphate and the accumulation and fermentation of hexose phosphates. Werkman and his collaborators showed that added fluoride plus a hydrogen acceptor prevented the formation of the normal products and caused 3-phosphoglycerate to accumulate.[282-285] In the absence of fluoride, hexose diphosphate, 3-phosphoglycerate, and α-glycerol phosphate were fermented slowly to the normal products. Barker and Lipmann[286] showed that dried *P. pentosaceum* transferred phosphate from

TABLE XIV

PROPIONIC ACID FERMENTATIONS

Products	mMoles/100 mmoles of C_3 fermented											
	Propionibacterium arabinosum[268]	Propionibacterium pentosaceum[269,273]						Clostridium propionicium[270]			Micrococcus lactilyticus[271]	Cytophaga succinicans[313a]
	Glucose	Glucose	Glucose[a]	Lactate	Pyruvate	Glycerol	Glycerol	Glucose	Lactate	Acrylate	Lactate	Glucose
Propionic acid	74.4	76	33.0	63.7	43.7	100.0	55.8	66.0	33.3	58.2	63.7	0
Acetic acid	5.0	20.6	11.6	33.9	57.5	4.9	2.9	33.0	66.7	29.1	39.5	39
Carbon dioxide	31.8	19.6	0	35.1	58.0	3.8	−37.7	36.5	61.6	30.6	39.1	−39
Succinate	3.9	10.8	0	6.9	7.1	6.8	42.1	—	—	—	—	59
Formate	—	—	—	—	—	—	—	—	—	—	—	21
Hydrogen	—	—	—	—	—	—	—	—	—	—	14.2	—
Propionic/acetic	14.7	3.9	2.8	1.9	0.77	20.0	19.2	20	0.5	2.0	1.6	—
Carbon recovery, %	94.0	111.0	78	107.0	111.0	114.0	101	100	98	89	103.0	99
O/R balance	0.9	0.64	0.88	1.2	0.86	1.1	1.17	1.1	0.9	1.1	1.0	1.02

[a] Sulfite added, 29.2 mmoles pyruvate, 7.2 mmoles lactate also formed.

adenosine triphosphate to an ester linkage with glucose, arabinose, glycerol, and several other substrates.

In contrast to the definite labeling patterns obtained with lactic acid bacteria, the fermentation of position-labeled glucoses by *P. arabinosum* revealed that all of the carbon atoms of hexose appeared to some extent in all of the carbon atoms of the products.[287, 288] Illustrative of the difficulties in interpreting the isotope data is the observation of Leaver *et al.*[310] that C^{14} from lactate-3-C^{14} is found in all carbons of propionate and succinate as well as both carbons of acetate and CO_2. Although a large amount of study has been necessary to interpret these results, it is evident that the labeling patterns reflect a substantial conversion of glucose to pyruvate via the Embden-Meyerhof pathway. For instance, with glucose-3,4-C^{14} the highest labeling appears in the carbon dioxide, presumably arising by decarboxylation of carboxyl-labeled pyruvate. The acetate methyl carbon along with positions 2 and 3 of propionate are highest labeled when glucose-1-C^{14} and glucose-6-C^{14} were fermented. These presumably arise from methyl-labeled pyruvate. These patterns would be predicted from the Embden-Meyerhof route.

Concurrently, however, evidence has accumulated which cannot be explained by the presence of a single route for hexose degradation. It was observed several times that fluoride did not completely inhibit glucose fermentation as it did for glycerol.[282, 283] It was clearly pointed out at the time that another fermentation mechanism must exist. Although the interpretation of the old data on fluoride inhibition is made more difficult by the finding of new routes for glucose fermentation which also yield phosphoglycerate, and by complicated effects of fluoride upon cell integrity,[289] newer information obtained with labeled substrates gives the same indications. With glucose-1-C^{14}, for instance, considerable radioactivity appears in the carbon dioxide as would be expected if an anaerobic hexose monophosphate pathway were functioning.[287, 288] However, there is no direct resemblance with the anaerobic hexose monophosphate route found in lactic acid bacteria, or with the anaerobic version of the hexose monophosphate route of Entner and Doudoroff which is found in *Pseudomonas*; the labeling patterns do not fit a combination of the Embden-Meyerhof pathway and one of these routes. Further, tests for the cleavage of 6-phosphogluconate to pyruvate and glyceraldehyde-3-phosphate as in the Entner-Doudoroff mechanism have been negative in two instances.[264, 290] There is, however, evidence for a hexose monophosphate system in which pentose phosphate is not cleaved simply to form 3 and 2 carbon units as in the heterolactic organisms.[290] Thus, a pathway from pentose phosphate to fructose-6-phosphate via sedoheptulose phosphate is indicated (see Fig. 5 for a detailed account of this mechanism). Since it is likely the pentose could be formed from glucose, its further metabolism via the transaldolase-transketolase mechanism as found in *Aerobacter aerogenes* (Section III, D, 1, b) could lead to more complicated labeling patterns in hexose monophosphate, which either enters the Embden-Meyerhof system or recycles through the hexose monophosphate pathway. This possibility is supported by the labeling patterns obtained in the fermentation of pentoses by *Propionibacterium*.

Wood and Leaver[277] have found that the quantitative relationship among the products in the fermentations of glycerol, erythritol, adonitol, and mannitol are very similar. The distribution of fixed CO_2 was similar to that incurred in the fermentation of C_3 and C_6 substrates, thereby indicating that unique mechanisms are not involved for the C_4 and C_5 compounds.

The pathway for conversion of pyruvate to succinate and propionate has only recently been clarified.[309a,b] Of greatest significance, in fact the opening of this problem resulted from, the discovery of heterotrophic carbon dioxide fixation in *Propionibacterium arabinosum* by Wood and Werkman.[272, 274, 291, 292] First, it was found that the carbon content of the fermentation products was greater than of the substrate consumed. In addition, a net decrease of carbon dioxide was demonstrated; and the carbon recoveries and oxidation-reduction balances were more satisfactory when the uptake in carbon dioxide was taken into account. It was also observed that the yield of succinate rose with increasing carbon dioxide content of the medium. A clear-cut demonstration of heterotrophic carbon dioxide fixation was obtained by fermentation of glycerol in the presence of $C^{13}O_2$. Under these circumstances little carbon dioxide is produced and both succinate and propionate became carboxyl-labeled.[292, 293] Similar experiments were performed with $C^{11}O_2$ by Carson *et al.*[294, 295] Although there followed attempts to explain the data by separate routes for propionate and succinate formation,[268, 272] evidence has continuously accumulated to indicate that succinate is a precursor of propionate.[269, 275, 292, 293, 296] Werkman and Wood[291] suggested that carbon dioxide fixation with pyruvate as the acceptor ought to form oxalacetate which would yield succinate, as shown in Fig. 9. Krebs and Eggleston[297] demonstrated that the postulated reactions occur at a rapid enough rate to account for the observed rate of propionate formation. In addition it was found that fumarate could be formed from glycerol.

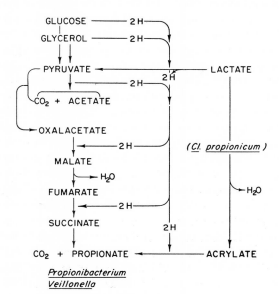

FIG. 9. Propionic acid fermentation.

More recent studies by Delwiche[298] and by Johns[299, 300] further confirmed the existence of this dicarboxylic acid pathway to succinate.

A direct fixation of carbon dioxide by a reversal of the well-known oxalacetic decarboxylase has been postulated and sought for some time. An incorporation of $C^{14}O_2$ into oxalacetic acid by crude preparations has been obtained, but not net CO_2 fixation. Three other reactions, both widely distributed, could serve the same purpose:

$$\text{pyruvate} + 2 \text{ H} + CO_2 \xrightarrow[\text{malic enzyme}]{} \text{malate}$$

$$\text{phosphoenolpyruvate} + CO_2 + \text{ADP} \xrightarrow[\substack{\text{phosphoenolpyruvate}\\\text{carboxykinase}}]{} \text{oxalacetate} + \text{ATP}$$

$$\text{phosphoenolpyruvate} + CO_2 \xrightarrow[\substack{\text{phosphoenolpyruvate}\\\text{carboxylase}}]{} \text{oxalacetate} + \text{iP}$$

A net CO_2 fixation has been obtained with extracts of *P. arabinosum* during the fermentation of glucose, glycerol, or hexose diphosphate.[288] More recently Pomerantz[301] found an exchange of $C^{14}O_2$ into oxalacetic acid which was stimulated by ATP (carboxykinase); net synthesis was obtained with phosphoenolpyruvate and $C^{14}O_2$, but ADP was not required. Hence, there is evidence for the existence of a plant-type phosphoenolpyruvate carboxylase. This pathway of CO_2 fixation could well function in glucose and glycerol fermentation, but its role in pyruvate or lactate fermentation would require the formation of phosphoenolpyruvate from pyruvate. Although pyruvate kinase is freely reversible, an expenditure of one mole of ATP would be required initially. Malic enzyme could serve the same purpose without a similar expenditure of energy.[302, 303] Evidence in favor of a role of this enzyme is lacking, however.

Although considerable evidence exists in favor of a dicarboxylic acid pathway to propionate, the process may not be as straight-forward as outlined in Fig. 9. Wood and Leaver[277] report that CO_2 turnover is much lower than would be required for propionate formation via the dicarboxylic acid pathway as depicted. Thus it has been suggested from these data and from enzyme experiments discussed below that a C_1 compound other than CO_2, but convertible to CO_2, is involved.

Succinate decarboxylation has been demonstrated repeatedly for *Propionibacterium* species and *Veillonella gazogenes*.[304-309] It has also been demonstrated that labeled carbon dioxide and labeled propionate can form labeled succinate to some extent.[275, 294, 306, 308, 309] Studies by Whiteley[307] and by Phares *et al.*[305, 309] with extracts reveal that the process is highly complicated and that coenzyme A derivatives of propionate and succinate play an important role. In addition, data obtained with cell-free extracts suggest that carbon dioxide and the carboxyl group may give rise to other one carbon compounds as part of the decarboxylation process.

A series of recent discoveries in animal and microbial systems has clarified the CO_2 fixation and succinate decarboxylation reactions. Swick and Wood[309a] and Stadtman et al.[309b] have demonstrated a biotin-containing transcarboxylase in P. shermannii. In addition the interconverion of succinyl~SCoA to methylmalonyl~SCoA by an isomerase requiring dimethylbenzimidazole-B_{12}-coenzyme (isolated by Barker et al.[309c] from P. shermannii) has been established.[309b] From these findings and other data a cyclic process for pyruvate carboxylation and succinate decarboxylation was proposed.[309a, 309b]

$$\text{succinyl~SCoA} \xrightarrow{\text{B}_{12}} \text{methylmalonyl~SCoA}$$

$$\text{methylmalonyl~SCoA} + \text{enz-biotin} \longrightarrow \text{propionyl~SCoA} + \text{enz-biotin-CO}_2$$

$$\text{enz-biotin-CO}_2 + \text{pyruvate} \rightarrow \text{oxalacetate} + \text{enz-biotin}$$

$$\text{oxalacetate} + 4\text{ H} \rightarrow \text{succinate} + \text{H}_2\text{O}$$

$$\text{propionyl~SCoA} + \text{succinate} \rightarrow \text{succinyl~SCoA} + \text{propionate}$$

$$\text{pyruvate} + 4\text{ H} \rightarrow \text{propionate} + \text{H}_2\text{O}$$

Lynen et al.[309d] has suggested that the net formation of enzyme-biotin-CO_2 may occur as follows via ATP activation. Though not clarified completely, a mechanism was suggested thus:

$$\text{enzyme-biotin} + \text{ATP} + \text{ADP~enzyme-biotin} + \text{iP}$$

$$\text{ADP~enzyme-biotin} + \text{CO}_2 \rightarrow \text{enzyme-biotin-CO}_2 + \text{ADP}$$

b. Participation of Formaldehyde in Fermentation.[311] Leaver,[312] and Carson et al.[313] have shown that glucose fermented in the presence of labeled formaldehyde leads to a more or less random distribution of isotope in all positions of the products. Similarly the fermentation of glucose labeled in various positions with unlabeled formaldehyde yielded radioactive formaldehyde. The significance of these observations with respect to the normal fermentations mechanisms is currently not known. Rate of these reactions is considerably slower than the fermentation rate, however.

c. Veillonella gazogenes. The pathway from pyruvate to propionate for Veillonella gazogenes appears to be similar to that in propionibacteria,[271] though differences in the details of succinate decarboxylation have been reported.[300, 305-307] The greatest departures from fermentation displayed by propionibacteria are its inability to ferment glucose and the presence of hydrogen among the products.

d. Cytophaga succinicans. This organism has an obligatory requirement for CO_2 for glucose fermentation.[313a] Succinate, acetate, and formate are the major fermentation products (Table XIV). The fermentations may be considered a variation of the propionic system in which succinate does not undergo decarboxylation. Hence the requirement for CO_2 to produce dicarboxylic acids, which are the hydrogen acceptors for the fermentation.

e. Clostridium propionicum. One hypothesis of long standing as to the mechanisms of propionate formation involves dehydration of lactate to acrylate and reduction of acrylate to propionate (Fig. 9). For the propionibacteria this pathway was eliminated when Barker and Lipmann[314] found that sodium fluoride inhibited lactate fermentation but not that of pyruvate. In addition, acrylate was not fermented. Although these observations were not necessarily conclusive, the need for the hypothesis vanished with the mounting evidence favoring the role of dicarboxylic acids as intermediates in the fermentation by *Propionibacterium* sp. It is interesting to note that the role of acrylate as an intermediate cannot be completely dismissed, for in *Clostridium propionicum*[270, 315, 316] the evidence favors its existence.[317, 318] *C. propionicum* neither forms nor decarboxylates succinate.[317, 318] In contrast to *Propionibacterium arabinosum*, lactate-3-C^{14} was fermented to acetate and propionate labeled almost exclusively in the methyl or methylene carbons. Randomization between α- and β-carbon atoms of propionate was not observed.[310] Cardon and Barker[270] observed the reduction of acrylate to propionate. Further, Johns[318] was unable to obtain an incorporation of $C^{14}O_2$ into propionate. In this connection, the finding of Stadtman[317] that propionyl coenzyme A can be oxidized to acrylyl coenzyme A in *Clostridium propionicum* suggests that the CoA derivatives function in propionate formation and further supports the hypothesis for an alternate route to propionate involving acrylate.

f. Energy Yields. It is impossible to assess accurately the energy yields in these fermentations. By either the Embden-Meyerhof system or a hexose monophosphate pathway involving fructose-6-phosphate synthesis from pentose phosphate followed by glycolysis, the yields approximate 2 moles of ATP per mole of glucose fermented. There is no evidence that energy is derived or consumed in the conversion of pyruvate to propionate, but the amount of pyruvate oxidized and the manner of phosphoenolpyruvate carboxylation (carboxykinase or carboxylase) affect the energy yield. With pyruvate or lactate as substrates, pyruvate oxidation to acetyl$\frown$SCoA appears to be the sole source of energy. Since CO_2 produced in succinate decarboxylation would be recycled by the transcarboxylase reaction, energy of the carbon-carbon bond is conserved. However, net CO_2 fixation, at least via phosphoenolpyruvate carboxylase, or CO_2 activation to biotin-enzyme-CO_2 level would be energy-requiring. The available data, or growth, indicate energy yields excess of 2 ATP/mole of glucose fermented (see Chapter 1).

2. MIXED POLYOL FERMENTATION BY YEASTS

A group of osmophilic yeasts isolated from brood comb and flower parts produce ethanol, glycerol, D-arabitol, erythritol, and mannitol.[319] Although

TABLE XV

POLYOL FERMENTATION BY OSMOPHILIC YEASTS[a]

Product	μMoles/100 of μmoles glucose fermented	Position	Relative specific activity[b]	
			Glucose-1-C^{14}	Glucose-2-C^{14}
Ethanol	68.9	Total	26.7	43.5
		CH_3—	26.4	2.62
		—CH_2OH	0.3	40.8
Glycerol	26.1	Total	29.1	30.3
		CH_2OH—	28.9	28.8
		—CHOH—	0.2	1.5
D-Arabitol	28.1	Total	40.4	58.8
		C_1	23.2	34.7
		C_2	0.5	12.5
		C_3	0.4	0.7
		C_4	0.2	7.85
		C_5	16.0	2.7
Succinate	1.7	—	—	—
Carbon dioxide	147.0	—	—	—
C^{14} recovery, %	—	—	94	—

[a] Spencer, Neish, Blackwood, and Sallans.[322]
[b] Specific activity of labeled carbon of glucose = 100.

these products are obtained in varying yields and combinations, depending upon the strain studied, combined yields of glycerol and D-arabitol as high as 60% have been obtained in the rapidly growing strains.[320] The yield of arabitol and glycerol is increased by aeration.[321]. Thus the fermentation departs considerably from the normal yeast fermentation. Since appreciable glycerol is produced without "steering" with sulfite, the fermentation has attracted interest because of its commercial possibilities.

Pathways distinct from the classical Embden-Meyerhof system must function, at least in the production of D-arabitol. Spencer *et al.*[322] have investigated the fermentation mechanism with uniquely labeled glucoses (Table XV). An ingenious method for stepwise degradation of D-arabitol was developed in which the D-arabitol was oxidized to D-xylulose with *Acetobacter suboxydans* and then fermented to acetate and lactate by *L. mesenteroides*. Since the labeling pattern obtained in the xylulose fermentation has been shown by Altermatt *et al.*[323] to be identical to that of xylose, it was possible to measure the isotope content of each carbon atom in D-arabitol. When glucose-1-C^{14} and glucose-2-C^{14} were fermented, the ethanol and glycerol

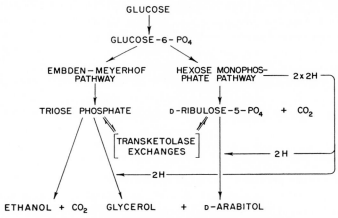

Fig. 10. Polyol fermentation by osmophilic yeasts.

were labeled as would be predicted from the exclusive operation of the classical glycolytic system, that is, methyl-labeled ethanol and glycerol-1-C^{14} were obtained from glucose-1-C^{14}, whereas carbinol-labeled ethanol and glycerol-2-C^{14} were obtained from glucose-2-C^{14}. With D-arabitol formed from glucose-1-C^{14}, carbon atoms 1 and 5 were labeled (57 % and 40 %) and from glucose-2-C^{14}, carbon atoms 1, 2, and 4 were labeled (59, 21, and 14 %). This labeling pattern was explained by assuming that (*a*) part of the glucose is converted to pentose phosphate and carbon dioxide by the hexose mono-phosphate pathway; (*b*) transketolase catalyzes exchange reactions utiliz-ing triose phosphate formed by aldolase, thereby altering the labeling pattern of pentose phosphate; and (*c*) transketolase causes an exchange of carbon atoms 1 and 2 of fructose-6-phosphate utilizing triose phosphate as the acceptor. By appropriate combinations of these well-established reac-tions, seven differently composed pentose phosphates can be formed. In these processes carbon atom 1 of glucose should appear only in carbon atoms 1 and 5 of arabitol, whereas carbon atom 2 of glucose should appear in car-bon atoms 1, 2, and 4 (Fig. 10). These results agree fairly well with the values obtained (Table XV). Therefore, in this fermentation, glycerol and ethanol plus carbon dioxide arise by glycolysis, whereas D-arabitol (pre-sumably produced from D-ribulose-5-phosphate) arises from the hexose monophosphate pathway (Fig. 5). The mechanism of erythritol formation in other strains is presumed to be equally complicated, (perhaps arising from erythrose phosphate), but remains to be studied.

D. Influence of Chain Length upon Fermentation

Increases and decreases in chain length relative to the hexose chain in most cases greatly alters the fermentation. With the pentoses that have received the most study, two new pathways come into play. Sedoheptulose (7 carbon ketose) fermentation also utilizes the pathway common to the pentoses but with differences in detail. Little is known of 4 carbon sugar fermentation but it can be inferred from the fermentation balance for L-erythrulose (see below) that the mechanism largely involves new reactions. Trioses and glycerol are closely related to intermediates of glucose metabolism. Their fermentation therefore requires only a few reactions for conversion of these substrates to intermediates in the hexose fermentation pathway.

1. Pentose Fermentation

All four D-aldopentoses—D-ribose, D-arabinose, D-xylose, and D-lyxose—as well as L-arabinose and L-xylose, are fermented by microorganisms. It is indeed curious that L-arabinose is usually fermented more rapidly than the D-pentoses,[324] and in some cases is fermented as rapidly as glucose. Homo- and heterolactic acid bacteria, propionibacteria, clostridia, the Enterobacteraceae, and many other organisms attack pentoses. In most cases the fermentation pattern is qualitatively similar to that displayed for hexose fermentation by the same organism. The only major deviation occurs among the homolactic acid bacteria, which also produce acetic acid when pentoses are the substrate. The reactions of pentose metabolism in a number of cells and tissues have recently been elucidated by the use of radioisotopes and enzyme preparations. From these studies it has become possible to understand the mechanism of pentose fermentation in great detail. Of key importance in this era have been the researches of Horecker and of Racker and their collaboraters, who established the reactions of pentose phosphate which participate in glucose catabolism via the hexose monophosphate pathway.

a. Pathway Involving 3–2 Cleavage of the Five Carbon Chain. In the fermentation of several pentoses by lactic acid bacteria, lactic and acetic acids are always formed in equimolar quantities.[325] This fact has led to the hypothesis that the five carbon chain undergoes cleavage into 2 and 3 carbon units which later become acetate and lactate, respectively. Recent discoveries concerning the reactions of pentose phosphate metabolism have substantiated this hypothesis[239] (see also below).

Peterson and associates investigated the pentose-fermenting lactic acid bacteria, which carry out the normal silage fermentation.[326, 327] It was found that two fermentation types exist. One type represented by *Lactobacillus pentosus*, did not produce mannitol during the fructose fermentation, whereas the second type, represented by *L. pentoaceticus*, did. Both types produced equimolar quantities of DL-lactate and acetate from several pentoses (Table XVI).[327] Subsequent taxonomic studies have led to the

TABLE XVI
PENTOSE FERMENTATIONS INVOLVING A CLEAVAGE BETWEEN CARBON ATOMS 2 AND 3

Products	μMoles/100 μmoles of pentose fermented				
	Lactobacillus pentosus[327]		*Lactobacillus pentoaceticus*[327]		*Fusarium lini*[328]
	L-arabinose	D-Xylose	L-Arabinose	D-Xylose	D-Xylose[a]
Lactic acid	95.5	96.9	89.3	89.8	—
Acetic acid	94.5	95.3	89.4	98.6	110.2
Carbon dioxide	4.3	4.3	8.1	6.3	92.3
Ethanol	—	—	—	—	83.2
Carbon recovered, %	96.0	97.0	89.0	95.0	96.0

[a] Resting cell suspension.

recognition of the homo- and heterofermentative groups of lactobacilli to which these organisms belong.

Further study of pentose fermentation by *Leuconostoc mesenteroides*, *Lactobacillus pentoaceticus*, and *E. coli* revealed that growth on pentose was required for a resting-cell fermentation of the same pentose to occur. This observation led Karström[329] to the recognition of adaptive, or inducible, and constitutive enzymes. The inducible nature of pentose metabolizing systems and enzymes has since been extended to *L. pentosus*[330] and further documented in *E. coli*.[331]

Lampen *et al.*[332, 333] and Barker *et al.*[334] showed that fermentation of D-xylose-1-C[14] by *L. pentosus* and L-arabinose-1-C[14] by *L. pentoaceticus* produced unlabeled lactate and acetate labeled in the methyl group. In subsequent studies by Bernstein[335] of C[14]-ribose fermentation by *L. pentosus* and by Altermatt *et al.*[323] of D-xylose-1-C[14], 2-C[14], and 5-C[14] fermentation by *Leuconostoc mesenteroides*, it was shown that lactate arose from carbon atoms 3, 4, and 5 of the pentose, as shown in Fig. 11. In a similar fashion resting cells of *Fusarium lini*[328] ferment D-xylose-1-C[14] to equimolar amounts of acetate, ethanol, and CO_2 (Table XVI); only the methyl group of acetate contained appreciable label. Thus certain molds as well as lactic acid bacteria degrade pentoses by a 3–2 cleavage mechanism. With the mold pyruvate arising from carbon atoms 4, 5, and 6 is converted to ethanol and carbon dioxide rather than to lactate. Since the acetate, lactate, ethanol, and carbon dioxide may be recovered and degraded separately, the *L. mesenteroides* fermentation has provided a valuable analytical tool for determining the labeling patterns of pentoses and related compounds.

The lactic acid bacteria convert the various pentoses to the common in-

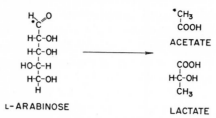

Fig. 11. Labeling pattern of pentose fermentation via 3–2 cleavage.

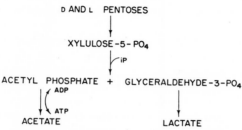

Fig. 12. Pentose fermentation—3–2 cleavage.

termediate, D-xylulose-5-phosphate, by means of a series of inducible isomerases, kinases, and epimerases.[336, 337] D-Xylulose-5-phosphate is then cleaved by phosphoketolase to form acetyl phosphate and D-glyceraldehyde-3-phosphate.[239] This process superficially resembles the phosphorolytic cleavage of pyruvate in that diphosphothiamine and inorganic phosphate are required and that an acetyl compound is formed. Acetyl phosphate is then converted to acetate, presumably by transfer of the phosphoryl group to adenosine diphosphate; glyceraldehyde-3-phosphate is metabolized to lactate via the lower portion of the Embden-Meyerhof pathway (Fig. 12). With the discovery of phosphoketolase in *Lactobacillus pentosus* by Heath et al.,[239] all of the steps in this pathway of pentose fermentation became known. Further, the known reactions accounted for the labeling patterns of the products obtained in the fermentation of 1-C[14] pentoses.

In the 3-2 cleavage route, one mole of adenosine triphosphate is required to form the pentose phosphate and at least two moles of adenosine triphosphate are formed in the conversion of glyceraldehyde-3-phosphate to pyruvate. If a third ATP is formed in the conversion of acetyl phosphate to acetate, the yield would be the same as obtained from fermentation of an equivalent amount of hexose, via Embden-Meyerhof pathway and one more than fermentation of hexose by HMP pathway (see Chapter 1). For pentose:

$$\text{pentose} + 2\text{ iP} + 2\text{ ADP} \rightarrow \text{lactate} + \text{acetate} + 2\text{ ATP} + 2\text{ H}_2\text{O}$$

b. Pathway Involving Hexose Synthesis. In contrast to lactobacilli, pentose fermentation by other organisms is more complex. The same products are formed, but the relative amounts are altered.[338, 339] In some instances, however, more than one mole of lactate is produced per mole of pentose.[340, 341] Thus it appears that the hexose pathway is followed, at least in the final stage. The postulate has been advanced that pentose is first converted to hexose, perhaps by addition of a single carbon atom, and that the hexose is then fermented in the normal fashion. Particularly illustrative are the discussions of Stanier and Adams[190] concerning D-xylose fermentation by *Aeromonas hydrophila*. Recent research has borne out the general idea of this hypothesis.

The first evidence for a pathway of pentose fermentation involving initial hexose synthesis was obtained by Horecker *et al.*,[342] who showed that D-ribose-5-phosphate utilization by a liver preparation yielded heptulose and hexose phosphates. Further, when pentose phosphate-2,3-C^{14} was metabolized, 2,3,4-labeled hexose phosphate was formed. Direct evidence for a participation of a similar system in pentose fermentation was obtained by Neish and Simpson[343] from the fermentation of D-arabinose-1-C^{14} and L-arabinose-1-C^{14} by *Aerobacter aerogenes*. Later, similar experiments were conducted by Altermatt *et al.*[344] with D-xylose 1-C^{14}, 2-C^{14}, 5-C^{14}, and with ribose 1-C^{14}. With all of the pentoses the same products were obtained (Table XVII). When different pentoses with label in the same position were compared, the labeling patterns in the products were identical. The methyl group of lactate, ethanol, acetate, and 2,3-butanediol contained 30 to 40 % of the activity of carbon atom 1 of pentose-1-C^{14}, whereas the carbon dioxide, formic acid, and carboxyl group of lactate contained 15 to 20 % of the original specific activity.

Similar labeling patterns for pentose-1-C^{14} fermentations were obtained by Gibbs and associates. Resting cells of aerobically grown *E. coli* K-12[345] fermented D-xylose-1-C^{14} and L-arabinose-1-C^{14} to lactate 1,3-C^{14}, acetate 2-C^{14}, and formate-C^{14}. The methyl groups of lactate and acetate were similarly labeled and had 30 to 50 % of the specific activity of the lactate carboxyl or of formate. The fermentation of ribose-1-C^{14} by yeast extracts yielded ethanol and carbon dioxide.[346] Twenty to 27 % of the specific activity of carbon 1 of ribose was present in the methyl groups and 15 % was present in carbon dioxide. Inhibition of product formation caused an accumulation of hexose monophosphate. When D-ribose-1-C^{14} was fermented by *Clostridium perfringens* and D-xylose-1-C^{14} was fermented by *C. beijerincki* and *C. butylicum*,[117] 1.2 to 1.3 moles of carbon dioxide were produced per mole of pentose fermented; the specific activity was about 20 % of that of the first carbon of the pentose employed. In addition, acetate and ethanol were similarly labeled in contrast to earlier findings with glucose fermentations,[116]

TABLE XVII

COMPLEX PENTOSE FERMENTATIONS

Products	mMoles/100 mmoles of pentose fermented							
	Propionibacterium sp.[338]		*Aerobacillus polymyxa*[190]	*Aeromonas hydrophila*[190]	*Aerobacter aerogenes*[343, 344]			
	L-Arabinose	D-Xylose	D-Xylose	D-Xylose	D-Ribose	D-Xylose	L-Arabinose	D-Arabinose
Lactic acid	21.6	56.7	—	20.4	3.5	3.3	10.8	3.2
Acetic acid	33.8	44.6	7.7	9.3	54.6	61.0	25.8	50.0
Carbon dioxide	38.2	30.0	161.0	134.7	60.0	46.0	78.7	29.1
Ethanol	—	—	63.0	48.9	59.6	55.6	38.0	52.6
2,3-Butanediol	—	—	38.0	39.0	10.3	3.7	23.3	2.8
Formic acid	—	—	—	—	59.4	72.3	44.5	79.6
Succinic acid	14.8	12.0	—	1.1	11.0	6.0	4.4	8.7
Propionic acid	98.3	44.5	—	—	—	—	—	—
Hydrogen	—	—	82.0	53.9	a	a	a	a
Acetoin	—	—	2.5	2.6	—	—	—	—
Carbon in cell	—	—	—	—	7.0	9.6	17.0	14.2
Carbon recovered, %	105.0	94.0	92.9	96.6	95.7	89.6	82	77.7
O/R balance	0.93	1.62	0.96	1.04	—	—	—	—

a Hydrogen not determined.

and were methyl-labeled to the extent of 40 % of the initial specific activity of carbon 1 of pentose.

Pentose fermentation by propionibacteria also results in the formation of the same products as obtained with hexoses (Table XVII), with the proportion of products varying in some cases whereas in others it remained the same as for hexoses.[274, 338, 347] The fermentation of L-arabinose-1-C[14] by *Propionibacterium arabinosum* studied by Rappoport and Barker[348] did not yield clear-cut evidence for the existence of either pathway of pentose fermentation. The highest specific activity (37 % of C-1 of pentose) was found in the acetate methyl group. However, the carboxyl group of acetate, all carbons of propionate, and the carbon dioxide were labeled as well. Although the high label in the methyl group was considered indicative of a 3-2 cleavage, as in the lactic acid bacteria, more recent evidence on the mechanism of pentose fermentation suggests that the same result would also be obtained in the hexose synthesis pathway. The experiments of Leaver et al.[310] show that carbon atoms 2 and 3 of lactate and pyruvate enter carbon dioxide and both carbon atoms of acetate and propionate. Thus the labeling pattern of the pyruvate, indicating the pathway involved, cannot be ascertained by examining the fermentation products. In addition, the labeling data obtained from glucose-C^{14} fermentation[287] (Section III, C, 1, a) shows that if a hexose monophosphate cycle involving transaldolase and transketolase were involved, highly complicated labeling patterns could arise which would not be interpretable in regard to the pathway involved. It appears likely as in the glucose fermentation by propionibacteria that clear-cut answers cannot be obtained from fermentation of labeled substrates.

In the hexose synthesis pathway, although the products formed vary greatly as a function of the organism involved, all of the products from pentose-1-C^{14} are labeled as if derived from pyruvate containing 40 % of the specific activity of carbon 1 of the pentose in the methyl group and 20 % of the specific activity of carbon 1 in the carboxyl group (Fig. 13). These specific activities are then carried into the products (Fig. 14). Neish and Simpson[343] and Gibbs et al.[345] independently postulated that such a labeling pattern can arise, as shown in Fig. 5. Three moles of pentose phosphate-1-C^{14} are converted to 5 moles of pyruvate. The three moles of unlabeled pyruvate arise from glyceraldehyde-3-phosphate and from the lower half of fructose-6-phosphate. The fourth mole of pyruvate, methyl-labeled, and the fifth mole, methyl- and carboxyl-labeled, arise from carbon atoms 1, 2, and 3 of fructose-6-phosphate.

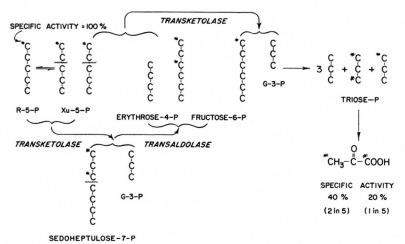

FIG. 13. Pyruvate labeling via hexose resynthesis (distribution of carbon).

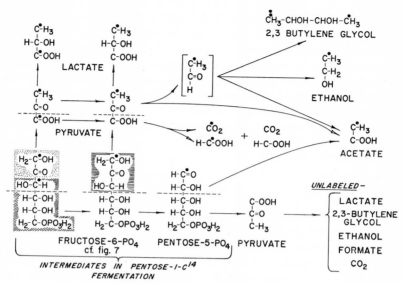

FIG. 14. Pathways of pentose fermentation.

Further evidence in support of the hexose resynthesis hypothesis has been obtained in *A. aerogenes*[349] and in *M. lacticum*[350] by showing the conversion of L-arabinose and D-ribose-5-phosphate to esters of ribulose, D-xylulose, sedoheptulose, D-fructose, and D-glucose. In addition, transketolase, pentose phosphate isomerase, and epimerases as well as isomerases and kinases for the free pentoses have been demonstrated. Also many of the enzymes of the Embden-Meyerhof pathway are known to be present.

In the hexose synthesis pathway, for every three moles of pentose fermented five moles of adenosine triphosphate are consumed (three to activate the substrate and two to phosphorylate fructose-6-phosphate). Ten moles of adenosine triphosphate would be generated in reaching the pyruvate stage. At this point two moles of adenosine triphosphate have been generated per mole of pentose fermented. Additional adenosine triphosphate may be generated to the extent of the acetyl phosphate formed but not reduced to ethanol. Hence, there is a possibility of an energy yield greater than that available in the homolactic or homoethanolic fermentation of glucose.

$$3 \text{ pentose} + 5 \text{ iP} + 5 \text{ ADP} \rightarrow 5 \text{ pyruvate} + 10 \text{ H} + 5 \text{ ATP} + 5H_2O$$

Thus two pentose fermentation patterns exist, one a 3-2 cleavage, which is restricted to lactic acid bacteria and *Fusarium*, and the second involving hexose synthesis, which is widely distributed. The fermentation pathway is determined by the type of the pentose phosphate-cleaving enzyme synthesized, i.e., transketolase and transaldolase for the hexose synthesis system, or phosphoketolase for the 3-2 cleavage.

c. *Conversion of Pentoses to the Main Pathway.* In virtually all organisms the enzymes for the initial steps in pentose metabolism are inducible and in each pathway D-xylulose-5-phosphate is the common intermediate through which all pentoses pass. Thus D-ribose and D-arabinose undergo isomerization at carbon atoms 1 and 2, phosphorylation at carbon 5, and epimerization of carbon 3 to reach D-xylulose-5-phosphate, whereas D-xylose requires only isomerization and phosphorylation. L-Arabinose fermentation involves its conversion to D-xylulose-5-phosphate in both fermentative types (*L. pentosus* and *A. aerogenes*) by isomerization, phosphorylation, and epimerization of carbon 4. The latter reaction is responsible for change from L- to D-configuration.[337, 351]

2. 2-Deoxy-D-Ribose Fermentation

Hoffman and Lampen[352] observed that the fermentation of hypoxanthine deoxyriboside and thymine deoxyriboside by *E. coli* yielded the free bases and one mole each of formate, acetate, and ethanol. It was postulated that deoxyribose-1-phosphate and deoxyribose-5-phosphate were intermediates in the fermentation. Subsequently, an aldolase was discovered in *E. coli* by Racker[353] which catalyzes the reaction:

D-glyceraldehyde-3-phosphate

$+$ $\rightarrow$ 2-deoxy-D-ribose-5-phosphate

acetaldehyde

Thus the reverse reaction would cleave deoxyribose-5-phosphate with ethanol arising by reduction of acetaldehyde which is coupled to the oxidation of the triose phosphate formed. The pyruvate thus formed would then be converted to acetate and formate. A similar fermentation, studied by Domagk and Horecker[354] in *L. plantarum*, forms lactate, acetaldehyde, ethanol, and acetate. When bisulfite is added, only lactate and acetaldehyde accumulate. It was also shown that 2-deoxy-D-ribose-5-phosphate is produced from deoxyribose and cleaved by an inducible kinase and aldolase, respectively. Presumably, the energy for growth is derived from the conversion of glyceraldehyde-3-phosphate to pyruvate and the oxidation of acetaldehyde to acetyl phosphate:

$$2 \text{ deoxyribose} + 2 \text{ ATP} \rightarrow 2 \text{ deoxyribose-5-phosphate} + 2 \text{ ADP}$$

$$2 \text{ glyceraldehyde-3-phosphate} + 4 \text{ ADP} + 2 \text{ iP} \rightarrow 2 \text{ lactate} + 4 \text{ ATP}$$

$$2 \text{ acetaldehyde} + \text{iP} \rightarrow \text{ethanol} + \text{acetyl}\smallfrown\text{P}$$

$$\text{acetyl}\smallfrown\text{P} + \text{ADP} \rightarrow \text{ATP} + \text{acetate}$$

$$\overline{2 \text{ deoxyribose} + 3 \text{ ADP} + 3 \text{ iP} \rightarrow \text{lactate} + \text{ethanol} + \text{acetate} + 3 \text{ ATP}}$$

Thus the energy yield would approximate 1.5 moles of ATP per mole of deoxyribose fermented.

TABLE XVIII

FERMENTATION OF SEDOHEPTULOSE AND L-ERYTHRULOSE
BY *Aerobacter aerogenes*[a]

Product	mMoles/100 mmoles fermented	
	L-Erythrulose	D-Sedoheptulose
2,3-Butanediol	0.9	22.4
Acetoin	0.1	—
Ethanol	11.4	80.0
Acetic acid	39.8	52.1
Formic acid	1.7	1.17
Succinic acid	6.8	5.7
Erythritol	39.9	—
Glycolic acid	23.0	—
Lactic acid	—	7.35
Hydrogen	11.0	—
Carbon dioxide	27.7	177.0
Cell carbon	—	100.0
Carbon recovered, %	92.2	96.8
O/R balance	1.12	—

[a] Neish and Blackwood,[355] and Tattrie and Blackwood.[356]

3. SEDOHEPTULOSE FERMENTATION

The products of sedoheptulose fermentation by *Aerobacter aerogenes* were determined by Neish and Blackwood.[355] As with the pentoses and hexoses, ethanol, 2,3-butanediol, acetic, formic, succinic, and lactic acids and carbon dioxide were produced (Table XVIII). The quantities and distribution of C^{14} in the products from sedoheptulose-2-C^{14} and -3-C^{14} are presented in Table XIX. From sedoheptulose-3-C^{14} the carbinol groups of ethanol and 2,3-butanediol, the carboxyl group of acetate, and both carbon atoms of succinate were labeled, whereas the carbon dioxide was unlabeled. From sedoheptulose-3-C^{14}, the methyl groups of ethanol, 2,3-butanediol, acetic, and lactic acids were labeled. In addition, the carboxyl groups of lactate and succinate and carbon dioxide were highly labeled. The labeling pattern suggested involvement of the pathway utilized for pentose fermentation via hexose phosphate and the glycolytic pathway. In this process sedoheptulose phosphate presumably served as substrate for transketolase which by two transfers of a two carbon unit, yielded first pentose phosphate, then triose phosphate. Since sedoheptulose phosphate also is a substrate for transaldolase, which utilizes triose phosphate as the acceptor in a transfer of a dihydroxyacetone unit, sedoheptulose-7-phosphate would yield hexose phosphate. The remaining four carbon atoms of sedoheptulose phosphate can then serve as an acceptor for two carbon units transferred in the trans-

TABLE XIX[a]

DISTRIBUTION OF C[14] IN PRODUCTS FROM THE DISSIMILATION
OF SEDOHEPTULOSE-2-C[14] AND -3-C[14]

Product	Relative specific activity[b]	
	Sedoheptulose-2-C[14]	Sedoheptulose-3-C[14]
Ethanol		
CH_3—	0.20	11.0
—CH_2OH	39.2	3.3
2,3-Butanediol		
CH_3—	0.17	8.6
—CHOH—	34.6	3.0
Acetic acid		
CH_3—	0.12	8.9
—COOH	32.8	1.7
Lactic acid		
CH_3	—	7.0
—CHOH—	—	0.75
—COOH	—	25.1
Succinic acid		
—CH_2—	23.0	10.5
—COOH	14.8	24.1
Carbon dioxide	1.3	27.3
Cell carbon	15.7	13.2

[a] Neish and Blackwood.[355]

[b] Expressed as per cent of the specific activity of the labeled carbon atom in the sedoheptulose fermented.

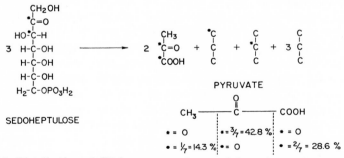

FIG. 15. Distribution of C[14] in pyruvate from sedoheptulose-1-C[14] and sedoheptulose-2-C[14].

ketolase reaction, also forming fructose-6-phosphate. Fructose-6-phosphate would form pyruvate with the distribution of label shown in Fig. 15. Twice as much sedoheptulose must be utilized by transaldolase as by transketolase cleavage in order to form the necessary two carbon acceptors.

$$2 \text{ S-7-P} + 2 \text{ G-3-P} \xrightarrow{\text{transaldolase}} 2 \text{ F-6-P} + 2 \text{ E-4-P}$$

$$\text{S-7-P} + 2 \text{ E-4-P} \xrightarrow{\text{transketolase}} 2 \text{ F-6-P} + \text{G-3-P}$$

$$4 \text{ F-6-P} \rightarrow 8 \text{ G-3-P}$$

$$3 \text{ S-7-P} \rightarrow 7 \text{ pyruvate}$$

In the absence of complicating processes, particularly exchange reactions, sedoheptulose-2-C^{14} would yield three out of seven moles of pyruvate labeled only in the carboxyl group. Thus the specific activity would be $\frac{3}{7}$ or 42% of the activity originally present in carbon atom 2 of sedoheptulose. It can be seen from Table XIX that the products appear to have been derived from pyruvate labeled mainly in the carboxyl group. The specific activity is low, however, and the activity in ethanol is high relative to that of 2,3-butanediol and acetic acid, all presumably derived from a common precursor. With sedoheptulose-3-C^{14}, one mole of pyruvate, 1- and 3-labeled, and 2 moles of pyruvate 1-labeled, out of the seven moles of pyruvate are produced. This corresponds to 14 and 28% of the original specific activity, respectively. As shown in the table, the products of sedoheptulose-3-C^{14} fermentation appear to have been derived mainly from pyruvate which was 1- and 3-labeled. However, the activity of the methyl group is lower than would be expected and activity is also present in carbon atoms derived from the carboxyl group of pyruvate. Thus, the data do not yield a clear-cut interpretation. Undoubtedly unknown reactions have an important role in sedoheptulose fermentation.

4. L-ERYTHRULOSE FERMENTATION

The fermentation of L-erythrulose by *A. aerogenes* was shown by Tattrie and Blackwood[356] to yield mainly ethanol, acetate, succinate, carbon dioxide, erythritol, glycolate, and hydrogen (Table XVIII). Most of these products are also found in glucose fermentation. However, new processes appear to be involved because (a) L-erythrulose is reduced to erythritol in a manner similar to the reduction of fructose to mannitol by heterolactic organisms, (b) the carbon chain is cleaved by yield one, two, and presumably three carbon compounds; (c) glycolic acid, not usually encountered as a fermentation product, is present in large quantity, and (d) the fermentation furnishes two carbon precursors of ethanol and acetate which are not also precursors of acetoin and 2,3-butanediol. D-Threose and D-erythrose also were fermented to the same products but at slower rates. Since little is known of 4-carbon sugar metabolism except for the role of erythrose-4-phosphate in pentose metabolism (Fig. 5),[357] the oxidation of erythritol to L-erythrulose by *Acetobacter* species[358] and the oxidation of D-erythrose by *Alcaligenes faecalis*,[359] further study is required to establish the fermentation mechanism employed.

E. Effect of Oxidation-Reduction State

In the closed system of a true fermentation, the aggregate oxidation-reduction state of the products corresponds to that of the substrate. Thus with hexitols which are more reduced than the corresponding hexoses by two hydrogen atoms, reduced products such as glycerol, hydrogen or ethanol are found in proportionately higher quantities; little alteration of the fermentation mechanism takes place, however. Substrates more oxidized than glucose, i.e., gluconic or glucuronic, 2-ketogluconic, and citric acids yield more oxidized products of which carbon dioxide is the major component (Table XX). As described below, different fermentation systems are in-

TABLE XX

Fermentation Balances for Substrates of Various
Oxidation-Reduction States

Products	mMoles/100 mmole of substrate fermented							
	Aerobacillus polymyxa[190]	Escherichia freundi[361]	Leuconostoc mesenteroides[362]			Streptococcus faecalis[363]	Erwinia carotovora[197]	
	Mannitol	Glycerol	Fructose	Gluconate	2-Ketogluconate	Gluconate	Galacturonate	Glucose
Carbon dioxide	147.7	7.63	67.0	96	98	54,49[a]	51.7	13.1
Ethanol	100.6	7.95	47.3	41	Trace	Trace	Trace	66.2
Acetate	19.7	9.0	15.7	52.5	101	Trace	149	64.2
Lactate	57.2	11.2	63.5	98	99	150, 175[a]	8.1	23.1
Succinate	5.7	4.0	Trace	Trace	0	—	22.7	11.2
Mannitol	—	—	33.	—	—	—	—	15.0
2,3-Butanediol	13.7	0	—	—	—	—	13.4	15.0
Formate	—	9.9	—	—	—	Trace	104.0	134.0
Hydrogen	169.9	2.5	—	—	—	—	—	—
Acetoin	0.8	—	—	—	—	—	—	—
Trimethylene glycol	—	55.6	—	—	—	—	—	—
Acrolein	—	4.20	—	—	—	—	—	—
Carbon recovered, %	106.8	105.0	97.0	96.0	99.0	—	103.8	97.0
O/R balance	0.969	0.975	1.05	1.05	0.98	—	0.96	0.97

[a] In the presence of arsenite.

volved even though the products do not differ materially from those encountered in glucose fermentation.

1. MANNITOL

Aerobacillus polymyxa,[190] propionic acid bacteria,[360] Enterobacteriaceae, and lactic acid bacteria ferment mannitol.[246, 247, 274] In the case of *Lactobacillus pentoaceticus*, mannitol is produced in the fermentation of fructose, but is later converted to acetic and lactic acids. *A. polymyxa*[190] produces more ethanol and hydrogen and less carbon dioxide and 2,3-butanediol. The propionibacteria produce the same products as obtained from glucose, but one or more moles of propionate are produced per mole of mannitol utilized (see Section III, C, 1.).

2. GLYCEROL

Glycerol fermentation readily occurs among the propionibacteria and Enterobacteriaceae. Under aerobic conditions, lactic acid bacteria also "ferment" this polyol. With the propionibacteria the change of oxidation-reduction state toward a more reduced substrate shifts the fermentation away from acetic acid and carbon dioxide production. Propionate is the major product formed (see Table XIV).

The glycerol fermentation of the Enterobacteriaceae has attracted considerable attention because of the unique products formed. Freund first noted the production of trimethyleneglycol from glycerol by a "coli-aerogenes" intermediate which Braak[360a] has since studied and named *E. freundi*. The fermentation data obtained by Braak and by Mickelson and Werkman[361] for *Citrobacter (Escherichia) freundi* (Table XX) show that in addition to the normal fermentation products trimethylene glycol in yields of 30 to 60 % can be obtained. In one fermentation, appreciable acrolein was produced but this unsaturated aldehyde was not fermented when added. Conditions were obtained whereby *A. aerogenes*, *E. coli*, and the intermediate types fermented glycerol in a mineral medium and without added hydrogen acceptors. In the presence of sulfite, trimethyleneglycol formation was not depressed, but considerable acrolein accumulated. Fumarate was reduced but its presence did not depress trimethylene glycol formation. In a comparison between *A. aerogenes* and *Citrobacter freundi*, trimethyleneglycol (45 %), acetoin, and 2,3-butanediol were produced by *A. aerogenes*, whereas *Citrobacter freundi* produced succinate but not acetoin or 2,3-butanediol.[364] Heterolactobacilli[364a, 364b] and *Bacillus amaracrylus*[364c] also produce acrolein from glycerol. Voisenet[364c] concluded that glycerol was first dehydrated to β-hydroxypropionaldehyde and then converted to acrolein by spontaneous chemical process.

The production of acrolein in distillery grain mashes has been identified with a lactobacillus,[364a, 364b] and results from a combined fermentation of glucose and glycerol. Sobolov and Smiley[365] have shown that: (*a*) glucose and glycerol fermentations proceed independently of each other; (*b*) in the presence of glucose glycerol is converted largely to trimethylene glycol and traces of β-hydroxypropionic acid; (*c*) glucose yields the products of the heterolactic fermentation (Section III, B, 2, a), except that ethanol formation was depressed in favor of acetate; (*d*) glycerol alone yielded equivalent amounts of trimethylene glycol and β-hydroxypropionic acid; and (*e*) acrolein was neither formed nor utilized, but could be produced in the analytical procedures. It was concluded that acrolein is not produced in glycerol fermentation, but arises chemically from β-hydroxypropionaldehyde, an intermediate in trimethylene glycol formation.

Although glycerol alone did not support growth, the cell yield on limiting glucose plus glycerol was nearly doubled relative to glucose alone. In view of the increased production of trimethylene glycol at the expense of ethanol, it was postulated that the reduction of a hydrogen acceptor produced from glycerol (presumably β-hydroxypropionaldehyde) is preferred to the reduction of acetyl phosphate to ethanol. If the acetyl phosphate can then yield ATP, the energy yield of the heterolactic fermentation would be doubled and account for the increased growth.

$$\text{glucose} + \text{ATP} \rightarrow \text{glucose-6-P}$$

$$\text{glucose-6-P} \rightarrow \text{xylulose-5-P} + CO_2 + 2 \times 2H$$

$$\text{xylulose-5-P} + \text{iP} \rightarrow \text{glyceraldehyde-3-P} + \text{acetyl-P} + H_2O$$

$$\text{glyceraldehyde-3-P} + \text{iP} + 2\ \text{ADP} \rightarrow \text{lactate} + 2\ \text{ATP} + H_2O$$

$$\text{acetyl-P} + \text{ADP} \rightarrow \text{acetate} + \text{ATP}$$

$$2\ \text{glycerol} \rightarrow 2\ \beta\text{-hydroxypropionaldehyde} + 2\ H_2O$$

$$2\ \beta\text{-hydroxypropionaldehyde} + 2 \times 2H \rightarrow 2\ \text{trimethyleneglycol}$$

$$\text{glucose} + 2\ \text{glycerol} + 2\ \text{iP} + 2\ \text{ADP} \rightarrow \text{lactate} + \text{acetate} + CO_2 +$$
$$2\ \text{trimethyleneglycol} + 2\ \text{ATP} + 4\ H_2O$$

Gunsalus and Sherman[366] found that streptococci could utilize glycerol as an energy source only if external hydrogen acceptors were present. However, some enterococci and a lactobacillus did produce acid from glycerol anaerobically. After an initial oxidation the process is fermentative in nature.

$$\text{glycerol} + O_2 \rightarrow \text{lactate} + H_2O_2$$

Some strains require oxygen whereas others may utilize fumarate.

$$\text{glycerol} + \text{fumarate} \rightarrow \text{lactate} + \text{succinate}$$

Since the phosphorylation of glycerol could be demonstrated, the pathway was considered to involve the formation α-glycerol phosphate followed by its dehydrogenation to dihydroxyacetone phosphate which then follows the lower portion of the Embden-Meyerhof pathway.[367] Recently Jacobs and Vandemark[368] found that *S. faecalis*, grown anaerobically on glucose, does not phosphorylate glycerol but oxidized it to dihydroxyacetone. Aerobic cells, however, did not oxidize glycerol but were able to form α-glycerol phosphate.

Following the discovery that citrate has biological asymmetry,[369] it was suspected that glycerol, though chemically symmetrical, has D and L forms which are biologically recognizable. Swick and Nakao[370] obtained biosynthetic glycerol-1-C^{14} (or 1,3-C^{14} depending on the outcome of the experiment) from the fermentation of glucose-3,4-C^{14} by yeast. After administration of the labeled glycerol to rats, the glycogen was isolated, and hydrolyzed; the glucose produced was then fermented by *Lactobacillus casei*. The radioactivity was found in the 3 and 4 positions of the glucose isolated from glycogen and in the carboxyl group of lactate, respectively. Hence, either "D" or "L" glycerol-1-C^{14} was produced. If random formation or utilization of the glycerol had been involved, the glucose would have been labeled in carbon atoms 1,3,4, and 6 and the lactate would have been 1,3-labeled. Similar results were obtained by Schambye *et al.*[371] using different methods. Karnovsky *et al.*[372] synthesized D- and L-glycerol-1-C^{14} and studied the utilization of these substrates by animals, while Rush *et al.*[373] studied their metabolism by different strains of *A. aerogenes*. Two systems were found in different strains, one involving phosphorylation and oxidation of α-glycerol phosphate as found in aerobic *S. faecalis*, the second involving direct oxidation to dihydroxyacetone. Pyruvate was formed in both cases. By degrading the pyruvate, it was established that the pathway utilizing α-glycerol phosphate preserved the asymmetric labeling, because all of the activity was present in the pyruvate carboxyl group. In the organism utilizing direct oxidation, the pyruvate was 1,3-labeled, showing that the asymmetry had been destroyed. In the latter case, conversion of glycerol to dihydroxyacetone destroys the asymmetry, whereas in the former pathway the asymmetry is preserved by the presence of the phosphate group (Fig. 16).

3. HEXONIC ACIDS

The effect of oxidation-reduction state and structure of the substrate on the fermentation pattern of *L. mesenteroides* is particularly well demonstrated by the balances obtained by Blackwood and Blakley[362] (Table XX). The fructose fermentation (compare with glucose, Section III, B, 2, a) follows the typical pattern for heterolactic acid bacteria in that mannitol is

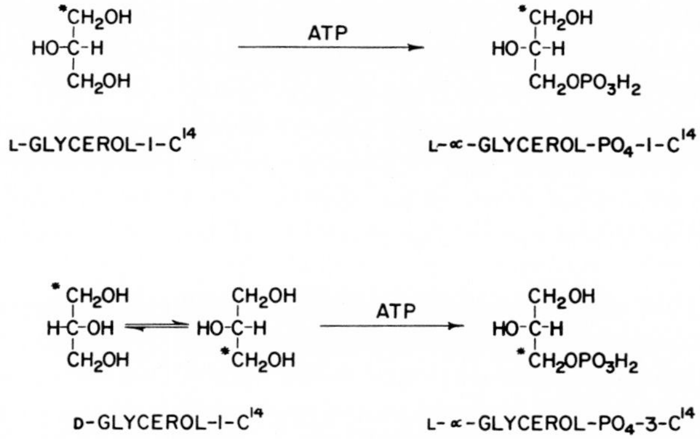

FIG. 16. Symmetry of glycerol phosphorylation [from Rush *et al.*, *J. Biol. Chem.* **226**, 891 (1957)].

formed. With gluconate and 2-ketogluconate, however, ethanol production decreases while the acetate and carbon dioxide increase. The process resembles the glucose fermentation in that all three fit the following general equation:

$$
\begin{array}{c}
\text{glucose} \\
\searrow \\
\text{gluconate} \longrightarrow \text{lactate} + 1 \left\{ \begin{array}{l} \text{ethanol} \\ + \\ \text{acetate} \end{array} \right. + \text{CO}_2 \\
\nearrow \\
\text{2-ketogluconate}
\end{array}
$$

Since gluconate and 2-ketogluconate have two and four less hydrogen atoms than glucose, respectively, $\frac{1}{2}$ mole each of ethanol and acetate would be expected from gluconate and only acetate from 2-ketogluconate. In the fermentation of 1-C^{14} hexonic acids all of the label was found in the carbon dioxide, whereas with 6-C^{14} hexonic acids, methyl-labeled lactate was formed. In contrast to *S. faecalis* (see below) the labeling patterns are identical to those expected from the hexose monophosphate pathway (entered at 6-phosphogluconate stage). Hence the same pathway is utilized in both glucose and gluconate fermentation. Since the labeling pattern excludes the Entner-Doudoroff and Embden-Meyerhof pathways, the fermentation of gluconate-2-C^{14}, which gave the most valuable data for *S. faecalis*, was not required to establish the pathway involved.

With more oxidized substrates, it is not necessary to carry out the energy-wasting reduction of acetyl phosphate to ethanol as a means of consuming the hydrogen atoms generated. Thus, if *L. mesenteroides* is able to transfer the phosphoryl groups from acetyl phosphate to adenosine diphosphate, an increase in energy yield amounting to 0.5 mole and 1 mole of adenosine triphosphate for gluconate and 2-ketogluconate respectively, can be obtained.

Sokatch and Gunsalus[363] have shown the existence of multiple pathways for gluconate fermentation in *Streptococcus faecalis*. Cells grown on gluconate fermented glucose, gluconic, and 2-ketogluconic acids, whereas glucose-grown cells were unable to attack the hexonic acids. Using growth as the criterion, the energy obtained from gluconate approximates that obtained from glucose. The products formed from gluconate are mainly lactate and carbon dioxide with traces of formate, acetate, and ethanol also being produced. The fermentation of gluconate-1-C^{14} yields $C^{14}O_2$ and carboxyl-labeled lactate. Gluconate-2-C^{14} yields lactate labeled in all positions with the carbinol position having the highest activity.

It has been possible to reconcile both the stoichiometry and labeling patterns by postulating that gluconate is phosphorylated to 6-phosphogluconate and that two pathways function equally for 6-phosphogluconate dissimilation. One of these routes involves (a) oxidation of 6-phosphogluconate, (b) conversion of pentose phosphate to hexose phosphate by the pathway which functions in the Enterobacteriaceae for pentose fermentation, and (c) fermentation by the Embden-Meyerhof pathway as follows:

$$3 \text{ 6-phosphogluconate} \rightarrow 3 \text{ pentose phosphate} + 3 \text{ } CO_2 + 3 \times 2H$$

$$3 \text{ pentose phosphate} \rightarrow 2 \text{ F-6-P} + \text{G-3-P}$$

$$2 \text{ F-6-P} + \text{G-3-P} \rightarrow 5 \text{ lactate}$$

$$3 \text{ 6-phosphogluconate} \rightarrow 5 \text{ lactate} + 3 \text{ } CO_2 + 3 \times 2H \tag{1}$$

The second route, which is coupled to the first series by utilizing the excess hydrogen atoms, follows the Entner-Doudoroff pathway and lower portion of the glycolytic system as follows:

$$3 \text{ 6-phosphogluconate} \rightarrow 3 \text{ pyruvate} + 3 \text{ G-3-P}$$

$$3 \text{ G-3-P} \rightarrow 3 \text{ lactate}$$

$$3 \text{ pyruvate} + 3 \times 2H \rightarrow 3 \text{ lactate}$$

$$3 \text{ 6-phosphogluconate} + 3 \times 2H \rightarrow 6 \text{ lactate} \tag{2}$$

Therefore, the over-all stoichiometry would be:

$$\text{6-phosphogluconate} \rightarrow 11 \text{ lactate} + 3 \text{ } CO_2$$

or

$$\text{6-phosphogluconate} \rightarrow 1.83 \text{ lactate} + 0.5 \text{ } CO_2 \tag{3}$$

When arsenite was added to prevent pyruvate oxidation, cell suspensions fermented 1 mole of gluconate to 0.5 moles of carbon dioxide and 1.75 moles of lactate, in close agreement with the above formulation.

The specific activities in the products from labeled gluconates compared with the values expected from the above system are shown in Table XXI.

TABLE XXI

LABELING PATTERNS IN THE GLUCONATE-C^{14} FERMENTATION
BY *Streptococcus faecalis*[a]

Substrate	Carbon dioxide		Lactic acid[b]					
			—COOH		—CHOH—		CH$_3$—	
	Yield, %	Sp. act.	Yield, %	Sp. act.	Yield, %	Sp. act.	Yield, %	Sp. act.[c]
Glucose-1-C^{14}								
Expected	50.0	100.0	50.0	27.3	0	—	0	—
Found	53.0	91.5	36.0	18.2	0	—	0	—
Glucose-2-C^{14}								
Expected	0	—	33.3	18.2	50.0	27.3	16.6	9.1
Found	0.6	—	8.5	5.4	44.0	29.5	17.8	12.0
Glucose-2-C^{14} + AsO_3^-								
Expected	0	—	33.3	18.2	50.0	27.3	16.6	9.1
Found	0	—	24.0	13.8	62.0	35.5	17.8	10.1
Glucose-6-C^{14}								
Expected	0	—	0	—	0	—	100.0	54.5
Found	0	—	0.5	—	0.9	—	52.0	31.8

[a] Sokatch and Gunsalus.[363]

[b] Calculated from a yield of 1.5 moles of lactate per mole of gluconate without arsenate, or 1.75 moles of lactate per mole of gluconate with arsenate.

[c] Specific activity of labeled carbon of gluconate taken as 100%.

The expected values are based upon the known labeling patterns of the Entner-Doudoroff pathway (Fig. 9) and hexose synthesis pathway for pentose fermentation (Fig. 5). Except where technical difficulties were encountered, the specific activities observed correspond rather closely to the expected values. Thus, growth on gluconic acid evokes the formation of at least portions of two pathways heretofore not observed in lactic acid bacteria. The new routes together with the Embden-Meyerhof pathway function in gluconate fermentation.

The details of 2-ketogluconate fermentation have not been elucidated. It may be predicted, however, by analogy with *Aerobacter cloacae*[374-376] and *Pseudomonas fluorescens*[377, 378] that 2-ketogluconate would be phosphorylated and that 2-keto-6-phosphogluconate would be reduced to 6-phosphogluconate at the expense of the equivalent reduction of pyruvate to lactate. The pyruvate remaining would then undergo either (*a*) dismutation to lactate, acetate, and carbon dioxide, (*b*) phosphoroclastic cleavage to formate and acetate, or (*c*) conversion to acetoin and carbon dioxide.

Based upon known energy-yielding sequences and the adenosine triphosphate requirement for substrate phosphorylation, a yield of 8 moles of adenosine triphosphate from 6 moles of gluconate (1.33 adenosine triphosphate per gluconate) would be predicted.

$$6 \text{ gluconate} + 8 \text{ iP} + 8 \text{ ADP} \rightarrow 11 \text{ lactate} + 3 \text{ CO}_2 + 8 \text{ ATP} + 8 \text{ H}_2\text{O}$$

Thus the gluconate fermentation in the presence of arsenite would yield 66 % of the energy obtained from glucose. The growth on limiting gluconate in the absence of aresenite corresponded to 90 % of that on equivalent glucose. It is possible that additional energy is obtained when pyruvate is further metabolized (absence of arsenite).

4. URONIC ACIDS

Another change of product distribution and pathway of fermentation is indicated from the data for uronic acid fermentation. Compared to glucose fermentation, the fermentation of galacturonic acid by *Erwinia carotovora*[197] (Table XX) resulted in increased carbon dioxide, succinate, and acetate, whereas the ethanol, formate and lactate are decreased. Further study is required to reveal the steps of the pathway involved. A consideration of the uronic acid structure suggests that new mechanisms are involved.

IV. Organic Acid Fermentations

Many organic acids serve as a source of carbon and energy for growth under anaerobic conditions. The fermentation of the tricarboxylic acid cycle intermediates such as malate, fumarate, and citrate are all similar and belong to the type which first yields pyruvate. The pyruvate is then fermented with acetyl⁓SCoA being the high energy intermediate. A second fermentative group utilizes fatty acids as substrates along with CO_2 as the hydrogen acceptor and generates energy by a form of oxidative phosphorylation which as yet is only partially understood.[1d]

A. CITRATE

Early recognition of citrate utilization in milk and in glucose-citrate broth by Hammer,[379] Hucker and Pederson,[380] and Van Beynum and Pette[381] led to the appreciation of the role of *Streptococcus lactis*, *S. citrovorous*, and *S. paracitrovorous* in better flavor development through the production of acetoin and diacetyl. In most cases, however, a fermentable sugar also was required to obtain citrate fermentation. Thus, interpretation of the early studies was complicated by the simultaneous carbohydrate fermentation. Brewer and Werkman,[382] for instance, found pyruvate in the citrate-glucose fermentation by *S. paracitrovorous*, but were unable to implicate citrate as its precursor, as was later established in citrate fermentations in the ab-

TABLE XXII
CITRIC ACID FERMENTATIONS

Product	mMoles/100 mmoles of citrate fermented						
	Aerobacter indologenes[388]		*Streptococcus zymogenes*[389]	*Lactobacillus casei*[389]	*Streptococcus paracitrovorous*[387]		
	Growing	Resting	Final pH, 7.0	Final pH, 6.2	Citrate	Oxalacetate	Pyruvate
Hydrogen	7.2	41.6	—	—	20.6	24.2	32.7
Carbon dioxide	166.0	169.3	130	115	128.8	129.6	51.9
Formic acid	6.4	—	34	73	18.1	18.2	15.8
Acetic acid	163.9	158.7	157	175	158.7	59.8	68.3
Ethanol	1.2	0.7	—	31	—	—	—
Acetoin	1.8	0	1.0	0.6	—	—	—
2,3-Butanediol	1.8	2.0	—	—	—	—	—
Lactic acid	1.0	1.0	42	12	14.0	15.6	17.0
Succinic acid	15.5	14.1	—	—	24.8	20.5	—
Carbon recovered, %	97.0	92.6	101.0	97.0	100.1	97.8	85.2
O/R index	1.11	1.02	0.97	0.96	0.94	0.92	0.93

sence of glucose.[383] Citrate fermentation in *A. aerogenes* was formulated by Deffner and Franke[384, 385] as follows:

$$4 \text{ citrate} \rightarrow 7 \text{ acetate} + 5 \text{ CO}_2 + \text{formate} + \text{succinate}$$

The initial cleavage of citrate was postulated to yield oxalacetate and acetate. More detailed fermentation balances were obtained by Brewer and Werkman[386-388] (Table XXII). Carbon dioxide and acetic acid were the major products, and as such were not different than obtained with glucose.

Brewer and Werkman[386, 387] obtained evidence that oxalacetate and pyruvate are intermediates in citrate fermentation by *S. paracitrovorous* by establishing the fermentability of these substrates (Table XXII). This experiment exemplifies the usefulness of balances in the study of fermentation mechanisms. As the table shows, the fermentation of oxalacetate closely resembled that of citrate except that acetate production decreased about 100 mmoles per 100 mmoles of oxalacetate fermented. Similarly, with pyruvate, the amounts are roughly similar to that obtained with oxalacetate except that about 80 mmoles less of CO_2 were produced. Thus, there is support for the following steps in citrate fermentation:

$$\text{citrate} \xrightarrow{\quad} \begin{array}{c} \text{oxalacetate} \\ + \\ \text{acetate} \end{array} \xrightarrow{\quad} \begin{array}{c} \text{pyruvate} \\ + \\ \text{CO}_2 \end{array}$$

Although the lactic fermentation was considered to be the sole mechanism for energy generation by homolactic acid bacteria, Campbell and Gunsalus[389, 390] showed that energy can be derived from citrate in the absence of carbohydrate fermentation and lactate production. The distribution of products is markedly dependent upon pH. With increasing pH more acetate and formate and less lactate and CO_2 are obtained. Above pH 7 virtually no lactate is produced and the fermentation follows the equation.

$$\text{citrate} \rightarrow CO_2 + \text{formic acid} + 2 \text{ acetic acid}$$

At an acid pH acetylmethylcarbinol and lactate become major products. The following reactions were considered to account for the products:[390, 391]

$$\text{citrate} \rightarrow \text{oxalacetate} + \text{acetate}$$

$$\text{oxalacetate} \rightarrow \text{pyruvate} + CO_2$$

$$\text{pyruvate} \rightarrow \text{acetate} + \text{formate}$$

$$2 \text{ pyruvate} \rightarrow \text{acetate} + CO_2 + \text{lactate}$$

$$2 \text{ pyruvate} \rightarrow \text{acetoin} + 2 CO_2$$

The role of oxalacetate and pyruvate in citrate fermentation has been further established by demonstration of a citrate-cleaving enzyme (citritase or citrate desmolase) and oxalacetic decarboxylase in many microorganisms. The citrate-cleaving enzyme is present in S. faecalis,[392] A. aerogenes,[393, 394] and E. coli[395] when grown on citrate. Although citrate is formed biologically by condensation of acetyl‿SCoA and oxalacetate, the cleavage of citrate in microbial fermentations is catalyzed by a distinct enzyme which does not involve CoA.[396-400]

B. THE ETHANOL-ACETATE FERMENTATION OF Clostridium kluyveri

Clostridium kluyveri was discovered as a contaminant in enrichments of Methanobacterium omelianski which would divert the normal oxidation of ethanol to acetate during methane fermentation in a way that yielded caproate.[401, 402] Although mixed cultures grew in a simple medium containing ethanol, pure cultures of C. kluyveri were unable to grow on ethanol unless a large quantity of yeast extract was added. The yeast extract could be replaced by acetate, propionate, or less effectively by butyrate.[403] It can be seen from the fermentation balances (Table XXIII) that ethanol and acetate are quantitatively converted to butyrate, caproate, and hydrogen, whereas a mixture of ethanol and propionate yielded valerate, heptanoate, and hydrogen as the main products. Small quantities of butyrate and caproate also were produced.[404] When acetate is present in excess of the ethanol, butyrate is the main product.

$$\text{ethanol} + \text{acetate} \rightarrow \text{butyrate} + H_2O$$

TABLE XXIII
Fatty Acid Fermentation by *Clostridium kluyveri*[404]

	μMoles/100 ml. of medium	
Substrates fermented		
Ethanol	4.55	12.2
Acetate	2.18	—
Propionate	—	10.00
Butyrate	—	—
Products formed		
Acetate	—	2.9
Butyrate	1.04	0.65
Valerate	—	7.2
Caproate	1.46	0.7
Heptanoate	—	0.25
Hydrogen	1.11	2.4
Carbon recovered, %	96.0	93.0
O/R index	1.00	1.18

With excess ethanol, the production of caproate (more reduced) is favored.

$$2 \text{ ethanol} + \text{acetate} \rightarrow \text{caproate} + 2 \text{ H}_2\text{O}$$

The above equations are not adhered to strictly because some of the hydrogen atoms normally going into butyrate synthesis appear as hydrogen gas, with the result that more acetate and less butyrate and caproate are produced than would be expected from the equations. Thus, the ethanol fermentation of *C. kluyveri* resembles the fermentation of *C. butyricum* and its variants (*C. tyrobutyricum* and *C. lactoacetophilum*) in that acetate is required as a hydrogen acceptor in each case (see Section III, A, 3). Since *C. kluyveri* is unable to ferment glucose or amino acids, this unique fermentation system for fatty acid synthesis is the obligatory mechanism of energy generation in this organism. Bornstein and Barker[404] demonstrated that this type of condensation and reduction pathway yielding higher fatty acids is exergonic and could yield energy for growth.

Stadtman and Barker and their associates have unraveled the details of the fermentation by the use of labeled substrates and biochemical studies with enzyme preparations[405] which are capable of fermenting acetate and ethanol. The following information, which has contributed to their formulation of the fermentation mechanism, has been summarized recently by Barker.[406]

(*a*) Incubation of carboxyl-labeled butyrate with unlabeled ethanol yielded β-labeled caproate. With carboxyl-labeled propionate and unlabeled ethanol, labeled propanol, valerate, and heptanoate were produced, whereas the smaller amounts of acetate, butyrate, caproate were unlabeled.[407] Thus, a 2-carbon compound (acetate), derived from ethanol, was shown to be the condensing unit. In addition, the condensation involved the carboxyl group of butyrate and the methyl group of acetate. The odd series of fatty acids are produced because propionate is the 2-carbon acceptor.[407]

(b) Oxidation of ethanol or butyrate yielded acetylphosphate.[408] In addition, butyrate could be synthesized from acetylphosphate and hydrogen but not from acetate and hydrogen.[409] With purified enzyme preparations, it was subsequently found that ethanol[410] and butyrate oxidations yielded acetyl⁓SCoA[411] and that this thiol ester is the reactant in the C_2 condensation leading to precursors of butyrate.[412, 413] An enzyme (phosphotransacetylase) present in the cruder preparations was capable of exchanging inorganic phosphate (or arsenate) for CoA.[414-416]

(c) β-Hydroxybutyrate and acetoacetate, the predicted intermediates in butyrate synthesis, did not yield butyrate or acetylphosphate at rates or under conditions required.[417, 418] Vinylcetate did yield butyrate and acetylphosphate, but its formation during butyrate synthesis was definitely disproved.[419]

(d) Extracts contained an enzyme, CoA transphorase, which catalyzed the exchange between the acylphosphates or CoA thiol esters of fatty acids and free fatty acids including acetate, propionate, butyrate, valerate, caproate, lactate, and vinylacetate. Crotonate, β-hydroxybutyrate, and vinyl-acetate did not react, however.[420, 421]

(e) With dialized extracts CoA was required for butyrate oxidation.[405] In addition, butyryl⁓SCoA was oxidized to acetoacetyl⁓SCoA, and acetoacetyl⁓SCoA, in the presence of CoA, yielded 2 acetyl⁓SCoA.[411]

(f) A role of vinylacetyl⁓SCoA or crotonyl⁓SCoA in the pathway is indicated from the formation of vinylacetyl⁓SCoA by CoA transphorase (see (d) above), from the acetyl⁓SCoA requirement for vinylacetate reduction[422] and from the discovery of an isomerase which interchanges vinyl-acetyl⁓SCoA and crotonyl⁓SCoA.[423]

The foregoing observations together with those made in animal tissues have resulted in the widely accepted concept for butyrate synthesis expressed by Barker[406] and shown in Fig. 17. In this cycle acetate or ethanol are converted to acetyl⁓SCoA, two of which then condense to form acetoacetyl⁓SCoA. Acetoacetyl⁓SCoA is reduced to β-hydroxybutyryl⁓SCoA and dehydrated to form vinylacetyl⁓SCoA or crotonyl⁓SCoA. One of these unsaturated carboxylic-thiol esters is then reduced to butyryl⁓SCoA. Another molecule of acetate can then accept CoA in a transfer reaction which yields free butyrate. The acetyl⁓SCoA so formed then re-enters a second cycle of butyrate synthesis. Similar though less extensive evidence indicates that the addition of another acetyl⁓SCoA to butyryl⁓SCoA leads to caproate synthesis, presumably via β-ketocaproyl⁓SCoA.[424]

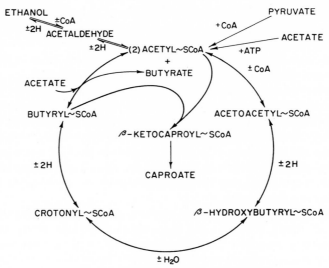

Fig. 17. Fatty acid synthesis in clostridia.

Although this mechanism explains many of the details of butyrate synthesis, it does not suggest the mechanism for energy generation. The oxidation of ethanol to acetyl⌣SCoA forms a potentially useful high energy thiol ester bond which can be utilized to form ATP. However, most of the acetyl⌣SCoA is consumed in butyrate and caproate synthesis, a process required to furnish hydrogen acceptors for the oxidation of ethanol and acetaldehyde. This problem was clearly recognized by Barker,[406] who suggested that energy could be derived in electron transport between the oxidation of ethanol and acetaldehyde and the reduction of crotonyl⌣SCoA. The potential drop in this system at pH 7 is about 0.39 volts or about 18 kcal. Thus there could be one or two moles of ATP synthesized per mole of ethanol oxidized in this system. Shuster and Gunsalus[1d] have provided the evidence that oxidative phosphorylation does occur in this pathway by showing ATP formation during the oxidation of hydrogen or of DPNH using crotonyl⌣SCoA as the acceptor.

The studies with *C. kluyveri* have greatly widened the concept of fermentation by showing the mechanism of butyrate synthesis and by establishing another method for energy generation in fermentation.

C. Methane Fermentations

The production of methane in sewage treatment plants, in mud, and in the first stomach of ruminants indicates a wide distribution of the methane-producing organisms in nature. Although important use and value are derived in the gasification of organic wastes by methane fermentation, the same process in the rumen appears to rob the host of both carbon and energy.

Because the methane bacteria are highly anaerobic and relatively difficult to isolate and subculture, rigorously pure cultures were unknown until 1940 when Barker[425] isolated *Methanobacterium omelianski*. Since that time three other species, *Methanobacterium formicicum*, *Methanosarcina barkeri*, and *Methanococcus vannielii*, have been isolated by Stadtman and Barker,[426] and by Schnellen.[427] Four other species were successfully transferred on solid media and obtained in a purified state with only one methane-producing type being present. Thus, the data on methane fermentations come from studies of both mixed or stabilized and purified cultures. All of the above cultures were obtained from mud and sewage sludge. There is increasing evidence that a similar array of species also inhabits the rumen. In fact, two species, *Methanobacterium formicicum* and *Methanobacterium ruminantium*, a type not heretofore encountered, have been isolated by Hungate and associates.[428, 429]

As a group, the methane bacteria are unique in that relatively few alcohols, organic acids, and other compounds are fermented, whereas normal energy sources such as carbohydrates and amino acids are not attacked. Within the group there is a marked substrate specificity which makes pure cultures incapable of completely degrading fatty acids C_3 through C_6 and alcohols. In the natural environment or in impure cultures, however, a sufficient variety of methane bacteria is present to effect complete utilization of more complex materials. The better known species and the substrates fermented are shown in Table XXIV. It can be seen that the fermentation of valeric acid, for instance, requires the presence of three species, one to

TABLE XXIV

SPECIFICITY OF METHANE-PRODUCING BACTERIA

Organism	Pure culture	Substrates
Methanobacterium formicicum[427]	Yes	H_2, CO_2, formate
Methanobacterium propionicum[430]	No	Propionate
Methanobacterium söhngenii[406]	No	Acetate, butyrate
Methanobacterium suboxydans[430]	No[a]	Butyrate, valerate, caproate
Methanobacterium omelianski[431, 432]	Yes	H_2, ethanol, primary and secondary alcohols
Methanococcus mazei[406]	No[a]	Acetate, butyrate
Methanococcus vanneilii[433]	Yes	Formate, hydrogen
Methanosarcina barkeri[427]	Yes	H_2, CO, methanol, acetate
Methanosarcina methanica[406]	No[a]	Acetate, butyrate (?)

[a] Purified until free of other methane-producing types.

form acetate and propionate, another to convert propionate into acetate and CO_2, and a third to ferment the acetate. Buswell and associates[434, 435] have shown that a number of other compounds, including higher fatty acids, aromatic compounds such as benzoic acid, and fermentation end products such as succinate, acetone, and 2,3-butanediol, are converted quantitatively by mixed cultures to methane and CO_2. Thus, in addition to the unique specificity, the unusual product, methane, and CO_2 are produced from all substrates. The primary insight into this phenomenon was furnished by Van Niel (see Barker[436]), who proposed that the oxidation of the substrates was coupled to the reduction of carbon dioxide to methane. The observations of Söhngen,[437] Barker,[432] and Kluyver and Schnellen[438] of fermentation of hydrogen in the presence of CO_2 to yield methane furnished obvious support for this theory.

$$4 \, H_2 + CO_2 \rightarrow CH_4 + 2 \, H_2O$$

Further, the fact that several species do not oxidize the substrates to carbon dioxide but stop at intermediate points has demonstrated that substrate carbon does not supply the carbon of methane.[439] *Methanobacterium omelianski*, for instance, oxidizes ethyl alcohol almost quantitatively to acetate.[431] The process, originally considered to be limited by the amount of carbon dioxide available, has recently been found to yield acetate and hydrogen in the absence of CO_2.[439a]

$$2 \text{ ethyl alcohol} + CO_2 \rightarrow 2 \text{ acetate} + \text{methane}$$

The CO_2 reduction hypothesis was further established by showing that the fermentation of unlabeled ethanol in the presence of $C^{14}O_2$ yielded methane of the same specific activity as the $C^{14}O_2$ supplied.[440] The fermentation of butyrate by *Methanobacterium suboxydans*[430] follows the same principle in that the $C^{14}O_2$ was the sole source of methane.

$$2 \text{ butyrate} + 2 \, H_2O + CO_2 \rightarrow 4 \text{ acetate} + \text{methane}$$

The situation becomes more involved, however, when CO_2 is also produced in the oxidation of the substrate. In the propionate fermentation by *Methanobacterium propionicum*,[430] for instance, a portion of the CO_2 produced is utilized in methane production.

Oxidation: $4 \text{ propionate} + 8 \, H_2O \rightarrow 4 \text{ acetate} + 4 \, CO_2 + 24 \, H$

Reduction: $3 \, CO_2 + 24 \, H \rightarrow 3 \text{ methane} + 6 \, H_2O$

Observed: $4 \text{ propionate} + 2 \, H_2O \rightarrow 4 \text{ acetate} + CO_2 + 3 \text{ methane}$

Again by the use of $C^{14}O_2$ it was shown that CO_2 was reduced to methane. The results were more difficult to interpret in this case, however, because the specific activity of the added $C^{14}O_2$ is continuously diminished by unlabeled CO_2 arising from propionate.

Although there is ample evidence in support of the carbon dioxide reduction theory, another system for methanogenesis is known to function in two cases. *Methanosarcina*, for instance, was shown by Schnellen[427] to convert methyl alcohol to methane.

$$4\ CH_3OH \rightarrow 3\ CH_4 + CO_2 + 2\ H_2O$$

Although the oxidation of methanol to CO_2 was considered likely, tracer studies showed that the methane arose exclusively from methyl alcohol, not from carbon dioxide.[441] Another unique but similar pathway for acetate fermentation was found by Buswell and Sollo,[442] who showed that $C^{14}O_2$ was not utilized during acetate fermentation, thereby suggesting the direct cleavage of acetate to the observed equal molar ratio of methane and CO_2. Stadtman and Barker[440, 441] showed that acetate-1-C^{14} and acetate-2-C^{14} were fermented so that the carboxyl group yields carbon dioxide exclusively and the methyl group yields methane without involving carbon dioxide reduction.

$$\overset{\prime}{C}H_3\overset{\circ}{C}OOH \rightarrow \overset{\prime}{C}H_4 + \overset{\circ}{C}O_2$$

In further studies with deuteroacetate and D_2O, Pine and Barker[443] and Pine and Vishniac[444] showed that the methyl group of both acetate and methanol are converted to methane intact with the fourth hydrogen atom coming from the medium.

$$CD_3COOH \xrightarrow{H_2O} CD_3H + CO_2$$

$$CH_3COOH \xrightarrow{D_2O} CH_3D + CO_2$$

$$4\ CH_3OH \xrightarrow{D_2O} 3\ CH_3D + CO_2$$

On the other hand, Buswell[445] has shown that enrichments which are capable of complete propionate fermentation convert all three carbon atoms of propionate C^{14} to methane and CO_2. Based upon the above reactions, carbon-3 of propionate (carbon-2 of acetate) should yield only methane. Thus, it is necessary to postulate a different reaction sequence for propionate fermentation in this mixed culture.

Virtually nothing is known of the mechanism of methane formation. Two of the expected intermediates, formate and methanol, are fermented by some species while in other organisms these and formaldehyde are not converted to methane. Also, carbon monoxide and formate do not participate in methane formation directly since these substrates first are converted to carbon dioxide and hydrogen. A unified concept of methane formation from all of the substrates has been proposed by Barker,[406] as shown in Fig. 18. The main feature of this scheme is the reduction of CO_2, methanol, and acetate after transfer of a single carbon unit to a carrier HX. The C_1-X compound can exist at the level of formate, formaldehyde, and methyl.

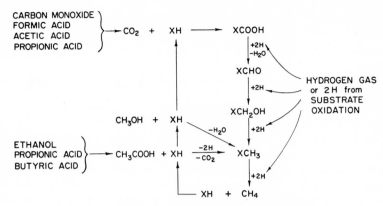

FIG. 18. Possible pathways of methane fermentation.

In addition to providing a *rationale* for CO_2 reduction, the scheme also takes into account the requirements for methanol and acetate utilization. Although the postulated system is suggested only as a guide, the use of carrier X is fully justified in view of the role of tetrahydrofolic acid as a carrier for formyl, hydroxymethyl, and formimino groups. The interconversion of formyl and hydroxymethyl tetrahydrofolic acids by oxidation-reduction also has been demonstrated, although similar enzymic information for methyl carriers and their interconversion with the hydroxymethyl level is not available.

The difficulty of growing pure cultures of methane bacteria in large quantity has prevented biochemical studies with this group of microorganisms. Thus, nothing is known of the mechanism of energy generation. It is evident, however, particularly in the fermentation of hydrogen and CO_2, or of carbon monoxide, that substrate phosphorylation is not involved. Thus, it is likely that the oxidation of substrates coupled to the carbon dioxide reduction allows ATP formation by a system resembling oxidative phosphorylation.

REFERENCES

[1] S. R. Elsden and J. L. Peel, *Ann. Rev. Microbiol.* **12**, 145 (1958).

[1a] I. C. Gunsalus, *Proc. Intern. Congr. Biochem., 4th Congr., Vienna, 1958* **13**, 444 (1959).

[1b] F. Lipmann, *Advances in Enzymol.* **1**, 99 (1941).

[1c] H. A. Barker, "Bacterial Fermentations," p. 95. Wiley, New York, 1957.

[1d] C. W. Shuster and I. C. Gunsalus, *Federation Proc.* **17**, 310 (1958).

[1e] H. G. Wood and C. H. Werkman, *Biochem. J.* **30**, 48 (1936).

[1f] A. Lavoisier, "Traité Élémentaire de Chymie," Chapter XIII. Cf. references 19 and 20a.

[2] A. C. Neish, "Analytical Methods for Bacterial Fermentations." Saskatoon, Saskatchewan, 1952.

[3] M. J. Johnson, W. H. Peterson, and E. B. Fred, *J. Biol. Chem.* **91,** 569 (1931).

[4] C. Erb, H. G. Wood, and C. H. Werkman, *J. Bacteriol.* **31,** 595 (1936).

[5] H. A. Barker, *Enzymologia* **2,** 175 (1937).

[6] M. Gibbs, R. Dumrose, F. A. Bennett, and M. R. Bubeck, *J. Biol. Chem.* **184,** 545 (1950).

[7] D. E. Koshland, Jr. and F. H. Westheimer, *J. Am. Chem. Soc.* **72,** 3383 (1950).

[8] M. Gibbs and R. D. DeMoss, *Arch. Biochem. Biophys.* **34,** 478 (1951).

[9] M. Gibbs and R. D. DeMoss, *Federation Proc.* **10,** 189 (1951).

[10] I. C. Gunsalus and M. Gibbs, *J. Biol. Chem.* **194,** 871 (1952).

[11] H. G. Wood, R. Stjernholm, and F. W. Leaver, *J. Bacteriol.* **70,** 510 (1955).

[12] F. W. Leaver, H. G. Wood, and R. Stjernholm, *J. Bacteriol.* **70,** 521 (1955).

[13] D. J. O'Kane and W. W. Umbreit, *J. Biol. Chem.* **142,** 25 (1952).

[14] R. W. Stone and C. H. Werkman, *Biochem. J.* **31,** 1516 (1937).

[15] I. C. Gunsalus, B. L. Horecker, and W. A. Wood, *Bacteriol. Revs.* **19,** 79 (1955).

[16] S. R. Elsden, *in* "The Enzymes" (J. B. Sumner and K. Myrbäck, eds.) Vol. II, Part I, p. 791. Academic Press, New York, 1952.

[17] D. Burk, *Cold Spring Harbor Symposia Quant. Biol.* **7,** 420 (1939).

[18] F. F. Nord and S. Weiss, *in* "The Chemistry and Biology of Yeasts" (A. H. Cook, ed.), p. 323. Academic Press, New York, 1958.

[19] S. C. Prescott and C. G. Dunn, "Industrial Microbiology," pp. 67, 260. McGraw-Hill, New York, 1940.

[19a] L. Pasteur, *Compt. rend.* **45,** 913 (1857).

[20] L. J. Gay-Lussac, *Ann. chim. et phys.* **95,** 311 (1815).

[20a] A. Harden, "Alcoholic Fermentation," Longmans, Green, London, 1923.

[21] A. C. Neish and A. C. Blackwood, *Can. J. Technol.* **29,** 123 (1951).

[22] E. Buchner, *Ber.* **30,** 117 (1897).

[23] E. C. Heath, D. Nasser, and H. Koffler, *Arch. Biochem. Biophys.* **64,** 80 (1956).

[24] E. A. Robbins and P. D. Boyer, *J. Biol. Chem.* **224,** 121 (1957).

[25] C. Neuberg and E. Reinfurth, *Biochem. Z.* **92,** 234 (1918).

[26] C. Neuberg and E. Reinfurth, *Biochem. Z.* **89,** 365 (1918).

[27] C. Neuberg and E. Reinfurth, *Ber.* **52,** 1677 (1919).

[28] C. Neuberg and J. Hirsch, *Biochem. Z.* **98,** 141 (1919).

[29] W. Connstein and K. Ludecke, *Ber.* **52,** 1385 (1919).

[30] W. Connstein and K. Ludecke, *Ber.* **52,** 99 (1919).

[31] C. Neuberg and E. Farber, *Biochem. Z.* **78,** 238 (1917).

[32] C. Neuberg and J. Hirsch, *Biochem. Z.* **96,** 175 (1919).

[33] C. Neuberg and J. Hirsch, *Biochem. Z.* **100,** 304 (1919).

[34] C. Neuberg, J. Hirsch, and E. Reinfurth, *Biochem. Z.* **105,** 307 (1920).

[35] C. Neuberg and W. Ursum, *Biochem. Z.* **110,** 193 (1920).

[36] W. J. Nickerson and W. R. Carroll, *Arch. Biochem.* **7,** 257 (1945).

[37] C. Neuberg and M. Kobel, *Ber.* **63,** 1986 (1930).

[38] C. Neuberg and M. Kobel, *Biochem. Z.* **219,** 490 (1930).

[39] C. Neuberg and M. Kobel, *Biochem. Z.* **229,** 446 (1930).

[40] M. Kobel and M. Scheuer, *Biochem. Z.* **229,** 238 (1930).

[41] M. Kobel, *Biochem. Z.* **243,** 406 (1931).

[42] A. J. Kluyver and H. L. Donker (1924); see A. J. Kluyver, *Ergeb. Enzymforsch.* **4,** 230 (1935).

[43] S. Orla-Jensen, *Kgl. Danske Videnskab. Selskabs, Skrifter, Naturvidenskab. math. Afdel.* [8] **5,** 51 (1919).

[44] I. C. Gunsalus and C. F. Niven, Jr., *J. Biol. Chem.* **145,** 131 (1942).

[45] T. B. Platt and E. M. Foster, *J. Bacteriol.* **75,** 453 (1958).

[46] H. D. Slade, H. G. Wood, A. O. Nier, A. Hemingway, and C. H. Werkman, *J. Biol. Chem.* **143,** 133 (1942).

[46a] J. T. Sokatch and I. C. Gunsalus, *J. Bacteriol.* **73,** 452 (1957).

[46b] G. Buyze, J. A. van den Hamer, and P. G. de Haan, *Antonie van Leeuwenhoek, J. Microbiol. Serol.* **23,** 345 (1957).

[46c] T. Wilken, *Proc. Intern. Congr. Biochem., 4th Congr., Vienna, 1958* **13,** 433 (1959).

[47] R. H. Deibel, J. B. Evans, and C. F. Niven, Jr. *Bacteriol. Proc. (Soc. Am. Bacteriologists)* p. 114 (1958).

[48] H. W. Seeley and P. J. Vandemark, *J. Bacteriol.* **61,** 27 (1951).

[48a] I. C. Gunsalus, *in* "The Mechanism of Enzyme Action" (W. D. McElroy and B. Glass, eds.), p. 545. Johns Hopkins Press, Baltimore, Maryland 1954.

[48b] W. D. Bancroft and H. L. Davis, *J. Phys. Chem.* **35,** 2508 (1931).

[49] L. M. Kopeloff, N. Kopeloff, J. L. Etchells, and E. Posselt, *J. Bacteriol.* **33,** 331 (1937).

[50] R. S. Breed, E. G. D. Murray, and A. P. Hitchens, eds., "Bergey's Manual of Determinative Bacteriology," 6th ed. Williams & Wilkins, Baltimore, Maryland, 1948.

[51] E. B. Fred, W. H. Peterson, and H. R. Stiles, *J. Bacteriol.* **10,** 63 (1925).

[52] M. Brin, R. E. Olson, and F. J. Stare, *Arch. Biochem. Biophys.* **39,** 214 (1952).

[53] E. L. Tatum and W. H. Peterson, *Ind. Eng. Chem.* **27,** 1493 (1935).

[54] C. S. Pederson, *Bacteriol. Revs.* **13,** 225 (1949).

[55] A. A. Anderson and J. E. Greaves, *Ind. Eng. Chem.* **34,** 1522 (1942).

[56] C. S. Pederson, W. H. Peterson, and E. B. Fred, *J. Biol. Chem.* **68,** 151 (1926).

[57] S. Kaufman, S. Korkes, and A. Del Campillo, *J. Biol. Chem.* **192,** 301 (1951).

[58] H. Katagiri and K. Kitahara, *J. Agr. Chem. Soc. Japan* **12,** 1217 (1937).

[59] H. Katagiri and K. Kitahara, *Biochem. J.* **31,** 909 (1937).

[60] H. Katagiri and K. Kitahara, *Biochem. J.* **32,** 1654 (1938).

[61] K. Kitahara, *J. Agr. Chem. Soc. Japan* **15,** 19 (1939).

[62] H. Katagiri and S. Murakimi, *J. Agr. Chem. Soc. Japan* **15,** 1135 (1939).

[63] H. Katagiri and S. Murakami, *J. Agr. Chem. Soc. Japan* **15,** 1141 (1939).

[64] K. Kitahara, *J. Fermentation Technol.* **27,** 125 (1950).

[65] K. Kitahara, A. Obayashi, and S. Fukui, *J. Agr. Chem. Soc. Japan* **26,** 162 (1952).

[66] K. Kitahara, A. Obayashi and S. Fukui, *J. Agr. Chem. Soc. Japan* **27,** 306 (1953).

[67] K. Kitahara and A. Obayashi, *J. Agr. Chem. Soc. Japan* **28,** 232 (1954).

[68] H. Katagiri and K. Imai, *Bull. Agr. Chem. Soc. Japan* **19,** 15 (1955).

[69] H. Katagiri, K. Imai, T. Sugimori, M. Komaki, and M. Okuzumi, *Kôso Kagaku Shimpojiumu* **12,** 103 (1957); *Chem. Abstr.* **47,** 10576 (1953).

[70] E. L. Tatum, W. H. Peterson, and E. B. Fred, *Biochem. J.* **26,** 846 (1933).

[71] E. L. Tatum, W. H. Peterson, and E. B. Fred, *Biochem. J.* **30,** 1892 (1936).

[72] E. L. Tatum and W. H. Peterson, *J. Bacteriol.* **32,** 122 (1936).

[73] W. B. Christensen, M. J. Johnson, and W. H. Peterson, *J. Biol. Chem.* **127,** 421 (1939).

[74] F. M. Huennekens, H. R. Mahler, and J. Nordmann, *Arch. Biochem.* **30,** 77 (1951).

[75] W. A. Pierce, Jr. and A. G. C. White, *J. Bacteriol.* **63,** 301 (1952).

[76] R. H. Steele, A. G. C. White, and W. A. Pierce, Jr., *J. Bacteriol.* **67,** 86 (1954).

[77] A. G. C. White, R. H. Steele, and W. A. Pierce, Jr., *J. Bacteriol.* **70,** 82 (1955).

[78] W. A. Pierce, Jr., *J. Bacteriol.* **74,** 186 (1957).

[79] C. F. Sprague and W. D. Bellamy, *J. Bacteriol.* **57,** 95 (1949).

[80] S. K. Suzuki, E. G. Hastings, and E. B. Hart, *J. Biol. Chem.* **7,** 431 (1910).

[81] A. J. Kluyver, "Chemical Activities of Microorganisms." Univ. of London Press, London, 1931.

[82] M. P. Bryant and L. A. Burkey, *J. Bacteriol.* **71,** 43 (1956).

[83] J. V. Bhat and H. A. Barker, *J. Bacteriol.* **54**, 381 (1947).
[84] T. E. Freidemann and T. E. Kmieciak, *Proc. Soc. Exptl. Biol. Med.* **47**, 84 (1941).
[85] A. M. Pappenheimer, Jr. and E. Shaskan, *J. Biol. Chem.* **155**, 265 (1944).
[86] E. M. Lerner and M. J. Pickett, *Arch. Biochem.* **8**, 183 (1945).
[87] C. E. Clifton, *J. Bacteriol.* **39**, 485 (1940).
[88] H. A. Barker and V. Haas, *J. Bacteriol.* **47**, 301 (1944).
[89] L. Pine, V. Haas, and H. A. Barker, *J. Bacteriol.* **68**, 227 (1954).
[90] H. A. Barker, M. D. Kamen, and V. Haas, *Proc. Natl. Acad. Sci. U. S.* **31**, 355 (1945).
[91] L. Pine and H. A. Barker, *J. Bacteriol.* **68**, 216 (1954).
[92] H. A. Barker, *Federation Proc.* **13**, 742 (1954).
[93] J. B. Van der Lek, Ph.D. Thesis, Technische Hoogeschool, Delft, Holland, 1930.
[94] W. H. Peterson and E. B. Fred, *Ind. Eng. Chem.* **24**, 237 (1932).
[95] H. R. Stiles, W. H. Peterson, and E. B. Fred, *J. Biol. Chem.* **84**, 437 (1929).
[96] R. Davies, *Biochem. J.* **36**, 582 (1942).
[97] R. W. Brown, C. L. Stahly, and C. H. Werkman, *Iowa State Coll. J. Sci.* **12**, 245 (1938).
[98] R. Davies, *Biochem. J.* **37**, 230 (1943).
[99] H. W. Seeley and P. J. Vandemark, *J. Bacteriol.* **59**, 381 (1950).
[100] O. L. Osburn, R. W. Brown, and C. H. Werkman, *J. Biol. Chem.* **121**, 685 (1937).
[101] O. L. Osburn, R. W. Brown, and C. H. Werkman, *Iowa State Coll. J. Sci.* **12**, 275 (1937).
[102] A. F. Langlykke, W. H. Peterson and E. B. Fred, *J. Bacteriol.* **34**, 443 (1937).
[103] W. Kempner, *Biochem. Z.* **257**, 41 (1933).
[104] W. Kempner and F. Kubowitz, *Biochem. Z.* **265**, 246 (1933).
[105] F. Kubowitz, *Biochem. Z.* **274**, 285 (1934).
[106] E. Simon, *Arch. Biochem.* **13**, 237 (1947).
[107] A. M. Hanson and N. E. Rodgers, *J. Bacteriol.* **51**, 568 (1946).
[107a] L. Smith, *Bacteriol. Revs.* **18**, 106 (1954).
[108] E. M. Lerner and J. H. Mueller, *J. Biol. Chem.* **181**, 43 (1949).
[109] L. B. Pett and A. M. Wynne, *J. Biol. Chem.* **97**, 177 (1932).
[110] B. Rosenfeld and E. Simon, *J. Biol. Chem.* **186**, 395 (1950).
[111] B. Rosenfeld and E. Simon, *J. Biol. Chem.* **186**, 495 (1950).
[112] G. Cohen-Bazire and G. N. Cohen, *Ann. inst. Pasteur* **77**, 718 (1949).
[113] M. J. Johnson, W. H. Peterson, and E. B. Fred, *J. Biol. Chem.* **101**, 145 (1933).
[114] R. C. Bard and I. C. Gunsalus, *J. Bacteriol.* **59**, 387 (1950).
[115] K. Shankar and R. C. Bard, *J. Bacteriol.* **69**, 436 (1955).
[116] L. M. Paege, M. Gibbs, and R. C. Bard, *J. Bacteriol.* **72**, 65 (1956).
[117] M. A. Cynkin and M. Gibbs, *J. Bacteriol.* **75**, 335 (1958).
[118] H. G. Wood, R. W. Brown, and C. H. Werkman, *J. Bacteriol.* **45**, 15 (1943).
[119] H. G. Wood, R. W. Brown, and C. H. Werkman, *Arch. Biochem.* **6**, 243 (1945).
[120] R. W. Brown, H. G. Wood, and C. H. Werkman, *Arch. Biochem.* **5**, 423 (1944).
[121] H. J. Koepsell and M. J. Johnson, *J. Biol. Chem.* **145**, 379 (1942).
[122] H. J. Koepsell, M. J. Johnson, and J. S. Meek, *J. Biol. Chem.* **154**, 535 (1944).
[123] G. Kalnitsky and C. H. Werkman, *J. Bacteriol.* **44**, 256 (1942).
[124] G. Kalnitsky and C. H. Werkman, *Arch. Biochem.* **2**, 113 (1943).
[125] M. F. Utter and C. H. Werkman, *Arch. Biochem.* **2**, 491 (1943).
[126] F. Lipmann, *J. Biol. Chem.* **155**, 55 (1944).
[126a] F. Lipmann, *Advances in Enzymol.* **6**, 231 (1946).
[127] H. D. Slade and C. H. Werkman, *Arch. Biochem.* **2**, 97 (1943).
[128] J. Wilson, L. O. Krampitz, and C. H. Werkman, *Biochem. J.* **42**, 598 (1948)

[129] R. S. Wolfe and D. J. O'Kane, *J. Biol. Chem.* **215,** 637 (1955).

[130] R. S. Wolfe and D. J. O'Kane, *J. Biol. Chem.* **205,** 755 (1953).

[131] A. L. Shug and P. W. Wilson, *Federation Proc.* **15,** 355 (1956).

[132] R. P. Mortlock and R. S. Wolfe, *Bacteriol. Proc.* (*Am. Soc. Bacteriologists*) p. 112 (1956).

[133] R. D. Hamilton and R. S. Wolfe, *Bacteriol. Proc.* (*Am. Soc. Bacteriologists*) p. 128 (1957).

[134] L. E. Mortenson and P. W. Wilson, *J. Bacteriol.* **62,** 513 (1951).

[135] H. Gest, *Bacteriol. Revs.* **18,** 43 (1954).

[136] H. D. Peck, Jr. and H. Gest, *Federation Proc.* **15,** 325 (1956).

[137] H. D. Peck, Jr. and H. Gest, *J. Bacteriol.* **73,** 569 (1957).

[138] F. E. Fontaine, W. H. Peterson, E. McCoy, M. J. Johnson, and G. J. Ritter, *J. Bacteriol.* **43,** 701 (1942).

[139] K. T. Wieringa, *Antonie van Leeuwenhoek, J. Microbiol. Serol.* **3,** 263 (1936).

[140] K. T. Wieringa, *Antonie van Leeuwenhoek, J. Microbiol. Serol.* **6,** 251 (1939).

[141] H. A. Barker, *Proc. Natl. Acad. Sci. U. S.* **30,** 88 (1944).

[142] H. A. Barker and M. D. Kamen, *Proc. Natl. Acad. Sci. U. S.* **31,** 219 (1945).

[143] H. G. Wood, *J. Biol. Chem.* **194,** 905 (1952).

[144] H. G. Wood, *J. Biol. Chem.* **199,** 579 (1952).

[145] K. Lentz and H. G. Wood, *J. Biol. Chem.* **215,** 645 (1955).

[146] J. V. Bhat and H. A. Barker, *J. Bacteriol.* **56,** 777 (1948).

[147] H. A. Barker, S. Ruben, and J. V. Beck, *Proc. Natl. Acad. Sci. U. S.* **26,** 477 (1940).

[148] H. A. Barker, B. E. Volcani, and B. P. Cardon, *J. Biol. Chem.* **173,** 803 (1948).

[149] A. Harden, *J. Chem. Soc.* **79,** 610 (1901).

[150] J. L. Stokes, *J. Bacteriol.* **57,** 147 (1949).

[151] H. D. Kay, *Biochem. J.* **20,** 321 (1926).

[152] M. A. Scheffer, Thesis, Technische Hoogeschool, Delft, Holland, 1928.

[153] J. Tikka, *Biochem. Z.* **279,** 264 (1935).

[154] A. C. Blackwood, A. C. Neish, and G. A. Ledingham, *J. Bacteriol.* **72,** 497 (1956).

[155] M. Doudoroff, *J. Bacteriol.* **44,** 461 (1942).

[156] J. L. Stokes, *J. Bacteriol.* **72,** 269 (1956).

[157] J. Blass, *Ann. inst. Pasteur* **73,** 885 (1947).

[158] I. P. Crawford, *J. Bacteriol.* **68,** 734 (1954).

[159] H. Gest and M. Gibbs, *Brookhaven Symposium on Major Metabolic Fuels* **5,** 157 (1952).

[160] S. Endo, *Biochem. Z.* **296,** 56 (1938).

[161] M. F. Utter and C. H. Werkman, *J. Bacteriol.* **42,** 665 (1941).

[162] M. F. Utter, F. Lipmann, and C. H. Werkman, *J. Biol. Chem.* **158,** 521 (1945).

[163] J. Wilson, L. O. Krampitz, and C. H. Werkman, *Biochem. J.* **42,** 598 (1948).

[164] H. J. Strecker, H. G. Wood, and L. O. Krampitz, *J. Biol. Chem.* **182,** 525 (1950).

[165] H. Chantrenne and F. Lipmann, *J. Biol. Chem.* **187,** 757 (1950).

[166] H. J. Strecker, *J. Biol. Chem.* **189,** 815 (1951).

[167] W. W. C. Pakes and W. H. Jollyman, *J. Chem. Soc.* **79,** 386 (1901).

[168] J. H. Quastel and M. D. Whetham, *Biochem. J.* **19,** 520 (1925).

[169] M. Stephenson and L. H. Stickland, *Biochem. J.* **25,** 205 (1931).

[170] M. Stephenson and L. H. Stickland, *Biochem. J.* **27,** 1528 (1933).

[171] M. Stephenson, *Ergeb. Enzymforsch.* **6,** 139 (1937).

[172] M. J. Pinsky and J. L. Stokes, *J. Bacteriol.* **64,** 337 (1952).

[173] M. J. Pinsky and J. L. Stokes, *J. Bacteriol.* **64,** 151 (1952).

[174] D. Billen and H. C. Lichstein, *J. Bacteriol.* **60,** 311 (1950).

[175] D. Billen and H. C. Lichstein, *J. Bacteriol.* **61,** 515 (1951).

[176] D. Billen, *J. Bacteriol.* **62,** 793 (1951).
[177] M. Stephenson, "Bacterial Metabolism," 3rd ed., p. 80. Longmans, Green, New York, 1949.
[178] E. J. Ordal and H. O. Halvorson, *J. Bacteriol.* **38,** 199 (1939).
[179] H. Gest and H. D. Peck, Jr., *J. Bacteriol.* **70,** 326 (1955).
[180] H. D. Peck, Jr. and H. Gest, *J. Bacteriol.* **73,** 706 (1957).
[181] H. C. Lichstein and R. B. Boyd, *J. Bacteriol.* **67,** 335 (1954).
[182] W. S. Waring and C. H. Werkman, *Arch. Biochem.* **1,** 303, 425 (1943).
[183] H. Gest and M. Gibbs, *J. Bacteriol.* **63,** 661 (1952).
[184] G. A. Ledingham and A. C. Neish, *in* "Industrial Fermentations" (L. A. Underkofler and R. J. Hickey, eds.), Vol. 2, p. 27. Chemical Publ., New York, 1954.
[185] A. Harden and G. S. Walpole, *Proc. Roy. Soc.* **B77,** 399 (1906).
[186] G. S. Walpole, *Proc. Roy. Soc.* **B83,** 272 (1911).
[187] A. Harden and O. Norris, *Proc. Roy. Soc.* **B84,** 492 (1912).
[188] A. Harden and D. Norris, *Proc. Roy. Soc.* **B85** 73 (1913).
[189] G. A. Adams and R. Y. Stanier, *Can. J. Research* **B23,** 1 (1945).
[190] R. J. Stanier and G. A. Adams, *Biochem. J.* **38,** 168 (1944).
[191] E. I. Fullmer, L. M. Christianson, and A. R. Kendall, *Ind. Eng. Chem.* **25,** 798 (1933).
[192] H. Reynolds and C. H. Werkman, *J. Bacteriol.* **32,** 123 (1936).
[193] H. Reynolds and C. H. Werkman, *J. Bacteriol.* **33,** 603 (1937).
[194] D. Paretsky and C. H. Werkman, *Arch. Biochem.* **14,** 11 (1947).
[195] B. H. Olson and M. J. Johnson, *J. Bacteriol.* **55,** 209 (1948).
[196] C. S. Pederson and R. S. Breed, *J. Bacteriol.* **16,** 163 (1928).
[197] A. J. Kraght and M. P. Starr, *J. Bacteriol.* **64,** 259 (1952).
[198] A. C. Blackwood, A. C. Neish, W. E. Brown, and G. A. Ledingham, *Can. J. Research* **B25,** 56 (1947).
[199] G. Knaysi and I. C. Gunsalus, *J. Bacteriol.* **47,** 381 (1944).
[200] M. Hooreman, J. P. Aubert, M. Lemoigne, and J. Millet, *Ann. inst. Pasteur* **78,** 497 (1950).
[201] M. Puziss and S. C. Rittenberg, *J. Bacteriol.* **73,** 48 (1957).
[202] H. A. Altermatt, F. J. Simpson, and A. C. Neish, *Can. J. Microbiol.* **1,** 473 (1955).
[203] A. C. Neish, A. C. Blackwood, F. M. Robertson, and G. A. Ledingham, *Can. J. Research* **B26,** 335 (1948).
[204] A. C. Neish, *Can. J. Botany* **31,** 265 (1953).
[205] H. Reynolds, B. J. Jacobsson, and C. H. Werkman, *J. Bacteriol.* **34,** 15 (1937).
[206] M. N. Mickelson, H. Reynolds, and C. H. Werkman, *J. Bacteriol.* **36,** 657 (1938).
[207] M. N. Mickelson and C. H. Werkman, *J. Bacteriol.* **37,** 619 (1939).
[208] M. Mickelson and C. H. Werkman, *J. Bacteriol.* **36,** 67 (1938).
[209] A. C. Neish and G. A. Ledingham, *Can. J. Research* **B27,** 694 (1949).
[210] G. J. Sigurdsson and A. J. Wood, *J. Fisheries Research Board Can.* **6,** 45 (1942).
[211] A. C. Neish, A. C. Blackwood, F. M. Robertson, and G. A. Ledingham, *Can. J. Research* **B25,** 65 (1947).
[212] F. H. Gallagher and R. W. Stone, *J. Bacteriol.* **38,** 235 (1939).
[213] A. C. Neish, A. C. Blackwood, and G. A. Ledingham, *Can. J. Research* **B23,** 290 (1945).
[214] I. C. Gunsalus, *J. Bacteriol.* **48,** 262 (1944).
[215] N. D. Gary and R. C. Bard, *J. Bacteriol.* **64,** 501 (1952).
[216] R. D. DeMoss, R. C. Bard, and I. C. Gunsalus, *J. Bacteriol.* **62,** 499 (1951).
[217] C. Neuberg and J. Hirsch, *Biochem. Z.* **115,** 282 (1921).
[218] C. Neuberg and L. Liebermann, *Biochem. Z.* **121,** 311 (1921).

[219] C. Neuberg and H. Ohle, *Biochem. Z.* **127,** 327 (1922).

[220] C. Neuberg and H. Ohle, *Biochem. Z.* **128,** 610 (1922).

[221] C. Neuberg and E. Reinfurth, *Biochem. Z.* **143,** 553 (1923).

[222] D. E. Green, D. Herbert, and V. Subrahmanyan, *J. Biol. Chem.* **138,** 327 (1941).

[223] T. P. Singer and J. Pensky, *Arch. Biochem. Biophys.* **31,** 457 (1951).

[224] D. E. Green, W. W. Westerfeld, B. Vennesland, and W. E. Knox, *J. Biol. Chem.* **145,** 69 (1942).

[225] Y. Tomiyasu, *Enzymologia* **3,** 263 (1937).

[226] E. Juni, *J. Biol. Chem.* **195,** 715 (1952).

[227] E. Juni and G. A. Heym, *Federation Proc.* **13,** 238 (1954).

[228] P. F. Smith and D. Hendlin, *J. Bacteriol.* **65,** 440 (1953).

[229] H. Nahm and W. Dirscherl, *Chem. Ber.* **83,** 415 (1950).

[230] M. Lemoigne, M. Hooreman, and M. Croson, *Ann. inst. Pasteur* **76,** 303 (1949).

[231] M. Mickelson and C. H. Werkman, *J. Bacteriol.* **34,** 137 (1937).

[232] M. Silverman and C. H. Werkman, *J. Biol. Chem.* **138,** 35 (1941).

[233] F. C. Happold and C. P. Spencer, *Biochim. et Biophys. Acta* **8,** 18 (1952).

[234] M. I. Dolin and I. C. Gunsalus, *J. Bacteriol.* **62,** 199 (1951).

[235] A. C. Neish, *Can. J. Research* **23B,** 10 (1945).

[236] F. M. Robertson and A. C. Neish, *Can. J. Research* **26B,** 737 (1948).

[237] G. E. Ward, O. G. Pettijohn, L. B. Lockwood, and R. D. Coghill, *J. Am. Chem. Soc.* **66,** 541 (1944).

[238] O. Warburg and W. Christian, *Biochem. Z.* **242,** 206 (1931).

[239] E. C. Heath, J. Hurwitz, B. L. Horecker, and A. Ginsburg, *J. Biol. Chem.* **231,** 1009 (1958).

[240] U. Gayon and E. Doubourg, *Ann. inst. Pasteur* **8,** 108 (1894).

[241] U. Gayon and E. Doubourg, *Ann. inst. Pasteur* **15,** 527 (1901).

[242] W. H. Peterson and E. B. Fred, *J. Biol. Chem.* **42,** 273 (1920).

[243] C. S. Pederson, *N. Y. State Agr. Expt. Sta.* (Geneva, NY) *Tech. Bull. No.* **151,** (1929).

[244] M. E. Nelson and C. H. Werkman, *J. Bacteriol.* **30,** 547 (1935).

[245] M. E. Nelson and C. H. Werkman, *J. Bacteriol.* **31,** 603 (1936).

[246] M. E. Nelson and C. H. Werkman, *Iowa State Coll. J. Sci.* **14,** 359 (1940).

[247] W. H. Peterson and E. B. Fred, *J. Biol. Chem.* **41,** 431 (1920).

[248] M. Gibbs, J. T. Sokatch, and I. C. Gunsalus, *J. Bacteriol.* **70,** 572 (1955).

[249] H. R. Stiles, W. H. Peterson, and E. B. Fred, *J. Biol. Chem.* **64,** 643 (1925).

[250] G. W. Jordian, H. Koffler, and H. R. Garner, *Bacteriol. Proc.* (*Soc. Am. Bacteriologists*) p. 97 (1958).

[251] R. D. DeMoss, I. C. Gunsalus, and R. C. Bard, *Bacteriol. Proc.* (*Soc. Am. Bacteriologists*) p. 125 (1951).

[252] R. D. DeMoss, *J. Cellular Comp. Physiol.* **41,** Suppl. 1,207 (1953).

[253] R. DeMoss, *Bacteriol. Proc.* (*Soc. Am. Bacteriologists*) p. 81 (1953).

[254] R. D. DeMoss, *Bacteriol. Proc.* (*Soc. Am. Bacteriologists*) p. 109 (1954).

[255] J. Hurwitz, *Biochim. et Biophys. Acta* **28,** 599 (1958).

[256] R. W. Eltz and P. J. Vandemark, *Bacteriol. Proc.* (*Soc. Am. Bacteriologists*) p. 122 (1957).

[257] I. A. Bernstein, K. Lentz, M. Malm, P. Schambye, and H. G. Wood, *J. Biol. Chem.* **215,** 137 (1955).

[258] A. J. Kluyver and W. J. Hoppenbrouwers, *Arch. Mikrobiol.* **2,** 245 (1931).

[259] R. D. DeMoss and M. Gibbs, *Bacteriol. Proc.* (*Soc. Am. Bacteriologists*) p. 146 (1952).

[260] M. Gibbs and R. D. DeMoss, *J. Biol. Chem.* **207,** 689 (1954).

[261] N. Entner and M. Doudoroff, *J. Biol. Chem.* **196,** 853 (1952).

[262] J. MacGee and M. Doudoroff, *Bacteriol. Proc. (Soc. Am. Bacteriologists)* p. 108 (1954).

[263] R. Kovachevich and W. A. Wood, *J. Biol. Chem.* **213,** 245 (1955).

[264] R. Kovachevich and W. A. Wood, *J. Biol. Chem.* **213,** 757 (1955).

[264a] M. Schramm, V. Klybas, and E. Racker, *J. Biol. Chem.* **233,** 1283 (1958).

[265] A. Fitz, *Ber.* **11,** 1896 (1878).

[266] S. Orla-Jensen, *Centr. Bakteriol. Parasitenk.* **4,** 325 (1898).

[267] E. von Freudenreich and S. Orla-Jensen, *Centr. Bakteriol. Parasitenk.* **17,** 529 (1906).

[268] H. G. Wood and C. H. Werkman, *Biochem. J.* **30,** 618 (1936).

[269] H. G. Wood, R. W. Stone, and C. H. Werkman, *Biochem. J.* **31,** 349 (1937).

[270] B. P. Cardon and H. A. Barker, *Arch. Biochem.* **12,** 165 (1947).

[271] E. L. Toubert and H. C. Douglas, *J. Bacteriol.* **56,** 35 (1948).

[272] H. G. Wood and C. H. Werkman, *Biochem. J.* **30,** 48 (1936).

[273] C. B. Van Niel, Ph.D. Thesis, Technische Hoogeschool, Delft, Holland, 1928.

[274] H. G. Wood and C. H. Werkman, *Biochem. J.* **34,** 7 (1940).

[275] F. W. Leaver and H. G. Wood, *J. Cellular Comp. Physiol.* **41,** Suppl. 1, 225 (1953).

[276] Y. Ichikawa, *Nippon Nôgei-kagaku Kaishi* **29,** 353 (1955); *Chem. Abstr.* **51,** 11458 (1957).

[277] H. G. Wood and F. W. Leaver, *Biochim. et Biophys. Acta* **12,** 207 (1953).

[278] A. I. Virtanen, *Soc. Sci. Fennica, Commentationes Phys. Math.* **1,** 1 (1923).

[279] A. I. Virtanen, *Soc. Sci. Fennica, Commentationes Phys. Math.* **2,** 1 (1925).

[280] A. I. Virtanen and H. Karström, *Acta Chem. Fennica* **7,** 17 (1931).

[281] L. B. Pett and A. M. Wynne, *Trans. Roy. Soc. Can. Inst.* **27,** 119 (1933).

[282] C. H. Werkman, R. W. Stone, and H. G. Wood, *Enzymologia* **4,** 24 (1937).

[283] W. P. Wiggert and C. H. Werkman, *Biochem. J.* **33,** 1061 (1939).

[284] R. W. Stone and C. H. Werkman, *Iowa State Coll. J. Sci.* **10,** 341 (1936).

[285] R. W. Stone, H. G. Wood, and C. H. Werkman, *J. Bacteriol.* **33,** 101 (1937).

[286] H. A. Barker and F. Lipmann, *J. Biol. Chem.* **179,** 247 (1949).

[287] H. G. Wood, R. Stjernholm, and F. W. Leaver, *J. Bacteriol.* **70,** 510 (1955).

[288] H. G. Wood, R. G. Kulka, and N. L. Edson, *Biochem. J.* **63,** 177 (1956).

[289] W. A. Volk, *J. Biol. Chem.* **208,** 777 (1954).

[290] P. J. Vandemark and G. M. Fukui, *J. Bacteriol.* **72,** 610 (1956).

[291] C. H. Werkman and H. G. Wood, *Advances in Enzymol.* **2,** 135 (1942).

[292] H. G. Wood, C. H. Werkman, A. Hemingway, and A. O. Nier, *J. Biol. Chem.* **139,** 377 (1941).

[293] H. G. Wood, C. H. Werkman, A. Hemingway, and A. O. Nier, *J. Biol. Chem.* **139,** 365 (1941).

[294] S. F. Carson and S. Ruben, *Proc. Natl. Acad. Sci. U. S.* **26,** 422 (1940).

[295] S. F. Carson, J. W. Foster, S. Ruben, and H. A. Barker, *Proc. Natl. Acad. Sci. U. S.* **27,** 229 (1941).

[296] H. G. Wood, C. H. Werkman, A. Hemingway, and A. O. Nier, *Proc. Soc. Exptl. Biol. Med.* **46,** 313 (1941).

[297] H. A. Krebs and L. V. Eggleston, *Biochem. J.* **35,** 676 (1941).

[298] E. A. Delwiche, *J. Bacteriol.* **56,** 811 (1948).

[299] A. T. Johns, *Nature* **164,** 620 (1949).

[300] A. T. Johns, *J. Gen. Microbiol.* **5,** 326 (1951).

[301] S. R. Pomerantz, *Federation Proc.* **17,** 290 (1958).

[302] S. Ochoa, J. B. V. Salles, and P. J. Ortiz, *J. Biol. Chem.* **187,** 863 (1950).

[303] S Korkes, A. Del Campillo, and S. Ochoa, *J. Biol. Chem.* **187,** 891 (1950).

[304] C. Erb, Ph.D. Thesis, Iowa State College, Ames, Iowa, 1934.

[305] E. A. Delwiche, E. F. Phares, S. F. Carson, M. V. Long, and S. Berger, *J. Bacteriol.* **71**, 598 (1956).

[306] S. Barban and S. J. Ajl, *J. Biol. Chem.* **192**, 63 (1951).

[307] H. R. Whiteley, *Proc. Natl. Acad. Sci. U. S.* **39**, 772 (1953).

[308] H. G. Wood, R. Stjernholm, and F. W. Leaver, *J. Bacteriol.* **72**, 142 (1956).

[309] E. F. Phares, E. A. Delwiche, S. F. Carson, and M. V. Long, *J. Bacteriol.* **71**, 604 (1956).

[309a] R. W. Swick and H. G. Wood, *Proc. Natl. Acad. Sci. U. S.*, **46**, 28 (1960).

[309b] E. R. Stadtman, P. Overath, H. Eggerer, and F. Lynen, *Biochem. Biophys. Research Communs.* **2**, 1 (1960).

[309c] H. A. Barker, R. D. Smyth, H. Weissbach, J. I. Toohey, J. N. Ladd, and B. E. Volcani, *J. Biol. Chem.* **235**, 480 (1960).

[309d] F. Lynen, J. Knappe, E. Lorch, G. Jutting, and E. Ringelmann, *Angew. Chem.* **71**, 481 (1959).

[310] F. W. Leaver, H. G. Wood, and R. Stjernholm, *J. Bacteriol.* **70**, 521 (1955).

[311] H. G. Wood and C. H. Werkman, *J. Bacteriol.* **30**, 652 (1935).

[312] F. W. Leaver, *J. Am. Chem. Soc.* **72**, 5326 (1950).

[313] S. F. Carson, J. W. Foster, S. Ruben, and M. D. Kamen, *Science* **92**, 433 (1940).

[313a] R. L. Anderson and E. J. Ordal, *J. Bacteriol.* **81**, 139 (1961).

[314] H. A. Barker and F. Lipmann, *Arch. Biochem.* **4**, 361 (1944).

[315] B. P. Cardon and H. A. Barker, *J. Bacteriol.* **52**, 629 (1946).

[316] B. P. Cardon and H. A. Barker, *J. Biol. Chem.* **173**, 803 (1948).

[317] E. R. Stadtman, *Federation Proc.* **15**, 360 (1956).

[318] A. T. Johns, *J. Gen. Microbiol.* **6**, 123 (1952).

[319] J. F. T. Spencer and H. R. Sallans, *Can. J. Microbiol.* **2**, 72 (1956).

[320] F. F. T. Spencer, J. M. Roxburgh, and H. R. Sallans, *J. Agr. Food Chem.* **5**, 64 (1957).

[321] J. F. T. Spencer and P. Shu, *Can. J. Microbiol.* **3**, 559 (1957).

[322] J. F. T. Spencer, A. C. Neish, A. C. Blackwood, and H. R. Sallans, *Can. J. Biochem. Physiol.* **34**, 495 (1956).

[323] H. A. Altermatt, A. C. Blackwood, and A. C. Neish, *Can. J. Biochem. Physiol.* **33**, 622 (1955).

[324] S. A. Koser and E. F. Vaughn, *J. Bacteriol.* **33**, 587 (1937).

[325] E. B. Fred, W. H. Peterson, and A. Davenport, *J. Biol. Chem.* **42**, 175 (1920).

[326] W. H. Peterson and E. B. Fred, *J. Biol. Chem.* **41**, 181 (1920).

[327] E. B. Fred, W. H. Peterson, and J. A. Anderson, *J. Biol. Chem.* **48**, 385 (1921).

[328] M. Gibbs, V. W. Cochrane, L. M. Paege, and H. Wolin, *Arch. Biochem. Biophys.* **50**, 237 (1954).

[329] H. Karström, *Ergeb. Enzymforsch.* **7**, 350 (1938).

[330] J. O. Lampen and H. R. Peterjohn, *J. Bacteriol.* **62**, 281 (1951).

[331] S. S. Cohen and R. Raff, *J. Biol. Chem.* **188**, 501 (1951).

[332] J. O. Lampen, H. Gest, and J. C. Sowden, *J. Bacteriol.* **61**, 97 (1951).

[333] H. Gest and J. O. Lampen, *J. Biol. Chem.* **194**, 555 (1952).

[334] H. A. Barker, D. A. Rappoport, and W. Z. Hassid, *Arch. Biochem. Biophys.* **31**, 326 (1951).

[335] I. A. Bernstein and F. Tiberio, *J. Biol. Chem.* **205**, 309 (1953).

[336] D. P. Burma and B. L. Horecker, *J. Biol. Chem.* **231**, 1039 (1958).

[337] D. P. Burma and B. L. Horecker, *J. Biol. Chem.* **231**, 1053 (1958).

[338] M. Foote, E. B. Fred, and W. H. Peterson, *Centr. Bakteriol. Parasitenk.* **82**, 379 (1930).

[339] M. J. Johnson, W. H. Peterson, and E. B. Fred, *J. Biol. Chem.* **91**, 569 (1931).
[340] L. A. Nutting and S. F. Carson, *J. Bacteriol.* **63**, 575 (1952).
[341] L. A. Nutting and S. F. Carson, *J. Bacteriol.* **63**, 581 (1952).
[342] B. L. Horecker, M. Gibbs, H. Klenow, and P. T. Smyrniotis, *J. Biol. Chem.* **207**, 393 (1954).
[343] A. C. Neish and F. J. Simpson, *Can. J. Biochem. Physiol.* **32**, 147 (1954).
[344] H. A. Altermatt, F. J. Simpson, and A. C. Neish, *Can. J. Biochem. Physiol.* **33**, 615 (1955).
[345] M. Gibbs, L. M. Paege, and J. M. Earl, *Bacteriol. Proc. (Soc. Am. Bacteriologists)* p. 111 (1954).
[346] M. Gibbs, J. M. Earl, and J. L. Ritchie, *J. Biol. Chem.* **217**, 161 (1955).
[347] C. H. Werkman, R. M. Hixon, E. I. Fulmer, and C. H. Rayburn, *Proc. Iowa Acad. Sci.* **36**, 111 (1929).
[348] D. A. Rappoport and H. A. Barker, *Arch. Biochem. Biophys.* **49**, 249 (1954).
[349] F. J. Simpson, M. J. Wolin, and W. A. Wood, *J. Biol. Chem.* **230**, 457 (1958).
[350] P. J. Vandemark and W. A. Wood, *J. Bacteriol.* **71**, 385 (1956).
[351] M. J. Wolin, F. J. Simpson, and W. A. Wood, *J. Biol. Chem.* **232**, 559 (1948).
[352] C. E. Hoffman and J. O. Lampen, *J. Biol. Chem.* **198**, 885 (1952).
[353] E. Racker, *J. Biol. Chem.* **196**, 347 (1952).
[354] G. F. Domagk and B. L. Horecker, *J. Biol. Chem.* **233**, 283 (1958).
[355] A. C. Neish and A. C. Blackwood, *Can. J. Biochem. Physiol.* **33**, 323 (1955).
[356] N. H. Tattrie and A. C. Blackwood, *Can. J. Microbiol.* **3**, 945 (1957).
[357] B. L. Horecker, P. Z. Smyrniotis, H. Hiatt, and P. Marks, *J. Biol. Chem.* **212**, 827 (1955).
[358] G. Bertrand, *Compt. rend.* **130**, 1330 (1900).
[359] H. H. Hiatt and B. L. Horecker, *J. Bacteriol.* **71**, 649 (1956).
[360] B. R. Ford and C. H. Werkman, *J. Bacteriol.* **35**, 206 (1938).
[360a] H. R. Braak, Ph.D. Thesis, Technische Hoogeschool, Delft, Holland, 1928.
[361] M. N. Mickelson and C. H. Werkman, *J. Bacteriol.* **39**, 709 (1940).
[362] A. C. Blackwood and E. R. Blakley, *Can. J. Microbiol.* **2**, 741 (1956).
[363] J. T. Sokatch and I. C. Gunsalus, *J. Bacteriol.* **73**, 452 (1957).
[364] M. N. Mickelson and C. H. Werkman, *Enzymologia* **8**, 252 (1940).
[364a] D. E. Mills, W. D. Baugh, and H. A. Conner, *Appl. Microbiol.* **2**, 9 (1954).
[364b] W. C. Serjak, W. H. Day, J. M. Vanlanen, and C. S. Boruff, *Appl. Microbiol.* **2**, 14 (1954).
[364c] C. E. Voisenet, *Ann. inst. Pasteur* **32**, 476 (1918).
[365] K. L. Smiley and M. Sobolov, *J. Bacteriol.* **79**, 261 (1960).
[366] I. C. Gunsalus and J. M. Sherman, *J. Bacteriol.* **45**, 155 (1943).
[367] I. C. Gunsalus and W. W. Umbreit, *J. Bacteriol.* **49**, 347 (1945).
[368] N. J. Jacobs and P. J. Vandemark, *Bacteriol. Proc. (Soc. Am. Bacteriologists)* p. 104 (1958).
[369] A. G. Ogston, *Nature* **162**, 963 (1948).
[370] R. W. Swick and A. Nakao, *J. Biol. Chem.* **206**, 883 (1954).
[371] P. Schambye, H. G. Wood, and G. Popjak, *J. Biol. Chem.* **206**, 875 (1954).
[372] M. L. Karnovsky, G. Hauser, and D. Elwyn, *J. Biol. Chem.* **226**, 881 (1957).
[373] D. Rush, D. Karibian, M. L. Karnovsky, and B. Magasanik, *J. Biol. Chem.* **226**, 891 (1957).
[374] J. DeLey, *Enzymologia* **16**, 99 (1953).
[375] J. DeLey, *Biochim. et Biophys. Acta* **13**, 302 (1954).
[376] J. DeLey and S. Verhofstede, *Naturwissenschaften* **21**, 584 (1955).
[377] S. A. Narrod and W. A. Wood, *J. Biol. Chem.* **220**, 45 (1956).

[378] E. W. Frampton and W. A. Wood, *Bacteriol. Proc. (Soc. Am. Bacteriologists)* p. 122 (1957).

[379] B. W. Hammer, *Iowa State Coll. Agr. Exptl. Sta. Bull.* **63,** (1920).

[380] G. J. Hucker and C. S. Pederson, *N. Y. State Agr. Expt. Sta. Tech. Bull.* **167,** (1930).

[381] J. Van Beynum and J. W. Pette, *J. Dairy Research* **10,** 250 (1939).

[382] C. R. Brewer and C. H. Werkman, *J. Bacteriol.* **36,** 261 (1938).

[383] H. D. Slade and C. H. Werkman, *J. Bacteriol.* **41,** 675 (1941).

[384] M. Deffner, *Ann.* **536,** 44 (1938).

[385] M. Deffner and W. Franke, *Ann.* **541,** 85 (1939).

[386] C. R. Brewer and C. H. Werkman, *Enzymologia* **6,** 273 (1939).

[387] C. R. Brewer and C. H. Werkman, *Antonie van Leeuwenhoek, J. Microbiol. Serol.* **6,** 110 (1940).

[388] C. R. Brewer and C. H. Werkman, *Enzymologia* **8,** 318 (1940).

[389] J. J. R. Campbell and I. C. Gunsalus, *J. Bacteriol.* **48,** 71 (1944).

[390] I. C. Gunsalus and J. J. R. Campbell, *J. Bacteriol.* **48,** 455 (1944).

[391] J. J. R. Campbell, W. D. Bellamy, and I. C. Gunsalus, *J. Bacteriol.* **46,** 573 (1943).

[392] D. C. Gillespie and I. C. Gunsalus, *Bacteriol. Proc. (Soc. Am. Bacteriologists)* p. 80 (1953).

[393] S. Dagley and E. A. Dawes, *Nature* **172,** 345 (1953).

[394] S. Dagley and E. A. Dawes, *J. Bacteriol.* **66,** 259 (1953).

[395] M. Grunberg-Monago and I. C. Gunsalus, *Bacteriol. Proc. (Soc. Am. Bacteriologists)* p. 73 (1953).

[396] R. W. Wheat, D. T. O. Wong, and S. J. Ajl, *J. Bacteriol.* **68,** 19 (1954).

[397] R. W. Wheat and S. J. Ajl, *Arch. Biochem. Biophys.* **49,** 7 (1954).

[398] R. W. Wheat and S. J. Ajl, *J. Biol. Chem.* **217,** 897 (1955).

[399] R. W. Wheat and S. J. Ajl, *J. Biol. Chem.* **217,** 909 (1955).

[400] R. A. Smith, J. Stamer, and I. C. Gunsalus, *Biochim. et Biophys. Acta* **19,** 567 (1956).

[401] H. A. Barker and S. M. Taha, *J. Bacteriol.* **43,** 347 (1942).

[402] H. A. Barker, *Arch. Mikrobiol.* **8,** 415 (1937).

[403] B. T. Bornstein and H. A. Barker, *J. Bacteriol.* **55,** 223 (1948).

[404] B. T. Bornstein and H. A. Barker, *J. Biol. Chem.* **172,** 659 (1948).

[405] E. R. Stadtman and H. A. Barker, *J. Biol. Chem.* **180,** 1085 (1949).

[406] H. A. Barker, "Bacterial Fermentations," p. 28. Wiley, New York, 1956.

[407] E. R. Stadtman, T. C. Stadtman, and H. A. Barker, *J. Biol. Chem.* **178,** 677 (1949).

[408] E. R. Stadtman and H. A. Barker, *J. Biol. Chem.* **180,** 1095 (1949).

[409] E. R. Stadtman and H. A. Barker, *J. Biol. Chem.* **180,** 1117 (1949).

[410] R. M. Burton and E. R. Stadtman, *J. Biol. Chem.* **202,** 873 (1953).

[411] E. R. Stadtman, *Federation Proc.* **12,** 692 (1953).

[412] E. R. Stadtman, M. Doudoroff, and F. Lipmann, *J. Biol. Chem.* **191,** 377 (1951).

[413] F. Lynen, *Harvey Lectures, Ser.* **48,** 210 (1952).

[414] E. R. Stadtman, G. D. Novelli, and F. Lipmann, *J. Biol. Chem.* **191,** 365 (1951).

[415] E. R. Stadtman, *J. Biol. Chem.* **196,** 527 (1952).

[416] E. R. Stadtman, *J. Biol. Chem.* **196,** 535 (1952).

[417] E. R. Stadtman and H. A. Barker, *J. Biol. Chem.* **180,** 1169 (1949).

[418] E. P. Kennedy and H. A. Barker, *J. Biol. Chem.* **191,** 419 (1951).

[419] E. R. Stadtman and H. A. Barker, *J. Biol. Chem.* **181,** 221 (1949).

[420] E. R. Stadtman, *J. Biol. Chem.* **203,** 501 (1953).

[421] E. R. Stadtman and H. A. Barker, *J. Biol. Chem.* **184,** 769 (1950).

[422] J. R. Peel and H. A. Barker, *Biochem. J.* **62,** 323 (1956).

[423] R. G. Bartsch, Ph.D. Thesis, University of California, Berkeley 1956.

[424] I. Lieberman and H. A. Barker, *J. Bacteriol.* **68,** 329 (1954).

[425] H. A. Barker, *Antonie van Leeuwenhoek, J. Microbiol. Serol.* **6,** 201 (1940).

[426] T. C. Stadtman and H. A. Barker, *J. Bacteriol.* **62,** 269 (1951).

[427] C. G. T. P. Schnellen, Ph.D. Thesis, Technische Hoogeschool, Delft, Holland, 1947.

[428] R. L. Mylroie and R. E. Hungate, *Can. J. Microbiol.* **1,** 55 (1954).

[429] P. H. Smith and R. E. Hungate, *J. Bacteriol.* **75,** 713 (1958).

[430] T. C. Stadtman and H. A. Barker, *J. Bacteriol.* **61,** 67 (1951).

[431] H. A. Barker, *J. Biol. Chem.* **137,** 153 (1941).

[432] H. A. Barker, *Proc. Natl. Acad. Sci. U. S.* **29,** 184 (1943).

[433] T. C. Stadtman and H. A. Barker, *J. Bacteriol.* **62,** 269 (1951).

[434] A. M. Buswell and W. D. Hatfield, *Illinois State Water Survey Bull.* **32,** 1 (1936).

[435] A. M. Buswell and H. F. Mueller, *Ind. Eng. Chem.* **44,** 550 (1952).

[436] H. A. Barker, *Arch. Mikrobiol.* **7,** 420 (1936).

[437] N. L. Söhngen, *Rec. trav. chim.* **29,** 238 (1910).

[438] A. J. Kluyver and C. G. T. P. Schnellen, *Arch. Biochem.* **14,** 57 (1947).

[439] H. A. Barker, *Arch. Mikrobiol.* **7,** 404 (1936).

[439a] A. T. Johns and H. A. Barker, *J. Bacteriol.* **80,** 837 (1960).

[440] T. C. Stadtman and H. A. Barker, *Arch. Biochem.* **21,** 256 (1949).

[441] T. C. Stadtman and H. A. Barker, *J. Bacteriol.* **61,** 81 (1951).

[442] A. M. Buswell and F. W. Sollo, *J. Am. Chem. Soc.* **70,** 1778 (1948).

[443] M. J. Pine and H. A. Barker, *J. Bacteriol.* **71,** 644 (1956).

[444] M. J. Pine and W. Vishniac, *J. Bacteriol.* **73,** 736 (1957).

[445] A. M. Buswell, L. Fina, H. F. Mueller, and A. Yarhiro, *J. Am. Chem. Soc.* **73,** 1809 (1951).

CHAPTER 3

Fermentations of Nitrogenous Organic Compounds

H. A. BARKER

I. Introduction

Living organisms commonly contain from 1 to 10% nitrogen on a dry weight basis. Most of this nitrogen is present in proteins and other polymeric compounds, although many monomeric compounds, such as urea, uric acid, creatine, glutamine, and asparagine, also occur in many organisms in lesser amounts. The majority of these organic nitrogenous compounds are at an oxidation level between carbohydrates and fats and are potentially useful as sources of carbon, nitrogen, and energy for both aerobic and anaerobic microorganisms.

Many monomeric compounds can be used directly as fermentation substrates by anaerobic microorganisms. The more abundant polymeric compounds, on the contrary, must be hydrolyzed or otherwise degraded into their component monomers before they can be fermented. This depolymerization is catalyzed by a variety of mostly hydrolytic enzymes that attack more or less specific linkages in proteins, polypeptides, nucleic acids, nucleotides, and related compounds. Such enzymes, commonly present in microorganisms, will not be discussed in this chapter. Nevertheless the depolymerizing enzymes are of major importance in the microbial decomposition of organic materials in nature because they usually catalyze the rate-limiting step in the over-all process. Once the component amino acids, purines, pyrimidines, and related compounds are liberated, they are frequently decomposed rapidly by mixed microbial populations.

This chapter is devoted to a systematic consideration of the decomposition of amino acids, purines, pyrimidines, and a few other nitrogenous compounds by bacteria under anaerobic conditions without the intervention of inorganic oxidizing agents such as sulfate, nitrate, or carbonate. This excludes such processes as sulfate reduction, denitrification, and the methane fermentation. The processes discussed are mostly fermentations in which either a single organic nitrogenous compound, or a pair of such compounds, or products of the decomposition of one or more such compounds undergo coupled oxidation-reduction reactions. Generally such fermentations, like fermentations of carbohydrates, provide the energy and metabolic intermediates required for growth of the organism in an appropriate medium. However, some anaerobic processes that will be discussed have been studied only with cell suspensions and are not yet known to be capable of supporting growth. A few reactions are mentioned which are known not to support growth but deserve attention for some other reason. Emphasis is placed upon the over-all chemical transformations of bacterial fermentations and on the metabolic pathways by which these transformations occur.

A. EARLY STUDIES

Much of the early chemical work on the anaerobic decomposition of nitrogenous compounds by "putrefactive" bacteria was confused by the use of either mixed cultures or very complex substrates like meat extract, or both. Observations made on such cultures demonstrated that bacteria can live by the anaerobic decomposition of amino acids with the production of ammonia, carbon dioxide, hydrogen sulfide, fatty acids, and a variety of other more or less volatile substances, often having unpleasant odors. However, these studies did little to establish the specific substrates decomposed or the chemical reactions catalyzed by individual species. Information of this type was probably first obtained by Naviasky,[1] who inoculated a medium containing asparagine as the main energy source with a pure culture of *Bacillus proteus vulgaris* and demonstrated the formation of carbon dioxide, ammonia, acetate, and succinate. Shortly thereafter, similar observations were made by Brasch[2] on the fermentation of glutamate by *Bacillus* (*Clostridium*) *putrificus* and by Liebert[3] on the fermentation of uric acid by *Bacillus* (*Clostridium*) *acidiurici*. These and other observations demonstrated that the fermentation of single nitrogenous compounds, like the fermentation of sugars, can support the growth of anaerobic bacteria. A quarter of a century later Stickland[4] used suspensions of washed cells of *Clostridium sporogenes* grown on a complex medium, to demonstrate that this species normally obtains energy by oxidation-reduction reactions between pairs of different amino acids. Subsequently it was shown that each of these types of amino acid fermentation is used by many species of anaerobic bacteria.[5]

II. Fermentations of Single Nitrogenous Compounds

A. AMINO ACIDS

About twenty species of anaerobic or facultatively anaerobic bacteria are known to ferment single amino acids. Table I lists these bacteria and indi-

TABLE I
Amino Acids Fermented by Anaerobic Bacteria

Species	Alanine	Arginine	Aspartate	Cysteine	Δ-Aminovalerate	Glutamate	Glycine	Histidine	Hydroxyproline	Isoleucine	Leucine	Lysine	Methionine	Phenylalanine	Proline	Serine	Tryptophan	Threonine	Tyrosine	Valine	Stickland reaction
Clostridium botulinum[6,7]											±				+						+
Clostridium cochlearium[8]						+															−
Clostridium perfringens[9,10]			+	+		+									+			+			
Clostridium propionicum[11]	+	−	±	+		−	−	−	−		−		±		+	−	+	−	±		−
Clostridium saccharobutyricum[12]		+				+		+							+			+			
Clostridium sporogenes[13,14]	−	+	−	+		−	−	−	−	−	+	−	+	+	+	+	+	+		−	+
Clostridium sticklandii[15]		+				−							+		+		+				+
Clostridium tetani[16,17]	−	+				+	−	+						−	+						−
Clostridium tetanomorphum[18]	−	−	+	+		+	−	+	−				±		+				+		−
Clostridium species[19]					+																
Fusobacterium nucleatum[20]	−	±	±	+		+	−	+	−		+				+		+		+		
Diplococcus glycinophilus[21]	−	−	−	−		−	+	−	−	−	−	−	−		±						
Micrococcus aerogenes[22]	−	−	−	−		+	−	+	−	−	−	−	−	−	+	−	+	−	−	−	−
Micrococcus anaerobius[23]	−	−	−	−		−	+	−													
Micrococcus variabilis[23]	−	−	−	−		−	+	−													
Micrococcus prevotii[22]	−	−	−	−		+	−	+	−	−	−	−	−	−	+	−	+	−	−	−	−
Micrococcus activus[22]	−	−	−	−		+	−	+	−	−	−	−	−	−	+	−	+	−	−	−	−
Micrococcus asaccharolyticus[22]	−	−	−	−		+	−	+	−	−	−	−	−	−	+	−	+	−	−	−	−
Coccus LC[24]				+											+		+				
Escherichia coli[25]															+		+				

Key: +, fermented rapidly; ±, fermented slowly; −, not, fermented.

cates the amino acids that are attacked. The ability to catalyze an oxidation-reduction reaction between pairs of different amino acids (Stickland reaction) is also indicated.

The bacteria presently known to ferment amino acids fall mainly into two groups, the anaerobic spore-formers (*Clostridium* species) and the anaerobic cocci (*Micrococcus* and *Diplococcus* species). Only one nonsporulating, obligately anaerobic, rod-shaped bacterium is listed, namely, *Fusobacterium nucleatum*. Probably other species of this general morphological and physiological group (family Bacteriodaceae) also will be found to ferment amino acids. Although most of the bacteria that ferment nitrogenous compounds are obligately anaerobic, one facultative species, *Escherichia coli*, is probably able to ferment certain amino acids.

All of the amino acids listed in Table I, with the exception of proline, hydroxyproline, and isoleucine, are known to be fermented by at least one bacterial species. The three exceptional amino acids are readily decomposed by clostridia that catalyze the Stickland reaction (see Table I). Undoubtedly in time bacteria will be found that ferment these amino acids.

1. ALANINE

A fermentation of alanine has so far been observed only with *Clostridium propionicum*,[11] which also ferments β-alanine,[26] serine, threonine, lactate, pyruvate, and acrylate. With all these substrates, except threonine, the products are acetate, propionate, and carbon dioxide; ammonia is also formed from the amino acids. The fermentation of alanine is represented by equation (1).

$$3CH_3CHNH_2COOH + 2H_2O \rightarrow 3NH_3 + 2CH_3CH_2COOH + CH_3COOH + CO_2 \quad (1)$$

The non-nitrogenous products of the alanine fermentation are the same as those formed by the propionic acid bacteria[27] (genus *Propionibacterium*) or *Micrococcus lactilyticus*[28] from lactate, except that *C. propionicum* does not produce succinate. Despite the similarity in products, there is substantial evidence that the chemistry of the two processes differs significantly. With both propionic acid bacteria[29] and *M. lactilyticus*,[30] succinate has been shown to be a precursor of propionate. In extracts of *M. lactilyticus*, succinate is first converted to succinyl-CoA and then decarboxylated to pro-

$$HOOCCH_2CH_2COSCoA \rightarrow CO_2 + CH_3CH_2COSCoA \quad (2)$$

pionyl-CoA, the immediate precursor of propionate. *C. propionicum*, on the contrary, neither forms nor decarboxylates succinate[31] or succinyl-CoA. Additional evidence against the participation of a symmetrical compound like succinate is the absence of randomization of the α- and β-carbon atoms of lactate during its conversion to propionate.[32] Also, *C. propionicum*, unlike the propionic acid bacteria, is unable to incorporate carbon dioxide carbon into propionate.[31] The formation of succinate from a C_3 substrate is known to involve carbon dioxide.

An indication of the path of propionate formation in *C. propionicum* was provided by the observation that acrylate is fermented by cell suspensions as rapidly as alanine or lactate.[11] This suggested the possibility that the latter substrates are converted to acrylate which is then reduced to propionate according to the scheme shown on page 155.

This reaction sequence is similar to that involved in the synthesis and oxidation of butyric acid by *Clostridium kluyveri*,[33] except that in the latter organism the coenzyme A derivatives of the acids are the actual reactants. The occurrence of such reactions in the reverse direction was investigated by Stadtman[34] by studying the oxidation of propionate with extracts and dried cell preparations of *C. propionicum*. Dried cells catalyzed the oxida-

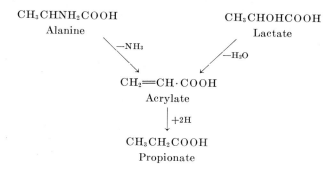

CH_3CHNH_2COOH
Alanine

$CH_3CHOHCOOH$
Lactate

$-NH_3$

$-H_2O$

$CH_2{=}CH{\cdot}COOH$
Acrylate

$+2H$

CH_3CH_2COOH
Propionate

tion of propionate, lactate, pyruvate, or alanine to acetate and carbon dioxide using oxygen as an electron acceptor. The oxidation of propionate was found to be absolutely dependent upon the addition of catalytic amounts of acetyl phosphate. Since enzymic reactions are known by which propionyl-CoA can be synthesized from propionate, acetyl phosphate, and coenzyme A, it seemed probable that acetyl phosphate was required for the synthesis of propionyl-CoA. This conclusion was supported by the observation that cell-free extracts, unlike dried cell preparations, were unable to oxidize propionate even in the presence of acetyl phosphate; however, propionyl-CoA was oxidized readily. Apparently the enzymic system responsible for the synthesis of propionyl-CoA was inactive in extracts.

The immediate oxidation product of propionyl-CoA has not been directly identified because of its instability in the enzymic system. However, indirect evidence for the formation of acrylyl-CoA was obtained. Synthetic acrylyl-CoA was shown to react rapidly with ammonium ion to form β-alanyl-CoA [equation (3)] in the presence of an extract of cells of *C. propionicum* grown on alanine.[26, 35] This reaction is reversible, but the equilibrium strongly

$$CH_2{:}CHCO{\cdot}SCoA + NH_3 \rightleftharpoons CH_2NH_2CH_2CO{\cdot}SCoA \qquad (3)$$

favors the formation of β-alanyl-CoA. When C^{14}-labeled propionate was oxidized in the presence of ammonium ion and catalytic amounts of acetyl phosphate and coenzyme A, C^{14}-labeled β-alanine was formed. Since the enzyme preparation catalyzed reaction (3), the accumulation of β-alanine provided presumptive evidence for the intermediate formation of acrylyl-CoA and β-alanyl-CoA. The latter compound could lose the CoA moiety by hydrolysis or a transfer reaction. The role of β-alanyl-CoA in the metabolism of alanine by *C. propionicum* is still completely obscure.

The reduction of acrylyl thioester to the propionyl derivative is also catalyzed by extracts of *C. propionicum* under certain circumstances. This type of reaction has been observed with acrylyl pantetheine, using a dye, reduced safranine, as reducing agent.[26] All the available evidence indicates that acrylyl-CoA is probably an intermediate in propionate formation by *C. propionicum.*

All attempts to demonstrate an enzymic conversion of alanine to acrylyl-CoA have been unsuccessful. There is no evidence for the formation of alanyl-CoA from alanine or for an interconversion of alanyl-CoA and acrylyl-CoA.

The reversible amination of acrylyl-CoA to β-alanyl-CoA under the influence of the enzyme acrylyl coenzyme A aminase suggests that β-alanyl-CoA may be an intermediate in the fermentation of β-alanine in accordance with the following sequence:

$$\beta\text{-alanine} \xrightarrow{\text{CoA}} \beta\text{-alanyl-CoA} \underset{}{\overset{\mp NH_3}{\rightleftharpoons}} \text{acrylyl-CoA} \underset{}{\overset{\pm 2H}{\rightleftharpoons}} \text{propionyl-CoA}$$

This suggestion is strengthened by the observation that the aminase is about 100 times more active in cells grown on β-alanine than in cells grown on α-alanine.[26] However, the initial reaction in this sequence, the conversion of β-alanine to β-alanyl-CoA, has not been demonstrated.

A reversible hydration of an acrylyl thioester to a lactoyl thioester [re-

$$CH_2{=}CHCO{-}CoA + H_2O \rightleftharpoons CH_3CHOHCOCoA \qquad (4)$$

action (4)] could not be detected in extracts of *C. propionicum.* This reaction in the forward direction has so far been observed only with extracts of a *Pseudomonas* species which was grown aerobically on propionate.[26]

2. δ-AMINOVALERATE

An unnamed clostridium, isolated from sewage sludge after a preliminary anaerobic enrichment in a medium containing δ-aminovalerate as the main energy source has been shown[19] to convert this substrate to ammonia, valerate, propionate, and acetate according to the following equation:

$$2H_2NCH_2CH_2CH_2{*}CH_2COOH + 2H_2O \rightarrow$$
$$2NH_3 + CH_3CH_2CH_2{*}CH_2COOH + CH_3CH_2COOH + {*}CH_3COOH \qquad (5)$$

In a fermentation of 2-C^{14}-δ-aminovalerate, the C^{14} was found only in the α-carbon of valerate and in the methyl carbon of acetate. These results suggest that the fermentation involves a reductive deamination and a β-oxidation of valerate or some intermediate C_5 compound to propionate and acetate. No enzymic studies have been reported. The substrate specificity of the organism is rather high since several compounds related to δ-aminovalerate, including β-alanine, γ-aminobutyrate, norvaline, ornithine, and ε-aminocaproic acid, cannot support its growth.

3. ARGININE, CITRULLINE, AND ORNITHINE

No fermentations of these compounds have been reported. Arginine can serve as a hydrogen acceptor in the Stickland reaction for *Clostridium sporo-*

genes, probably after an initial conversion to ornithine, since three moles of ammonia are formed per mole of arginine and ornithine serves as a hydrogen acceptor.[36] *Clostridium sticklandii* is able to use arginine, citrulline, or ornithine as an oxidant.[15]

The conversion of arginine to ornithine has been demonstrated with *C. perfringens*,[37] *Streptococcus faecalis*,[38] *S. lactis*,[39] and *S. haemolyticus*.[40] At least two enzymic steps are involved. Cell-free extracts of these organisms convert arginine to citrulline under appropriate conditions according to the equation:

$$
\begin{array}{ccc}
\text{NH} & & \text{NH} \\
| & & | \\
\text{C}=\text{NH} & & \text{C}=\text{O} \\
| & & | \\
\text{NH} & & \text{NH} \\
| & +\ \text{H}_2\text{O} \rightarrow & | \qquad +\ \text{NH}_3 \qquad\qquad (6)\\
(\text{CH}_2)_3 & & (\text{CH}_2)_3 \\
| & & | \\
\text{CHNH}_2 & & \text{CHNH}_2 \\
| & & | \\
\text{COOH} & & \text{COOH} \\
\text{Arginine} & & \text{Citrulline}
\end{array}
$$

With extracts of *S. faecalis* or *S. lactis* a large accumulation of citrulline requires the absence of orthophosphate. The enzyme responsible for the deamination is called arginine desiminase.[41] The cleavage of the ureido group of citrulline has been demonstrated with extracts of *S. faecalis*[38, 42] and *S. lactis*[39] and with cell suspensions of *C. perfringens*.[37] With the former organisms, the reaction requires the presence of orthophosphate and a phosphate acceptor such as adenosine-5'-phosphate or adenosine diphosphate. The reaction probably proceeds according to equation (7), although a stoichio-

$$\text{citrulline} + \text{Pi} + \text{ADP} \rightarrow \text{ornithine} + \text{CO}_2 + \text{NH}_3 + \text{ATP} \qquad (7)$$

metric yield of adenosine triphosphate (ATP) has not been observed because of the presence of ATPase in the enzyme preparations.[43] The enzyme system catalyzing reaction (7) has been called "citrullinase" or "citrulline ureidase." However, it is now known that two enzymic steps are involved in the reaction,[39] one being a phosphorolysis of citrulline [reaction (8)] to ornithine and carbamylphosphate, the other being the transfer of the phosphoryl group from carbamylphosphate to adenosine diphosphate (ADP) to form ATP [reaction (9)]. Carbamylphosphate has been shown to serve

$$\text{L-citrulline} + \text{HPO}_4^= \rightleftharpoons \text{L-ornithine} + \text{NH}_2\text{COOPO}_3^= \qquad (8)$$

$$\text{NH}_2\text{COOPO}_3^= + \text{ADP} \rightleftharpoons \text{NH}_3 + \text{CO}_2 + \text{ATP} \qquad (9)$$

both as a carbamyl donor in citrulline synthesis [the reverse of reaction (8)] and as a phosphate donor to ADP [reaction (9)] in the presence of extracts of *S. faecalis*.[44] The enzymes catalyzing the reactions have been separated and partially purified.[45] The equilibrium in reaction (8) is far to the left. Therefore the decomposition of citrulline is dependent upon the removal of carbamylphosphate by reaction (9). The equilibrium in the latter reaction is far in the direction of ATP formation.

The multienzyme system responsible for the conversion of arginine to ornithine, carbon dioxide, and ammonia was formerly called "arginine dihydrolase" in the mistaken belief that the reaction was caused by a single enzyme.

Although a fermentation of ornithine has not been described, reactions are known by which an extensive decomposition of ornithine can occur in a system containing a suitable reducing agent and a mixture of two clostridia. An organism catalyzing the Stickland reaction can reduce ornithine to δ-aminovalerate which can be fermented by an unnamed clostridium[19] (see Section II, A, 2 on δ-aminovalerate).

4. Aspartate and Asparagine

Asparagine was probably the first amino acid shown to be decomposed anaerobically by a pure bacterial culture. In 1908 Naviasky[1] found that *Bacillus proteus vulgaris* can ferment asparagine with the formation of several products among which succinate, acetate, carbon dioxide, and ammonia were positively identified. Since this early work, relatively few studies on the fermentation of asparagine or aspartate have been carried out.

The products of aspartate fermentation by *Clostridium tetani* (Table II) are ammonia, carbon dioxide, volatile acids (acetate and butyrate), hydroxy acids (lactate and malate), and alcohol (ethanol and possibly butanol). Although succinate was not mentioned as a product of aspartate fermentation, it is probably formed because succinate is a major product (yield about 50%) of the fermentation of malate by *C. tetani*.[17] *Clostridium*

TABLE II

Products of l-Aspartate Fermentation by *Clostridium tetani*[16]

Product	Yield[a]
Ammonia	(100)
Carbon dioxide	105
Acetate	18[b]
Lactate	55[c]
Ethanol	30

[a] The yield of product is expressed in moles per 100 moles of substrate decomposed. Cell suspension experiment.

[b] Probably includes some butyrate.

[c] Probably includes some malate.

saccharobutyricum was reported[46] to form acetic and butyric acids from aspartate in a molar ratio of 2 to 1.

The available data are insufficient to permit firm conclusions concerning the path of aspartate decomposition. Many facultative bacteria form the enzyme aspartase,[47] which deaminates aspartate according to equation (10).

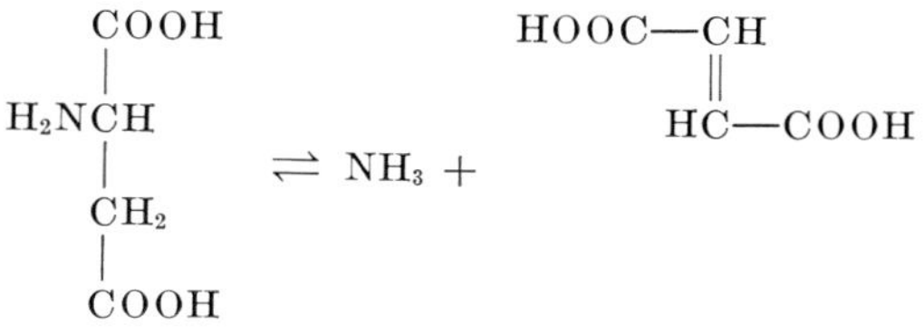

$$
\begin{array}{ccc}
\text{COOH} & & \text{HOOC—CH} \\
| & & \| \\
\text{H}_2\text{NCH} & & \text{HC—COOH} \\
| & \rightleftharpoons \text{NH}_3 + & \\
\text{CH}_2 & & \\
| & & \\
\text{COOH} & &
\end{array}
\qquad (10)
$$

L-Aspartate   Fumarate

However, the presence of this enzyme has not been demonstrated in any obligately anaerobic bacterium.

Clostridium welchii has been shown[48, 49] to catalyze a decarboxylation of

$$\text{COOH·CH}_2\text{CHNH}_2\text{COOH} \rightarrow \text{CO}_2 + \text{CH}_3\text{CHNH}_2\text{COOH} \qquad (11)$$

L-aspartate to L-alanine [reaction (11)]. This decarboxylation is greatly accelerated by pyruvate and a variety of other α-keto acids and is inhibited by carbonyl reagents. The stimulation by pyruvate has been interpreted to mean that the reaction involves a transamination between aspartate and pyruvate to give alanine and oxalacetate [equation (12)] followed by decarboxylation of the latter compound[49] [equation (13)]. This interpretation

$$\text{aspartate} + \text{pyruvate} \rightarrow \text{oxalacetate} + \text{alanine} \qquad (12)$$

$$\text{oxalacetate} \rightarrow \text{pyruvate} + \text{CO}_2 \qquad (13)$$

is incorrect, because Meister *et al.*[48] have shown that C^{14}-labeled pyruvate is not incorporated into alanine as the above reactions predict. The mechanism by which keto acids stimulate aspartate decarboxylation has not been determined.

$$\text{COOH·CH}_2\text{CHNH}_2\text{COOH} \rightarrow \text{COOH·CH}_2\text{CH}_2\text{NH}_2 + \text{CO}_2 \qquad (14)$$

A very slow decarboxylation of L-aspartate to β-alanine [reaction (14)] is also catalyzed by some bacteria[50] but is not known to occur in clostridia.

The reaction sequence involved in the reductive conversion of L-aspartate to threonine[51, 52] should also be considered as a possible path of aspartate fermentation. If this reaction sequence does occur in anaerobic bacteria, the decomposition of aspartate must be coupled with suitable oxidative reactions.

At present there is no evidence that any of the above reactions of L-aspartate is directly involved in its fermentation by anaerobic bacteria.

5. Cysteine, Homocysteine, and Methionine

Some microorganisms and animal tissues have long been known to contain an enzyme, cysteine desulfhydrase, that converts cysteine to pyruvate, ammonia, and hydrogen sulfide according to the following reaction.[53] This

$$HSCH_2CHNH_2COOH + H_2O \rightarrow H_2S + NH_3 + CH_3COCOOH \qquad (15)$$

enzyme has been found in *Proteus vulgaris*,[54] *P. morganii*,[55] *Escherichia coli*,[56] *Propionibacterium pentosaceum*,[57] and *Bacillus subtilis*.[58] The *E. coli* and *B. subtilis* enzymes attack only L-cysteine, whereas extracts of *P. pentosaceum* act on D and L isomers at the same rate. These differences may indicate the existence of two stereospecific desulfhydrases or of a cysteine racemase.

The fermentation of cysteine with formation of ammonia and hydrogen sulfide and other products has been shown with an obligately anaerobic coccus (Table III), but a stoichiometric formation of the products of the cysteine desulfhydrase reaction has not been demonstrated with any anaerobic species. Formation of pyruvate from cysteine by rumen coccus LC[24] is probable because the products of fermentations of pyruvate and cysteine by this organism are very similar except for ammonia and hydrogen sulfide. Quantitative data on the products of cysteine fermentation by other anaerobic bacteria are not available.

On the basis of the above evidence it is probable that fermentations of cysteine generally involve conversion of the substrate to pyruvate by the cysteine sulfhydrase reaction, followed by a fermentation of pyruvate according to the enzymic constitution of the organism.

DL-Homocysteine is decomposed by cell-free extracts of *Proteus morganii* more rapidly than DL-cysteine, DL-serine, or DL-threonine. The products of

TABLE III

PRODUCTS OF L-CYSTEINE FERMENTATION BY COCCUS LC[24]

Product	Yield[a]
Ammonia	100
Hydrogen	8
Hydrogen sulfide	+
Carbon dioxide	103
Formate	14
Acetate	26
Propionate	2
Butyrate	31
Valerate	5

[a] The figures give the yield of product in moles per 100 moles of cysteine decomposed.

homocysteine decomposition are ammonia, hydrogen sulfide, and α-keto-

$$HSCH_2CH_2CHNH_2COOH + H_2O \rightarrow H_2S + NH_3 + CH_2CH_2COCOOH \quad (16)$$

butyrate [reaction (16)]. The enzyme catalyzing this reaction apparently requires pyridoxal phosphate as a cofactor.[59] The enzymes attacking cysteine and homocysteine appear to be different. No information appears to be available concerning the anaerobic decomposition of α-ketobutyrate by *P. morganii.*

Methionine is attacked slowly by several anaerobic bacteria (Table I). Chemical and enzymic studies of methionine decomposition have been carried out only with *Clostridium sporogenes.*[14] Extracts of this organism were found to convert L-methionine to α-ketobutyrate, ammonia, and meth-

$$CH_3S—CH_2CH_2CHNH_2COOH + H_2O \rightarrow CH_3SH + NH_3 + CH_3CH_2COCOOH \quad (17)$$

ylmercaptan [reaction (17)]. The enzyme system responsible for this reaction has been called both methionine demercapto-deaminase[14] and dethiomethylase.[60] In *C. sporogenes*, the enzyme system does not act upon D-methionine, although in some bacteria the dethiomethylase is accompanied by a methionine racemase which permits the utilization of both isomers. The partially purified dethiomethylase has been shown to require pyridoxal phosphate as a coenzyme.

The further transformations of α-ketobutyrate and the final products of methionine fermentation by *C. sporogenes* have not been determined.

6. GLUTAMATE

Glutamate is fermented with great facility by *Clostridium tetanomorphum*[18, 61, 62]; indeed it appears to be the preferred substrate for this species. The rate of glutamate decomposition is similar to that of glucose decomposition by other organisms. For example, when a suitable medium containing 0.1 M glutamate is inoculated with 1 volume per cent of an active culture of *C. tetanomorphum*, the substrate is completely decomposed within 18 to 24 hours at 37°C.

The main products of glutamate fermentation are acetate, butyrate, ammonia, carbon dioxide, and hydrogen (Table IV). The yields of ammonia and carbon dioxide are essentially constant at one mole per mole of glutamate under a variety of conditions. The yields of the other three products are somewhat dependent on the pH of the medium.[61] When the pH is increased from 7 to 8 the yield of hydrogen is about doubled and the molar ratio of acetate to butyrate is increased from 2.9 to 3.8.

The path of glutamate decomposition in *C. tetanomorphum* is of considerable interest because it is completely different from the well-known path of glutamate metabolism via α-ketoglutarate and the tricarboxylic acid cycle.

TABLE IV

PRODUCTS OF GLUTAMATE FERMENTATION[a]

Product	Clostridium tetanomorphum[63] glutamate	Clostridium tetani[17] glutamate	Micrococcus aerogenes[22] glutamate
Ammonia	(100)	(100)	103
Carbon dioxide	91	94	98
Formate	0	—	0
Hydrogen	5	—	5
Acetate	116	90	101
Butyrate	41	45	45
Lactate	0	trace	0

[a] The figures give the yield in moles per 100 moles of substrate decomposed. The data were obtained with cell suspensions.

The first indication of an unusual path of glutamate breakdown was provided by the low yield of carbon dioxide. A conversion of glutamate to acetate and carbon dioxide via the tricarboxylic cycle would produce 3 moles of carbon dioxide per mole of glutamate instead of the observed 1 mole. A significant reutilization of carbon dioxide was excluded by an experiment with C^{14}-labeled carbon dioxide.

Further information concerning the fate of the individual carbon atoms of glutamate was obtained by tracer experiments.[61, 63, 64] Samples of glutamate labeled with C^{14} in positions 1, 2, 4, or 5 were fermented by washed cells, and the products were isolated and degraded to locate the isotope. The results of these experiments are summarized diagrammatically in Fig. 1. Glutamate carbon atoms 1 and 2 are converted largely to acetate, with only a small conversion to butyrate. Carbon atoms 3 and 4 are converted mainly to butyrate in such a way that carbon atom 4 appears in the carboxyl and presumably the β-carbon atoms of butyrate, whereas carbon atom 3 probably occupies the α- and γ-positions of butyrate. Carbon atom 5 is converted exclusively to carbon dioxide. These results indicate the formation of two different C_2 units during glutamate fermentation. One unit, derived from glutamate carbon atoms 1 and 2, is converted to free acetate which is not readily activated by this organism for conversion to butyrate. The sec-

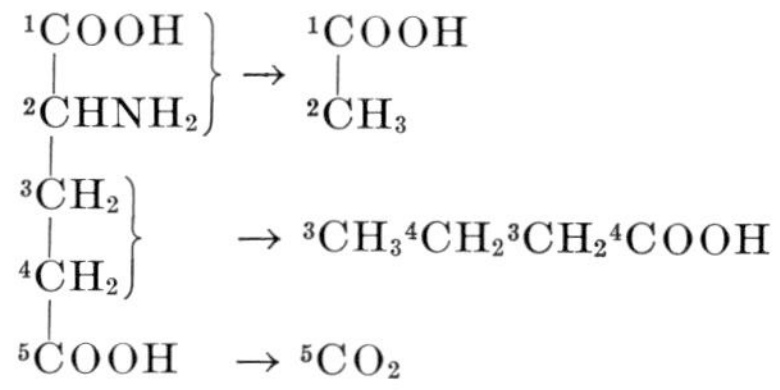

$$
\begin{array}{l}
\left.\begin{array}{l} {}^{1}\text{COOH} \\ {}^{2}\text{CHNH}_2 \end{array}\right\} \rightarrow \begin{array}{l} {}^{1}\text{COOH} \\ {}^{2}\text{CH}_3 \end{array} \\[2ex]
\left.\begin{array}{l} {}^{3}\text{CH}_2 \\ {}^{4}\text{CH}_2 \end{array}\right\} \rightarrow {}^{3}\text{CH}_3{}^{4}\text{CH}_2{}^{3}\text{CH}_2{}^{4}\text{COOH} \\[2ex]
{}^{5}\text{COOH} \rightarrow {}^{5}\text{CO}_2
\end{array}
$$

FIG. 1. Fermentation of C^{14}-glutamate by Clostridium tetanomorphum.

ond C_2 unit, derived from glutamate carbon atoms 3 and 4, must be an activated acetyl group, since it is preferentially converted to butyrate. The results of the tracer experiments are consistent with the idea that pyruvate, derived from glutamate carbon atoms 3, 4, and 5, is an intermediate in the fermentation.

Further analysis of the chemical reactions in the glutamate fermentation was done with enzyme preparations.[65] Crude, particle-free extracts of *C. tetanomorphum* convert glutamate anaerobically to ammonia, acetate, carbon dioxide, hydrogen, and several minor products including pyruvate and mesaconate, but do not form butyrate under the same conditions. The identification of mesaconate (methylfumarate) by Wachsman[65] was a major contribution because it pointed the way to the further elucidation of the role of branched chain dicarboxylic acids in glutamate breakdown. When mesaconate was added as a substrate, it was rapidly decomposed by cell-free extracts to carbon dioxide, hydrogen, pyruvate, and acetate. Both the rate of mesaconate formation from glutamate, and the rate of its decomposition are more than adequate to justify the conclusion that mesaconate is an intermediate in glutamate fermentation.

During the decomposition of mesaconate by crude extracts an additional product sometimes accumulated in appreciable amounts. This compound, which was detectable either by paper chromatography or by partition chromatography on a silica gel column, had the properties of a dicarboxylic acid containing one or more hydroxyl groups. Not enough of the acid was at first available to permit its identification by chemical methods, but a consideration of the structure of mesaconate and the possibility of the enzymatic hydration of its double bond, suggested that the dicarboxylic acid might be either α- or β-methylmalic acid. The former compound, also known as citramalic acid, seemed to be a more likely intermediate because a simple aldol type cleavage would yield pyruvate and acetate, known products of mesaconate decomposition in this system. DL-Citramalic acid was synthesized and found to be decomposed rapidly to pyruvate and acetate by cell-free extracts.

Figure 2 shows the reactions involved in the conversion of mesaconate to pyruvate and acetate by *C. tetanomorphum*. The reversible hydration of the

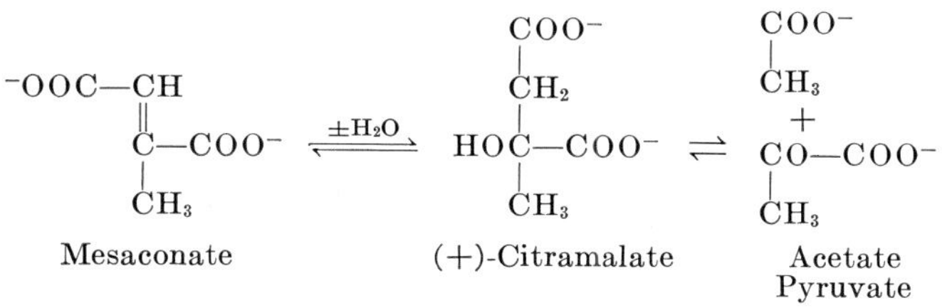

FIG. 2. Conversion of mesaconate to acetate and pyruvate.

double bond of mesaconate to form (+)-citramalate is catalyzed by an enzyme referred to as mesaconase. This enzyme has not been studied in detail, but it appears to be distinct from fumarase and aconitase. The activity of mesaconase is dependent upon the presence of ferrous ion and cysteine. The enzyme is strongly inhibited by chelating agents such as α,α'-dipyridyl or o-phenanthroline, which combine with ferrous ion. This inhibition provides a convenient method for blocking the path of glutamate fermentation at the mesaconate level. The equilibrium of the mesaconase reaction favors the formation of citramalate ($K_{eq.} \approx 8$).

The conversion of (+)-citramalate to pyruvate and acetate is catalyzed by the enzyme citramalase. This enzyme is highly active but very unstable, having a half-life in extracts of only a few hours at 0°C. When extracts are incubated at 37°C. for an hour, they completely lose the ability to decompose citramalate. Since most of the other enzymes involved in glutamate fermentation are more stable, this provides a method for obtaining an accumulation of citramalate during the decomposition of other substrates.

Citramalase shows a high degree of substrate specificity. (+)-Citramalate is the only substrate so far found to be decomposed by the enzyme at an appreciable rate. The equilibrium of the reaction strongly favors the decomposition of citramalate

$$K_{eq.} = \frac{[\text{pyruvate}][\text{acetate}]}{[\text{citramalate}]} \approx 7$$

particularly when the substrate concentration is low. The only cofactor known to be required for the citramalase reaction is magnesium ion.

The conversion of glutamate to mesaconate and ammonia involves at least two reactions, shown in Fig. 3. The first reaction results in a rearrangement of the carbon chain of L-glutamate with formation of L-*threo*-β-methylaspartate, a branched-chain C_5 dicarboxylic amino acid. The second reaction is a deamination of β-methylaspartate to mesaconate.

The formation of β-methylaspartate in the *C. tetanomorphum* system was

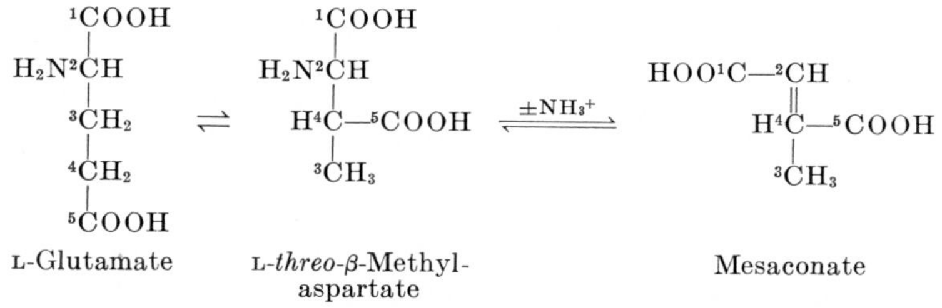

Fig. 3. Conversion of glutamate to mesaconate.

detected while studying the effect of charcoal treatment on the ability of cell-free extracts to interconvert glutamate, mesaconate, and ammonia. Untreated extracts catalyze the reaction in both directions. After charcoal treatment, the decomposition of glutamate was largely suppressed, whereas the formation of amino acid from mesaconate and ammonia proceeded at an undiminished rate. This result indicated that an amino acid other than glutamate had been formed by the charcoal-treated extract. This was confirmed by the observation that the amino acid was not decarboxylated by the specific L-glutamic decarboxylase of *E. coli*. Later, a procedure was developed for isolating several grams of the crystalline product of the enzymic reaction.[66] The compound was shown to be an L-β-methylaspartate, probably the L-*threo* isomer.

Following the isolation of β-methylaspartate, the enzyme β-methylaspartase that catalyzes the reversible conversion of the amino acid to mesaconate and ammonia was purified about 45-fold.[67] The enzyme was found to have a high substrate specificity, L-*threo*-β-methylaspartate being the only amino acid decomposed at a rapid rate.

The equilibrium constant of the β-methylaspartase reaction

$$K_{eq.} = \frac{[\text{mesaconate}][\text{NH}_4^+]}{[\beta\text{-methylaspartate}]}$$

is 0.24 at pH 7.9 and 25°C. The equilibrium strongly favors the formation of mesaconate and ammonia at relatively low substrate concentrations ($< 0.01\ M$). Therefore the enzyme can be used as a convenient reagent for the quantitative estimation of L-*threo*-β-methylaspartate, using a spectrophotometric method based upon the ultraviolet light absorption of mesaconate at 240 mμ. At high substrate concentrations, the equilibrium favors the synthesis of the amino acid. Consequently the enzyme can also be used for the preparation of L-*threo*-β-methylaspartate.

Another property of the enzyme that proved to be useful in studying the role of β-methylaspartate in glutamate fermentation is its sensitivity to inhibition by calcium ion. Relatively low concentrations of calcium ion, of the order of 0.01 M, cause a high degree of inhibition by competing with the essential magnesium ion. Addition of calcium ion to crude extracts can be used to inhibit β-methylaspartase specifically and cause the accumulation of L-*threo*-β-methylaspartate under appropriate conditions.

With the aid of the above information the role of L-*threo*-β-methylaspartate as an intermediate between glutamate and mesaconate has been established. The formation of β-methylaspartate from glutamate was demonstrated by decomposing glutamate with a crude extract in the presence of 0.015 M calcium ion and showing that β-methylaspartate accumulated to a concentration 30 times that permitted by the β-methylaspartase equilibrium. In the absence of calcium ion, the conversion of β-methylaspartate to mesaconate and ammonia is extremely rapid in relation to the rate of glutamate breakdown. Extracts usually contain sufficient β-methylaspartase to decompose 350 μmoles of L-*threo*-β-methylaspartate per minute per milliliter at 37°C. Most extracts decompose glutamate at less than one-tenth of that rate.

The equilibrium constant for the reaction

$$\text{L-glutamate} \rightleftharpoons \text{L-}threo\text{-}\beta\text{-methylaspartate} \tag{18}$$

expressed by the equation

$$K_{eq.} = \frac{[\beta\text{-methylaspartate}]}{[\text{L-glutamate}]}$$

is approximately 0.13 at pH 8. Since the equilibrium constant for the β-methylaspartase reaction is 0.24, the equilibrium constant for the over-all conversion of L-glutamate to mesaconate and ammonium ion [reaction (19)]

$$\text{L-glutamate} \leftrightarrow \text{mesaconate} + NH_4 \tag{19}$$

is 0.032. This corresponds to a standard free energy change (ΔF) at pH 7.9 of 2.0 kilocalories. Despite this somewhat unfavorable standard free energy change, the reaction is pulled in the direction of glutamate decomposition by the formation of two products and by the subsequent conversion of mesaconate to pyruvate and acetate via citramalate.

The rearrangement of the straight C_5 chain of glutamate to the branched chain of β-methylaspartate is a reaction of considerable interest because no similar reaction has been observed in other enzymic systems. The chemical mechanism of this rearrangement is not known, but the origin of the individual carbon atoms of β-methylaspartate has been established by tracer experiments. Reference to Fig. 4 will facilitate interpretation of the results.

The numbering of the carbon atoms in compounds of Fig. 4 is based upon the previously mentioned tracer experiments, in which glutamate variously labeled with C^{14} was fermented by intact cells. The results, considered in relation to the known and relatively simple reactions from β-methylaspartate to the final products, indicate that the methyl group of β-methylaspartate originates from carbon atom 3 of glutamate and is attached to carbon atom 4 of glutamate. This conclusion was confirmed by an experiment in which glutamate-4-C^{14} was converted to mesaconate, which was degraded chemically to establish the position of the isotope.[68] The results proved that the carbon atom adjacent to the methyl group was derived exclusively from glutamate carbon atom 4. Since β-methylaspartate and mesaconate have identical carbon skeletons, the same conclusion applies to β-methylaspartate.

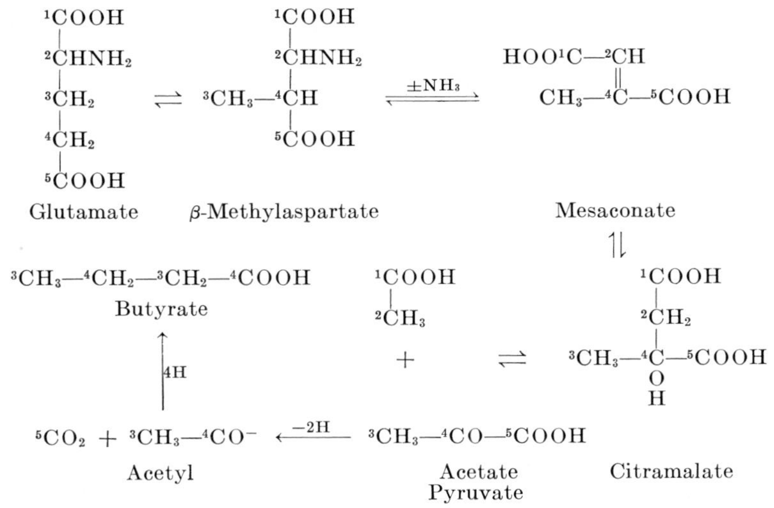

$$
\begin{array}{ccc}
^1COOH & ^1COOH & \\
| & | & \\
^2CHNH_2 & ^2CHNH_2 & HOO^1C-^2CH \\
| & | \xrightarrow{\pm NH_3} & \parallel \\
^3CH_2 \rightleftharpoons ^3CH_3-^4CH & CH_3-^4C-^5COOH \\
| & | & \\
^4CH_2 & ^5COOH & \\
| & & \\
^5COOH & &
\end{array}
$$

Glutamate   β-Methylaspartate   Mesaconate

$$\Updownarrow$$

$$^3CH_3-^4CH_2-^3CH_2-^4COOH \qquad ^1COOH \qquad\qquad ^1COOH$$

Butyrate $^2CH_3$ $^2CH_2$

$$\uparrow 4H \qquad\qquad + \qquad \rightleftharpoons \qquad ^3CH_3-^4\underset{\underset{H}{O}}{C}-^5COOH$$

$$^5CO_2 + {}^3CH_3-^4CO^- \xleftarrow{-2H} {}^3CH_3-^4CO-^5COOH$$

Acetyl   Acetate   Citramalate
                 Pyruvate

Fig. 4. Path of glutamate fermentation.

From a knowledge of the correspondence of carbon atoms in glutamate and β-methylaspartate, the nature of the reaction involved in the interconversion of the straight- and branched-chain carbon structures is apparent. A cleavage must occur between carbon atoms 2 and 3 of glutamate. The C_2 group, consisting of glutamate carbon atoms 1 and 2, is then transferred, directly or indirectly, back to the C_3 moiety so as to form a new bond between carbon atoms 2 and 4. This leaves carbon atom 3 on the side in the methyl group. There is no evidence that the C_3 chain consisting of carbon atoms 3, 4, and 5 is broken during the C_2 transfer reaction.

The effect of charcoal treatment of crude extracts on the decomposition of glutamate has already been mentioned. This effect was shown to be caused by the removal of an essential coenzyme. The coenzyme has recently been isolated from *C. tetanomorphum* and shown to be a yellow-orange compound which is rapidly inactivated by exposure to visible light.[69] It is a derivative of pseudovitamin B_{12} containing an additional molecule of adenine. The precise function of the coenzyme in the interconversion of glutamate and β-methylaspartate has not been determined.

The decomposition of pyruvate and the formation of butyrate have not been studied extensively in the *C. tetanomorphum* system. However, the formation of hydrogen, carbon dioxide, and acetate from pyruvate under certain conditions suggests the functioning of a pyruvate-decomposing system similar to that found in *Clostridium butyricum* [70, 71] shown in reaction

$$CH_3COCOOH + HSCoA \rightarrow CH_3COSCoA + CO_2 + H_2 \qquad (20)$$

(20). The further conversion of the acetyl group derived from pyruvate to butyrate may follow the path used by *Clostridium kluyveri*.[33]

So far the chemical reactions of glutamate fermentation have been intensively studied only in *C. tetanomorphum*. Several other species, including *Micrococcus aerogenes*, *C. saccharobutyricum*, *C. tetani*, *C. botulinum*, and *Fusobacterium nucleatum*, are known to ferment glutamate readily (Table I). Presumptive evidence for the mesaconate path of glutamate decomposition is provided by the observation that these species, like *C. tetanomorphum*, form approximately one mole of carbon dioxide per mole of glutamate fermented. However, cells or cell extracts of *M. aerogenes*, grown on glutamate, were found not to decompose β-methylaspartate, mesaconate or DL-citramalate.[22] This apparently eliminates these compounds from consideration as intermediates, but does not exclude participation of their coenzyme A derivatives. Itaconyl-CoA and possibly mesaconyl-CoA are involved in the decomposition of itaconic acid by rat liver mitochondria.[72]

7. GLYCINE

The only anaerobic bacteria known to carry out a true fermentation of glycine are *Diplococcus glycinophilus*,[21] *Micrococcus anaerobius*, and *M. variabilis*.[23] The *Diplococcus* and *Micrococcus* species may be more closely related than the different generic names imply. All three organisms have a similar morphology and they form almost the same products.

The fermentation of glycine is described approximately by equation (21).

$$4CH_2NH_2COOH + 2H_2O \rightarrow 4NH_3 + 2CO_2 + 3CH_3COOH \tag{21}$$

In addition to the products shown, hydrogen gas is formed by *D. glycinophilus* in significant but variable amounts. The variability is determined by the fact that the hydrogen-producing reaction is readily reversible. Hydrogen is evolved only when the partial pressure of the gas in the medium is low. At a pressure of about 0.3 atmosphere equilibrium is reached; at higher pressures hydrogen is consumed. Because of these relations and the low solubility of hydrogen in water, a considerable evolution of hydrogen is observed only when the medium is shaken and the gas phase above the culture is large. The formation of hydrogen results in an increased yield of carbon dioxide and a decreased yield of acetic acid. The two *Micrococcus* species do not form hydrogen from glycine.

Inspection of equation (21) suggests that the fermentation of glycine consists of a dismutation in which the complete oxidation of one mole of glycine is coupled with the reduction of three moles of glycine to acetate and ammonia. Tracer experiments in which C^{14}-labeled glycine was fermented by cell suspensions of *D. glycinophilus* have shown that this interpretation is incorrect.[73] With glycine-1-C^{14} as substrate, C^{14} was found mainly in carbon dioxide but also in lesser amounts in both carbons of acetate. The specific activity of the carbon dioxide was almost the same as that of the carboxyl carbon of the substrate. With glycine-2-C^{14} as substrate, both carbon atoms of acetate were strongly labeled whereas carbon dioxide was very weakly labeled. With CO_2-C^{14}, both carbons of acetate were again labeled. These results show that the carbon dioxide is derived mainly from the carboxyl carbon of glycine, whereas both carbons of acetate are derived partly from the methylene carbon of glycine and partly from carbon dioxide. The data exclude both a complete oxidation of glycine to carbon dioxide and a significant direct reduction of glycine to acetate. They demonstrate that the formation of acetate involves a condensation of the methylene carbon atoms of two molecules of glycine or a derivative thereof.

Further elucidation of the actual path of the glycine fermentation had to await the development of concepts concerning the interconversions of glycine and serine in other organisms and the role of tetrahydrofolic acid in this process.[74] On the basis of such concepts and by the application of recently developed spectrophotometric techniques for detecting various derivatives of tetrahydrofolic acid (THFA), Sagers and Gunsalus[75] obtained evidence that crude cell-free extracts of *D. glycinophilus* catalyze the following reactions, which may account for the conversion of glycine to pyruvate.

$$\overset{*}{C}H_2NH_2COOH + THFA \xrightarrow{-2H} (-\overset{*}{C}H_2-THFA) + CO_2 + NH_3 \quad (22)$$

$$(-\overset{*}{C}H_2-THFA) + \overset{*}{C}H_2NH_2COOH \rightarrow \overset{*}{C}H_2OH\overset{*}{C}HNH_2COOH + THFA \quad (23)$$

$$\overset{*}{C}H_2OH\overset{*}{C}HNH_2COOH \rightarrow \overset{*}{C}H_3\overset{*}{C}OCOOH + NH_3 \quad (24)$$

Reaction (22) was not observed directly, but the formation of methylene-THFA, a cyclic compound containing the C_1 unit at the oxidation level of formaldehyde, was deduced from the fact that C^{14}-formaldehyde was formed on acidification of the reaction mixture, presumably by chemical decomposition of the enzymic product. Furthermore, when the reaction was carried out in the presence of substrate amounts of triphosphopyridine nucleotide (TPN), a more oxidized product, methenyl-THFA, containing the C_1 unit at the oxidation level of formate, was found to accumulate. The immediate product of glycine oxidation would be expected to be glyoxylic acid, which is known to be formed from glycine by a *Pseudomonas* and an *Achromobacter* species. However, this compound has not yet been identified as an intermediate in the *D. glycinophilus* fermentation.

Reaction (23) represents the transfer of THFA-bound formaldehyde to glycine with formation of serine. The occurrence of this reaction was deduced from observations on the reverse reaction. The serine dehydrase reaction [reaction (24)] was observed directly. In this connection it may be noted that serine is decomposed much more slowly than glycine by cell suspensions of *D. glycinophilus* probably because of a permeability barrier.

The above reactions result in the conversion of glycine-2-C^{14} to pyruvate-2,3-C^{14}. Pyruvate is slowly decomposed by intact cells. Evidence for the oxidation of pyruvate to acetate and carbon dioxide by *D. glycinophilus* has not yet been presented. If this oxidation does occur, the path of formation of acetate-1,2-C^{14} and unlabeled carbon dioxide from glycine-2-C^{14} is clearly indicated, though not yet conclusively established.

The path of glycine oxidation in *D. glycinophilus* appears to be identical with that in the purine-fermenting clostridia[75] but quite different from that in *Pseudomonas* species.[76] Glycine is metabolized in an entirely different manner by organisms using the Stickland reaction.

The previously mentioned tracer experiments with intact cells demonstrated that the partial oxidation of glycine is coupled with a reduction of carbon dioxide to acetic acid. The chemistry of this type of carbon dioxide reduction has not been elucidated. Carbon dioxide could be incorporated into the methyl carbon of acetate via formate, formyl-THFA, hydroxymethyl-THFA, serine, and pyruvate. However, this path does not account for the preferential incorporation of carbon dioxide carbon into the carboxyl group of acetate by *D. glycinophilus*[73] and *Butyribacterium rettgeri*.[77] With the latter organism evidence has been obtained which indicates that pyruvate probably is not an intermediate in acetate synthesis.[78] For example, when glucose was fermented in the presence of $C^{14}O_2$ under conditions permitting the accumulation of both pyruvate and acetate, it was found that the specific activity of the methyl carbon atom of acetate was much higher than that of pyruvate. The chemistry of acetate synthesis from carbon dioxide still needs extensive study.

D. glycinophilus decomposes several glycine-containing peptides with subsequent fermentation of the glycine moiety.[21] The peptides decomposed most rapidly are hippuric acid, *p*-aminohippuric acid, DL-leucylglycine, DL-alanylglycine, diglycine, acetylglycine and hippurylglycine. The nonglycine moieties are not attacked. The peptidases responsible for the decomposition of peptides in this organism have not been studied.

8. HISTIDINE

This amino acid is fermented by *Clostridium*, *Fusobacterium*, and *Micrococcus* species (Table I). The fermentation products of three species are given in Table V. The paths of histidine degradation by these organisms appear to be similar to those used by aerobic systems such as mammalian liver,[79] *Pseudomonas fluorescens*,[80] and *Aerobacter aerogenes*.[81, 82] Most of the basic studies of the path of histidine breakdown were done with aerobic organisms.

TABLE V

PRODUCTS OF HISTIDINE FERMENTATION[a]

Product	Clostridium tetanomorphum[63, 83, 84]	Clostridium tetani[17]	Micrococcus aerogenes[22]
Ammonia	~200	293	290
Carbon dioxide	63	68	103
Formamide	82	—	0
Formate	0	—	5
Hydrogen	16	0	0
Acetate	93	211	191
Butyrate	33	31	5
Lactate	0	—	35

[a] The figures give the yield of products in moles per 100 moles of substrate decomposed. The data were obtained with cell suspensions.

The first step in histidine breakdown by all of the above species is a deamination to urocanate which can be readily detected and identified by its

$$
\begin{array}{ccccc}
\text{Histidine} & \xrightarrow{-NH_3} & \text{Urocanate} & \xrightarrow{+2H_2O} & \text{Formiminoglutamate} \quad (25)
\end{array}
$$

characteristic ultraviolet absorption spectrum. This deamination, catalyzed by the enzyme histidase, appears to be irreversible. Formation of urocanate from histidine has been shown with *C. tetanomorphum*,[83] *A. aerogenes*,[81] and *Micrococcus aerogenes*.[22] These bacteria, or enzymic preparations derived from them, also degrade urocanate to the same products formed from histidine. The rate of urocanate breakdown under appropriate conditions is adequate to justify the assumption it is on the main path of histidine decomposition.

Urocanate is further degraded to L-α-formiminoglutamate by an enzyme system called urocanase. Formiminoglutamate has been isolated as a product of urocanate decomposition in relatively crude enzyme preparations derived from mammalian liver[79] and *P. fluorescens*,[80] and its properties have been carefully compared with those of the synthetic compound. The evidence for the accumulation of formiminoglutamate in extracts of *C. tetano-*

morphum and *A. aerogenes* is less complete but fairly convincing. It consists in the demonstration of the accumulation in reaction mixtures supplied with histidine or urocanate of a compound which, like α-formiminoglutamate, yields equimolar quantities of glutamate, formate, and ammonia on treatment with strong alkali.[83] The compound also moves like α-formiminoglutamate during paper chromatography and, like it, reacts very slowly with ninhydrin to give the purple color characteristic of amino acids.[84]

The chemistry of the urocanase reaction has not been elucidated in detail. However, some evidence has been obtained with the cat liver enzyme[85] that imidazoloneacrylic acid and imidazolonepropionic acid are intermediates.

Both *C. tetanomorphum*[84, 86] and *A. aerogenes*[81] have been shown to form formamide and glutamate during the decomposition of histidine or urocanate. These products appear to be formed more or less directly from α-

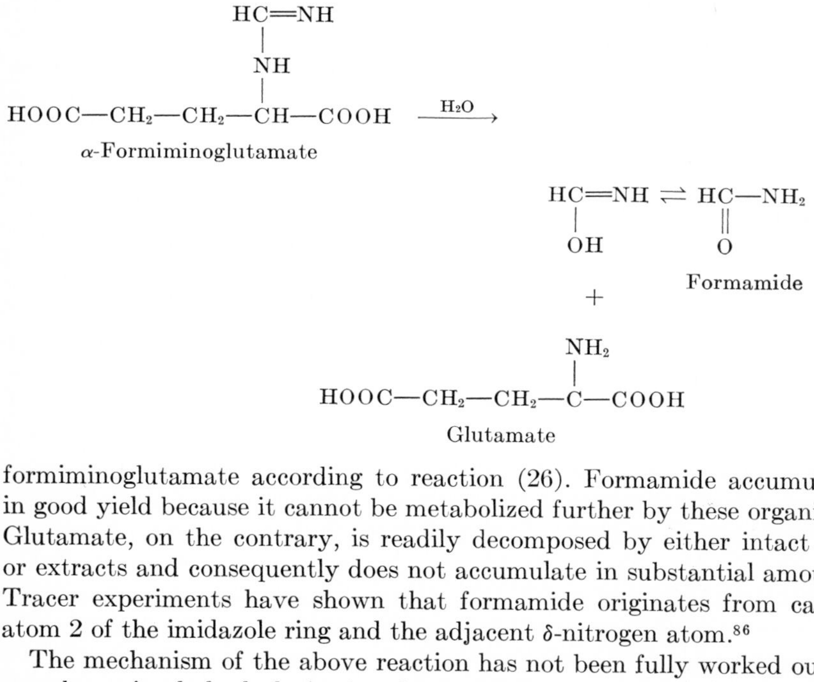

$$
\begin{array}{c}
HC{=\!=}NH \\
| \\
NH \\
| \\
HOOC{-}CH_2{-}CH_2{-}CH{-}COOH \quad \xrightarrow{\text{H}_2\text{O}}
\end{array}
$$

α-Formiminoglutamate

$$
\begin{array}{c}
HC{=\!=}NH \rightleftharpoons HC{-}NH_2 \\
| \qquad\qquad \| \\
OH \qquad\qquad O \\
\end{array} \qquad (26)
$$

Formamide

$+$

$$
\begin{array}{c}
NH_2 \\
| \\
HOOC{-}CH_2{-}CH_2{-}C{-}COOH
\end{array}
$$

Glutamate

formiminoglutamate according to reaction (26). Formamide accumulates in good yield because it cannot be metabolized further by these organisms. Glutamate, on the contrary, is readily decomposed by either intact cells or extracts and consequently does not accumulate in substantial amounts. Tracer experiments have shown that formamide originates from carbon atom 2 of the imidazole ring and the adjacent δ-nitrogen atom.[86]

The mechanism of the above reaction has not been fully worked out. It may be a simple hydrolysis. Another possibility is a transfer of the formimino group to tetrahydrofolic acid (THFA) to give glutamate and N^5-formimino-THFA, a compound known to be formed by enzymes in liver[87] and *C. cylindrosporum*.[88] N^5-Formimino-THFA could then be either hydrolyzed to formamide and THFA or be converted via $N^{5,10}$-methenyl-THFA to N^{10}-formyl-THFA, which can serve as a source of formyl and hydroxymethyl groups for synthetic reactions. The utilization of the formimino group for such purposes may account for the fact that the yield of formamide is always less than one mole per mole of histidine decomposed.

Glutamate is a transient intermediate in the fermentation of histidine by *C. tetanomorphum* and *A. aerogenes*. The final products of glutamate and histidine fermentation are generally similar except for the formamide and extra ammonia formed from the latter substrate. However, Whiteley[22] has found that *Micrococcus aerogenes* produces neither formamide nor equivalent amounts of formate from histidine and forms more acetate and lactate and less butyrate from histidine than from glutamate (compare Tables IV and V). This organism must have an accessory enzymic system for utilizing the formyl group derived from carbon atom 2 of the imidazole ring.

The products of histidine fermentation by *Clostridium tetani* are similar to those formed by *M. aerogenes*, except that with the former organism the yield of carbon dioxide is lower and the yields of acetate and butyrate are appreciably higher.[17] These differences suggest that *C. tetani*, like some other anaerobic bacteria,[89] may be able to synthesize acetate from carbon dioxide. The analytical methods used in determining the products of histidine fermentation by *C. tetani* do not permit a conclusion concerning the possible formation of formamide.

Several other paths of histidine degradation have been observed in aerobic organisms[80] but there is no evidence that these are involved in the energy metabolism of anaerobic bacteria. Histidine is decarboxylated to histamine under favorable conditions by several clostridia including *C. welchii* and *C. paludis*.[90] However, histidine decarboxylase, like other amino acid decarboxylases, is formed and is active only in acid media which are relatively unfavorable for growth. Histamine can be converted by extracts of a *Pseudomonas* species to aspartate and formate via imidazole acetic acid, imidazolone acetic acid, formiminoaspartic acid, and formylaspartic acid.[91] The formation of imidazole acetic acid from histamine is an oxidative reaction involving molecular oxygen. No similar transformation of histamine is known to occur in clostridia.

9. Leucine, Isoleucine, and Valine

The oxidation of these amino acids in the Stickland reaction to branched-chain fatty acids containing one less carbon atom is described in Section III, A (Stickland reaction). No fermentation of any of these amino acids has been reported.

10. Lysine

The decomposition of lysine has been studied to a limited extent with a mixed culture of two strains of *E. coli* and with *Clostridium sticklandii*.

When a medium containing L-lysine as the main carbon source was inoculated with bovine rumen fluid and incubated anerobically, the lysine was decomposed to ammonia, acetate, and butyrate.[92] The predominant organisms in the medium were small Gram-negative rods. After ten transfers several strains of bacteria were isolated from the enrichment culture. These strains mostly belong to two slightly different colony types, designated type E and type F. Both types were identified as strains of *E. coli*. When these two types of *E. coli* were tested separately neither one was able to grow appreciably or to ferment lysine in the medium used for the enrichment culture. However, lysine was fermented when the medium was inoculated simultaneously with both types.

Quantative determination of the products formed by mixed growing cultures established that for each 100 moles of L-lysine fermented the indicated number of moles of each product was formed: ammonia, 200; carbon dioxide, 0.4; acetate, 95; and buytrate, 95. In several experiments the ratio of acetate to butyrate was very close to unity. The small amount of carbon dioxide probably was derived from the yeast extract present in the medium. The above data show that the mixed culture lysine fermentation conforms to the following equation:

$$CH_2NH_2CH_2CH_2CH_2CHNH_2COOH + 2H_2O \rightarrow$$
$$2NH_3 + CH_3COOH + CH_3CH_2CH_2COOH \quad (27)$$

A similar type of lysine degradation is catalyzed by *C. sticklandii*, although with this organism the decomposition of lysine appears to be stimulated by the simultaneous decomposition of formate plus arginine or ornithine.[93] When a medium containing DL-lysine-2-C^{14}, DL-ornithine, formate, and a little yeast extract was fermented by a growing culture of *C. sticklandii* and the products were separated, C^{14} was found mainly in acetate and butyrate. The acetate was labeled almost exclusively in the methyl carbon atom, and the butyrate was labeled about five times more strongly in carbon atom 2 than in carbon atom 4. When DL-lysine-2-C^{14} was decomposed by dried cells of *C. sticklandii*,[94] the butyrate was labeled exclusively in carbon atom 2. With DL-lysine-6-C^{14} as a substrate, dried cells formed methyl-labeled acetate and butyrate labeled in carbon atom 4. These results have been interpreted to indicate that the C_6 chain of lysine is broken into a C_2 fragment, converted to acetate, and a C_4 fragment, converted to butyrate, in two ways, by cleavage between lysine carbon atoms 2 and 3 or between carbon atoms 4 and 5. A cleavage between carbon atoms 2 and 3 would give acetate derived from lysine carbon atoms 1 and 2 and butyrate derived from lysine carbon atoms 3–6, whereas a cleavage between carbon atoms 4 and 5 would give acetate derived from lysine carbon atoms 5 and 6 and butyrate derived from lysine carbon atoms 1–4. The

$$\overset{6}{C}H_3\overset{5}{C}H_2\overset{4}{C}H_2\overset{3}{C}OOH + \overset{2}{C}H_3\overset{1}{C}OOH$$

2-3 cleavage

$$\overset{6}{C}H_2NH_2\overset{5}{C}H_2\overset{4}{C}H_2\overset{3}{C}H_2\overset{2}{C}HNH_2\overset{1}{C}OOH$$

4-5 cleavage

$$\overset{6}{C}H_3\overset{5}{C}OOH + \overset{4}{C}H_3\overset{3}{C}H_2\overset{2}{C}H_2\overset{1}{C}OOH$$

relatively small formation of butyrate labeled in both the α and γ positions during the decomposition of lysine-2-C^{14} by growing cells shows that synthesis of butyrate from acetate or acetate precursors is a relatively slow reaction. It has been suggested that 2-ketocaproic acid and 5-ketocaproic acid or suitably activated derivatives of these compounds may be the intermediates that undergo the cleavage reaction. This suggestion is consistent with known mechanisms of fatty acid oxidation, but it is not as yet supported by direct evidence.

Fusobacterium nucleatum probably decomposes lysine in much the same way as do the bacteria already mentioned.[20] The evidence for this conclusion is that cell suspensions of *F. nucleatum* form ammonia but not carbon dioxide from lysine. The identity of the other products has not been established.

11. PROLINE AND HYDROXYPROLINE

These amino acids are not known to be fermented. They can be reduced by bacteria catalyzing the Stickland reaction. The product of proline reduction, δ-aminovalerate, can be fermented (see Section II, A, 2 on δ-aminovalerate). The product of hydroxyproline reduction has not been characterized and its further metabolism is not known.

12. SERINE

An enzyme that converts serine to pyruvate and ammonia [equation

$$CH_2OHCHNH_2COOH \rightarrow CH_3COCOOH + NH_3 \qquad (28)$$

(28)] is frequently found in anaerobic bacteria and appears to be responsible for the first step in serine fermentation. This enzyme, referred to as serine dehydrase or deaminase, sometimes is specific for L-serine and sometimes appears to act also on L-threonine.[95, 96] A separate enzyme acting on D-serine and D-threonine also occurs in some bacteria. Serine dehydrase activity has been observed in *Micrococcus aerogenes*,[22] coccus LC,[24] *E. coli*,[97] and other species.

Since pyruvate is formed in the first step of serine fermentation, the final products are determined by the enzymic systems available to the

TABLE VI

PRODUCTS OF SERINE FERMENTATIONS[a]

Product	Clostridium botulinum[6]	Clostridium propionicum[21]	Clostridium tetani[16]	Coccus LC[24]	Fusobacterium nucleatum[20]	Micrococcus aerogenes[22]
Ammonia	(100)	(100)	(100)	100	(100)	102
Hydrogen	—	—	—	50	—	96
Carbon dioxide	86	66	100	98	91	95
Formate	—	—	—	7	—	0
Acetate	53	66	23	30	26	96
Propionate	—	33	—	7	—	0
Butyrate	—	0	23	18	26	0
Valerate	—	—	—	2	—	—
Ethanol	57	—	24	—	19	—
Lactate	—	—	—	—	8	0

[a] The figures give the yield of products in moles per 100 moles of substrate decomposed.

organism for fermenting pyruvate. The products formed by several serine-fermenting species are given in Table VI. The chemistry of pyruvate fermentations is discussed in Chapter 2 of this volume.

Clostridium sticklandii ferments serine with the formation of carbon dioxide and alanine;[15] the other products have not been identified but they probably include ammonia and acetate, since these compounds are formed from other amino acids by this organism.

13. THREONINE

This amino acid is fermented by several species (Table VII). Observations on the chemistry of the fermentation have been made mainly with *Clostridium propionicum*, rumen coccus LC, *Micrococcus aerogenes*, and *M. lactilyticus*.

The initial step in threonine breakdown in all species studied appears to be a deamination and rearrangement to give α-ketobutyrate [reaction (29)].

$$CH_3CHOHCHNH_2COOH \rightarrow CH_3CH_2COCOOH + NH_3 \qquad (29)$$

This reaction is catalyzed by the enzyme threonine dehydrase (deaminase), which has been extensively purified from extracts of rumen coccus LC[98] and *E. coli*.[96] Evidence for the occurrence of α-ketobutyrate as an intermediate is provided by the transient accumulation of the compound under certain conditions and its decomposition at the same rate and with virtually the same yield of products as observed with threonine.[22, 24, 99]

TABLE VII

PRODUCTS OF THREONINE FERMENTATIONS[a]

Product	Coccus LC[24] cell suspension	Micrococcus aerogenes[22] dried cells	Clostridium propionicum[21] growing cells
Ammonia	100	101	100
Hydrogen	30	98	0
Carbon dioxide	80	100	75
Formate	3.8	0	—
Acetate	6.2	0	0
Propionate	78	102	67
Butyrate	3.0	0	34
Valerate	11	—	—

[a] The figures give the yield of products in moles per 100 moles of substrate decomposed.

The ultimate end products of the fermentation of threonine or α-keto-butyrate depend upon the enzymic constitution of the organism. Table VII gives data on the products formed by three species from threonine.

Micrococcus aerogenes catalyzes a simple dehydrogenation of α-keto-bu-tyrate according to the equation

$$CH_3CH_2COCOOH \rightarrow CH_3CH_2COOH + CO_2 + H_2 \qquad (30)$$

An esterification of inorganic phosphate is probably coupled with this reaction.

Rumen coccus LC, probably a *Neisseria* or *Moraxella* species, combines an oxidative decarboxylation of α-ketobutyrate to propionate with other reactions. A considerable part of the substrate evidently undergoes a C_2—C_2 cleavage with the formation of acetate. This might occur by a direct cleavage of threonine to acetaldehyde and glycine [reaction (31)] followed by an

$$CH_3CHOHCHNH_2COOH \rightarrow CH_3CHO + CH_2NH_2COOH \qquad (31)$$

oxidation of acetaldehyde to acetate, or possibly by a novel rearrangement of α-ketobutyrate to acetoacetate or acetoacetyl-CoA followed by a thioclastic cleavage of the latter to acetyl-CoA. A possible but as yet unknown mechanism for the conversion of α-ketobutyrate to acetoacetyl-CoA involves α-ketobutyryl-CoA, α-hydroxybutyryl-CoA, crotonyl-CoA, and β-hydroxybutyryl-CoA as intermediates. Acetyl-CoA could be converted to acetate or condensed with propionyl-CoA to give β-ketovaleryl-CoA which could be reduced to valerate via valeryl-CoA. The organism is known to synthesize valerate from C_3 and C_2 compounds. The small amount of formate may be derived from hydrogen and carbon dioxide by the reversible formic hydrogen lyase reaction.

C. propionicum converts threonine to butyrate, propionate, carbon di-

$$3CH_3CHOHCHNH_2COOH + 2H_2O \rightarrow$$
$$CH_3CH_2CH_2COOH + 2CH_3CH_2COOH + 2CO_2 + 3NH_3 \quad (32)$$

oxide, and ammonia according to the following equation. The over-all process represents an oxidation of two moles of threonine (or α-ketobutyrate) to propionate and carbon dioxide coupled with a reduction of one mole to butyrate.

The usual path of butyrate formation in bacterial fermentations involves a condensation of C_2 units in the form of acetyl-CoA. This path of butyrate synthesis can be readily demonstrated in most organisms by adding a little C^{14}-acetate to the fermenting medium and observing the incorporation of the isotope into both halves of the butyrate molecule. In the threonine fermentation by *C. propionicum* such incorporation of acetate carbon into butyrate does not occur.[100] This suggests that threonine is converted to butyrate by a more direct process not involving C_2 units. This conclusion is further supported by the observation that butyrate is not formed by *C. propionicum* from the C_3 amino acids serine and alanine.[21] The path of butyrate formation in *C. propionicum* is not known, but a possible reaction sequence for the conversion of α-ketobutyrate to acetoacetyl-CoA, a precursor of butyrate, has already been described. In view of the observations of Stadtman[35] on the role of coenzyme A in the reductive formation of propionate by *C. propionicum*, a similar role of coenzyme A in butyrate formation is probable.

The fermentation of threonine [equation (33)] by *Micrococcus aerogenes*

$$CH_3CHOHCHNH_2COOH + H_2O \rightarrow NH_3 + CO_2 + H_2 + CH_3CH_2COOH \quad (33)$$

undoubtedly goes via α-ketobutyrate, since this compound accumulates in considerable amounts under favorable conditions. When α-ketobutyrate is added as a substrate it decomposes at the same rate as threonine and gives the same products, excluding ammonia.

14. TRYPTOPHAN

Clostridium sporogenes has been reported to catalyze a slow fermentation of tryptophan.[13] The observed products per mole of tryptophan were indolepropionic acid, 0.5 mole; ammonia, 1 mole; and a small amount of carbon dioxide. No other products were identified, but it was suggested that the reduction of tryptophan to indolepropionic acid was coupled with the oxidation of a second mole of tryptophan to indolepyruvic acid [reaction (34)]. Presumably a slow further oxidation of indolepyruvic acid to indoleacetic acid accounts for the observed carbon dioxide formation.

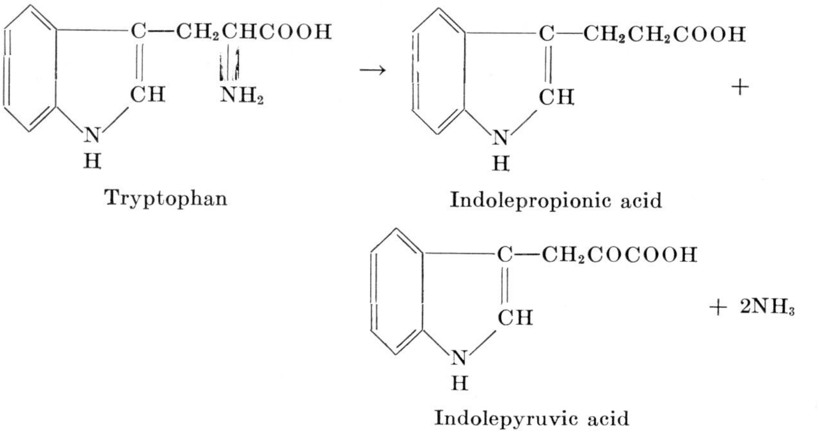

$$
\begin{array}{ccc}
\text{Tryptophan} & \rightarrow & \text{Indolepropionic acid} \\
\end{array}
$$

(34)

Indolepyruvic acid

$$+ 2NH_3$$

Indoleacetic acid has been identified as a product of tryptophan oxidation by aerobic fungi.[101]

E. coli and certain other facultatively and obligately anaerobic bacteria decompose tryptophan to indole, pyruvate, and ammonia by the so-called tryptophanase reaction:[102]

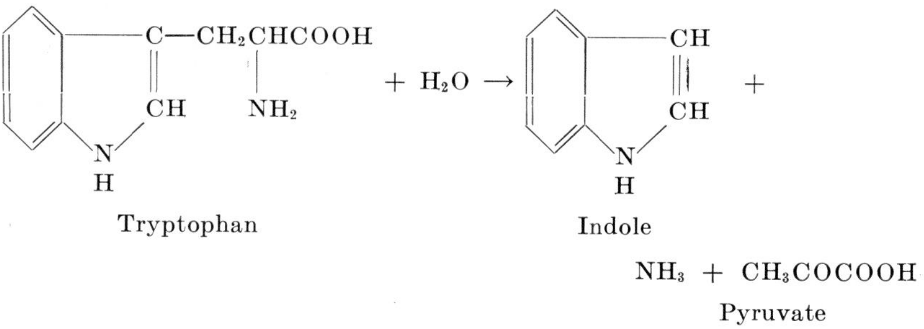

$$+ H_2O \rightarrow$$

$$
\begin{array}{cc}
\text{Tryptophan} & \text{Indole} \\
\end{array}
$$

(35)

$$NH_3 + CH_3COCOOH$$

Pyruvate

Serine appears not to be an intermediate in this reaction.[103] Since pyruvate is readily fermented by many bacteria, the tryptophanase reaction theoretically could initiate a fermentation of tryptophan, but this has not been demonstrated. Generally the formation of indole appears to be a relatively minor reaction which has more interest for taxonomists than for physiologists.

15. TYROSINE AND PHENYLALANINE

Relatively little information is available concerning the anaerobic decomposition of these amino acids. One or both amino acids are attacked by *Fusobacterium nucleatum*,[20] *C. tetanomorphum*,[18] *C. sporogenes*,[13, 104] and mixed rumen bacteria.[105] The products, other than ammonia, carbon dioxide and hydrogen, have generally not been determined. Quantitative data on tyrosine fermentation by *C. tetanomorphum* show that approximately one mole of carbon dioxide and ammonia and 0.4 mole of hydrogen are formed per mole of substrate. *C. sporogenes* both oxidizes and reduces tyrosine at a moderate rate, but only oxidizes phenylalanine.

Some early studies on the decomposition of tyrosine were focused on the formation of phenol and *p*-cresol, products which were rather easily detected and which were thought to be harmful to man. Several facultatively and obligately anaerobic bacteria, including *Bacterium coli phenologenes*,[106] *Clostridium (Bacillus) pseudotetanique*,[107] *C. (B.) tetani*,[108] and *Bacillus phenologenes*[109] were isolated from soil or fecal material and shown to form phenol under appropriate conditions. *B. phenologenes*, a coli-like organism, forms phenol from L- or DL-tyrosine, glycyl-1-tyrosine or protein digests. In a relatively simple medium containing 0.1 % of L-tyrosine, 0.8 gram of phenol per liter (80 % of the theoretical yield) accumulated during a 15-day incubation. In most other studies quantitative data were not reported. *Clostridium (Bacillus) cresologenes*, a strictly anaerobic species, forms *p*-cresol when grown in complex media, but there is no direct evidence that it is derived from tyrosine.[107] An unnamed Gram-negative bacterium of uncertain classification, isolated from a marine sediment, was reported to convert tyrosine or *p*-hydroxyphenylacetic acid to *p*-cresol in small yield.[110] No organism has been reported to produce both phenol and *p*-cresol.

The immediate precursor of phenol is thought to be *p*-hydroxybenzoic acid. This is based upon the observation that *Bacterium coli phenologenes*

$$HO\langle\underline{\quad}\rangle COOH \longrightarrow HO\langle\underline{\quad}\rangle H + CO_2 \tag{36}$$

forms phenol from tyrosine or *p*-hydroxybenzoic acid but not from several related compounds.[106] The same type of evidence suggests that *p*-hydroxyphenylacetic acid may be decarboxylated to *p*-cresol:[110]

$$HO\langle\underline{\quad}\rangle CH_2COOH \longrightarrow HO\langle\underline{\quad}\rangle CH_3 + CO_2 \tag{37}$$

Other products formed from tyrosine by *E. coli communis*, *Proteus vulgaris*, or *Bacillus subtilis* are *p*-hydroxyphenyllactic acid, *p*-hydroxyphenylacrylic acid, and *p*-hydroxyphenylacetic acid. These products are probably formed by an oxidative rather than a fermentative process. L-Tyrosine is converted to the D(+) isomer of *p*-hydroxyphenyllactic acid by *P. vulgaris* and to the L(−) isomer by *B. subtilis*.[111] The formation of *p*-hydroxyphenyllactic acid from tyrosine by both organisms is favored by a neutral or alkaline medium and by the presence of glycerol as a second substrate.[112]

Probably tyroxine is first oxidized to p-hydroxyphenylpyruvic acid and then reduced as follows:

$$HO\langle\_\rangle CH_2CHNH_2COOH \xrightarrow[-2H]{H_2O} HO\langle\_\rangle CH_2COCOOH + NH_3$$

Tyrosine p-Hydroxyphenylpyruvic acid

H_2O
$-2H$
$-CO_2$ $+2H$

$$HO\langle\_\rangle CH_2COOH \qquad HO\langle\_\rangle CH_2CHOHCOOH$$

p-Hydroxyphenylacetic acid p-Hydroxyphenyllactic acid

p-Hydroxyphenylpyruvic acid under appropriate conditions may also be oxidized to p-hydroxyphenylacetic acid. There is also some evidence that p-hydroxyacrylic acid may be an intermediate in the conversion of tyrosine to p-hydroxyacetic acid by $P.$ $vulgaris.$[113] In a culture growing on tyrosine under semiaerobic conditions, the acrylic acid derivative first accumulated and was then replaced by the acetic acid derivative. The formation of p-hydroxybenzoic acid from tyrosine apparently has not been demonstrated with any anaerobic organism.

Further studies are needed to give a coherent picture of the anaerobic decomposition of tyrosine and phenylalanine.

B. HETEROCYCLIC COMPOUNDS

Eight species of anaerobic bacteria have been reported to ferment heterocyclic compounds (Table VIII). Like the amino acid fermenting species, these bacteria also are mostly anaerobic sporeformers and cocci: $Zymobacterium$ $oroticum$ is the only species not belonging to one of these two groups. Relatively few studies have been made of bacteria causing fermentations of heterocyclic compounds. Probably many more species of this physiological group remain to be discovered.

1. PURINES

Purines are fermented by $Clostridium$ $acidiurici,$ $C.$ $cylindrosporum,$ $Micrococcus$ $aerogenes,$ and $M.$ $lactilyticus.$ The chemistry of purine fermentation by the clostridia has been studied most extensively and therefore will be discussed first.

Growing cultures of the purine-fermenting clostridia readily decompose

TABLE VIII

FERMENTATIONS OF HETEROCYCLIC COMPOUNDS

Species	Adenine	Guanine	Hypoxanthine	Uric acid	Xanthine	Cytosine	Orotic acid	Thymine	Uracil	Allantoin	Nicotinic acid
Clostridium acidiurici[114]	−	+	+	+	+					−	
Clostridium cylindrosporum[114]	−	+	+	+	+					−	
Clostridium uracilicum[115]									+		
Clostridium species[116]											+
Micrococcus aerogenes[117]	+	+	+	−	+	±		±	±	−	
Micrococcus lactilyticus[118]	±	±	+	±	+				−	±	
Streptococcus allantoicus[119]				−						+	
Zymobacterium oroticum[120]							+				

xanthine, guanine, 6,8-dihydroxypurine, and guanosine, and attack hypoxanthine and inosine more slowly or after a period of adaptation.[114, 121] The nucleosides are first converted to the free bases by a nucleoside phosphorylase that acts on inosine and guanosine but not on adenosine or xanthosine.

Chemical balance studies of purine fermentations by *C. acidiurici* have shown the main products to be ammonia, carbon dioxide, and acetate; in addition a little formate usually accumulates (Table IX). By disregarding the small yield of formate the fermentation of xanthine can be represented

$$
\begin{array}{l}
\text{N}\!=\!\text{COH} \\
\quad | \quad | \\
\text{HOC} \quad \text{C}\!-\!\text{N} \\
\quad \| \quad \| \qquad \diagdown \\
\qquad\qquad\qquad \text{CH} \ + \ 6\text{H}_2\text{O} \ \rightarrow \ 4\text{NH}_3 \ + \ 3\text{CO}_2 \ + \ \text{CH}_3\text{COOH} \\
\quad \| \quad \| \qquad \diagup \\
\text{N}\!-\!\text{C}\!-\!\text{NH}
\end{array}
\qquad (38)
$$

Xanthine

approximately by equation (38). Guanine, which is at the same oxidation level as xanthine, gives the same products plus an extra mole of ammonia. With the more oxidized purine uric acid, the yield of carbon dioxide is increased to 3.5 moles and the yield of acetic is decreased to 0.7 mole, whereas with the more reduced purine hypoxanthine the yield of carbon dioxide is decreased to 2 moles and the yield of acetate is increased to 1.25 moles. With all these substrates the purine nitrogen is converted virtually quantitatively to ammonia, without any detectable accumulation of urea. The same products are formed by *C. cylindrosporum*, except that the yield of

TABLE IX
PRODUCTS OF PURINE FERMENTATIONS[a]

Product	Clostridium cylindrosporum[122] Substrate: urate	Clostridium acidi-urici[114,122,123] Substrate			Micrococcus aerogenes[117] Substrate			Micrococcus lactilyticus[118] Substrate	
		Urate	Xanthine	Hypoxanthine	Hypoxanthine	Xanthine	Adenine	Hypoxanthine	Xanthine
Carbon dioxide	275	340	264	199	270	304	275	198	154
Hydrogen	—	—	—	—	53	0	49	80	7
Formate	48	(18)[b]	(18)[b]	—	—	—	—	—	—
Acetate	37	72	101	127	26	30	0	72	37
Propionate	—	—	—	—	1	8	0	20	11
Lactate	—	—	—	—	47	48	66	—	—
Glycine	14	0	—	—	—	—	—	—	—
Ammonia	356	397	380	370	400	399	506	208	188
Urea	0	0	0	0	—	—	—	98	11
Uric acid	—	—	—	—	—	—	—	—	47

[a] The figures give moles of product per 100 moles of substrate fermented. Cell suspension experiments.

[b] Estimated from a separate experiment.

formate is higher, 0.5–1.0 mole per mole decomposed, and 0.14–0.45 mole of glycine accumulates.

Xanthine has been identified as the compound that actually undergoes ring cleavage in the purine fermentation. The first definite indication of the key role of xanthine was obtained in experiments on the influence of the growth substrate on the relative rates of decomposition of xanthine, guanine, hypoxanthine, and uric acid.[124] Xanthine was immediately decomposed by washed cells that had been grown on any of the four purines, whereas uric acid, hypoxanthine, and to a lesser extent guanine were attacked rapidly only after a period of adaptation. This suggested that the other purines were converted to xanthine according to the scheme shown.

$$\text{Guanine}$$
$$\Big| \; -NH_3$$
$$\text{Hypoxanthine} \xrightarrow{-2H} \text{Xanthine} \xleftarrow{+2H} \text{Uric acid}$$
$$\Big|$$
$$\text{Products}$$

In support of this scheme, cells grown on guanine were shown to contain an active guanase that converts guanine to xanthine and ammonia.[125, 126] Cells grown on uric acid were found to attack rapidly both uric acid and xanthine. The addition of 2,4-dinitrophenol prevented uric acid breakdown without inhibiting the fermentation of xanthine. A direct reduction of uric acid to xanthine was later observed with purified preparations of a xanthine dehydrogenase isolated from extracts of *C. cylindrosporum* grown on uric acid.[127] The same enzyme converts hypoxanthine to xanthine by a rather roundabout path; hypoxanthine (6-hydroxypurine) is oxidized first to 6,8-dihydroxypurine, then on to uric acid (2,6,8-trihydroxypurine) which is finally reduced to xanthine (2,6-dihydroxypurine). It is not known whether a more direct oxidation of hypoxanthine to xanthine occurs in cells adapted to hypoxanthine.

Tracer experiments with guanine or uric acid specifically labeled with C^{14} have established the origin of the carbon atoms of the products formed by *C. cylindrosporum*.[122, 128] Similar experiments with unlabeled purines and C^{14}-labeled glycine, formate, or carbon dioxide have demonstrated that these fermentation products undergo further transformations and interconversions. The results of a number of tracer experiments, summarized in Table X, indicate that carbon dioxide, formate, and glycine are primary

TABLE X

ORIGIN OF THE CARBON ATOMS IN THE PRODUCTS OF PURINE[a] FERMENTATION
BY *C. cylindrosporum*[122]

Source	Percentage of product carbon atoms derived from indicated source					
			Product			
	CO_2	HCOOH	Acetate		Glycine	
			COOH	CH_3	COOH	CH_2
Carbon dioxide	—	29	5	24	40	0
Formate	10	—	2	20	2	2
Glycine, COOH	2	1	1	0	—	0
Glycine, CH_2	0	1	17	6	1	—
Purine, C-2	26	12	0	2	13	2
Purine, C-4	27	3	0	2	37	2
Purine, C-5	7	0	83	37	2	74
Purine, C-6	35	1	0	0	2	0
Purine, C-8	5	28–91	2	10	1	1
	112	76–139	110	101	98	81

[a] Most of the experiments were done with C^{14}-labeled guanine or uric acid.

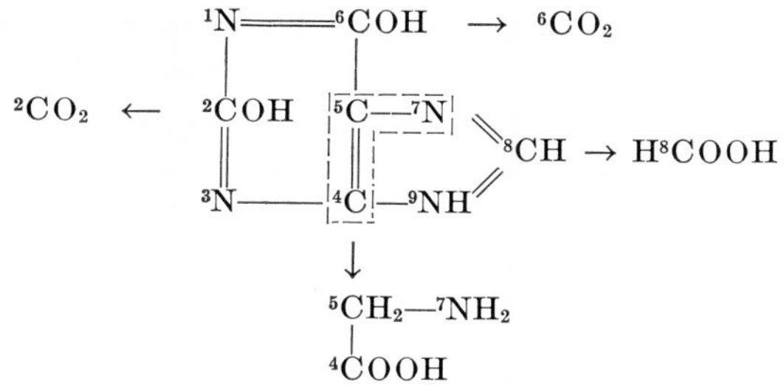

$$^1N =\!\!=\!\!= {}^6COH \quad \rightarrow \quad {}^6CO_2$$

$$^2CO_2 \leftarrow \quad ^2COH \quad |^5C-\!^7N| \atop \diagdown$$

$$^8CH \rightarrow H^8COOH$$

$$^3N-\!|^4C|-\!^9NH \atop \diagup$$

$$\downarrow$$

$$^5CH_2-\!^7NH_2$$

$$^4COOH$$

FIG. 5. Origin of some products of xanthine fermentation.

products of purine decomposition and originate as shown in Fig. 5. Carbon dioxide is derived from purine carbon atoms 2, 4, and 6. Purine carbon atom 4 is probably converted to carbon dioxide via the carboxyl carbon of glycine or a glycine derivative, although this is not shown by the data of Table X. Formate is derived directly from purine carbon atom 8 and indirectly from other carbon atoms, probably via carbon dioxide. Glycine carbon is derived mainly from the 4 and 5 positions in the purine and also from the nitrogen atom in position 7, as shown by experiments with uric acid-7-N^{15}.[122] Other purine carbon atoms also contribute to the glycine carboxyl carbon atom, probably via carbon dioxide. There is no explanation for the fact that purine carbon 2 is incorporated into the glycine carboxyl position more readily than purine carbon 6.

The tracer experiments indicate that acetate is formed by secondary conversions of glycine, formate, and carbon dioxide or their precursors. Most of the acetate carboxyl carbon is derived from purine carbon atom 5, probably via glycine. The acetate methyl carbon appears to originate largely from purine carbon atoms 5 and 8, probably via glycine, formate, and carbon dioxide. The relatively small incorporation of the methylene carbon of added glycine into acetate, as compared with purine carbon 5, may indicate either that glycine is not utilized as readily as a glycine precursor or that labeled glycine in the medium is not in equilibrium with glycine within the bacteria. It should be noted that acetate, unlike the other fermentation products, does not participate in further catabolic reactions.

The tracer experiments showed that glycine is an intermediate in the purine fermentation. Even before the tracer method was available, other experiments led to the same conclusion.[114] Following the discovery that glycine is formed from purines by *C. cylindrosporum*, cell suspensions of *C. acidiurici*, which does not accumulate glycine, were found to decompose glycine when it was supplied together with uric acid, and the amount of glycine decomposed was shown to be dependent upon the amount of uric acid fermented. Furthermore, methylene blue reduction tests by the Thunberg technique established that in the presence of washed cells of *C. acidi-*

urici glycine functions as a very active reducing agent. These observations suggested that the oxidation of glycine is coupled with the reduction of uric acid to xanthine. More direct evidence for this conclusion was provided by the discovery that the decomposition of uric acid under some conditions is dependent on the presence of glycine.[129] Some thoroughly washed and aged cell suspensions of *C. acidiurici* were found to ferment uric acid only after a lag period. The lag was abolished completely by the addition of a catalytic amount of glycine.

The enzymic steps in the decomposition of xanthine were investigated with cell-free extracts of *C. acidiurici*[130] and *C. cylindrosporum*.[121, 131] Extracts from both species were found to convert xanthine anaerobically to ammonia, carbon dioxide, formate, and glycine, or to compounds that yield these products in the analytical procedures used. In addition, appreciable amounts of one or more amino imidazoles were detected by means of paper chromatography and the Pauly and Bratton-Marshall tests. These observations indicated that the pyrimidine ring of xanthine is first attacked in such a way as to form an imidazole derivative which is then further degraded stepwise.

The individual reactions in the enzymic conversion of xanthine to glycine, formate, carbon dioxide, and ammonia are shown in Fig. 6. Reaction I represents the hydrolytic cleavage of the pyrimidine ring of xanthine between positions 1 and 6 resulting in the formation of 4-ureido-5-imidazolecarboxylic acid. A large accumulation of this compound can be obtained by incubating crude extracts of *C. cylindrosporum* with xanthine in the presence of 10^{-3} M ethylenediaminetetraacetic acid (EDTA) which completely suppresses the further conversion of the ureido compounds.[132] Reaction II represents a decomposition of the ureido group of 4-ureido-5-imidazolecarboxylic acid with formation of ammonia, carbon dioxide, and 4-amino-5-imidazolecarboxylic acid.[133] The latter compound accumulates in a weakly alkaline reaction mixture containing crude cell-free extract. The reaction is dependent upon the presence of Mn^{++}, Fe^{++}, or Mg^{++}. The mechanism of reaction II has not been studied in detail, but since orthophosphate is not required, the reaction appears to be hydrolytic. Reaction III is an enzymic decarboxylation of 4-amino-5-imidazolecarboxylic acid to 4-aminoimidazole which accumulates in the presence of EDTA.[133] The further conversion of 4-aminoimidazole to formiminoglycine and ammonia by reactions IV and V is again dependent on divalent cations such as Fe^{++} or Mn^{++}. Formiminoglycine has been isolated from enzymic reaction mixtures and fully characterized by comparison with the synthetic compound.[134] The enzyme 4-aminoimidazole hydrolase that catalyzes the decomposition of 4-aminoimidazole has been partially purified and shown to form ammonia but not formiminoglycine. The other product which accumulates

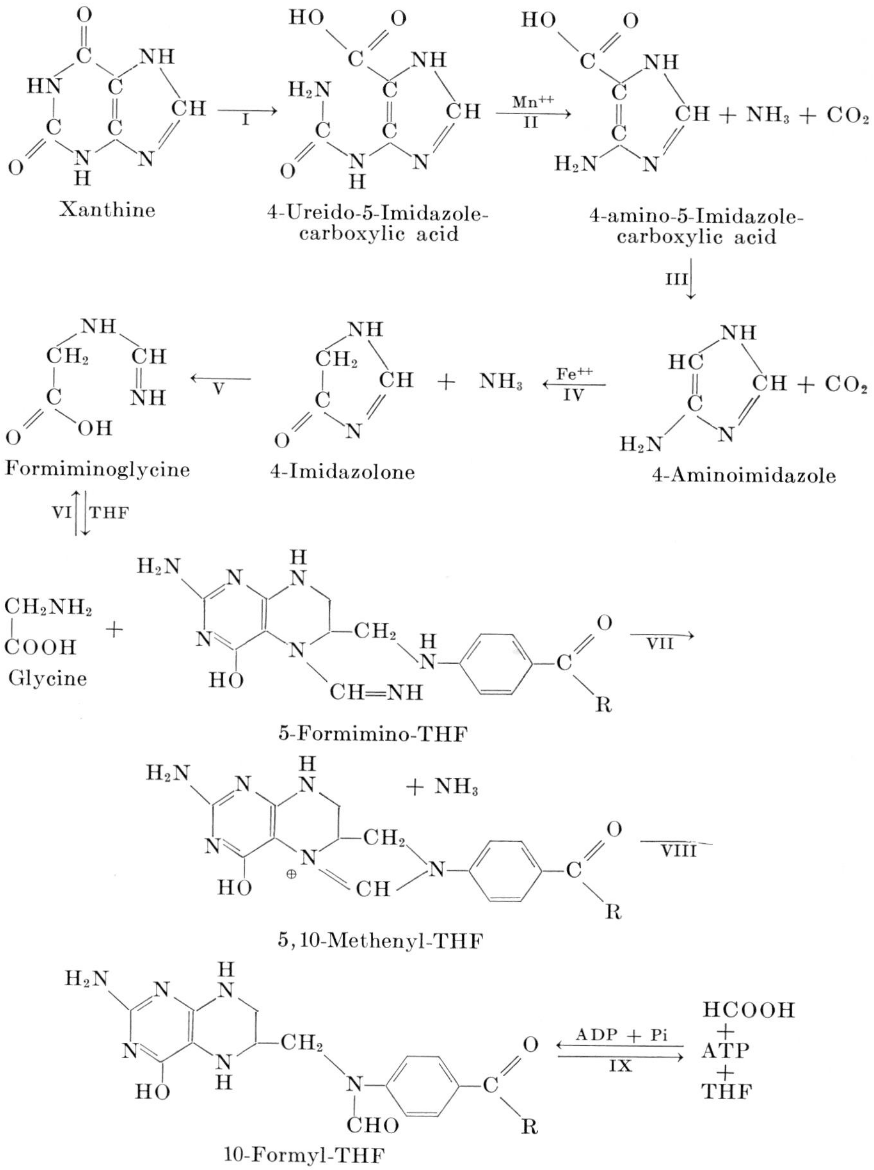

FIG. 6. Enzymic reactions in the conversion of xanthine to glycine, formate, carbon dioxide, and ammonia by *Clostridium cylindrosporum*.

has not been characterized, but may be the very unstable 4-imidazolone which is rapidly converted to formiminoglycine by crude extracts.[135]

Formiminoglycine is the major product formed from xanthine by crude extracts of *C. cylindrosporum*. In the early experiments on xanthine decomposition by extracts, formiminoglycine was mistakenly identified as a mixture of glycine, formate, and ammonia, because these compounds are rapidly formed nonenzymically from formiminoglycine under conditions used for their estimation.

The conversion of formiminoglycine to glycine involves a reversible enzymic reaction (VI) with tetrahydrofolic acid (THF). This reaction, which permits a rapid exchange between the glycine moiety of formiminoglycine and free glycine,[136] is essentially a transfer of the formimino group between glycine and THF. The second product of the reaction is 5-formimino-THF.[137, 138] The enzyme, called formiminoglycine formimino transferase, that catalyzes the formation of this product has been purified until it does not catalyze reaction VII. The latter reaction, which involves the removal of ammonia and cyclization to form 5,10-methenyl-THF, is catalyzed by the enzyme formimino-THF cyclodeaminase which also has been partially purified. The product of this apparently irreversible reaction has a strong ultraviolet absorption peak at 356 mμ and therefore can be readily identified and estimated. Reaction VIII, the hydrolytic conversion of 5,10-methenyl-THF to 10-formyl-THF, is catalyzed by the enzyme methenyl-THF cyclohydrolase which is present in extracts of *C. cylindrosporum*. The net result of reactions VI, VII, and VIII is the conversion of formimino-glycine and THF to glycine, ammonia, and 10-formyl-THF.

The enzymic decomposition of 10-formyl-THF is an apparently complex reaction (IX) that requires orthophosphate and adenosine diphosphate (ADP), and results in the formation of formate, THF, and adenosine triphosphate (ATP).[139, 140] This is the first ATP-generating reaction encountered during the purine fermentation. The equilibrium of this reaction rather strongly favors the formation of 10-formyl-THF. Therefore the decomposition of this compound depends upon coupled reactions consuming ATP and THF. The enzyme tetrahydrofolic formylase that catalyzes reaction IX is abundant in *C. cylindrosporum* and has been prepared in crystalline form from this source.[141]

The reactions shown in Fig. 6 account for the conversion of xanthine to glycine, formate, carbon dioxide, and ammonia, the major products formed by *C. cylindrosporum*. However, in the fermentation of xanthine by living cells of *C. acidiurici* very little glycine and formate accumulate; the main organic product is acetate. Therefore it is necessary to account for the conversion of glycine and formate or their known precursors to acetate. There is considerable evidence to show that this involves the reactions already described in the discussion of the fermentation of glycine by *Diplococcus glycinophilus*: a hydroxymethylation of glycine to serine by "active formaldehyde"; a deamination and rearrangement of serine to pyruvate; and an oxidation of pyruvate to acetate and carbon dioxide.[75] The "active formaldehyde" is probably derived from formiminoglycine via formimino-THF, methenyl-THF, methylene-THF, and hydroxymethyl-THF. The latter contains a C_1 group at the oxidation level of formaldehyde.

The above scheme is supported by a variety of tracer experiments with cell suspensions of *C. cylindrosporum* and *C. acidiurici* and also by experiments with extracts. The tracer experiments[142, 143] have shown that the carboxyl groups of both glycine and formiminoglycine are converted to carbon dioxide; glycine-2-C^{14} yields pyruvate-2-C^{14}; both glycine-2-C^{14} and formiminoglycine-2-C^{14} yield acetate-1-C^{14}; and formiminoglycine-C^{14} labeled in the formimino group is converted to acetate-2-C^{14}. The experiments with extracts have shown that enzymes are present that catalyze the transfer of the hydroxymethyl group from methylene-THF to glycine,[75] and the conversion of L-serine to pyruvate and ammonia.[142, 144] The reversible interconversion [reaction (39)] of hydroxymethyl-THF (formaldehyde oxidation level) and methenyl-THF (formate oxidation level), catalyzed by the enzyme hydroxymethyl-THF dehydrogenase, has been demonstrated. This

$$\text{hydroxymethyl-THF} + \text{TPN} \rightleftharpoons \text{methenyl-THF} + \text{TPNH} \qquad (39)$$

reaction in the reverse direction permits the formation of the hydroxymethyl group from formiminoglycine via formimino-THF and methenyl-THF. Relatively little information is available concerning the enzymic reactions involved in the formation of acetate by these organisms.[143, 145, 146]

We have seen that the formimino carbon of formiminoglycine can undergo two types of reactions: (1) It can be converted to formate via the tetrahydrofolic acid derivatives with the simultaneous formation of ATP, or (2) it can be reduced and transferred via the THF derivatives to glycine to give serine. The relative importance of these two processes depends upon the relative activities of the enzymes that act on methenyl-THF. With *C. cylindrosporum*, glycine and formate accumulate in substantial amounts and therefore the enzyme system leading to ATP formation is more active. With *C. acidiurici*, on the contrary, acetate is the main product, indicating a very active system for reducing the formyl group and transferring the product to glycine to form serine and eventually acetate.

Micrococcus lactilyticus ferments hypoxanthine and xanthine, and catalyzes a slow deamination of adenine and guanine.[118] The products of hypoxanthine fermentation are carbon dioxide, hydrogen, acetate, propionate, ammonia, urea, and under some conditions xanthine, uric acid, and uracil (Table IX). The hydrogen is formed at least in part during the anaerobic oxidation of hypoxanthine to xanthine. The initial steps in breakdown of the purine structure have not been determined. However, the appearance of about half of the total nitrogen as urea and the formation of small amounts of uracil suggest that the imidazole ring is attacked with formation of urea and a pyrimidine. Neither urea nor uracil is broken down at an appreciable rate. The mode of formation of ammonia, carbon dioxide and fatty acids by *M. lactilyticus* is not known.

Micrococcus aerogenes ferments adenine, hypoxanthine, guanine, and xanthine to form varying quantities of carbon dioxide, acetate, propionate, lactate, and ammonia (Table IX); hydrogen is produced from hypoxanthine or adenine, but not from xanthine or guanine.[117] In addition, the pyrimidine uracil appears as a transient intermediate during the decomposition of xanthine or guanine, and both uracil and thymine appear during the decomposition of the more reduced purines hypoxanthine or adenine.

The path of purine decomposition by *M. aerogenes* has not been determined. The pyrimidines do not appear to be on the main path of purine fermentation because of their slow rate of decomposition.

2. PYRIMIDINES

Pyrimidines are not fermented as readily as purines. Three anaerobic bacteria are known to destroy certain pyrimidines at a significant rate, namely, *Zymobacterium oroticum*, *Micrococcus aerogenes*, and *Clostridium uracilicum* (Table VIII). Of these three, only *Z. oroticum* appears to use a pyrimidine as a major energy source. Attempts to isolate species that readily ferment the common pyrimidines from soil or other natural sources by means of the enrichment culture method have generally been unsuccessful. However, a slow, continuous, and extensive decomposition of uracil or thymine by enrichment cultures containing a mixed bacterial flora has been observed.

Zymobacterium oroticum was isolated from black mud by enrichment in a medium containing the sodium salt of orotic acid as the main organic nutrient.[120, 147] This organism ferments orotic acid slowly with formation of ammonia, carbon dioxide, acetate, and one or more C_4 dicarboxylic acids, probably including succinic acid. Other pyrimidines are not known to be decomposed by this organism.

The early reactions in the fermentation of orotic acid have been identified by the use of cell-free extracts (Fig. 7). The first reaction is the DPN-linked reduction of orotic acid to L-dihydro-orotic acid.[147] The dihydro-orotic dehydrogenase responsible for this reaction has been partially purified. The equilibrium of the reaction strongly favors orotic acid reduction. The next step is a hydrolytic cleavage of the dihydropyrimidine ring by the enzyme dihydro-orotase to give L-ureidosuccinic acid.[148] This reaction is readily

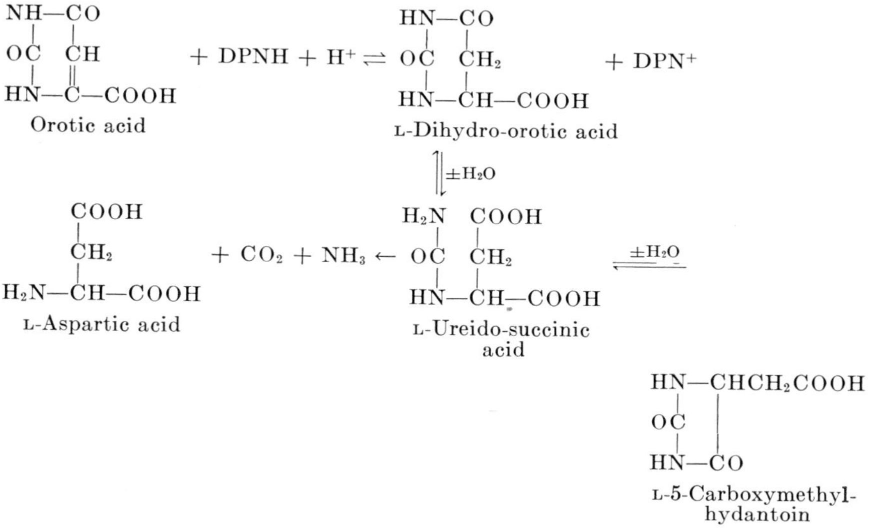

```
NH—CO                              HN—CO
 |    |                             |    |
OC   CH        + DPNH + H⁺ ⇌      OC   CH₂              + DPN⁺
 |    ||                            |    |
HN—C—COOH                         HN—CH—COOH
  Orotic acid                     L-Dihydro-orotic acid
```

$$\updownarrow \pm H_2O$$

```
 COOH                             H₂N  COOH
  |                                |    |
  CH₂      + CO₂ + NH₃  ←        OC   CH₂            ± H₂O
  |                                |    |             ⇌
H₂N—CH—COOH                       HN—CH—COOH
  L-Aspartic acid                 L-Ureido-succinic
                                       acid
```

```
                          HN—CHCH₂COOH
                           |    |
                          OC    |
                           |    |
                          HN—CO
                          L-5-Carboxymethyl-
                               hydantoin
```

FIG. 7. Reactions in orotic acid fermentation by *Zymobacterium oroticum.*

reversible; at equilibrium the molar ratio of ureidosuccinic acid to dihydro-orotic acid is about 2:1. Cell-free extracts of *Z. oroticum* also catalyze the reversible conversion of ureidosuccinic acid to L-5-carboxymethylhydantoin. This appears to be a side reaction not involved in the main path of orotic acid fermentation. The ureido group of ureidosuccinic acid is degraded by the enzyme ureidosuccinase with formation of ammonia, carbon dioxide, and L-aspartic acid.[149] This is an irreversible reaction which appears to be hydrolytic, since its rate is not dependent on the presence of phosphate or a phosphate acceptor.

The further conversions of L-aspartate have not been studied in detail. However, cell-free extracts catalyze the decomposition of aspartate to pyruvate, carbon dioxide, and ammonia.[149] This decomposition of aspartate was found to be dependent upon the presence of stoichiometric amounts of α-ketoglutarate. This indicated that a transamination occurred between aspartate and α-ketoglutarate [reaction (40)] and suggested that the following reactions may be involved in aspartate breakdown.

$$\text{aspartate} + \alpha\text{-ketoglutarate} \rightleftharpoons \text{oxalacetate} + \text{glutamate} \tag{40}$$

$$\text{oxalacetate} \rightarrow \text{pyruvate} + CO_2 \tag{41}$$

$$\text{glutamate} + \text{DPN} \rightleftharpoons \alpha\text{-ketoglutarate} + NH_3 + \text{DPNH} + H^+ \tag{42}$$

$$\text{aspartate} + \text{DPN} \rightarrow \text{pyruvate} + CO_2 + NH_3 + \text{DPNH} + H^+ \tag{43}$$

This sequence postulates a catalytic role of glutamate or α-ketoglutarate,

TABLE XI

PRODUCTS[a] OF PYRIMIDINE FERMENTATIONS BY *Micrococcus aerogenes*

Product	Substrate		
	Uracil	Cytosine	Thymine
Carbon dioxide	115	43	108
Hydrogen	55	12	39
Acetate	43	0	55
Lactate	67	24	72
Ammonia	169	131	99
Uracil	—	78	29

[a] The figures give moles of product per 100 moles of substrate fermented. Cell suspension experiments.

which has not yet been demonstrated. The reduced DPN formed in reaction (42) could be used for the conversion of orotic acid to dihydro-orotic acid, the first step in the fermentation.

The final steps in the orotic acid fermentation appear to be an oxidation of pyruvate to acetate and carbon dioxide coupled with a reduction of oxalacetate via malate and fumarate to succinate. The postulated enzymic reactions have not been studied in detail.

Micrococcus aerogenes ferments uracil, cytosine, and thymine slowly and often incompletely.[117] The main products are lactate, acetate, carbon dioxide, hydrogen, and ammonia (Table XI). Uracil is also formed during the decomposition of cytosine or thymine and appears to be an intermediate product. Nothing else is known about the chemistry of pyrimidine breakdown in *M. aerogenes*.

Clostridium uracilicum was isolated from soil by enrichment in a medium containing uracil and yeast extract.[115] The organism requires biotin, several amino acids, and a carbohydrate for growth. Uracil is not required and does not stimulate growth. Uracil is decomposed only by cells that have grown in the presence of this compound. Other pyrimidines appear not to be attacked.

The products of uracil decomposition by adapted cell suspensions of *C. uracilicum* are β-alanine, carbon dioxide, and ammonia.[150] Cell suspensions and cell-free extracts also convert dihydrouracil or β-ureidopropionic acid to the same products, and convert carbamylphosphate to orthophosphate, carbon dioxide, and ammonia. β-Alanine is not decomposed. Both dihydrouracil and β-ureidopropionic acid have been identified as intermediates in uracil breakdown by extracts. Furthermore, an enzyme which catalyzes the reversible reduction of uracil to dihydrouracil by DPNH has been demonstrated and partially purified. This reaction is analogous to the

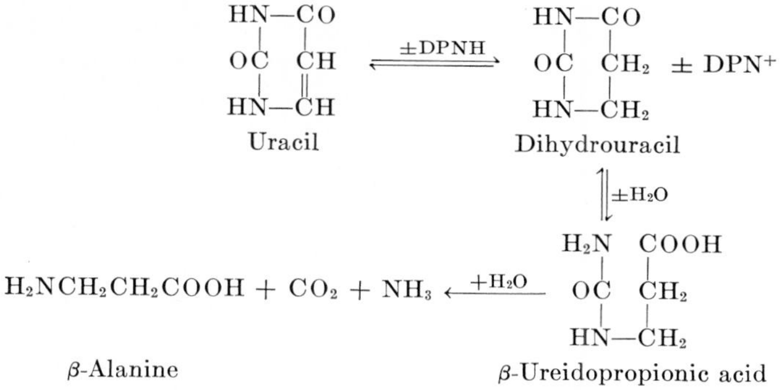

$$\underset{\text{Uracil}}{\begin{array}{c} \text{HN—CO} \\ |\quad| \\ \text{OC}\quad\text{CH} \\ |\quad|| \\ \text{HN—CH} \end{array}} \quad\underset{}{\overset{\pm\text{DPNH}}{\rightleftharpoons}}\quad \underset{\text{Dihydrouracil}}{\begin{array}{c} \text{HN—CO} \\ |\quad| \\ \text{OC}\quad\text{CH}_2 \\ |\quad| \\ \text{HN—CH}_2 \end{array}} \pm\text{DPN}^+$$

$\pm H_2O$

$$\text{H}_2\text{NCH}_2\text{CH}_2\text{COOH} + \text{CO}_2 + \text{NH}_3 \quad\xleftarrow{+\text{H}_2\text{O}}\quad \begin{array}{c} \text{H}_2\text{N}\quad\text{COOH} \\ |\quad\quad| \\ \text{OC}\quad\text{CH}_2 \\ |\quad\quad| \\ \text{HN—CH}_2 \end{array}$$

β-Alanine$\qquad\qquad\qquad\qquad\qquad$ β-Ureidopropionic acid

FIG. 8. Decomposition of uracil by *Clostridium uracilicum*.

reversible reduction of dihydro-orotic acid catalyzed by an enzyme from *Z. oroticum*. The accumulated evidence indicates that the decomposition of uracil involves the reactions shown in Fig. 8.

3. ALLANTOIN

Streptococcus allantoicus, a homofermentative lactic acid bacterium isolated from an enrichment medium containing allantoin, ferments this compound readily in a medium containing a little yeast extract.[119] The products in moles per mole of allantoin decomposed are the following: ammonia, 2.26; urea, 0.62; oxamic acid, 0.45; carbon dioxide, 1.68; formate, 0.09; acetate, 0.15; glycolate, 0.14; and lactate, 0.01. A small amount of glycine is also formed. Oxamic acid, the monoamide of oxalic acid, has not been observed elsewhere as a natural product.

A little information is available concerning the chemistry of allantoin fermentation. The first step appears to be the formation of allantoic acid

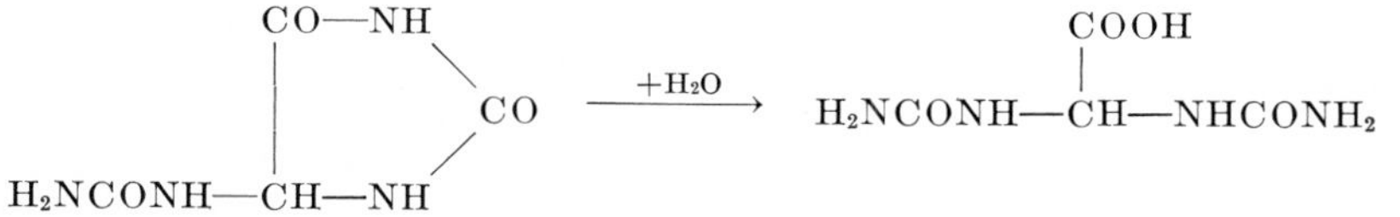

$$\underset{\text{Allantoin}}{\begin{array}{c} \text{CO—NH} \\ |\qquad\quad\diagdown \\ \qquad\qquad\text{CO} \\ |\qquad\quad\diagup \\ \text{H}_2\text{NCONH—CH—NH} \end{array}} \quad\xrightarrow{+\text{H}_2\text{O}}\quad \underset{\text{Allantoic acid}}{\begin{array}{c} \text{COOH} \\ | \\ \text{H}_2\text{NCONH—CH—NHCONH}_2 \end{array}} \quad(44)$$

by a hydrolytic reaction. The latter compound is both formed and decomposed at a relatively rapid rate. The presence of 0.05 M sodium fluoride strongly inhibits the decomposition of allantoic acid and causes it to accumulate during the breakdown of allantoin. Further steps in the fermentation are not known. However, since *S. allantoicus* forms both ammonia and urea but does not contain the enzyme urease, it is apparent that at least one ureido group is decomposed by a path not involving urea. Tracer experiments with $N^{15}H_3$ have shown that the nitrogen in oxamic acid is not derived from ammonia; therefore oxamic acid must be formed rather directly by cleavage and oxidation of allantoic acid rather than by ammonolysis of an oxalyl compound. Glyoxylate may be an intermediate in the fermentation since it is readily decomposed anaerobically by cell suspensions. The products, other than carbon dioxide, have not been identified.

The enzyme system involved in allantoin fermentation is adaptive. Cells grown on glucose are entirely inactive on allantoin.

4. Nicotinic Acid

An unidentified clostridium isolated by the enrichment culture method was shown to grow in a medium containing nicotinic acid, yeast extract, and peptone.[116] Nicotinic acid is required for growth and the amount of growth is roughly proportional to the concentration of nicotinic acid up to 0.2%.

The products of the anaerobic decomposition of nicotinic acid by washed cell suspensions are ammonia, carbon dioxide, acetate, and propionate.

$$\underset{\text{Nicotinic acid}}{\begin{array}{c} ^4CH \\ {}^5CH \quad {}^3C-COOH \\ | \quad\quad\quad || \\ {}^6CH \quad {}^2CH \\ {}^1N \end{array}} + 4H_2O \rightarrow NH_3 + CO_2 + CH_3COOH + CH_3CH_2COOH \quad (45)$$

The fermentation is rather accurately described by equation (45). The only related compound fermented by the organism is nicotinamide. Several other compounds, including pyridine, picolinic acid, isonicotinic acid, quinolinic acid, anthranilic acid, p-aminobenzoic acid, 3-hydroxyanthranilic acid, kynurenic acid, and N-methylnicotinamide, are not attacked.

Some evidence concerning the chemical steps in the nicotinic acid fermentation is available. Lyophilized bacteria contain an enzymic system that couples the oxidation of nicotinic acid to 6-hydroxynicotinic acid with the reduction of methylene blue.[151] Tracer experiments have established that nicotinic acid and 6-hydroxynicotinic acid are rapidly interconverted in the absence of an external oxidizing agent according to the reaction:

$$\text{nicotinic acid} + H_2O \rightleftharpoons \text{6-hydroxynicotinic acid} + 2H \quad (46)$$

6-Hydroxynicotinic acid is not definitely known to be on the path of nicotinic acid fermentation. However, it is possible that 6-hydroxynicotinic acid is an intermediate and is oxidized to the corresponding ketone, 6-pyridone. The 6-pyridone theoretically could undergo a hydrolytic cleavage between the carbon in the 6 position and the nitrogen to form an acyclic compound from which the fermentation products could be derived.

III. Fermentations of Pairs of Amino Acids (Stickland Reaction)

Many clostridia, growing on protein hydrolyzates or amino acid mixtures, appear to obtain most of their energy by a coupled oxidation-reduction between suitable amino acids, or amino acids and non-nitrogenous compounds (Table XII). The coupled decomposition of amino acids is commonly referred to as the Stickland reaction. The characteristic feature of the Stickland reaction is that single amino acids are not decomposed appreciably, but appropriate pairs of amino acids are decomposed rapidly. One member of the pair is oxidized while the other is reduced.

TABLE XII

BACTERIA CATALYZING THE STICKLAND REACTION

Clostridium acetobutylicum	C. histolyticum
C. aerofoetidum	C. indolicum
C. bifermentans	C. mitelmanii
C. botulinum, types A and B	C. saprotoxicum
C. butyricum	C. sordellii
C. caproicum	C. sporogenes
C. carnofoetidum	C. valerianicum
C. ghonii	C. sticklandii

Evidence for this formulation was obtained initially by studying the interaction between amino acids and suitable redox dyes in the presence of cell suspensions of C. sporogenes.[4] Alanine and some other amino acids were found to serve as substrates for the reduction of methylene blue. This indicated that these amino acids were oxidized. Glycine, proline, and hydroxyproline were ineffective for reducing methylene blue, but rapidly oxidized the reduced form of the low potential dye, benzyl viologen. This indicated that these amino acids were reduced. When one mole of the oxidizable amino acid alanine was combined with two moles of the reducible amino acid glycine, three moles of ammonia were formed rapidly in the presence of a cell suspension. This showed that both amino acids were deaminated. However, when one mole of alanine was incubated with an excess of proline only one mole of ammonia was formed. This suggested that proline was reduced by ring cleavage according to reaction (47) without formation of ammonia.

$$
\begin{array}{c}
\mathrm{CH_2-CH_2} \\
|\qquad\ | \\
\mathrm{CH_2}\quad \mathrm{CHCOOH} \;+\; 2\mathrm{H} \;\rightarrow\; \mathrm{CH_2}\quad \mathrm{CH_2COOH} \\
\ \diagdown\ \diagup \qquad\qquad\qquad\quad \diagdown \\
\mathrm{NH} \qquad\qquad\qquad\qquad \mathrm{NH_2}
\end{array}
\qquad (47)
$$

$$\mathrm{CH_2-CH_2}$$

Proline   δ-Aminovalerate

The correctness of this suggestion was established by identifying δ-aminovalerate as a major product of the reaction.[152] Once the product of proline reduction was identified, the other compounds formed in the coupled decomposition of alanine and proline could be recognized as products of alanine oxidation.[4] Quantitative analysis showed that one mole each of ammonia, carbon dioxide, and acetate were formed per mole of alanine added, according to the equation:

$$CH_3CHNH_2COOH + 2H_2O \xrightarrow{-4H} NH_3 + CH_3COOH + CO_2 \quad (48)$$

When one mole of alanine was incubated with an excess of glycine, three moles of ammonia, three moles of acetate, and one mole of carbon dioxide were formed. On the assumption that the same products were formed from alanine in the presence of glycine or proline, these data lead to the conclusion that glycine is reduced to acetate and ammonia [equation (49)].

$$CH_2NH_2COOH + 2H \rightarrow NH_3 + CH_3COOH \quad (49)$$

The reduction of glycine to acetate and ammonia was subsequently confirmed by experiments which were based upon the ability of some strains of *C. sporogenes* to use gaseous hydrogen as a reducing agent.[12] When a cell suspension was incubated with a known amount of glycine in a hydrogen atmosphere, the quantity of hydrogen consumed and products formed agreed well with equation (49).

Tracer experiments[153] have shown that the carboxyl and methyl carbon atoms of acetate are derived from the carboxyl and methylene carbon atoms of glycine, respectively. Two moles of glycine are necessary to oxidize one mole of alanine [equation (50)].

$$\text{alanine} + 2 \text{ glycine} + 2H_2O \rightarrow 3NH_3 + 3CH_3COOH + CO_2 \quad (50)$$

A. OXIDATIONS

A number of other amino acids can serve as reductants for clostridia catalyzing the Stickland reaction (see Table XIII). These amino acids may be divided into three groups[5]: (1) Aliphatic amino acids that are more reduced than α-keto acids, namely, alanine, leucine, isoleucine, norleucine, and valine. (2) Aliphatic amino acids that are in the same oxidation state as the keto acids, namely, serine, threonine, cysteine, methionine, arginine, citrulline, and ornithine. (3) Other amino acids, including histidine, phenylalanine, tryptophan, tyrosine, aspartate, and possibly glutamate. Not all of these amino acids are used by any one species and the rates of oxidation of the different amino acids by one organism may differ widely.

Clostridium sporogenes oxidizes amino acids of group 1 rapidly and with about equal facility, as judged by the rate of reduction of brilliant cresyl blue. Amino acids of the other groups are used at lower rates or not at all

TABLE XIII

AMINO ACIDS USED AS REDUCTANTS IN THE STICKLAND REACTION
BY VARIOUS CLOSTRIDIA

Amino acid	Relative rate[a]	Amino acid	Relative rate[a]
Alanine	100	Serine	16
Leucine	100	Asparagine	13
Isoleucine	100	Arginine	—
Norleucine	100	Citrulline	—
Valine	76	Ornithine	—
Histidine	37	Threonine	—
Phenylalanine	28	Cysteine	—
Tryptophan	17	Methionine	—
Tyrosine	16		

[a] The figures give relative rates of reduction (alanine = 100) of brilliant cresyl blue by a washed cell suspension of *Clostridium sporogenes* in the presence of the indicated amino acids.[104]

(Table XIII). *C. sticklandii*[15] is unable to oxidize alanine, but can oxidize arginine, citrulline, and ornithine. Obviously, the specific enzymic constitution of the organism is of primary importance in determining the manner of utilization of amino acids, particularly those of group 2, which, being readily convertible to α-keto acids by nonoxidative reactions, are capable of being either oxidized or reduced. The redox potential and the activity of the coupled system will determine the fate of the keto acid. It should be noted that the oxidation of certain non-nitrogenous compounds, such as pyruvate and ethanol, can be coupled with the reduction of amino acids in what can be described as a modified Stickland reaction.[104]

The final oxidation products of several amino acids by cell suspensions of *C. caproicum* or *C. valerianicum* have been determined using either proline or oxygen as oxidant.[154, 155] Oxygen can be used as an unphysiological oxidant by these obligately anaerobic species because they contain autoxidizable flavin enzymes. The type of oxidant does not appear to influence the nature of the final products. Valine, leucine, and isoleucine have been shown to be oxidized to fatty acids with one less carbon atom, namely, isobutyric acid, isovaleric acid, and a valeric acid, presumably the optically active α-methylbutyric acid, respectively. In addition to fatty acids, small amounts of α-keto acids of the same chain length as the amino acids accumulated when O_2 was used as the oxidant.[156] These α-keto acids were identified as the expected oxidation products of the amino acids. The keto acids have been shown to undergo oxidative decarboxylation to the corresponding fatty acids.[155] The role of the α-keto acids as intermediates in amino acid oxidation according to the following sequence is rather firmly established.

$$RCHNH_2COOH + H_2O \xrightarrow{-2H} NH_3 + RCOCOOH \xrightarrow{-2H} RCOOH + CO_2$$

The enzymic reactions involved in oxidation of group 1 amino acids to α-keto acids are not yet known with certainty. Two possibilities have been suggested[5]: (1) The amino acid undergoes a direct oxidative deamination by an enzyme analogous to glutamic dehydrogenase. (2) The amino acid undergoes a transamination with α-ketoglutarate to form the corresponding α-keto acid and glutamate [reaction (51)] and the latter is then oxidized to ammonia and α-ketoglutarate by glutamic dehydrogenase [reaction (52)].

$$RCHNH_2COOH + COOHCH_2CH_2COCOOH \rightleftharpoons$$
$$RCOCOOH + COOHCH_2CH_2CHNH_2COOH \tag{51}$$

$$COOHCH_2CH_2CHNH_2COOH + H_2O + DPN^+ \rightleftharpoons$$
$$COOHCH_2CH_2COCOOH + NH_3 + DPNH + H^+ \tag{52}$$

The regeneration of α-ketoglutarate by reaction (52) would permit this compound to function catalytically. The oxidations of alanine, valine, and leucine by *C. saccharobutyricum*, a species that does not catalyze a typical Stickland reaction, apparently involve the second mechanism since the anaerobic deamination of these amino acids occurs only in the presence of α-ketoglutarate.[157] With *C. sporogenes* there is no clear evidence for or against the participation of transaminase or glutamic dehydrogenase in the conversion of alanine to pyruvate, although the organism contains both enzymes.

Although the mechanism of oxidation of group 1 amino acids by *C. sporogenes* is not established, some factors affecting the rate and extent of alanine oxidation by crude cell-free extracts are known.[5] Both DPN (diphosphopyridine nucleotide) and orthophosphate (replaceable by arsenate) are required for rapid oxidation of alanine by oxygen. A stimulation by phosphate is also observed when DPN is used as the oxidant. There is some evidence that phosphate is involved in alanine oxidation as well as in pyruvate oxidation (see below), but the point is not firmly established. Additional studies with purified enzymes are needed to determine the mechanism of alanine oxidation by *C. sporogenes*.

The deamination of amino acids of groups 2 and 3 has already been discussed in connection with the fermentation of individual amino acids.

The oxidation of pyruvate by *C. sporogenes* appears to involve the same mechanism found in *E. coli*[158] and *S. faecalis*.[159] Three cofactors, CoA, DPN, and cocarboxylase, have been shown to stimulate pyruvate oxidation by dialyzed extracts.[160] Acetyl-CoA is probably an intermediate since addition

TABLE XIV

AMINO ACIDS USED AS OXIDANTS IN THE STICKLAND
REACTION BY *Clostridium sporogenes*

Compound	Relative rate[a]
Glycine	100
Proline	100
Hydroxyproline	100
Ornithine	100
Arginine	80
Tryptophan	67
Tyrosine	25
Cysteine	22
Cystine	16
Methionine	15
Aspartate	2

[a] The figures give the relative rates (glycine = 100) of hydrogen uptake, measured manometrically, in the presence of a washed suspension of *C. sporogenes* and the indicated amino acids.[13]

of phosphate results in formation of acetyl phosphate, presumably by the action of the enzyme phosphotransacetylase. Therefore, both high energy acetyl and phosphoryl groups are available for synthetic reactions. The oxidation of higher α-keto acids in the presence of phosphate also results in formation of the corresponding acyl phosphates.

B. REDUCTIONS

The most distinctive part of the Stickland reaction is the apparently direct reduction of certain amino acids, including glycine, proline, hydroxyproline, and ornithine (Table XIV). This type of reaction has been observed only in certain clostridia.

The reductions of glycine to acetic acid and ammonia and of proline to δ-aminovalerate during the coupled reaction with alanine have already been mentioned. Cells of *C. sporogenes*, grown in the presence of glucose, catalyze the same reductions using gaseous hydrogen as reductant.[13] The rate of hydrogen uptake can be followed manometrically. This provides a convenient and moderately sensitive method for identifying compounds that can be used as oxidants by *C. sporogenes*.

By this method the amino acids listed in Table XIV, and, in addition, a considerable number of non-nitrogenous compounds were shown to serve as oxidants. The reduction of hydroxyproline was shown to require one mole of hydrogen and to occur without the formation of ammonia; the presumed reduction product, γ-hydroxy-δ-aminovaleric acid, was not directly identified. Ornithine is reduced to δ-amino-n-valeric acid[13, 36] according to the equation:

$$NH_2(CH_2)_3CHNH_2COOH + H_2 \rightarrow NH_2(CH_2)_4COOH + NH_3 \qquad (53)$$

Ornithine $\qquad\qquad\qquad$ δ-Aminovaleric acid

Tryptophan is apparently reduced by hydrogen to indolepropionic acid

Tryptophan $\qquad\qquad\qquad\qquad\qquad$ Indolepropionic acid

and ammonia.[12] A derivative of indolepropionic acid was isolated and partially characterized. The expected stoichiometry according to equation (54) was not observed because tryptophan was simultaneously fermented to other products.

The enzymic reactions in proline reduction by *C. sticklandii* have been partially analyzed. Crude cell-free extracts catalyze a reduction of DL-proline by several dithiol compounds[161] according to equation (55). The most effective dithiol so far tested is 1,3-dimercaptopropanol. Several other

$$\text{DL-proline} + R(SH)_2 \rightarrow \text{δ-aminovalerate} + RS_2 \qquad (55)$$

dithiols, including 6,8-dimercapto-octanoate (reduced lipoic acid) and 1,2-dimercaptopropanol (BAL), are somewhat less active whereas monothiols like 2-mercaptoethanol are virtually inactive. Probably none of these compounds is the physiological reducing agent, since to be effective even 1,3-dimercaptopropanol must be used in a high concentration that is unlikely to occur in living cells. Furthermore, the reduction of proline by intact bacteria is relatively insensitive to inhibition by arsenite, whereas many reactions involving dithiols are extremely sensitive to this inhibitor. The physiological reducing agent has not been identified, but it is not reduced diphosphopyridine nucleotide.

The reduction of L-proline in the cell-free system apparently involves its conversion to D-proline [reaction (56)] followed by the reduction of the

$$\text{L-proline} \rightleftharpoons \text{D-proline} \qquad (56)$$

$$\text{D-proline} + R(SH)_2 \rightarrow \text{δ-aminovalerate} + RS_2 \qquad (57)$$

latter to δ-aminovalerate [reaction (57)].[162] The enzyme systems catalyzing these two reactions have been separated. Reaction (56) probably involves more than one enzyme, since there is evidence for the accumulation of an intermediate that has some but not all of the properties of D-proline.[163] The partially purified enzyme catalyzing reaction (57) cannot reduce L-proline.

Mg^{++}, Ca^{++}, and Mn^{++} stimulate the reduction of D-proline. There is no clear evidence for participation of either DPN or pyridoxal phosphate in the reaction.

The reduction of glycine by extracts of *C. sticklandii* can also be coupled with the oxidation of dithiols, but the reaction is more complex than the reduction of D-proline. A soluble enzyme system responsible for the reduction of glycine by 1,3-dimercaptopropanol appears to require orthophosphate and a phosphate acceptor such as adenosine monophosphate (AMP) or ADP for full activity.[153, 164] The orthophosphate and phosphate acceptor can be replaced by arsenate as in the triose phosphate dehydrogenase reaction. When orthophosphate (P_i) and ADP are used, one mole of ATP is formed per mole of glycine reduced in accordance with reaction (58). The

$$CH_2NH_2COOH + R(SH)_2 + P_i + ADP \rightarrow CH_3COOH + NH_3 + RS_2 + ATP \quad (58)$$

fact that arsenate can substitute for phosphate and ADP indicates that a high energy phosphoryl compound probably is formed as an intermediate and normally transfers its phosphoryl group to ADP. The identity of this intermediate has not been established but evidence for the existence of an intermediate between glycine and acetate has been presented.

The enzyme preparation responsible for the reduction of glycine also reduces proline. In the latter process, phosphate is not required and, when present, is not esterified. The difference between glycine and proline reduction, with respect to phosphorylation, may or may not also exist in intact bacteria. At present there is no indication that glycine is more effective than proline as an oxidant for growing cells.

IV. Conclusions

The energy metabolism of anaerobic organisms involves a coupling of the oxidation and reduction of organic substrates or products of substrate transformation. The oxidation reactions are frequently similar or identical to corresponding reactions catalyzed by aerobic organisms except for certain limitations imposed by the absence of oxygen. For example, the oxidative deamination of amino acids and the oxidative decarboxylation of keto acids occur in much the same ways in both aerobic and anaerobic species. However, the oxidation of aromatic compounds, like tyrosine, by anaerobic species appears to be generally restricted to an attack on the aliphatic side chain probably because of the need for direct participation of oxygen in hydroxylation and rupture of the benzene ring.[165] Aliphatic compounds are commonly oxidized to fatty acids which accumulate in the medium. Fatty acids are generally not decomposed by fermentative bacteria apparently because the first step in their oxidation occurs at such a high oxidation-reduction potential that it cannot be effectively coupled with other available oxidants. But aside from such limitations there is nothing distinctive about oxidations catalyzed by anaerobic bacteria.

The reduction reactions of fermentative organisms are more distinctive. The problem of providing organic oxidants has been solved in a variety of ways. Some species use a substrate directly as an oxidant. This is done, for example, by *Clostridium sporogenes* and other organisms that are capable of reducing glycine to acetic acid, proline to δ-aminovaleric acid, or trypto- phan to indolepropionic acid. Similarly, the purine-fermenting clostridia reduce uric acid to xanthine, and *Zymobacterium oroticum* reduces orotic acid to dihydro-orotic acid. Other species transform the nitrogenous sub- strate to a non-nitrogenous intermediate that is capable of serving as an oxidant. Examples of this are the conversion of serine to propionate, prob- ably via pyruvate, by *C. propionicum*, and the conversion of glutamate to butyrate via pyruvate and presumably acetyl-CoA by *C. tetanomorphum*. Another common method of accomplishing an anaerobic oxidation is by the removal of gaseous hydrogen. A striking example is the fermentation of threonine by *Micrococcus aerogenes* in which the oxidation of one mole of substrate to propionate and carbon dioxide is coupled with the forma- tion of one mole of hydrogen. This method of removing electrons is ob- viously only applicable when the reducing system operates at an oxidation- reduction potential well below that of the hydrogen electrode.

The fermentation reactions discussed in this chapter differ markedly with respect to the number of reactions that occur before the nitrogen is removed from the substrate. In several fermentations the nitrogen is re- moved in the first step. Examples of this are the nonoxidative deaminations of serine, threonine, and cysteine, the reductive deaminations of glycine and tryptophan, and the oxidative deamination or possibly transamination of various amino acids by bacteria utilizing the Stickland reaction. In other instances, one or more of the nitrogen atoms of the substrate are retained through a sequence of two or more reactions. Examples are the fermenta- tions of purines, pyrimidines, allantoin, arginine, histidine, and glutamate. In most fermentations of nitrogenous compounds much or all of the nitro- gen is ultimately converted to ammonia or urea. However, in a few fermen- tations some of the final products still retain a nitrogen atom. Some exam- ples are the accumulation of oxamic acid in the fermentation of allantoin by *Streptococcus allantoicus*, of glycine in the fermentation of purines by *C. cylindrosporum*, of indolepropionic acid in the fermentation of tryptophan by *C. sporogenes*, and of δ-aminovalerate in the reduction of proline or or- nithine by the same organism.

Only a few of these fermentations have been studied to the extent that we have a fairly comprehensive knowledge of all of their chemical steps. The Stickland reaction, and the fermentations of purines and glutamate are perhaps best understood, but conspicuous gaps exist in our knowledge of even these processes. In the Stickland reaction the mechanism of the reduction of glycine to acetic acid, coupled with the esterification of phosphate, is still obscure. In the purine fermentation, the path of acetate synthesis from carbon dioxide and the mechanism of the coupling between glycine or pyruvate oxidation and uric acid reduction are not understood. In the glutamate fermentation by *C. tetanomorphum* the novel reactions responsible for the conversion of glutamate to β-methylaspartate and the specific role of the pseudovitamin B_{12} coenzyme remain to be elucidated. Knowledge of the chemistry of most of the other fermentations is still highly fragmentary, in several instances consisting only of the quantitative identification of the products. Some fermentations of nitrogenous compounds undoubtedly still await discovery. Obviously this is an area which has not been thoroughly explored and in which significant discoveries can still be made.

REFERENCES

[1] P. Naviasky, *Arch. Hyg.* **66**, 209 (1908).
[2] W. Brasch, *Biochem. Z.* **18**, 380 (1909).
[3] F. Liebert, *Proc. Koninkl. Akad. Wetenschap. Amsterdam*, p. 990 (1909).
[4] L. H. Stickland, *Biochem. J.* **28**, 1746 (1934); **29**, 889 (1935).
[5] B. Nisman, *Bacteriol. Revs.* **18**, 16 (1954).
[6] C. E. Clifton, *Proc. Soc. Exptl. Biol. Med.* **43**, 588 (1940).
[7] C. E. Clifton, *J. Bacteriol.* **39**, 485 (1940).
[8] H. A. Barker, *Arch. Mikrobiol.* **10**, 376 (1939).
[9] E. Chargaff and D. B. Sprinson, *J. Biol. Chem.* **151**, 273 (1943).
[10] D. D. Woods and A. R. Trim, *Biochem. J.* **36**, 501 (1942).
[11] B. P. Cardon and H. A. Barker, *J. Bacteriol.* **52**, 629 (1946).
[12] G. N. Cohen, B. Nisman, and G. Cohen-Bazire, *Bull. soc. chim. biol.* **30**, 109 (1948).
[13] J. C. Hoogerheide and W. Kocholaty, *Biochem. J.* **32**, 949 (1938).
[14] S. Wiesendanger and B. Nisman, *Compt. rend. acad. sci.* **237**, 764 (1953).
[15] T. C. Stadtman, *J. Bacteriol.* **67**, 314 (1954).
[16] C. E. Clifton, *J. Bacteriol.* **44**, 179 (1942).
[17] M. J. Pickett, *J. Biol. Chem.* **151**, 203 (1943).
[18] D. D. Woods and C. E. Clifton, *Biochem. J.* **31**, 1774 (1937).
[19] J. K. Hardman, T. C. Stadtman, and J. Szulmajster, *Bacteriol. Proc. (Soc. Am. Bacteriologists)* p. 120 (1958).
[20] H. C. Jackins and H. A. Barker, *J. Bacteriol.* **61**, 101 (1951).
[21] B. P. Cardon and H. A. Barker, *Arch. Biochem.* **12**, 165 (1947).
[22] H. R. Whiteley, *J. Bacteriol.* **74**, 324 (1957).
[23] H. C. Douglas, *J. Bacteriol.* **62**, 517 (1951).
[24] D. Lewis and S. R. Elsden, *Biochem. J.* **60**, 683 (1955).
[25] W. A. Wood and I. C. Gunsalus, *J. Biol. Chem.* **181**, 171 (1949).
[26] E. R. Stadtman and P. R. Vagelos, *in "Proceedings of the International Symposium on Enzyme Chemistry*, Tokyo-Kyoto (1957)" (K. Ichihara, ed.), p. 86. Academic Press, 1958.
[27] F. W. Leaver, H. G. Wood, and R. Stjernholm, *J. Bacteriol.* **70**, 521 (1955).

[28] E. L. Foubert and H. C. Douglas, *J. Bacteriol.* **56,** 35 (1948).

[29] E. A. Delwiche, E. F. Phares, and S. F. Carson, *J. Bacteriol.* **71,** 598 (1956).

[30] H. R. Whiteley, *Proc. Natl, Acad. Sci. U. S.* **39,** 772, 779 (1953).

[31] A. T. Johns, *J. Gen. Microbiol.* **6,** 123 (1952).

[32] F. W. Leaver, H. G. Wood, and R. Stjernholm, *J. Bacteriol.* **70,** 521 (1955).

[33] H. A. Barker, "Bacterial Fermentations," p. 46. Wiley, New York, 1956.

[34] E. R. Stadtman, *Bull. soc. chim. biol.* **37,** 931 (1955).

[35] E. R. Stadtman, *J. Am. Chem. Soc.* **77,** 5765 (1955).

[36] D. D. Woods, *Biochem. J.* **30,** 1934 (1936).

[37] G. C. Schmidt, M. A. Logan, and A. A. Tytell, *J. Biol. Chem.* **198,** 771 (1952).

[38] H. D. Slade, *Arch. Biochem. Biophys.* **42,** 204 (1953).

[39] M. Korzenovsky and C. H. Werkman, *Arch. Biochem. Biophys,* **46,** 174 (1953).

[40] G. M. Hills, *Biochem. J.* **34,** 1057 (1940).

[41] B. Petrack, L. Sullivan, and S. Ratner, *Arch. Biochem. Biophys.* **69,** 186 (1957).

[42] S. Akumatsu and T. Sekine, *J. Biochem (Tokyo)* **38,** 349 (1951).

[43] H. D. Slade, C. C. Doughty, and W. C. Slamp. *Arch. Biochem. Biophys.* **48,** 338 (1954).

[44] M. E. Jones, L. Spector, and F. Lipmann, *J. Am. Chem. Soc.* **77,** 819 (1955).

[45] M. E. Jones, L. Spector, and F. Lipmann, *Proc. Intern. Congr. Biochem., 3rd Congr., Brussels 1955* p. 278 (1956).

[46] G. N. Cohen, B. Nisman, and G. Cohen-Bazire, *Bull. soc. chim. biol.* **30,** 109 (1948).

[47] A. I. Virtanen and N. Ellfolk, *in* "Methods in Enzymology" (S. P. Colowick and N. O. Kaplan, eds.), Vol. 2, p. 386. Academic Press, New York, 1955.

[48] A. Meister, H. A. Sober, and S. V. Tice, *J. Biol. Chem.* **189,** 577 (1951).

[49] R. M. Hicks, *Biochem. J.* **60,** iii (1955).

[50] D. Billen and H. C. Lichstein, *J. Bacteriol.* **58,** 215 (1949).

[51] S. Black and N. G. Wright, *in* "Symposium on Amino Acid Metabolism" (W. D. McElroy and B. Glass, eds.), p. 591. Johns Hopkins Press, Baltimore, Maryland, 1955.

[52] Y. Watanabe, S. Konishi, and K. Shimura, *J. Biochem. (Tokyo)* **44,** 299 (1957).

[53] C. Fromageot, *in* "The Enzymes: Chemistry and Mechanism of Action" (J. B. Sumner and K. Myrbäck, eds.), Vol. I, Part 2, Chapter 41, p. 1237. Academic Press, New York, 1951.

[54] H. L. A. Tarr, *Biochem. J.* **27,** 759 (1933).

[55] R. E. Kallio and J. R. Porter, *J. Bacteriol.* **60,** 607 (1950).

[56] P. Desnuelle and C. Fromageot, *Enzymologia* **6,** 80 (1939).

[57] P. Desnuelle, E. Wookey, and C. Fromageot, *Enzymologia* **8,** 225 (1940).

[58] C. Fromageot and T. P. Kiun, *Bull. soc. chim. biol.* **23,** 1471 (1941).

[59] R. E. Kallio, *J. Biol. Chem.* **192,** 371 (1951).

[60] R. E. Kallio and A. D. Larson, *in* "Symposium on Amino Acid Metabolism" (W. D. McElroy and B. Glass, eds.), p. 616. Johns Hopkins Press, Baltimore, Maryland, 1955.

[61] H. A. Barker, *Enzymologia* **2,** 175 (1937).

[62] H. A. Barker, *Arch. Mikrobiol.* **10,** 376 (1939).

[63] J. T. Wachsman and H. A. Barker, *J. Biol. Chem.* **217,** 695 (1955).

[64] B. A. Fry, *Biochem. J.* **60,** vi (1955).

[65] J. T. Wachsman, *J. Biol. Chem.* **223,** 19 (1956).

[66] H. A. Barker, R. D. Smyth, E. J. Wawszkiewicz, M. N. Lee, and R. M. Wilson, *Arch. Biochem. Biophys.* **78,** 468 (1958).

[67] H. A. Barker, R. D. Smyth, R. M. Wilson, and H. Weissbach, *J. Biol. Chem.* **234,** 320 (1959).

[68] A. Munch-Petersen and H. A. Barker, *J. Biol. Chem.* **230,** 649 (1958).

[69] H. A. Barker, H. Weissbach, and R. D. Smyth, *Proc. Natl. Acad. Sci. U.S.* **44,** 1093 (1958).

[70] R. S. Wolfe and D. J. O'Kane, *J. Biol. Chem.* **215,** 637 (1955).

[71] R. P. Mortlock and R. S. Wolfe, *Bacteriol. Proc. (Soc. Am. Bacteriologists)* p. 112 (1956).

[72] J. Adler, S. F. Wang, and H. A. Lardy, *J. Biol. Chem.* **229,** 865 (1957).

[73] H. A. Barker, B. E. Volcani, and B. P. Cardon, *J. Biol. Chem.* **173,** 803 (1948).

[74] F. M. Huennekens, M. J. Osborn, and H. R. Whiteley, *Science* **128,** 120 (1958).

[75] R. D. Sagers and I. C. Gunsalus, *Bacteriol. Proc. (Soc. Am. Bacteriologists)* p. 119 (1958).

[76] L. L. Campbell, *J. Biol. Chem.* **217,** 669 (1955).

[77] H. A. Barker, M. D. Kamen, and V. Haas, *Proc. Natl. Acad. Sci. U.S.* **31,** 355 (1945).

[78] L. Pine and H. A. Barker, *J. Bacteriol.* **68,** 216 (1954).

[79] H. Waelsch and A. Miller, *in* "Amino Acid Metabolism" (W. D. McElroy and B. Glass, eds.), p. 407. Johns Hopkins Press, Baltimore, Maryland, 1955.

[80] H. Tabor, *in* "Amino Acid Metabolism" (W. D. McElroy and B. Glass, eds.), p. 373. Johns Hopkins Press, Baltimore, Maryland, 1955.

[81] B. Magasanik and H. R. Bowser, *J. Biol. Chem.* **213,** 571 (1955).

[82] H. R. B. Revel and B. Magasanik, *J. Biol. Chem.* **233,** 930 (1958).

[83] R. L. Wickremasinghe and B. A. Fry, *Biochem. J.* **58,** 268 (1954).

[84] J. T. Wachsman, Ph.D. Thesis, University of California, Berkeley, California, 1955.

[85] A. Miller and H. Waelsch, *J. Biol. Chem.* **228,** 365 (1957).

[86] J. T. Wachsman and H. A. Barker, *J. Bacteriol.* **69,** 83 (1955).

[87] H. Tabor and J. C. Rabinowitz, *J. Am. Chem. Soc.* **78,** 5705 (1956).

[88] J. C. Rabinowitz and W. E. Pricer, Jr., *J. Am. Chem. Soc.* **78,** 5702 (1956).

[89] H. A. Barker, *Ann. inst. Pasteur* **77,** 361 (1949).

[90] E. F. Gale, *Biochem. J.* **35,** 66 (1941).

[91] O. Hayaishi, H. Tabor, and T. Hayaishi, *J. Biol. Chem.* **227,** 161 (1957).

[92] P. M. Dohner and B. P. Cardon, *J. Bacteriol.* **67,** 608 (1954).

[93] T. C. Stadtman and F. H. White, *J. Bacteriol.* **67,** 651 (1954).

[94] T. C. Stadtman, *in* "Amino Acid Metabolism" (W. D. McElroy and B. Glass, eds.), p. 493. Johns Hopkins Press, Baltimore, Maryland, 1955.

[95] A. Pardee and L. Prestidge, *J. Bacteriol.* **70,** 667 (1955).

[96] W. A. Wood and I. C. Gunsalus, *J. Biol. Chem.* **181,** 171 (1949).

[97] D. E. Metzler and E. E. Snell, *J. Biol. Chem.* **198,** 363 (1952).

[98] D. J. Walker, *Biochem. J.* **69,** 524 (1958).

[99] H. R. Whiteley and E. J. Ordal, *J. Bacteriol.* **74,** 331 (1957).

[100] H. A. Barker and T. Wiken, *Arch. Biochem.* **17,** 149 (1948).

[101] F. Kögl and D. G. Kostermans, *Z. physiol. Chem., Hoppe-Seyler's* **228,** 113 (1934).

[102] I. C. Gunsalus, C. C. Galeener, and J. R. Stamer, *in* "Methods in Enzymology" (S. P. Colowick and N. O. Kaplan, eds.), Vol. II, p. 238. Academic Press, New York, 1955.

[103] W. A. Wood, I. C. Gunsalus, and W. W. Umbreit, *J. Biol. Chem.* **170,** 313 (1947).

[104] W. Kocholaty and J. C. Hoogerheide, *Biochem. J.* **32,** 437 (1938).

[105] K. El-Shazly, *Biochem. J.* **51,** 647 (1952).

[106] M. Rhein, *Biochem. Z.* **87,** 123 (1918).

[107] M. Rhein, *Compt. rend. soc. biol.* **87,** 575 (1922).

[108] M. Rhein, *Compt. rend, soc. biol.* **84,** 561 (1921).

[109] A. Berthelot, *Compt. rend. acad. sci.* **164,** 196 (1917).

[110] R. W. Stone, H. E. Machamer, W. J. McAleer, and T. S. Oakwood, *Arch. Biochem.* **21,** 217 (1949).

[111] T. Sasaki and I. Otsuka, *J. Biol. Chem.* **32,** 533 (1917).

[112] T. Sasaki, *J. Biol. Chem.* **32,** 527 (1917).

[113] K. Hirai, *Biochem. Z.* **114,** 71 (1921).

[114] H. A. Barker and J. V. Beck, *J. Biol. Chem.* **141,** 3 (1941).

[115] L. L. Campbell, Jr., *J. Bacteriol.* **73,** 220 (1957).

[116] I. Harary, *J. Biol. Chem.* **227,** 815 (1957).

[117] H. R. Whiteley, *J. Bacteriol.* **63,** 163 (1952).

[118] H. R. Whiteley and H. C. Douglas, *J. Bacteriol.* **61,** 605 (1951).

[119] H. A. Barker, *J. Bacteriol.* **46,** 251 (1953).

[120] J. T. Wachsman and H. A. Barker, *J. Bacteriol.* **68,** 400 (1954).

[121] J. C. Rabinowitz and H. A. Barker, *J. Biol. Chem.* **218,** 161 (1956).

[122] J. C. Rabinowitz and H. A. Barker, *J. Biol. Chem.* **218,** 147 (1956).

[123] J. V. Beck, *J. Biol. Chem.* **176,** 1169 (1948).

[124] J. V. Beck, *Bacteriol. Proc.* (*Soc. Am. Bacteriologists*) p. 136 (1950).

[125] J. Rakosky, and J. V. Beck, *J. Bacteriol.* **69,** 563 (1955).

[126] J. Rakosky, L. N. Zimmerman, and J. V. Beck, *J. Bacteriol.* **69,** 566 (1955).

[127] W. H. Bradshaw, Ph.D. Thesis, University of California, Berkeley, California, 1957.

[128] J. L. Karlsson and H. A. Barker, *J. Biol. Chem.* **178,** 891 (1949).

[129] H. A. Barker, S. Ruben, and J. V. Beck, *Proc. Natl. Acad. Sci. U.S.* **26,** 477 (1940).

[130] W. H. Bradshaw and J. V. Beck, *Bacteriol Proc.* (*Soc. Am. Bacteriologists*) p. 86 (1953).

[131] N. Radin and H. A. Barker, *Proc. Natl. Acad. Sci. U.S.* **39,** 1196 (1953).

[132] J. C. Rabinowitz and W. E. Pricer, *J. Biol. Chem.* **218,** 189 (1956).

[133] J. C. Rabinowitz and W. E. Pricer, *J. Biol. Chem.* **218,** 175 (1956).

[134] J. C. Rabinowitz and W. E. Pricer, *J. Biol. Chem.* **222,** 537 (1956).

[135] K. Freter, J. C. Rabinowitz, and B. Witkop, *Ann.* **607,** 174 (1957).

[136] R. D. Sagers, J. V. Beck, W. Gruber, and I. C. Gunsalus, *J. Am. Chem. Soc.* **78,** 694 (1956).

[137] J. C. Rabinowitz and W. E. Pricer, Jr., *J. Am. Chem. Soc.* **78,** 5702 (1956).

[138] J. C. Rabinowitz and W. E. Pricer, Jr., *Federation Proc.* **16,** 236 (1957).

[139] J. C. Rabinowitz and W. E. Pricer, Jr., *J. Am. Chem. Soc.* **78,** 1513 (1956).

[140] J. C. Rabinowitz and W. E. Pricer, Jr., *J. Am. Chem. Soc.* **78,** 4176 (1956).

[141] J. C. Rabinowitz and W. E. Pricer, Jr., *Federation Proc.* **17,** 293 (1958).

[142] R. D. Sagers and J. V. Beck, *J. Bacteriol.* **72,** 199 (1956).

[143] J. C. Rabinowitz and W. E. Pricer, Jr., *Federation Proc.* **15,** 332 (1956).

[144] J. V. Beck, R. D. Sagers, and L. R. Morris, *J. Bacteriol.* **73,** 465 (1957).

[145] H. A. Barker and S. R. Elsden, *J. Biol. Chem.* **167,** 619 (1947).

[146] R. D. Sagers and J. V. Beck, *Arch. Biochem. Biophys.* **54,** 249 (1955).

[147] I. Lieberman and A. Kornberg, *Biochim. et. Biophys. Acta* **12,** 223 (1953).

[148] I. Lieberman and A. Kornberg, *J. Biol. Chem.* **207,** 911 (1954).

[149] I. Lieberman and A. Kornberg, *J. Biol. Chem.* **212,** 909 (1955).

[150] L. L. Campbell, Jr., *J. Bacteriol.* **73,** 225 (1957).

[151] I. Harary, *J. Biol. Chem.* **227,** 823 (1957).

[152] L. H. Stickland, *Biochem. J.* **29,** 288 (1935).

[153] T. C. Stadtman, P. Elliott, and L. Tiemann, *J. Biol. Chem.* **231,** 961 (1958).

[154] G. Cohen-Bazire, G. N. Cohen, and A.-R. Prévot, *Ann. inst. Pasteur* **75,** 291 (1948).

[155] B. Nisman and G. Vinet, *Ann. inst. Pasteur* **77,** 277 (1949).

[156] B. Nisman and G. Vinet, *Ann. inst. Pasteur* **78,** 115 (1950).

[157] B. Nisman, G. N. Cohen, M. Raynaud, and A. J. Rosenberg, *Bull. soc. chim. biol.* **29,** 650 (1947).

[158] S. Korkes, A. del Campillo, I. C. Gunsalus, and S. Ochoa, *J. Biol. Chem.* **193,** 721 (1951).

[159] I. C. Gunsalus, *in* "Mechanism of Enzyme Action" (W. D. McElroy and B. Glass, eds.), p. 545. Johns Hopkins Press, Baltimore, Maryland, 1954.

[160] B. Nisman and S. B. Wiesendanger, *Compt rend. acad. sci.* **238,** 292 (1954).

[161] T. C. Stadtman, *Biochem. J.* **62,** 614 (1956).

[162] T. C. Stadtman and P. Elliott, *J. Biol. Chem.* **228,** 983 (1957).

[163] T. C. Stadtman and L. Tiemann, *Abstr. Meeting Am. Chem. Soc., Miami* p. 25c (April 1957).

[164] T. C. Stadtman and P. Elliott, *J. Am. Chem. Soc.* **78,** 2020 (1956).

[165] H. S. Mason, *Advances in Enzymol.* **19,** 79 (1957).

CHAPTER 4

Cyclic Mechanisms of Terminal Oxidation

L. O. KRAMPITZ

I. Introduction

A. STATEMENT OF THE PROBLEM

Nature has endowed cells with unique and complicated cyclic mechanisms for the oxidation of foodstuffs to carbon dioxide and water. Teleologically one would assume the more direct these mechanisms, the more efficient the processes should be for the cell. Were the processes designed solely for obtaining energy for cellular functions by oxidation, one could question the rationale of the evolutionary processes. On the contrary, as if purposely to confuse researchers, a duality in purpose was conceived by nature. While the obtainment of energy through electron transfer for cellular functions is most important, the cell requires, in addition, carbon skeletons for the synthesis of cellular material. For example, if the only mechanism for the oxidation of carbohydrate substances were a cyclic pathway, none of the intermediates could be removed for biosynthesis of amino acids, fats, or other constituents of the cell, since the cyclic process would be interrupted and oxidation would cease. A cyclic mechanism with provisions for replacement of cyclic components appears to be a most efficient mechanism for the synthesis of these cellular components and for the yield of energy by oxidation. It is the intent of this chapter to describe these cyclic mechanisms, particularly as they relate to the way by which the various microbial cells obtain energy for their life processes and the synthesis of cellular components.

B. The Role of Cyclic Mechanisms

After the discovery of the Harden and Young ester (fructose 1,6-diphosphate) in 1906,[1] the elucidation of the mechanism of fermentation of glucose to lactic acid by muscle tissue and to ethyl alcohol and carbon dioxide by yeast was rapidly achieved (see Chapter 2, Vol. II). The two processes were found to be almost identical. The main difference concerns the fate of pyruvic acid, which is one of the common intermediates in the sequence of reactions catalyzed by both tissues. In muscle tissue, the pyruvic acid is reduced to lactic acid by the electrons involved in the oxidative step in the conversion of 3-phosphoglyceraldehyde to 1,3-diphosphoglyceric acid. Electron transfer is mediated by diphosphopyridine nucleotide (DPN+). In yeast, on the other hand, pyruvic acid is decarboxylated to acetaldehyde and carbon dioxide, and the electrons involved in the oxidative step referred to above reduce the acetaldehyde to ethyl alcohol. It was soon established that many microorganisms metabolized glucose via pyruvic acid in a similar manner. These processes are anaerobic and by definition are fermentative, i.e., the electrons involved in the oxidative step are transferred to an acceptor other than oxygen. In view of the fact that pyruvic acid appeared to be a cardinal intermediate of carbohydrate metabolism, many investigators turned their attention toward the elucidation of the mechanism of complete oxidation of this acid. Most of the early information was obtained employing tissues from mammalian origin. The reason was twofold: (1) considerable seemingly related information gained from experimental work with mammalian tissue was at hand, and (2) as will be shown subsequently, certain criteria for the ultimate proof of a metabolic series of events were more easily met by the use of mammalian tissue.

During the last two decades, a great deal of research has been done in an attempt to establish these pathways of oxidation in microorganisms, employing the same criteria which were so successful with mammalian tissue. In order fully to appreciate the problems concerned with microbial experimentation in this area, a brief historical account of the early events and a description of these criteria with mammalian tissue is pertinent. It is not the purpose of this chapter to describe the detailed enzymic mechanisms of the pathways of oxidative metabolism, which can be found in several excellent textbooks of biochemistry.

II. Historical Development of Cyclic Mechanisms

A. C$_4$ DICARBOXYLIC ACID CYCLE OF SZENT-GYÖRGYI

Szent-Györgyi[2] found that the oxidation of carbohydrate by minced muscle tissue was greatly stimulated by the addition of very small amounts of fumaric, malic, oxalacetic, and succinic acids. He recognized the importance of these C$_4$ dicarboxylic acids for the oxidative metabolism of carbohydrates, and proposed that they were acting catalytically as electron carriers to oxygen. Figure 1 illustrates his concept. It is important to observe that the C$_4$ dicarboxylic acids are *not* intermediates in the oxidation of the carbon skeleton of the carbohydrate. They serve only as electron carriers. Thus, while this so-called C$_4$ dicarboxylic acid cycle can explain the transfer of electrons to oxygen, the ultimate electron acceptor, with the formation of water, it provides no information as to the pathway of carbon dioxide formation. In the process, oxalacetic acid accepts two electrons from an oxidative step in carbohydrate oxidation, forming malic acid. The elements of water are removed from malic acid to form fumaric acid. The latter acid is reduced by another oxidative step in carbohydrate oxidation to succinic acid. The

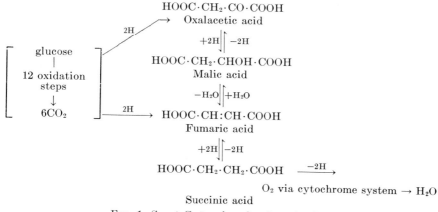

FIG. 1. Szent-Györgyi cycle of respiration.

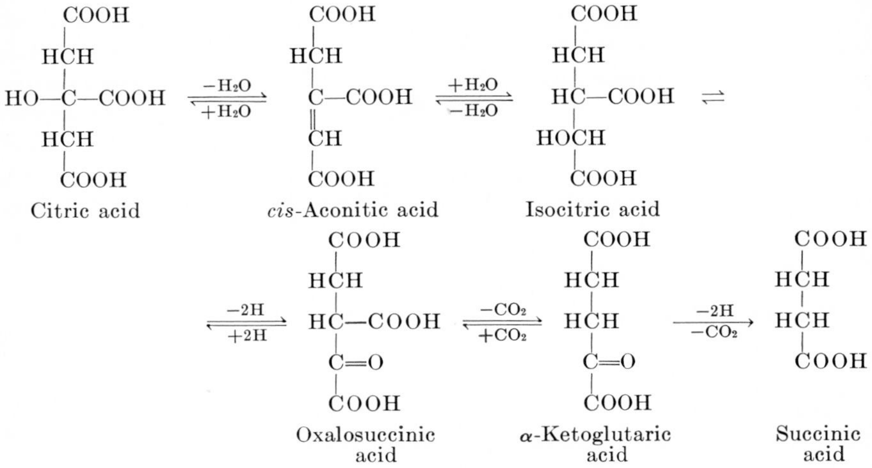

$$
\begin{array}{ccccc}
\text{COOH} & & \text{COOH} & & \text{COOH} \\
| & & | & & | \\
\text{HCH} & & \text{HCH} & & \text{HCH} \\
| & \xrightarrow[\,+H_2O\,]{\,-H_2O\,} & | & \xrightarrow[\,-H_2O\,]{\,+H_2O\,} & | \\
\text{HO—C—COOH} & & \text{C—COOH} & & \text{HC—COOH} \quad \rightleftharpoons \\
| & & \| & & | \\
\text{HCH} & & \text{CH} & & \text{HOCH} \\
| & & | & & | \\
\text{COOH} & & \text{COOH} & & \text{COOH} \\
\text{Citric acid} & & \textit{cis-}\text{Aconitic acid} & & \text{Isocitric acid}
\end{array}
$$

$$
\begin{array}{ccccccc}
& & \text{COOH} & & \text{COOH} & & \text{COOH} \\
& & | & & | & & | \\
& & \text{HCH} & & \text{HCH} & & \text{HCH} \\
& \xrightarrow[\,+2H\,]{\,-2H\,} & | & \xrightarrow[\,+CO_2\,]{\,-CO_2\,} & | & \xrightarrow[\,-CO_2\,]{\,-2H\,} & | \\
& & \text{HC—COOH} & & \text{HCH} & & \text{HCH} \\
& & | & & | & & | \\
& & \text{C=O} & & \text{C=O} & & \text{COOH} \\
& & | & & | & & \\
& & \text{COOH} & & \text{COOH} & & \\
& & \text{Oxalosuccinic} & & \alpha\text{-Ketoglutaric} & & \text{Succinic} \\
& & \text{acid} & & \text{acid} & & \text{acid}
\end{array}
$$

Fig. 2. Pathway of oxidation of citric acid.

succinic acid is reoxidized to oxalacetic acid with the electrons passing to oxygen via the cytochrome system with the formation of water. After twelve such oxidation steps the carbohydrate is oxidized to carbon dioxide. As mentioned previously, the proposed mechanism does not provide information concerning the intermediates of carbohydrate oxidation.

A series of reactions involving tricarboxylic acids which was apparently related to the C_4 dicarboxylic acid cycle was studied by Martius and Knoop.[3, 4] These investigators found that liver tissue rapidly oxidized citric acid to succinic acid. They presented evidence to indicate that the series of reactions depicted in Fig. 2 were involved. While not all of the intermediate steps in the oxidation of citric acid to succinic acid were rigorously proven, the scheme indicated a possible relationship between tricarboxylic and dicarboxylic acids which were rapidly metabolized by many types of tissue.

B. TRICARBOXYLIC ACID CYCLE OF KREBS

Krebs and Johnson in 1937[5] by brilliantly conceived experiments were able to establish the relationship and to demonstrate the pathway of carbohydrate oxidation by mammalian tissue. They showed that catalytic amounts of citric acid greatly stimulated the respiration of minced pigeon breast muscle, particularly if carbohydrate was present. Instead of assuming that citric acid was serving as an electron carrier, as had Szent-Györgyi for the dicarboxylic acids, Krebs believed that citric acid resulted from the condensation of some derivative of carbohydrate cleavage with oxalacetic acid. The oxidation of citric acid to succinate by reactions shown in Fig. 2, and of succinate to oxalacetate by the reactions shown in Fig. 1, completed

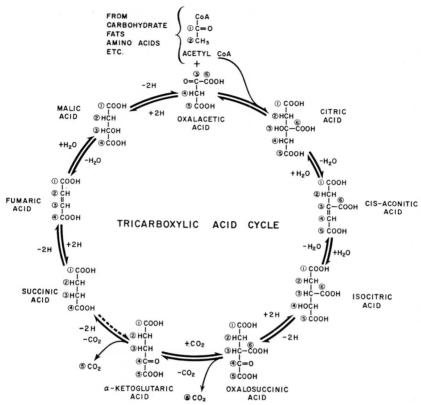

FIG. 3. Tricarboxylic acid cycle.

a cycle with the elimination of two carbon atoms (originally from carbohydrate) as carbon dioxide. After completion of the cycle, oxalacetate was condensed again with a carbohydrate derivative to form citric acid and the cycle initiated again. This cycle is referred to as the Krebs cycle or the tricarboxylic acid cycle (TCA cycle) and is shown in Fig. 3.

III. Criteria for Establishment of Cyclic Mechanisms

A. RATES OF REACTION

Krebs and Johnson established that the rates of all the individual oxidative reactions of the cycle they were able to test were commensurate with the total rate of oxidation of citrate. One of the premises held at that time was that for a proposed compound to be an intermediate in a sequence of metabolic reactions, it must be converted to the same end products as the parent compound, and at an equal or greater rate. While this assumption is reasonable, subsequent work, as will be discussed later, has shown that the rate of reactions, particularly with whole cell preparations, is not a reliable criterion for the establishment of intermediary sequences. Nevertheless, in these investigations by Krebs and co-workers, rate studies were of incalculable value. They were also able to confirm the observations made by Martius and Knoop[3, 4] who had shown the conversion of citric acid to α-ketoglutaric acid. Arsenite, a specific inhibitor of α-keto acid oxidation, was used to inhibit the further oxidation of α-ketoglutaric acid. The conversion of citric acid to succinic acid was also demonstrated by the use of malonic acid as an inhibitor of succinic acid oxidation.

It has been emphasized that the cycle provides a mechanism for the oxidation of carbohydrates to carbon dioxide. Because of the major position held by pyruvic acid in intermediary carbohydrate metabolism, it was thought that this acid was involved in the primary condensation reaction with oxalacetic acid. As a result of the excellent work by Lipmann[6] and his co-workers, Lynen[7] and co-workers, Ochoa[8] and co-workers, Gunsalus[9] and co-workers (see Chapter 1, Vol. II), and Green[10] and co-workers, it has been established that the acetyl derivative of coenzyme A (acetyl CoA) is the moiety derived from the oxidative decarboxylation of pyruvic acid, which condenses with oxalacetic acid to form citric acid.

Perhaps the most important contribution of Krebs and Johnson in 1937 was the demonstration of the synthesis of citric acid from oxalacetic acid. Prior to this time, considerable work had been done with various microorganisms which formed large quantities of citric acid, and it had been suggested that a C_4 dicarboxylic acid and a C_2 fragment were involved in the synthesis.[11, 12] Detailed evidence, however, was not available. The experiments by Krebs and Johnson employing minced pigeon breast muscle showed that large amounts of citric acid were synthesized anaerobically from oxalacetic acid. These investigators were not at that time able to ascertain the nature of the moiety which condensed with oxalacetic acid to form citric acid, but as stated above, we now know it to be acetyl CoA. Perhaps in these experiments acetyl CoA was endogenously present and pyruvic acid, which arose from the decarboxylation of a portion of the oxalacetic acid, was oxidized to acetyl CoA by an anaerobic dismutation reaction. Nevertheless, the synthesis of citric acid, a very important reaction for the concept of the TCA cycle, was demonstrated.

B. Quantitative Aspects and Malonate Inhibition

Krebs and Eggleston[13] later made the following significant observation which indicated the quantitative importance of the cycle in pigeon breast muscle. They demonstrated that malonate completely inhibited the oxidation of pyruvate by this tissue. This result was compatible with either the Szent-Györgyi C_4 dicarboxylic acid cycle or the TCA cycle, since succinic dehydrogenase is required by both mechanisms. In the former mechanism the flow of electrons would be interrupted inasmuch as the oxidation and reduction of succinic acid were inhibited. In the TCA cycle mechanism, the inhibitor prevented the formation of oxalacetate by inhibiting the oxidation of succinic acid, thereby stopping the cyclic mechanism. If the mechanism of the TCA cycle were valid, pyruvic acid should be aerobically oxidized by malonate poisoned muscle if the oxidation product of succinic acid, i.e., fumaric acid, were also added. In this manner oxalacetate could be derived from the oxidation of fumarate and the cycle could be initiated in spite of the inhibition of the oxidation of succinate. Such an experiment was performed and the following stoichiometry obtained:

$$\text{Pyruvate} + \text{fumarate} + 2O_2 \xrightarrow[\text{inhibited}]{\text{malonate}} \text{succinate} + 3CO_2 + H_2O$$

$$C_3H_4O_3 + C_4H_4O_4 + 2O_2 \longrightarrow C_4H_6O_4 + 3CO_2 + H_2O$$

Four oxidative steps occur which account for the four atoms of oxygen consumed. They are: (1) oxidation of fumarate via malate to oxalacetate; (2) oxidation of pyruvate to acetyl CoA and carbon dioxide; (3) oxidation of isocitrate, formed via citrate from acetyl CoA and oxalacetate, to oxalosuccinate; and (4) oxidation of α-ketoglutarate, formed by decarboxylation of oxalosuccinate, to succinate and carbon dioxide.

This experiment demonstrated clearly that succinate could arise oxidatively from pyruvate under conditions where the reductive pathway of succinate formation was inhibited by malonate. The oxidation of pyruvate by the inhibited muscle tissue could only occur when a C_4 dicarboxylic acid (a source of oxalacetate) other than succinic acid was simultaneously added.

While Krebs and co-workers were developing the important concept of the tricarboxylic acid cycle, Wood and Werkman[14] were developing the equally important concept of heterotrophic carbon dioxide fixation (see Chapter 2, Vol. III). It has been previously stated that in the TCA cycle, as it occurs in muscle tissue, if any of the C_4 dicarboxylic acids were removed for any other purpose, the cycle would be interrupted unless these acids were resynthesized. Working with the propionic acid bacteria, Wood and Werkman[15] showed that these organisms formed considerable quantities of succinic acid when glycerol was fermented in the presence of sodium bicarbonate. These results suggested that succinic acid was formed from oxalacetate which had been synthesized by carbon dioxide fixation with pyruvate. This reaction proved to be very important for the elucidation of the tricarboxylic acid cycle in liver tissue. In an attempt to demonstrate the TCA cycle in pigeon liver, Evans[16] demonstrated that the oxidative removal of pyruvic acid was not inhibited by malonate and that α-ketoglutarate and succinate accumulated. It appeared that an unknown mechanism for the synthesis of C_4 dicarboxylic acids existed in liver. These results were in direct contradiction with the results of similar experiments employing muscle tissue. Other experiments established that the TCA cycle was operative in liver tissue, thus posing the question of the mechanism by which liver tissue brought about a synthesis of C_4 dicarboxylic acids under conditions of malonate poisoning. Wood and Werkman[17] and Krebs and Eggleston[18] suggested that the carbon dioxide fixation reaction discovered by Wood and Werkman, i.e., pyruvate + carbon dioxide → oxalacetate, was the mechanism by which liver tissue synthesized the C_4 dicarboxylic acid required for the oxidation of pyruvate under conditions of malonate poisoning. Evans and Slotin[19] employed the isotope of carbon C^{11} to demonstrate that carbon dioxide was fixed in α-ketoglutarate, which indicated that the Wood and Werkman reaction was involved. Wood and collaborators[20] established that carbon dioxide fixation occurred, and determined some quantitative aspects of the TCA cycle in pigeon liver. In order to understand more easily the importance of this work, the reader is referred to Fig. 3. These investigators used pyruvic acid and $NaHC^{13}O_3$ as substrates under aerobic conditions, in the presence of malonate as an inhibitor of succinic dehydrogenase. If it is assumed that pigeon liver can catalyze the fixation of carbon dioxide with pyruvic acid to form oxalacetic acid and that the oxidation of pyruvic acid can occur with the formation of acetyl CoA, the latter will condense with the oxalacetic acid to form citric acid. The malonic acid will inhibit succinic dehydrogenase and therefore succinic acid cannot be formed by a reductive reaction, nor can it be oxidized after formation from the oxidation of α-ketoglutaric acid. Malic and fumaric acids will be formed by the reduction of the oxalacetate formed by carbon dioxide fixation and will consequently contain C^{13} in their carboxyl groups. The tracing of the isotope in the various compounds as illustrated in Fig. 3 should be done literally. As depicted two-dimensionally on paper, citric acid appears to be a symmetrical compound and as such one would expect aconitase to remove the elements of water in a symmetrical manner. That is, one-half of the molecules of aconitic acid would have the double bond above the center carbon atom, number 3 as written, and the remaining molecules would have the double bond below the center atom. The formation of isocitric acid by the action of aconitase would place the hydroxyl group alpha to carbon atom number one in half of the molecules, and gamma to carbon atom one in the other half of the molecules. After oxidation of the isocitric acid to succinic acid, isotope would appear in a carboxyl group of half of the succinic acid molecules. The experimental results (Table I) showed that the succinate did not contain isotope. Wood and co-workers interpreted these results to indicate that isocitric acid is the product of condensation of

TABLE I
DISTRIBUTION OF C^{13} IN TRICARBOXYLIC ACIDS BY PIGEON LIVER[a]

Compound	Excess C^{13} (%)
α-Ketoglutaric acid	
α-Carboxyl group carbon atom	1.1
Remaining 4 carbon atoms	0.03
Succinic acid	0.08
Citric, malic, and fumaric acid carboxyl group carbon atoms	0.8

[a] For particulars of experiments see ref. 20.

the moiety from pyruvic acid and oxalacetic acid and that the equilibrium catalyzed by aconitase (i.e., formation of citric acid) did not occur or was extremely sluggish. Subsequent work has shown that citric acid is the primary product but that enzymically it exhibits asymmetrical properties which account for the observed results. Under these circumstances it will be observed that the carboxyl group adjacent to the keto group of α-ketoglutaric acid does contain isotope which is evolved as carbon dioxide during the oxidative step to succinic acid. Under conditions of the experiment, i.e., malonic acid present as an inhibitor of succinic dehydrogenase, α-ketoglutarate accumulated sufficiently to permit its isolation and analysis for isotopic content. It was not understood why α-ketoglutarate accumulated; but for the establishment of the occurrence and quantitative importance of the TCA cycle under these conditions, this accumulation was indeed fortunate. It must be recalled that while Krebs and co-workers had established the framework of the TCA cycle, practically no information was available concerning the intimate mechanisms. Had α-ketoglutaric acid not accumulated, the employment of $C^{13}O_2$ as the tracer isotope would not have yielded any definitive results, since the succinate contained no isotope. By determining quantitatively the α-ketoglutaric acid and finding the C^{13} exclusively in the carboxyl group adjacent to the keto group, Wood and co-workers were able to confirm the existence of the TCA cycle and to establish the synthesis of oxalacetic acid from pyruvic acid and CO_2 as a mechanism for the synthesis of the C_4 decarboxylic acid so essential for maintenance of the TCA cycle. Within a short time all of the individual steps of the TCA cycle were clearly established.

From all of these results there could be no doubt as to the importance of the TCA cycle in mammalian tissue. Nevertheless very little data were at hand which permitted a rigorous evaluation as to its quantitative importance. The possibility remained that some other mechanism which included some of the same intermediates as the TCA cycle, but not in the same sequence, was equally as important. Until such data are at hand it is always dangerous to eliminate other mechanisms. The latter warning is exemplified particularly in the area of carbohydrate metabolism (see Chapter 2). A few years ago, the only mechanism which was well established for the breakdown of glucose was that referred to as the Embden-Meyerhof scheme. We now know there are several other mechanisms and that these mechanisms exist in organisms and tissues formerly believed to contain exclusively the Embden-Meyerhof pathway. This point will be referred to again.

IV. Criterion of Rates of Reaction Applied to Microorganisms

In their original work, Krebs and Johnson found that many mammalian tissues oxidized citric acid in addition to synthesizing it from oxalacetate. They concluded that these tissues possessed the TCA cycle. On the other hand, they inferred that yeast and *Escherichia coli* did not possess the cycle, since these organisms could not oxidize citric acid at an appreciable rate; furthermore, some of the other criteria applicable to mammalian tissue were not satisfied with these microbial systems. This immediately posed the problem of the mechanism employed by microorganisms to oxidize carbohydrates or their breakdown products. Furthermore, it is well known that many microorganisms can grow with acetic acid as the sole source of carbon. Since the TCA cycle required a source of dicarboxylic acid for continuance of the cycle, it was reasoned that these organisms must have an unknown mechanism for the synthesis of the C_4 dicarboxylic acid from acetic acid, or that an unknown pathway existed for the oxidation of acetic acid.

It can be readily shown that many microorganisms either will not oxidize citric acid, or oxidize it at a rate not commensurate with the rate of oxidation of glucose, pyruvate, or acetate. On the other hand, many of these same organisms will oxidize the C_4 dicarboxylic acids at a very rapid rate. This observation made it attractive to propose that microorganisms possessed a pathway of oxidation comparable to a scheme suggested by Thunberg many years ago.[21] Figure 4 outlines the essential features of this pathway. The important, yet not conclusively demonstrated, step is the oxidative condensation of two molecules of acetic acid to succinic acid. The remaining reactions have many features in common with the reactions involving C_4 dicarboxylic acid components of the TCA cycle. The oxidation process has essentially resulted in the oxidation of one mole of acetic acid to carbon dioxide and water. All of the steps, with the exception of the oxidative condensation of two molecules of acetic acid to succinic acid, can be demonstrated in many microorganisms. Many attempts have been made to demonstrate the condensation step, but no conclusive evidence exists that it occurs. In those cases where claims for its demonstration in bacteria have been made, the reaction appears to be so sluggish that it is of little

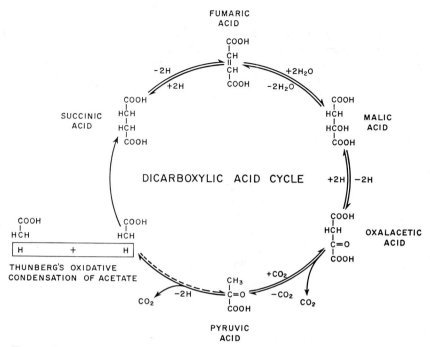

FIG. 4. Dicarboxylic acid cycle for oxidation of acetic acid. Net result: The oxidation of one molecule of acetic acid to carbon dioxide and water. Cycle repeats.

consequence.[22] In keeping with other warnings stated above it would be folly to deny the existence of the reaction; however, more definitive evidence is required. Evidence against this cycle in some microorganisms will be presented later. More important at this stage of the discussion is the fact that if the criterion of rates of reaction is taken as evidence for the operation of a cyclic mechanism in microorganisms, the occurrence of the TCA cycle would appear to be excluded. Much of the early work with microorganisms was done with *E. coli*, and additional evidence against the existence of the TCA cycle in this organism was the well-known fact that citric acid will not serve as the sole source of carbon for its growth. On the other hand, it is also known that if some readily metabolized nutrients, such as peptone, glucose, or acetate, are added to the growth medium, citrate will be readily metabolized.[23] Apparently the cell wall is impermeable to citrate and an inducible mechanism for its transfer is present which is facilitated by the presence of nutrients that are utilized in a noninducible manner. Unless all the intimate details (on an enzyme level) concerning rate studies of a series of reactions are known, caution must be exercised in interpreting the data obtained from such studies. This caution is well exemplified in the case of acetate oxidation by muscle tissue. It has been stated previously that Krebs and his co-workers were confident that some derivative from carbohydrate metabolism condensed with oxalacetate to form citric acid, i.e., the first reaction in the cycle. In an attempt to elucidate this step they came to the conclusion that pyruvic acid condensed with oxalacetate to form a seven-carbon compound which was oxidatively decarboxylated to citric acid. The main reason for this proposal was that acetate was not oxidized by muscle at a rate commensurate with the rate of oxidation of pyruvate. When pyruvate is oxidatively decarboxylated, acetyl CoA is an early product of the reaction, and it is this derivative and not the free acetic acid which condenses with oxalacetate to form citrate. When free acetate is added it must first be converted to acetyl CoA, and the preparations used by the early investigators were incapable of performing this metabolic act. Therefore in drawing conclusions from data obtained from rate studies, one must be aware of (1) the permeability problems, and (2) the possibility that the substrate one is dealing with is not the one actually employed by the cell.

V. Rate Studies with Bacteria: *Micrococcus lysodeikticus* and *Escherichia coli*

Rate studies have been extensively performed with two microorganisms, an aerobe, *Micrococcus lysodeikticus*, and a facultative anaerobe, *E. coli*. Typical results obtained with *M. lysodeikticus* are given in Table II.[24] With whole cells the rates of oxidation of acetate, α-ketoglutarate, fumarate, and succinate are all comparable. Citrate is not oxidized. Cells that have been partially lysed with lysozyme exhibit similar rates. Cells that have been disrupted by glass-grinding oxidize citrate rapidly but such preparations, in contrast to the whole cells or to cells which have been partially lysed by lysozyme, oxidize α-ketoglutarate very slowly. Neither of these preparations

TABLE II

RATES OF OXIDATION BY *Micrococcus lysodeikticus*[a]

Compound	μl. O_2 consumed at 60 min.		
	Whole cells	Partially lysed cells	Glass-ground cells
Acetate	214	210	122
Citrate	0	20	204
α-Ketoglutarate	229	260	82
Fumarate	235	205	242
Succinate	240	232	256

[a] For particulars of experiments see ref. 24.

TABLE III

RATES OF OXIDATION BY *Escherichia coli*[a]

Compound	μl. Oxygen consumed at 60 min.			
	E. coli (E-26)		E. coli (Crookes)	
	Whole cells	Extracts and particles	Whole cells	Extracts and particles
Citrate	2	110	3	241
cis-Aconitate	12	90	22	190
Isocitrate	12	87	20	210
α-Ketoglutarate	222	58	145	162
Succinate	741	334	800	292
Acetate	625	8	665	6

[a] For particulars of experiments see refs. 25, 26.

satisfies the rate criterion and on this basis if each preparation is taken individually the TCA cycle could be excluded. However, the combined properties of the lysed preparation and the glass-ground preparation are such that the rate criterion is satisfied.

Table III illustrates rates of oxidation of some of the tricarboxylic and dicarboxylic acids by whole cells and disrupted cells of two strains of *E. coli*.[25, 26] Whole cells of both strains are practically incapable of oxidizing citrate, *cis*-aconitate, or isocitrate. Their ability to oxidize α-ketoglutarate is greater, but cannot compare with the ability of these cells to oxidize acetate or succinate. Clearly on the basis of rate of oxidation the C_6 tricarboxylic acids or α-ketoglutaric acid are not intermediates in the oxidation of acetate. On the other hand, succinate could be an intermediate on this basis. Malic and fumaric acids, data for which are not shown in the table, are oxidized as rapidly as is succinate. An entirely different result is obtained with disrupted cells of these two strains. During the preparation of disrupted cells the enzymes responsible for the activation of acetic acid (formation of acetyl CoA) are damaged; therefore the rate of oxidation of pyruvate is more indicative of the true rate of oxidation of acetate. Of particular significance is that with both preparations and particularly with the preparation obtained from the Crookes strain, the rate of oxidation of citrate, *cis*-aconitate, and isocitrate has been considerably increased. It might be concluded that the whole cells do not oxidize acetate by way of the TCA cycle, and that the dicarboxylic acid cycle is of importance. On the other hand, the criterion of rate would indicate that the TCA cycle is in operation when the cells are disrupted.

These data obtained from experiments with *M. lysodeikticus* and *E. coli* illustrate vividly the dangers of depending exclusively on rate studies. It will be shown that the TCA cycle is the major pathway of oxidation of acetate by both of these organisms. In all probability, disrupted preparations are capable of oxidizing the tricarboxylic acids more rapidly than whole cells because a permeability barrier has been destroyed, although this has not been proved. The data on pyruvate and acetate oxidation by disrupted cells of both strains of *E. coli* also illustrate the difficulties sometimes encountered when a substrate which is only related to the actual substrate is added. Acetate is not the actual substrate, and cannot be converted to acetyl CoA, which is the substrate. It is obvious, therefore, that caution should be exercised when determining whether a compound is an intermediate. Even if the criterion of rates of reaction were satisfied, such data do not reveal any information concerning the sequence in which the reactions are occurring. In order to obtain evidence for the oxidation by the TCA cycle it is necessary to establish that the various reactions occur in the sequence dictated by the cycle. Sometimes this important fact is neglected. The mere demonstration of the presence of all the enzymes required for the TCA cycle does not give any indication of the quantitative importance of the entire cycle in the cell. It is obvious that even if the cycle accounted only for a small percentage of the total oxidation of acetate, the various enzymes could be readily demonstrated. If the remaining pathway of oxidation was entirely unknown, the experiments might not detect it. Furthermore, the demonstration of the existence of the enzymes of the TCA cycle does not reveal the sequence in which the reactions occur.

VI. Carrier Type of Experiments Employing Isotopes

An ideal approach to the problem of establishing the existence of a cyclic process such as the TCA cycle is the use of specific inhibitors, as done so successfully by Krebs and Wood and their co-workers. It will be recalled that Krebs and Eggleston added fumarate and pyruvate to the malonate-inhibited pigeon breast muscle preparation in order to initiate the cyclic events. It was demonstrated that under these conditions the cycle proceeded quantitatively with the accumulation of succinate. Unfortunately, these techniques have not been too successful in causing the accumulation of intermediates of the cycle with the various microorganisms thus far investigated. Therefore, the expedient of oxidizing an isotopically labeled substrate in the presence of a pool of nonlabeled compounds suspected of being intermediates has been employed. These types of experiments have been termed *carrier-type* experiments. The theory is that if the isotopic substrate were oxidized through an intermediate which is common to the nonisotopic pool, the two should mix and the compound of the pool should contain isotope, the pool being sufficiently large to permit isolation of the compound. By isolation and determination of the position of the isotope in the compound and its specific activity, one may draw conclusions concerning the possible mechanism of oxidation. Unfortunately, this rather simple technique has not been as fruitful as one might predict. The hypothesis upon which this technique rests assumes mixing or equilibration of the metabolically produced intermediate and the added carrier. There is considerable evidence that this is not always the case—both with the whole cell preparations and with soluble preparations. Results obtained from experiments of this type will be discussed, inasmuch as they have been frequently cited either to refute or substantiate the TCA cycle in microorganisms.

Saz and Krampitz[27] and Ajl and co-workers[28] conducted experiments of this type with *M. lysodeikticus*. Acetate-2-C[14] was oxidized in the presence of nonisotopic α-ketoglutarate and succinate. At the end of the experiment, the residual acetate, α-ketoglutarate, and succinate were isolated and degraded, and the specific radioactivity of the various carbon atoms determined (see Table IV). Examination of the specific radioactivities indicates serious inadequacies in the experimental approach. It will be observed that the specific activities of the carbon atoms of α-ketoglutarate are lower than those of the corresponding carbon atoms of succinate. If α-ketoglutarate is the precursor of succinate as it is in the TCA cycle, the specific radioactivity of the corresponding carbon atoms of the former cannot be lower, but must be equal to or greater than those of succinate. If the specific activity in α-ketoglutarate is greater, one can explain the results by postulating a source of succinate from some other nonisotopic source within the cell which will dilute the radioactivity of the succinate. Of particular sig-

TABLE IV

OXIDATION OF ACETATE-2-C[14] BY *M. lysodeikticus* IN THE PRESENCE OF NONISOTOPIC α-KETOGLUTARATE AND SUCCINATE[a]

Succinate	c.p.m./mmole	α-Ketoglutarate	c.p.m./mmole
COOH	2,943	COOH	661
H$_2$C, H$_2$C	5,217	H$_2$C, H$_2$C	2,241
COOH	2,943	C=O	661
		COOH	1,409
	Initial acetate	300,000	
	Final acetate	98,500	
	Respiratory CO$_2$	50,620	

[a] For particulars of experiments see ref. 27.

nificance is the fact that the specific activity of the respiratory CO_2 is *many times* greater than that of the carboxyl carbon atoms of either α-keto-glutarate or succinate. Since the carboxyl carbon atoms of the various acids in the TCA cycle are the precursors of the respiratory carbon dioxide, it is impossible, when the cycle operates, for the radioactivity of the respiratory carbon dioxide to be greater than that of the precursor carboxyl carbon atoms. The specific activity may be the same as or less than that of the corresponding carboxyl carbon atoms, but never greater. If it is less, carbon dioxide has been derived from other nonisotopic sources which will dilute the radioactive carbon dioxide. It would thus appear that if the TCA cycle is involved in the oxidation of acetate by *M. lysodeikticus*, it accounts for only a fraction of the total process, and some other unknown mechanism is more important. An alternative explanation is that the *added* succinate and α-ketoglutarate, i.e., the carrier compounds, may not completely equilibrate with the succinate and α-ketoglutarate which arise from the acetate via the oxidative cycle. In other words, there may have been substrate-enzyme or substrate-coenzyme complexes of succinate and α-ketoglutarate which arose as integral components of the cycle and did not mix thoroughly with the succinate and α-ketoglutarate which were added as carriers. The latter would obviously not contain the full complement of radioactivity present in the acetate.

Similar experiments performed with *E. coli*[29] produced results which can be interpreted in an entirely different manner (see Table V). The relative incorporation of acetate-2-C^{14} into α-ketoglutarate added as a carrier when compared to the succinate is much less than in *M. lysodeikticus*. The degree of incorporation of C^{14} into the succinate was indeed relatively great. The specific activities of the respiratory carbon dioxide and the carboxyl carbon

TABLE V

OXIDATION OF ACETATE-2-C^{14} BY *E. coli* IN THE PRESENCE OF NONISOTOPIC α-KETOGLUTARATE AND SUCCINATE[a]

Compound (c.p.m./mmole)		Distribution of isotope in succinate (c.p.m./mmole)	
Initial acetate	386,000	COOH	5,060
Final acetate	346,000	HCH	39,800
α-Ketoglutarate	1,500	HCH	39,800
Succinate	89,500	COOH	5,060
Respiratory CO_2	3,600		

[a] For particulars of experiments see ref. 29.

atoms of succinate are of the same order of magnitude, indicating that the latter may be precursors of the respiratory carbon dioxide. These results with *E. coli* would appear to exclude a mechanism involving both α-keto-glutarate and succinate (as in the TCA cycle), but would be in conformity with a cycle involving succinate. Such a cycle is the Thunberg dicarboxylic acid cycle. Supporting evidence for this concept, not shown in the table, is that only small amounts of radioactivity from acetate-2-C^{14} are incorporated into the tricarboxylic acids. Taken at face value, these data obtained by carrier experiments with *M. lysodeikticus* and *E. coli* suggested that the former oxidized acetate via the TCA cycle and the latter via the dicarb-oxylic acid cycle. Reasons for skepticism about such conclusions have already been presented.

VII. Noncarrier Type of Experiments Employing Isotopes

A. HYPOTHESIS OF TECHNIQUE

It is possible to circumvent the objection that the components of the TCA cycle are not in isotopic equilibrium with the carrier substances in the following manner. If it is assumed that a suspension of cells or an enzyme preparation which is oxidizing acetate contains small quantities of all the intermediates, it should be possible with proper micromethods to isolate the intermediates, if a sufficiently large quantity of cells or preparation is employed. In addition, if isotopic acetate is added in an amount which establishes the half maximal rate of oxidation of acetate by the enzyme preparation used, the size of the free pool of isotopic acetate is minimized, and conditions more or less ideal for equilibration of substrate and intermedi-ates are established. Secondly, if the time chosen for the experiment is sufficiently short, the possibility of extensive recycling is minimized. It can be readily shown (Fig. 3) that continuous recycling will randomly dis-tribute the isotope from acetate-2-C^{14} into all the intermediates. Should the experimental conditions be such to permit extensive recycling, it would be impossible to interpret the results in terms of a specific metabolic mechanism.

Results from this type of experiment employing *M. lysodeikticus* and *E. coli* will be discussed, in order that the reader may make a direct compari-son with the carrier type of experiment previously described.

Table VI lists the specific activities of the various acids isolated from a mixture obtained by permitting a partially lysed preparation of *M. ly-sodeikticus* to oxidize acetate-2-C^{14}.[27] The specific activities of the acetate and succinate indicate that the two are in isotopic equilibrium. Further-more, the α-ketoglutarate and citrate are also equilibrated. In fact, the specific activity of each of the latter two acids is greater than the specific

TABLE VI

SPECIFIC ACTIVITIES OF TCA ACIDS ISOLATED FROM *M. lysodeikticus*
AFTER OXIDATION OF ACETATE-2-C^{14a}

Compound	c.p.m./mmole	μmole isolated
Acetate (final)	2,608,200	4,190
Pyruvate	880,000	48
Succinate	2,734,150	175
α-Ketoglutarate	3,178,200	20
Citrate	3,957,950	4
Respiratory CO_2	221,390	1,320

[a] For particulars of experiments see ref. 27.

activity of the acetate or succinate, which indicates that there are probably
nonisotopic precursors of acetate and succinate in the enzyme preparation
which dilute the isotopic material. The complete equilibration of the
various acids which occurs in this type of experiment contrasts strikingly
with the lack of equilibration which occurs in the carrier type of experiments. These results offer supporting evidence for the TCA cycle in *M.
lysodeikticus*; however, the distribution pattern of the isotope in these
acids is even more informative, being fully in accord with that which
could be expected when acetate-2-C^{14} is oxidized by way of the TCA cycle.
The distribution data are given in Table VII and the reader is again referred to Fig. 3 to facilitate a visualization of the mechanism. In Table VII
the carbon atoms of citric acid have been numbered arbitrarily to denote
their origin in the TCA cycle from acetic and oxalacetic acids. Numbers 1
and 2 designate the carboxyl and methyl group of acetic acid and numbers
3, 4, 5, and 6 correspond to the appropriate carbon atoms in oxalacetic
acid—carbon 6 (tertiary carboxyl) designating the carboxyl group originally
adjacent to the carbonyl group of oxalacetic acid. The numbers assigned to
the carbon atoms of α-ketoglutaric and succinic acids correspond to their
origin from citric acid by the TCA cycle. Since the respiratory carbon dioxide contains radioactivity it is obvious that some recycling of the components of the cycle has occurred. During the first revolution of the cycle
the acetate-2-C^{14} will condense with nonisotopic oxalacetate which is endogenously present, and the respiratory carbon dioxide will not contain
isotope. However, the succinate formed will literally contain C^{14} in carbon
atom 2 as numbered in Table VII. Since succinic acid is a symmetrical
molecule, C^{14} will be statistically present in both carbon atoms number 2
and 3, i.e., one-half of the molecules will contain C^{14} in position 2 and one-
half in position 3. During the next turn of the cycle, acetate-2-C^{14} will condense with oxalacetate containing isotope in either position 2 or 3, since
the latter will be derived from the isotopic succinate (see Fig. 3). If the

TABLE VII

RECOVERY OF AND ISOTOPE DISTRIBUTION IN INTERMEDIATES OF
ACETATE-2-C^{14} OXIDATION BY *M. lysodeikticus*[a]

Compound	Structural formula	Specific activity (c.p.m./mmole)	Amount isolated (μmole)
Initial acetate	COOH	0	—
	CH$_3$	3,620,500	
Final acetate	1 COOH	33,800	4,190
	2 CH$_3$	2,608,200	
Citrate	1 COOH	439,630	4
	2 CH$_2$	1,278,000	
	6 COOH	522,700	
	3 C	1,122,000	
	OH		
	4 CH$_2$	1,278,000	
	5 COOH	439,630	
α-Ketoglutarate	1 COOH	450,300	20
	2 CH$_2$ 3 CH$_2$	1,945,400	
	4 C=O	450,300	
	5 COOH	332,200	
Succinate	1 COOH	448,300	175
	2 CH$_2$ 3 CH$_2$	1,837,550	
	4 COOH	448,300	
Respiratory CO$_2$	—	221,390	1,320

[a] For particulars of experiments see ref. 27.

original numbering system is maintained the citrate will statistically have the following isotopic content at the beginning of the second turn of the cycle:

$$
\begin{array}{ll}
\text{COOH} & \quad 1 \quad \text{COOH} \\
\text{HC}^{14}\text{H} & \quad 2 \quad \text{HC}^{14}\text{H} \quad \overset{6}{\text{COOH}} \\
\text{H} & \quad 3 \quad \text{C}^{14} \\
+ & \quad \rightarrow \\
\text{O}=\text{C}^{14}-\text{COOH} & \quad 4 \quad \text{HC}^{14}\text{H} \quad \text{OH} \\
\text{HC}^{14}\text{H} & \quad 5 \quad \text{COOH} \\
\text{COOH} &
\end{array}
$$

Since none of the carboxyl groups contain isotope, the respiratory carbon dioxide will not contain C^{14} during the second turn of the cycle. It will be observed, however, that at the conclusion of the second turn the carboxyl groups of succinic and oxalacetic acids contain C^{14}; therefore, during the third revolution of the cycle, the respiratory carbon dioxide will contain C^{14}. Carbon dioxide fixation into oxalacetate has not been considered in the above explanation. The amount of C^{14} found in the respiratory carbon dioxide from acetate-2-C^{14} is indicative of the degree of recycling which has occurred. It can also be seen that after an appropriate number of cycles a general distribution of C^{14} in the carbon atoms of the various acids will have occurred. The data given in Table VII show that limited recycling had occurred under the conditions chosen for the experiment. In the carrier type of experiments described previously the specific activity of the respiratory carbon dioxide was much greater than the specific activity of the carboxyl groups of the various acids. In the noncarrier type of experiments the specific activity of the respiratory carbon dioxide was somewhat lower than the specific activity of the carboxyl groups. In all probability, oxidations of endogenous substances to carbon dioxide diluted the radioactivity of the respiratory carbon dioxide evolved from the TCA cycle.

The specific activity of the individual carbon atoms of each of the acids agrees with the mechanism of oxidation of acetate-2-C^{14} by the TCA cycle. Since limited recycling had occurred, those carbon atoms which have as their precursor the methyl group of acetate-2-C^{14} have the highest specific activity. Note carbon atoms number 2, 3, and 4 of citric acid, 2 and 3 of α-ketoglutaric acid, 2 and 3 of succinic acid, and carbon number 2 of the residual acetate. Another important aspect of this noncarrier type of experiment is that over 90 % of the total radioactivity added as acetate-2-C^{14} can be found in the recovered acids and respiratory carbon dioxide. If some other mechanism of oxidation is important for the oxidation of acetate by *M. lysodeikticus*, the concentration of the intermediates in the unknown mechanism is extremely low and the specific activity very high.

TABLE VIII

SPECIFIC ACTIVITIES OF TCA ACIDS ISOLATED FROM *E. coli* AFTER OXIDATION OF ACETATE-2-C^{14} [a]

Compound	c.p.m./μmole	μmoles isolated
Citrate	11,800	6.3
α-Ketoglutarate	9,700	3.9
Succinate	8,500	136.0
Fumarate	7,920	10.2
Malate	9,215	9.9
Respiratory CO_2	860	1,765
Residual acetate	4,400	3,290
Isotope recovery	>90%	—

[a] For particulars of experiments see ref. 29.

Inasmuch as the results from carrier type experiments with *E. coli* were interpreted as showing that the oxidation of acetate occurred by means of the C$_4$ dicarboxylic acid cycle, it is interesting to analyze the results obtained with this organism by use of the noncarrier technique.[29] In contrast to carrier type experiments where isotopic acetate was incorporated into carrier succinate to a high degree, but into α-ketoglutarate or citrate in insignificant amounts, acetate-2-C^{14} has completely equilibrated with citrate and α-ketoglutarate as well as the C$_4$ dicarboxylic acids (see Table VIII). Actually the residual acetate has a lower specific activity than the other acids, indicating sources of nonisotopic acetate from endogenous substances which are oxidized to acetate. The data depicting the distribution pattern of the isotope in the carbon atoms of the various acids are not shown, but follow precisely the pattern expected from the oxidation of acetate-2-C^{14} by the TCA cycle. Furthermore the total recovery of C^{14} from all of the isolated compounds is greater than 90%, indicating the quantitative importance of the cycle. It can be concluded that *M. lysodeikticus* and *E. coli*, the former a strict aerobe and the latter a facultative anaerobe, both oxidize acetate by the TCA cycle. The reader is also referred to the work by Ajl and Wong[30] for an appraisal of the TCA cycle in *E. coli*.

B. THE PROBLEM WITH YEAST

One of the first observations of the biosynthesis of citric acid from acetic acid was made by Wieland and Sonderhoff.[11] They observed that brewer's yeast converted approximately 10% of total barium acetate present to citric acid. The concept of the TCA cycle had not been established, and these authors believed that the synthesis of citric acid which they observed was a cellular side reaction, the pathway of oxidation of acetate by yeast being via the Thunberg dicarboxylic acid cycle. On the other hand, the results obtained by Sonderhoff and Thomas[31] with deuterium-labeled acetate were in accordance with the TCA cycle. One of the objections to the occurrence of the TCA cycle in yeast was the inability to demonstrate many of the enzymes with whole cells. Lynen and Neciullah[32] demonstrated that such failures were due to the impermeability of the cell membrane of the yeast cell to these substrates. With cells whose structure was destroyed by freezing in liquid air, the various substrates of the TCA cycle were readily oxidized. Later, Lynen[33] showed that the oxidation of acetate by yeast was inhibited by malonate and concluded the TCA cycle was operative. Weinhouse and Millington[34] found that the isotope distribution in citrate produced by yeast in the presence of magnesium and barium acetate-C^{13} was in agreement with the TCA cycle. However, in order to account for the distribution of the amount of isotope in the carboxyl groups of the C_4 dicarboxylic acids, these authors suggested that in addition to the TCA cycle, a supplementary mechanism for the synthesis of a dicarboxylic acid from acetic acid was present. The mechanism proposed for the latter was the Thunberg condensation reaction.

In 1952, Krebs *et al.*[35] employed yeast preparations which had been made permeable to di- and tricarboxylic acids by treatment with dry ice. The results obtained from studies on the rate of substrate utilization, from carrier type of experiments and from additional criteria of the type frequently applied to mammalian systems, were interpreted as evidence that the tricarboxylic acid cycle was not the main oxidative pathway in yeast. They believed that the pathway existed in yeast, but only for the synthesis of carbon skeletons of compounds required for cellular components. Some unknown mechanism was apparently involved for the oxidative energy-yielding process. DeMoss and Swim[36] conducted experiments with baker's yeast employing acetate-2-C^{14} without the use of carriers, i.e., experiments similar to those previously described with *M. lysodeikticus* and *E. coli*. The results (Table IX) of these experiments were very similar to those ob-

TABLE IX

SPECIFIC ACTIVITIES OF TCA ACIDS ISOLATED FROM BAKER'S YEAST
AFTER OXIDATION OF ACETATE-2-C^{14a}

Compound	c.p.m./μmole	μmoles isolated
Acetate	5580	36
Citrate	4550	159
α-Ketoglutarate	4700	0.5
Succinate	4260	208
Fumarate	4150	56
Malate	4600	217
Respiratory CO_2	97	6590

[a] For particulars of experiments see ref. 36.

tained with the two bacterial species. One major difference was observed which is not indicated in the table. The degree of equilibration between the residual isotopic acetate and all of the di- and tricarboxylic acids was practically complete; however, while with the bacterial species a recovery of greater than 90 % of the total C^{14} was obtained in the components of the TCA cycle, the isotope recovery in these components isolated from yeast was lower. Therefore, the possibility existed that the methods employed did not detect intermediates not related to the cycle which were of importance for an alternate pathway. Yeast cells have an extremely large intracellular pool of amino acids, particularly glutamic acid and alanine. It will readily be recognized that the carbon skeletons of these acids have their source in α-ketoglutaric and pyruvic acids. If the size of the intracellular amino acid pool and the isotopic content of this pool is taken into consideration, together with the components of the TCA cycle, the total recovery of isotope is sufficiently large to indicate a quantitative importance of the cycle for oxidative purposes in yeast. These data do not exclude the existence of a related mechanism.

VIII. Quantitative Aspects of the TCA Cycle

A. FUMARATE AS ELECTRON ACCEPTOR FOR ACETATE OXIDATION

Reference has been made to the quantitative accumulation of intermediates of the TCA cycle resulting from the oxidation of pyruvate by muscle and liver tissue in the presence of inhibitors such as malonate. Individual reactions of the TCA cycle catalyzed by enzyme preparations from microorganisms can be inhibited by the various inhibitors used with mammalian tissue, but such preparations usually do not catalyze all of the reactions of the cycle. With intact microbial cells, inhibitors such as malonate have not been effective. Permeability barriers appear to be involved. For this reason, difficulty has been encountered in the design of experiments which would demonstrate the quantitative accumulation of intermediates. Krebs,[37] however, reported that acetate and a number of other substrates were oxidized under anaerobic conditions by nonproliferating suspensions of *E. coli* when fumarate was added as the oxidant. The observations resulted from the study of the role of fumarate in respiration and no consideration was given to the mechanism of acetate oxidation. The over-all reaction for the oxidation of acetate is illustrated in the following equation:

$$\text{Acetate} + 4 \text{ fumarate} + 2H_2O \rightarrow 2CO_2 + 4 \text{ succinate}$$

$$C_2H_4O_2 + 4C_4H_4O_4 + 2H_2O \rightarrow 2CO_2 + 4C_4H_6O_4$$

Since acetate was found to be practically inert oxidatively in muscle tissue, pyruvate was postulated as the substance which condensed with oxalacetate

TABLE X

OXIDATION OF ACETATE-1-C[14] BY *E. coli* IN PRESENCE OF FUMARATE[a]

Compound	Quantity (μmoles)	Specific activity (c.p.m./μmole)	Added C[14] (%)
Acetate	24.3	866	12.7
Succinate	370	362	81.2
Fumarate	31.8	41	0.8
Malate	57.6	46	1.6
Respiratory CO_2	162	23	2.2

[a] For particulars of experiments see ref. 38.

to initiate the TCA cycle. Therefore, it was difficult at that time to conceive how *E. coli* could oxidize acetate by a TCA cycle, particularily since such components as citrate, isocitrate, *cis*-aconitate, and α-ketoglutarate were not oxidized by the organism at a sufficiently high rate when compared to acetate. The equation shows that 2 moles of carbon dioxide are produced which are equivalent to the carbon atoms of acetate; since the conditions are anaerobic, fumarate is the oxidant, i.e., electron acceptor. Oxidatively and reductively the equation is satisfied by reduction of 4 moles of fumarate to 4 moles of succinate. Krebs therefore concluded that acetate was oxidized to carbon dioxide by some unknown mechanism, and that fumarate simply acted as the oxidant in place of oxygen. Swim and Krampitz[38] repeated the experiment performed by Krebs, substituting 1-C[14] acetic acid ($CH_3 \cdot C^{14}OOH$) for nonisotopic acetate. Their results are given in Table X.

If the carbon dioxide arose from the carbon atoms of acetate, the carbon dioxide would contain all of the radioactivity of the initial acetate. In fact, the specific activity of the carbon dioxide was very low, indicating that only a small fraction of the initial acetate was oxidized to CO_2. Upon closer examination these results can be interpreted to be in agreement with the TCA cycle (refer to Fig. 3). To initiate the TCA cycle the following steps would occur. (1) Two molecules of fumarate would undergo a dismutation forming one molecule of oxalacetate and one molecule of succinate. (2) The acetate (acetyl CoA) would condense with the oxalacetate to form citrate, with carbons 1 and 2 of the citric acid molecule containing carbon atoms originally present in the acetate. Carbon number 1 (carboxyl group) would contain the C[14] from $CH_3 \cdot C^{14}OOH$). (3) Transformation to α-ketoglutarate would then occur as outlined in Fig. 3, and during the process nonisotopic carbon number 6 of citric acid would be evolved as carbon dioxide. Fumarate would act as the electron acceptor for the oxidation of isocitrate to oxalosuccinate, forming another molecule of succinate. (4) The α-ketoglutarate would be oxidatively decarboxylated to succinate, evolving nonisotopic carbon atom 5 as carbon dioxide. The electrons in the oxidative step would reduce another molecule of fumarate to succinate. In summary, the observed data would be obtained: i.e., the evolution of two molecules of carbon dioxide, which are nonradioactive, and the formation of four molecules of succinate. Three molecules of succinate would result from the reduction of fumarate; one would arise through the operation of the TCA cycle, and would contain the isotope in one carboxyl group from the original isotopic acetate. Succinate would not be oxidized further because of the anaerobic conditions of the experiment, and a dismutation between it and a molecule of fumarate does not occur. The data in Table X show that the succinate present at the conclusion of the experiment contained the major portion of the isotope and that the carbon dioxide evolved contained insignificant amounts. Variations from the exact theoretical stoichiometry are due to endogenous reactions taking place in the whole cells.

B. EVIDENCE AGAINST C_4 DICARBOXYLIC ACID CYCLE

Although these results showed that the carbon atoms of acetate were not oxidized to carbon dioxide and that they could be accounted for by the TCA cycle, it is possible that part of the acetate was utilized by a Thunberg condensation (oxidative condensation of two molecules of acetate to form succinate) and that in some manner the oxidation of fumarate to carbon dioxide was linked with the utilization of acetate. It was possible, however, to determine the extent of the Thunberg condensation by mass analysis of the succinate formed from acetate-2-C^{13} ($C^{13}H_3 \cdot COOH$). By the same technique the extent of the occurrence of the TCA cycle can also be ascertained by the mass analysis of the succinate-C^{13}. If an experiment similar to the one referred to above is performed, except that acetate-2-C^{13} ($C^{13}H_3 \cdot COOH$) and fumarate are the substrates, and the succinate is isolated and examined for C^{13} content, the following alternative results could be expected, depending upon whether the Thunberg type of condensation or the TCA cycle occurred (refer to Fig. 3). A detailed description of the fate of acetic acid under these conditions was given previously. If $C^{13}H_3 \cdot COOH$ is substituted for $CH_3 \cdot C^{14}OOH$ it will be seen that the molecular species of the succinate formed by way of the TCA cycle will be:

$$HOOC^{12} \cdot C^{13}H_2 \cdot C^{12}H_2 \cdot C^{12}OOH$$

Emphasis should be placed upon the fact that the carbon atom which will contain the isotope of C^{13} is *one* of the methylene carbons. On the other hand, if the Thunberg condensation occurs, the molecular species of the succinate formed will be:

$$HOOC \cdot \overset{H}{\underset{H}{C^{13}}} \begin{array}{c} \hline H + H \\ \hline \end{array} \overset{H}{\underset{H}{C^{13}}} \cdot COOH \rightarrow HOOC \cdot C^{13}H_2 \cdot C^{13}H_2 \cdot COOH$$

In this case, *both* methylene groups of the succinate will contain the isotope of C^{13}. The isotope of carbon having a mass of 13 is a normal constituent of of all carbon and the normal complement of C^{13} is approximately 1.1 %; the remaining carbon has a mass of 12. Acetate-2-C^{13} is prepared from sources of carbon which have been enriched above the normal complement of 1.1 % and the amount of isotope the enriched material contains is expressed as per cent excess of C^{13}. In the following, C^{12} will refer to the normal carbon atom, i.e., ignoring the normal complement of C^{13}, and C^{13} will be used to refer to carbon atoms which have been enriched. The analysis for the isotope of C^{13} is performed with a mass spectrometer and the isotopic material is analyzed in the gaseous form. The spectrometer actually measures the mass of the compound. Therefore it is possible to determine which of the two molecular species described above is present or in what percentage combination they exist. In order to obtain the two methylene carbon atoms of succinate in the gaseous form, the molecule was degraded to obtain ethylene:

$$HOOC \cdot CH_2 \cdot CH_2 \cdot COOH \rightarrow CH_2{=}CH_2 + 2CO_2$$

The ethylene represents the two carbon atoms from the methylene groups of succinate. If the succinate contained no isotope the molecular species of the ethylene would be $C^{12}H_2{=}C^{12}H_2$. The molecular weight (mass) would be 28.

If the succinate contained only one C^{13} (TCA type) the molecular species of the ethylene would be $C^{13}H_2{=}C^{12}H_2$. The mass would be 29. In the case of the Thunberg condensation, the succinate would contain C^{13} in both methylene carbon atoms and the molecular species of the ethylene would be $C^{13}H_2{=}C^{13}H_2$. The mass would be 30.

The percentage of each type of ethylene obtained from the degradation of the succinate is shown in Table XI.

It will be recalled that four molecules of succinate are formed during the oxidation of acetate with fumarate as the electron acceptor. In the case of the TCA cycle, three molecules of succinate will be formed by the reduction of the nonisotopic fumarate and therefore will not contain the isotope C^{13} and the ethylene obtained will have a mass of 28. The fourth molecule of

TABLE XI

RELATIVE ABUNDANCE OF DOUBLY AND SINGLY LABELED ETHYLENE OBTAINED FROM C^{13}-LABELED SUCCINATE[a]

	Mass 30	Mass 29	Mass 28
Molecular species	$C^{13}H_2{=}C^{13}H_2$	$C^{13}H_2{=}C^{12}H_2$	$C^{12}H_2{=}C^{12}H_2$
Per cent	0.18	21.1	78.7

[a] For details of experiments see ref. 38.

succinate has its origin in the skeleton of the cycle and would contain the isotope C^{13} in *one* of the methylene groups. The mass of the ethylene would be 29. In other words, 75 % of the molecules will not contain an excess of C^{13} and 25 % of the molecules will contain an excess of C^{13} in only one of the two methylene groups. The data are in excellent agreement with these theoretical calculations. 78.7 % of the molecules of succinate did not contain isotope in the methylene carbons and 21.1 % of the molecules had only one of the methylene groups containing C^{13}.

The small variations from the theoretical calculations are due to anomalies in the experimental conditions and the reader is referred to the original publication for a more detailed description. From the data in Table XI it will be seen that the amount of succinate formed containing C^{13} in both methylene groups ($C^{13}H_2 \!=\! C^{13}H_2$, mass 30) was only 0.18 %. After certain corrections, too detailed to present here, are made for recycling of succinate, the percentage of molecules containing atoms of C^{13} in each of the methylene groups is so negligible so as to be within experimental error. It can therefore be concluded that under these conditions the TCA cycle accounts quantitatively for the metabolism of acetate and fumarate and that the Thunberg type of condensation of two molecules of acetate to form succinate does not occur.

IX. The Criterion of Sequential Induction

The principles of sequential induction of metabolic pathways in microorganisms were independently discovered by Stanier,[39] Karlsson and Barker,[40] and Suda *et al.*[41] (see Chapter 12, Vol. III). Briefly the principle is: for the metabolism of substance A, if B, C, D, etc., are intermediates and if the entire process is under inductive control, induction to substance A results in sequential induction to B, C, D, etc., i.e., ability to metabolize these compounds. If B, C, D, etc., are not intermediates they will not be immediately metabolized. This technique has been valuable for the elucidation of some metabolic pathways but unfortunately has led to some erroneous conclusions when employed to elucidate oxidative pathways. Karlsson and Barker [40] found that *Azotobacter agilis* when grown with acetate as the source of carbon was not induced to oxidize α-ketoglutarate, succinate, fumarate, malate, or pyruvate. Isotopic studies of a carrier type indicated that succinate and oxalacetate were not intermediates. From these and other results they concluded that the TCA cycle was not operative in this organism. Stone and Wilson[42, 43] investigated the inductive patterns of *Azotobacter vinelandii* grown on sucrose. Nonproliferating cells oxidized acetate and pyruvate immediately, but succinate, fumarate, malate, and α-ketoglutarate were oxidized only following long induction periods. Citrate was not oxidized. Cell-free extracts of these organisms rapidly oxidized succinate, fumarate, malate, and α-ketoglutarate. Acetate was rapidly oxidized after addition of small quantities of C_4 dicarboxylic acids to spark the initial condensation reaction of the TCA cycle. Campbell and Stokes[44] found that cells of *Pseudomonas aeruginosa* grown with acetate as the sole source of carbon did not immediately oxidize citrate, *cis*-aconitate, isocitrate, α-ketoglutarate, succinate, or fumarate, but oxidized acetate and malate without induction periods. When the cells were dried and then tested in the same manner, all of the above compounds were oxidized immediately at rapid rates. Lara and Stokes[45] observed that typical strains of *Escherichia coli* oxidized citrate after the cells were dried. The data obtained by these latter groups of investigators indicated that the cells from both species contained the enzymes necessary for the oxidation of components of the TCA cycle, but that permeability or transport problems existed in the untreated cells. Barret *et al.*[46] and Barret and Kallio[47] were able to show by well-designed experiments that the induction process was related to a mechanism of transport. It was observed that cells of *P. fluorescens* which had been grown on fumarate showed a long induction period for the oxidation of citrate, whereas growth on citrate yielded cells which immediately oxidized citrate. When the fumarate-grown cells were irradiated with ultraviolet light, a technique known to interfere with protein synthesis, the induction period with citrate was indefinitely prolonged. The same level of irradiation had no effect on the oxidation of citrate by cells which had been grown on citrate. These investigators also demonstrated that extracts prepared from induced and noninduced cells contained equivalent amounts of enzymes required for oxidizing citric acid. It would appear then that the inability of these microbial cells to oxidize components of the TCA cycle is not caused by the lack of the relevant metabolic enzymes, but rather by the lack of an enzyme system required for transfer of the substance through the cell membrane. During induction, there is a synthesis of an enzymic system capable of active transport. Clearly the criterion of sequential induction cannot be used alone to determine an oxidative pathway; other criteria must also be applied.

X. The Criterion of Microbial Mutant Analysis of Metabolic Pathways

Microbial mutants have been very useful for the elucidation and analysis of biosynthetic pathways. Most of the evidence indicates that the result of a single mutation may be the loss of one enzymic activity, in all likelihood the loss of the ability by the cell to synthesize a single enzyme. Therefore, if a mutant strain is obtained which has lost the ability to perform one of a series of indispensable enzymic reactions, the strain in question will not grow unless the product of the reaction is added to the growth medium. By obtaining mutant strains blocked at successive steps in the series of reactions and determining the products which will permit growth of the organism, the metabolic pathway can be determined. Gilvarg and Davis[48] used this approach very effectively in establishing the importance of the the TCA cycle in *E. coli* and *Aerobacter aerogenes*. The wild-type strain of *E. coli* can grow on a synthetic medium consisting of minerals, ammonia, and a simple carbon source. They obtained several mutant strains of *E. coli* which would grow on glucose, lactate, or succinate, provided that glutamate was also present. Some stage in the synthesis of glutamate was blocked in these mutant strains, since the wild-type strain would grow on the same substrates without the addition of glutamate. The mutant strains would not grow on acetate with glutamate present. Apparently glucose, lactate, or succinate could serve as a source of carbon for the mutant strains, whereas acetate could not. The possibility existed that different mutations had occurred, one pertaining to the utilization of acetate and a second for the synthesis of glutamate. Experience has shown that the occurrence of a double mutation is a rare event. Furthermore, Gilvarg and Davis irradiated one of their mutant strains with ultraviolet light to increase the rate of reversion back to the wild type. They selected for reverse mutant strains which had lost the glutamate requirement, and also for ones which had lost the acetate block. Several revertants of each were isolated; every one proved to have lost both blocks. These results showed clearly that the glutamate requirement and the inability to utilize acetate by the mutant strains were related phenomena. After a systematic survey for the location of the enzymic block, it was discovered that the organisms were lacking or very deficient in the enzyme which condenses acetyl CoA and oxalacetate to form citrate, i.e., condensing enzyme. All the other enzymes required for the activation of acetate and the TCA cycle were present in amounts comparable to those in the wild-type strain. The loss of the ability of the mutant strains to synthesize the condensing enzyme readily explains why the organism cannot utilize acetate as an energy source for growth, and also explains the requirement for glutamate. α-Ketoglutarate is the precursor of the carbon skeleton for glutamate synthesis by *E. coli*. Since α-ketoglutarate is obtained indirectly from citrate by reactions of the TCA cycle and the synthesis of citrate by the mutant cannot occur because of the absence of condensing enzyme, the glutamate requirement is obvious. The fact that the loss of ability of the mutant strain to synthesize one enzyme of the TCA cycle has created conditions under which the organism cannot survive unless special nutritional conditions are satisfied indicates the importance of the TCA cycle to the cell. The question of how the wild type strain of *E. coli* accomplishes the net synthesis of dicarboxylic acids from acetate when the latter serves as the sole source of carbon for growth is taken up on page 240.

The quantitative importance of the TCA cycle for the oxidation of carbohydrates in *E. coli* can be ascertained with these mutants. If alternative pathways do exist, the mutational block which is specifically in the TCA cycle should not affect any alternative pathways. Gilvarg and Davis obtained data which indicated that glucose and pyruvate were oxidized only as far as acetate; a total oxidation of these two substances did not occur. If important alternative pathways were present, total oxidation of the substrates would have occurred. These data demonstrate the quantitative significance of the TCA cycle in *E. coli* and *A. aerogenes*.

XI. Deviations from the TCA Cycle

While there can be no question as to the quantitative importance of the TCA cycle in many microorganisms, certain experimental evidence indicates that modifications of the cycle are involved in some microorganisms. One of the questions which has perplexed investigators is the means whereby microorganisms, which are able to utilize acetate as the sole source of carbon for growth, oxidize acetate, since the known mechanism requires a C_4 dicarboxylic acid. A mechanism is also required for the synthesis of carbon skeletons for cellular components.

It has been emphasized previously that there was no established mechanism by which a C_4 dicarboxylic acid could be synthesized from two molecules of acetate. The formation of oxalacetate by carbon dioxide fixation with pyruvic acid has been discussed. It is readily recognizable that if a mechanism existed for the synthesis of pyruvic acid from acetate and carbon dioxide or some other C_1 compound, it would be possible for the cell to synthesize a C_4 dicarboxylic acid. The oxidative decarboxylation of pyruvate is considered to be only sluggishly reversible or entirely irreversible. However, it is worthwhile to remember that this reaction is oxidative and that the initial stages of this reaction are not too well understood. It may be that the attempts which have been made to demonstrate the reversibility of the reaction have not been performed under the proper reductive conditions for reversibility. Pertinent to this point is the fact that the following reaction catalyzed by several of the members of the genus *Clostridium* has been shown to be reversible in *Clostridium butylicum*:

$$CH_3 \cdot CO \cdot COOH + H_3PO_4 \rightleftharpoons CH_3 \cdot CO \cdot OPO_3H_2 + H_2 + CO_2$$

This organism contains the enzyme hydrogenase, and the reaction can be considered as an oxidative decarboxylation of pyruvate with the electron transfer occurring through this enzyme with the formation of hydrogen. In those organisms which do not contain hydrogenase, it is possible that during growth the proper reductive conditions do exist. Under these conditions pyruvate would be synthesized from acetate and carbon dioxide, followed by a synthesis of oxalacetate by fixation of a second molecule of carbon dioxide. The oxalacetate would condense with acetate to form citrate, and by oxidation and decarboxylation of citrate a steady flow of carbon dioxide would be available for further synthesis of C_4 dicarboxylic acid. It should be emphasized that the net condensation of acetate and a C_1 fragment has not been adequately demonstrated.

A. ISOCITRITASE

Campbell *et al.*[49] made the very important observation that crude extracts of *Pseudomonas aeruginosa* formed glyoxylic and succinic acids from citrate and isocitrate. This was the basis for the development of the concept that the synthesis of a C_4 dicarboxylic acid occurred from two C_2 moieties, although the implications of the work were not immediately recognized.

The reaction is shown in the following equation:

$$
\begin{array}{cccc}
\text{COOH} & \text{COOH} & & \\
| & | & & \\
\text{HCH} & \text{HCH} & & \text{O=CH} \\
| & | & & | \\
\text{H C—COOH} & \rightleftharpoons \text{HCH} & + & \text{COOH} \\
| & | & & \\
\text{HOCH} & \text{COOH} & & \\
| & & & \\
\text{COOH} & & & \\
\text{Isocitric} & \text{Succinic} & \text{Glyoxylic} & \\
\text{acid} & \text{acid} & \text{acid} & \\
\end{array}
$$

Subsequent experiments by Smith and Gunsalus,[50] Saz and Hillary,[51] Olson,[52] and Wong and Ajl[53] demonstrated that isocitrate was the substrate for the enzyme, termed isocitritase. Smith and Gunsalus[54] purified the enzyme and demonstrated many of its properties. It did not require coenzyme A. The reaction was reversible, and the equilibrium for the reaction at physiological concentration was very much toward the formation of succinic and glyoxylic acids. The isocitritase reaction can be visualized as an alternate mechanism for the breakdown of citric acid via isocitric acid to succinic and glyoxylic acids. Succinic acid would be further metabolized through the conventional reactions of the TCA cycle. Certain microorganisms are known to oxidize glyoxylic acid to carbon dioxide and water. Campbell[55] obtained evidence with an unidentified *Pseudomonas* that allantoin was degraded to urea and glyoxylic acid and that the latter was oxidized via formic acid to carbon dioxide and water. The significance of direct glyoxylic acid oxidation is not known. However, the mechanism of oxidation of acetate via isocitric and glyoxylic acid may be of importance to some organisms.

B. MALATE SYNTHETASE

Shortly after the discovery of isocitritase, Wong and Ajl[56] in 1956 made a very significant observation which was obviously related to conversion of isocitrate to succinic and glyoxylic acids. They demonstrated the presence of an enzyme system capable of synthesizing malic acid from acetate and glyoxylic acid in cells of *E. coli* grown on acetate as the sole source of carbon. They named the enzyme malate synthetase. A study of the properties of the enzyme revealed that acetyl CoA condensed with glyoxylic acid as depicted in the following equation:

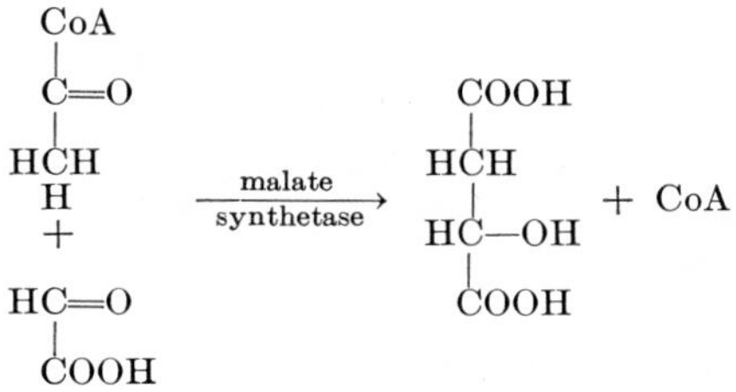

$$\begin{array}{ccc}
\begin{array}{c}
\text{CoA} \\
|\\
\text{C}{=}\text{O} \\
|\\
\text{HCH} \\
\text{H} \\
+ \\
\text{HC}{=}\text{O} \\
|\\
\text{COOH}
\end{array}
&
\xrightarrow[\text{synthetase}]{\text{malate}}
&
\begin{array}{c}
\text{COOH} \\
|\\
\text{HCH} \\
|\\
\text{HC}{-}\text{OH} \\
|\\
\text{COOH}
\end{array}
\;+\; \text{CoA}
\end{array}$$

Acetate was activated by acetokinase and phosphotransacetylase to form acetyl CoA. Attempts to demonstrate the reversibility of malate synthetase have not been successful. Subsequently these investigators[57] recognized the possibility of accounting for the synthesis of the C_4 dicarboxylic acid from two molecules of acetate, one of which yielded glyoxylate by reactions of the TCA cycle and isocitritase activity.

C. VARIATION OF THE TCA CYCLE

In 1957 Kornberg and Madsen[58] demonstrated the presence of isocitritase and malate synthetase in extracts of cells of *Pseudomonas* grown on acetate as the sole source of carbon. They also recognized the possibility of synthesis of cell constituents from C_2 units (acetate) by a cycle including many of the reactions of the TCA cycle, coupled with the synthesis of malic acid from acetic and glyoxylic acids (see Fig. 5). The reactions depicted in the figure are sufficient to account for the oxidation of acetate to carbon dioxide and water and at the same time account for the synthesis of *excess* C_4 dicarboxylic acids from acetate required for the synthesis of other cellular components during growth when acetate is the sole source of carbon. Kornberg *et al.* referred to the combined cyclic events as the glyoxylate cycle or the glyoxylate bypass. An excellent summary of the glyoxylate cycle has been presented by Kornberg and Krebs[59] and by Wong and Ajl.[57] The importance of the work by these two groups of investigators cannot be minimized. After speculations had so often been made about the oxidative condensation of two molecules of acetate (Thunberg condensation) to form succinate, in order to explain the synthesis of C_4 units from C_2 units, experimental evidence is now available for a concrete mechanism. It should be emphasized that the occurrence of malate synthetase has been demonstrated in microbial cells which have been grown on *acetate as*

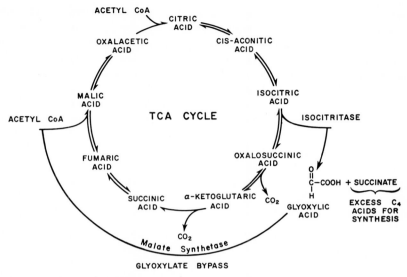

FIG. 5. Tricarboxylic acid cycle and glyoxylate bypass.

the sole source of carbon. The role of the above mechanism is therefore doubtful for cells grown under other conditions. The development of this mechanism by cells grown on acetate attests to the broad powers possessed by microorganisms for growth under varied nutritive conditions. The establishment of these cyclic events also reiterates that the demonstration of individual reactions of any cyclic mechanism does not establish that the reactions occur in an orderly sequence, nor can anything be said regarding the quantitative significance of the cycle in the living cell. For example, if *M. lysodeikticus,* an organism discussed previously in which the TCA cycle appeared to be of quantitative significance, contained isocitritase and malic synthetase, it is obvious that the same results would have been obtained and the same interpretations made. Yet a substantial proportion of the mechanism could well have involved the glyoxylate bypass. The organism was grown, however, on a complex medium containing glucose and other substances as the source of carbon and did not contain malate synthetase. It will be recalled that similar conclusions were made from results obtained employing *E. coli.* These organisms were grown with acetate as their major source of carbon and one might suspect that the glyoxylate bypass accounted for some of the oxidation of acetate. It is not likely that this occurred in these experiments. When the cells were extracted to obtain all of the isotopic organic acids that could have arisen from acetate-2-C14 and chromatographed, no unknown fractions were detected which had specific radioactivities comparable to the acids that are constituents of the TCA cycle. If significant quantities of glyoxylic acid had been present, an unknown fraction containing considerable radioactivity would have appeared.

The possibility also exists that the glyoxylic acid through transamination reactions was transformed to glycine and the latter incorporated into protein of the cell. Radioactivity determinations on the cellular protein revealed that insignificant amounts of isotope had been incorporated from the acetate-2-C^{14}. The fact has been stressed that when microbial cells are grown on acetate a mechanism must be present for the biosynthesis of C_4 dicarboxylic acids in order that cellular constituents can be synthesized. Under these conditions of stress it would appear that some microbial cells have the potential of employing the glyoxylate bypass for the synthesis of excess C_4 dicarboxylic acid. It may be, however, that when nonproliferating cells of this type oxidize acetate, the mechanism of the TCA cycle only is involved, since under these conditions the cell is not required to synthesize cellular constituents. When the organism is grown on more complex substances than C_2 compounds, such as glucose, it can synthesize C_4 dicarboxylic acids by mechanisms other than the glyoxylate bypass and consequently does not develop this mechanism. The genetic potential of the cell is apparently such that under conditions of growth the enzymic pattern of the cell is sufficiently adaptive to accommodate to a variety of conditions. It is difficult to imagine an environment in nature where acetate serves as the sole source of carbon for a microorganism. Nevertheless it is important to determine the enzymic potentials of these cells. Microorganisms, because of their versatility and the ease by which they can be manipulated, serve as excellent biological material to investigate metabolic phenomena.

XII. General Occurrence of TCA Cycle in Microorganisms: Bacteria, Molds, and Protozoa

For purposes of clarity the discussion thus far has centered around a limited number of microorganisms about which there has been controversy regarding the existence of the TCA cycle and the criteria employed to establish its existence. Many of the individual reactions of the TCA cycle have been demonstrated in a number of genera of bacteria. These include: *Salmonella typhosa* and *S. paratyphi*,[60] *Brucella abortus*,[61] *Mycobacterium tuberculosis*,[62] *Pasteurella pestis*,[63] *Rhodospirillum rubrum*,[64] and many others. It can be assumed that many bacteria have the potential to oxidize intermediates of the TCA cycle. Delwiche and Carson,[65] employing aerobically grown cells of *Propionibacterium pentosaceum*, demonstrated that, except for citrate, the intermediates of the TCA cycle were oxidized. A cell-free extract, however, oxidized citrate to α-ketoglutarate. This organism, and presumably other species of this genus, possess the potential for oxidation by the TCA cycle. Perhaps with this group of organisms the cycle is used primarily for synthesis of cellular constituents and the unique fermentative reactions are used for energy processes. It will be recalled that *E. coli* is capable of oxidizing acetate anaerobically with fumarate as the oxidant. Under growing conditions, combined reactions of the fermentative type and of the TCA cycle probably lead to the synthesis of carbon skeletons which are incorporated into cellular components as well as furnishing energy for cellular processes.

The following method has been used extensively by two groups of investigators (Roberts and co-workers[66] and Ehrensvärd and co-workers[67]) to establish the operation of the TCA cycle for the synthesis of carbon skeletons of amino acids in proteins under conditions of growth of microorganisms. It is known that the carbon skeletons of some amino acids are derived from intermediates of the TCA cycle. Therefore, the distribution pattern of C^{14} from acetate-2-C^{14} and acetate-1-C^{14} in carbon atoms of those amino acids obtained from hydrolyzates of cellular proteins of the cell should reflect the quantitative importance of the cycle to the cell. In general the results obtained by these two groups indicated that the cycle was of importance under conditions of growth for *E. coli*, *Rhodospirillum rubrum*, and *Torulopsis utilis*.

The possibility of the occurrence of the TCA cycle in fungi is suggested by the very nature of some of the end products of their metabolism of sugars. Citric acid and other tricarboxylic acids as well as dicarboxylic acids have been isolated from fermentation liquors produced by various fungi. Foster and co-workers have made excellent contributions in this area and the reader is referred to Foster[68] for comprehensive information in this field. Goldschmidt *et al.*[69] came to the conclusion that *Penicillium chrysogenum* oxidized isotopically labeled acetate to carbon dioxide and water by the mechanism of the TCA cycle.

There are several indications that protozoa also utilize the TCA cycle for oxidative purposes[70] and that rickettsiae[71] have at least some of the individual reactions of the cycle.

The reader is referred to the many reviews which are listed at the end of the chapter as supplementary reading material for a more thorough discussion of excellent investigations relating to the TCA cycle in microorganisms.

XIII. Alternate Pathways

Reference has already been made to what may be called a unitarian concept of carbohydrate dissimilation which was held until very recently.[72, 73, 74] The only mechanism well established was the Embden-Meyerhof pathway. The wide diversity of types of fermentation performed by various bacteria was interpreted as reflecting modifications of the mechanism by which pyruvic acid was anaerobically metabolized. Pyruvate was believed to be oxidized via acetyl CoA to carbon dioxide and water by the TCA cycle or deviations from it, as previously discussed. It is possible that obligate anaerobic microorganisms dissimilate carbohydrates mainly by the Embden-Meyerhof mechanism of glycolysis, and that facultative aerobic organisms in addition have other mechanisms for the degradation of carbohydrates. Our knowledge concerning the obligately aerobic organisms is incomplete, and evidence suggests that these organisms may degrade or oxidize carbohydrates by pathways other than the Embden-Meyerhof scheme and the TCA cycle.

No known mechanism exists for the *complete* oxidation of free carbohydrates (i.e., nonphosphorylated) to carbon dioxide. Oxidative processes involving free sugars or their intermediates usually terminate with an accumulation of organic products of oxidation in addition to carbon dioxide. It is not known how the energy released in these oxidations is coupled with cellular functions. Electron transfer via respiratory chains such as the cytochrome system may provide the coupled energy through oxidative phosphorylation. It is also not clear how the cell derives suitable intermediates for biosynthesis of cellular components from these types of oxidation, since the molecular structure of some of the intermediates is unrelated to the known precursors of cellular constituents. These direct and incomplete oxidative mechanisms performed by a variety of microorganisms are discussed in Chapter 2, Vol. II.

A. OXIDATIVE PENTOSE PHOSPHATE CYCLE

An alternative mechanism for the complete oxidation of phosphorylated carbohydrates to carbon dioxide and water by a cyclic method not involving the Embden-Meyerhof pathway and the TCA cycle has recently been discovered. The mechanism is referred to as the "hexosemonophosphate shunt" or the "oxidative pentose phosphate cycle." The following briefly describes some observations which led to the conclusion that some unknown pathway existed for the oxidation of carbohydrates.

Warburg and co-workers[75] demonstrated that glucose-6-phosphate was directly oxidized to 6-phosphogluconate. The dehydrogenase was triphosphopyridine nucleotide (TPN$^+$)-linked, and under aerobic conditions TPNH was reoxidized by way of the cytochrome system. Additional work by Warburg and by Dickens[76] and Lipmann[77] demonstrated that 6-phosphogluconate was further oxidized by a second TPN$^+$-linked dehydrogenase with the evolution of carbon dioxide. Dickens[78] was able to demonstrate the accumulation of a pentose during the latter oxidation, and proposed

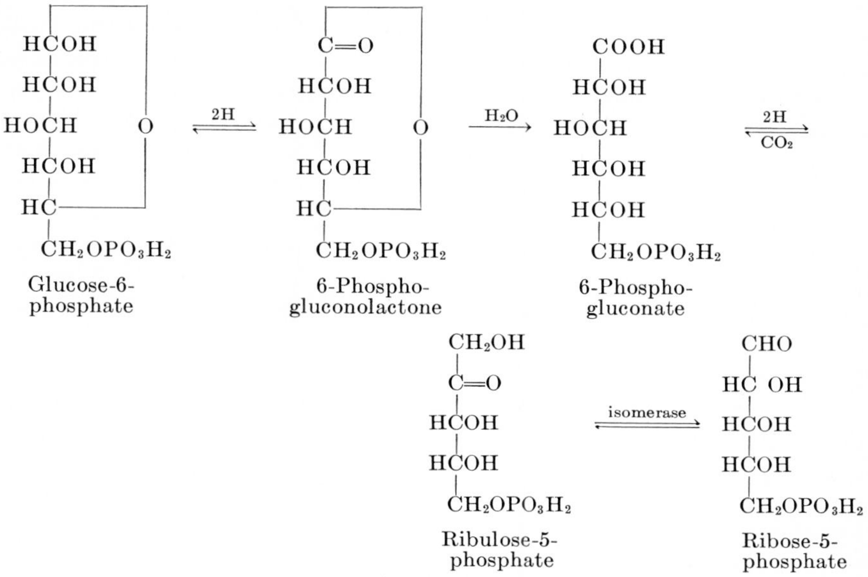

HCOH
HCOH
HOCH   O $\underset{}{\overset{2H}{\rightleftharpoons}}$
HCOH
HC⎽
CH₂OPO₃H₂

Glucose-6-
phosphate

C=O
HCOH
HOCH   O $\xrightarrow{H_2O}$
HCOH
HC⎽
CH₂OPO₃H₂

6-Phospho-
gluconolactone

COOH
HCOH
HOCH $\underset{CO_2}{\overset{2H}{\rightleftharpoons}}$
HCOH
HCOH
CH₂OPO₃H₂

6-Phospho-
gluconate

CH₂OH
C=O
HCOH $\overset{isomerase}{\rightleftharpoons}$
HCOH
CH₂OPO₃H₂

Ribulose-5-
phosphate

CHO
HC OH
HCOH
HCOH
CH₂OPO₃H₂

Ribose-5-
phosphate

FIG. 6. Oxidation of glucose-6-phosphate.

that ribose-5-phosphate was an intermediate in the oxidation of glucose-6-phosphate. In 1951 Scott and Cohen[79] presented evidence obtained with enzyme preparations from yeast and from ribose-adapted *E. coli* which showed that the pentose ester was ribose-5-phosphate. Horecker and Smyniotis[80] with a purified enzyme preparation from yeast established that ribulose-5-phosphate was the first product obtained from the oxidative decarboxylation of 6-phosphogluconate, and that an isomerase accounted for the formation of ribose-5-phosphate. The mechanism for the oxidation of glucose-6-phosphate to ribose-5-phosphate is shown in Fig. 6.

Dische[81] found that adenosine (a source of ribose) was metabolized by hemolysates of erythrocytes to hexosediphosphate and triose, and Schlenk and Waldvogel[82] identified glucose-6-phosphate as a product of ribose-5-phosphate metabolism by liver tissue. The formation of a six carbon ester (hexosediphosphate) from a five carbon ester (ribose-5-phosphate) could be explained by mechanisms in conformity with the Embden-Meyerhof pathway as follows:

2 ribose-5-phosphate → 2 "C₂ fragment" + 2 triose phosphate

2 triose phosphate → fructose-1,6-diphosphate

fructose-1,6-diphosphate → fructose-6-phosphate + inorganic phosphate

The fate of the C₂ fragment was not known. It was subsequently found

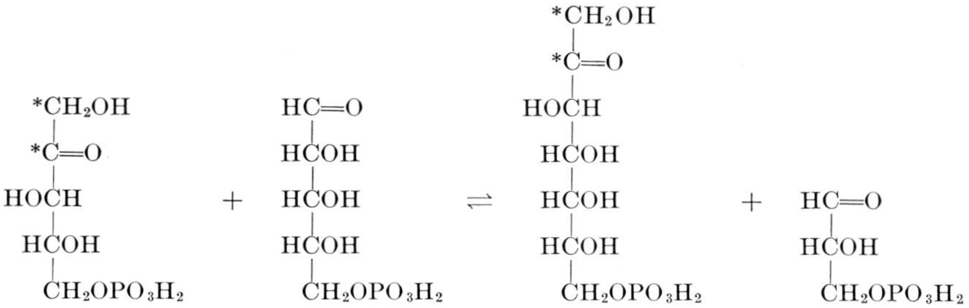

$$
\begin{array}{ccccccc}
 & & & & \text{*CH}_2\text{OH} & & \\
 & & & & \text{*C}=\text{O} & & \\
\text{*CH}_2\text{OH} & & \text{HC}=\text{O} & & \text{HOCH} & & \\
\text{*C}=\text{O} & & \text{HCOH} & & \text{HCOH} & & \\
\text{HOCH} & + & \text{HCOH} & \rightleftharpoons & \text{HCOH} & + & \text{HC}=\text{O} \\
\text{HCOH} & & \text{HCOH} & & \text{HCOH} & & \text{HCOH} \\
\text{CH}_2\text{OPO}_3\text{H}_2 & & \text{CH}_2\text{OPO}_3\text{H}_2 & & \text{CH}_2\text{OPO}_3\text{H}_2 & & \text{CH}_2\text{OPO}_3\text{H}_2
\end{array}
$$

Xylulose-5-phosphate + Ribose-5-phosphate $\rightleftharpoons$ Sedoheptulose-7-phosphate + Glyceraldehyde-3-phosphate

FIG. 7. Formation of sedoheptulose-7-phosphate by transketolase. Note the transfer of the two carbon atoms indicated with asterisks.

that the amount of hexosemonophosphate which accumulated was in excess of that which could be expected from the triose phosphate derived from ribose-5-phosphate. Therefore, the "C₂ fragment" from ribose-5-phosphate was also involved in the synthesis. Furthermore, hexosemonophosphate was formed from ribose-5-phosphate by hemolysates of erythrocytes which were unable to convert fructose diphosphate to the monophosphate ester, i.e., the lower equation depicted above. In view of the oxidative decarboxylation of 6-phosphogluconate to ribulose-5-phosphate and carbon dioxide, and the resynthesis of hexosemonophosphate, a cyclic mechanism for the oxidation of hexosemonophosphate was envisioned. The mechanism has been elucidated by the excellent research performed mainly by Horecker and Racker and their colleagues. Summaries of this work are found in references 72 and 73.

An enzyme which catalyzed the splitting of pentose phosphate to a C₂ moiety and glyceraldehyde-3-phosphate was crystallized from yeast and spinach. It was found that the substrate for the enzyme was xylulose-5-phosphate (see Fig. 7). The latter was derived from ribulose-5-phosphate by the action of the enzyme epimerase. The enzymic reaction did not proceed unless a suitable aldehyde acceptor was present to combine with the C₂ fragment. Therefore the enzyme catalyzed a transfer rather than a cleavage and the substrate possessed a keto linkage. It was called transketolase. Thiamine pyrophosphate was found to be a coenzyme for the apoenzyme. In view of the fact that the reaction would not proceed unless an acceptor aldehyde was present, a glycolaldehyde-thiamine pyrophosphate enzyme complex was envisioned. The entire complex was referred to as "active glycolaldehyde." When ribose-5-phosphate was present as the acceptor aldehyde, sedoheptulose-7-phosphate (a seven carbon keto sugar) and triose phosphate were formed from xylulose-5-phosphate.

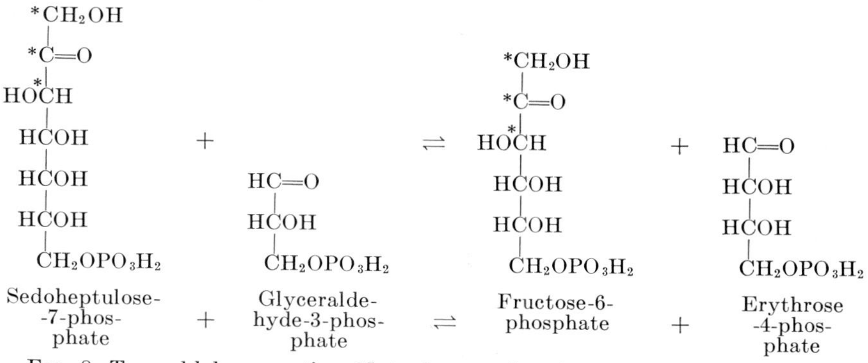

*CH₂OH
|
*C=O
|
HO*CH
|
HCOH   +   ⇌   *CH₂OH
| |
HCOH   HC=O   *C=O   +   HC=O
| | | |
HCOH   HCOH   HO*CH   HCOH
| | | |
CH₂OPO₃H₂   CH₂OPO₃H₂   HCOH   HCOH
                                               | |
                                               HCOH   CH₂OPO₃H₂
                                               |
                                               CH₂OPO₃H₂

Sedoheptulose-   Glyceralde-   Fructose-6-   Erythrose
-7-phos-   +   hyde-3-phos-   ⇌   phosphate   +   -4-phos-
phate   phate   phate

$$\text{*CH}_2\text{OH} \quad \text{*C=O} \quad \text{HO*CH} \quad \text{HCOH} \quad \text{HCOH} \quad \text{HCOH} \quad \text{CH}_2\text{OPO}_3\text{H}_2$$

FIG. 8. Transaldolase reaction. Note the transfer of the three carbon atoms indicated with asterisks.

Another enzyme was found in extracts from yeast and spinach which catalyzed a type of transfer depicted in Fig. 8. It will be observed that a transfer of an aldolase type occurred. The enzyme was called transaldolase. The reaction resembled the transketolase reaction in that no reaction occurred unless an acceptor aldehyde (glyceraldehyde-3-phosphate, erythrose-4-phosphate) for the dihydroxyacetone moiety was present.

A combination of the transketolase and transaldolase reactions accounted for the synthesis of fructose-6-phosphate from xylulose-5-phosphate and ribose-5-phosphate. These cyclic events are illustrated in Fig. 9. It will be noted that one molecule of glucose enters the cycle via 6-phosphogluconate and xylulose-5-phosphate and the remaining sequence of events is initiated by the action of transketolase on the latter ester and ribose-5-phosphate. Ribose-5-phosphate serves much the same purpose in this cycle as does oxalacetate in the TCA cycle, i.e., a carrier of a two carbon moiety. Similarly, ribose-5-phosphate is regenerated after a single revolution of the oxidative pentose phosphate cycle. The net result of a single turn of the cycle is represented in the following equation:

$$1 \text{ glucose} \rightarrow 3CO_2 + 1 \text{ glyceraldehyde-3-phosphate}$$

The glyceraldehyde-3-phosphate may be transformed by the action of triose phosphate isomerase to an equilibrium mixture of it and dihydroxyacetone phosphate from which fructose-1,6-diphosphate is formed (action of aldolase). The latter compound may be hydrolyzed to fructose-6-phosphate and isomerized to glucose-6-phosphate for entry into the cycle by oxidation to xylulose-5-phosphate. Two revolutions of the cycle are represented by the equation:

$$2 \text{ glucose} \rightarrow 6CO_2 + 1 \text{ glucose}$$

Therefore, for the equivalence of the complete oxidation of one molecule

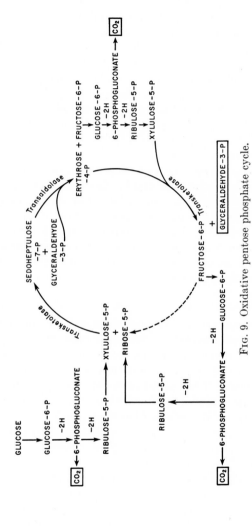

FIG. 9. Oxidative pentose phosphate cycle.

of glucose to carbon dioxide, two revolutions are required and the resynthesis of a molecule of a glucose ester occurs.

In the above description little attention has been given to the fate of the electrons during the two oxidative steps of glucose-6-phosphate to ribulose-5-phosphate. These oxidations are mediated by TPN^+, which under most conditions with microorganisms is reoxidized via the cytochrome system by oxygen. Since three molecules of carbon dioxide are evolved during one revolution of the cycle and two TPN^+-linked oxidative steps are required for the formation of each molecule of carbon dioxide, a total of six molecules of TPNH will be formed by one revolution. The oxidative pentose phosphate cycle for the oxidation of glucose is therefore an aerobic mechanism. On the other hand, a mechanism is known for the oxidation of TPNH by DPN^+ (transhydrogenase) which under proper conditions of equilibria to overcome unfavorable oxidation-reduction potentials may couple the oxidation steps with anaerobic reduction reactions. Under these conditions the oxidative pentose cycle could account for anaerobic dissimilation of glucose with the accumulation of reduced products of glucose dissimilation. As yet, no evidence exists for these cyclic events occurring anaerobically in microorganisms. There is evidence that TPNH may be required for fatty acid synthesis, and in certain mammalian tissues where rapid fat synthesis occurs the pentose phosphate pathway has been found to be of considerable importance.

B. OCCURRENCE OF CYCLE IN MICROORGANISMS

Since the discovery of the reactions comprising the oxidative pentose phosphate cycle there have been many attempts to determine the extent of its operation in various microbial cells. The reactions of this cycle and the Embden-Meyerhof pathway and the TCA cycle are demonstrable in many microorganisms. The difficulties which are encountered in the design of experiments that will clearly reveal the extent to which the two mechanisms are operative in the cell can be readily appreciated. It must be emphasized that the mere demonstration of the presence of all the enzymes responsible for the reactions of the cycle does not provide evidence for its quantitative importance to the cell.

One technique which has given some information concerning the relative contribution of the pentose phosphate cycle to the total oxidation of carbohydrates in microorganisms is the use of isotopically labeled sugars. A review of the Embden-Meyerhof pathway will illustrate that carbon atoms number 1 and 6 of the glucose molecule terminate in carbon atom 3 (methyl group) of each of the two molecules of pyruvate formed by the pathway. Therefore from an isotopic and metabolic point of view carbon atoms 1 and 6 of glucose are equivalent in this pathway. Carbon atoms 3 and 4 of the glucose molecule form the carbon atoms of the carboxyl group in each molecule of pyruvic acid. Since in the oxidation of pyruvate to acetyl CoA for entrance into the TCA cycle the carboxyl carbon atoms of pyruvic acid are evolved as carbon dioxide, it is obvious with glucose-$3,4$-C^{14} there will be an early appearance of isotopic carbon in the respiratory carbon dioxide. With glucose-6-C^{14} or glucose-1-C^{14} the appearance of isotope in the respiratory carbon dioxide will be considerably delayed if the dissimilation of the sugar occurred by the Embden-Meyerhof pathway. On the other hand, oxidation of glucose-1-C^{14} by the oxidative pentose phosphate cycle would result in the early appearance of the isotope in the respiratory carbon dioxide, since the initial step is the conversion of the phosphate ester of the sugar to ribulose-5-phosphate, through an oxidative decarboxylation of the intermediate 6-phosphogluconate (see Fig. 6). With glucose-6-C^{14} the appearance of the isotope in the respiratory carbon dioxide would be delayed by this cycle.

In addition to kinetic studies of this type the relative isotopic contribution of various carbon atoms from glucose to cellular constituents can be determined. With the use of specifically labeled glucose one can determine by the distribution pattern of the isotope in the cellular components derived from the dissimilation of glucose which of the two pathways is quantitatively important. These techniques would be readily applicable to the problem if the various species of microorganisms possessed either one or the other pathway. Unfortunately this is not the case, since the potential for both mechanisms exists in many cells and we have already seen that there are some intermediates common to both pathways. As a consequence, common pools of intermediates exist in the cell. Furthermore, it is observed from Fig. 9 that recycling of fructose-6-phosphate occurs in the pentose phosphate cycle and the amount of recycling will determine the degree of randomization of the isotope in the fructose-6-phosphate. Additional randomization will occur from the reversibility of the transketolase-transaldolase reactions. Because of these situations, it is very difficult to determine the relative contributions of the two pathways to the total metabolism of the microbial cell. It is also possible that in some microorganisms the oxidative pentose phosphate pathway may be responsible for the oxidation of a portion of the glucose molecule and the TCA cycle involved in the remainder. It is observed from Fig. 9 that with one revolution of the cycle three molecules of carbon dioxide and one molecule of glyceraldehyde-3-phosphate are formed from one molecule of glucose-6-phosphate. A conversion of the triose phosphate to pyruvate by an incomplete Embden-Meyerhof pathway and oxidation of the pyruvate via the TCA cycle would result in the complete oxidation of glucose.

In spite of these complexities, several investigations have demonstrated that the oxidative pentose cycle is of quantitative importance to some microorganisms. Reference will be made to a few of these investigations which give an indication of the techniques employed and the general problem of interpretation of results. Cohen[83] investigated the oxidation of gluconate-1-C^{14} and glucose-1-C^{14} by growing cells of *E. coli* and determined the contribution of the pentose-phosphate cycle to the oxidation of these substances and the synthesis of the ribose moiety of ribose nucleic acids. Under the experimental conditions used, more carbon dioxide was derived from carbon atom 1 of glucose than could be expected from the mechanism of the Embden-Meyerhof pathway. A minimum of 14% and a maximum of approximately 35% of the glucose was oxidized via pentose phosphate, more than that required for the ribose nucleic acid of the cell. The precise contribution of the cycle to the total oxidation of glucose could not be determined. The data obtained from experiments with nonproliferating cells and glucose-1-C^{14} gave no indication of a preferential liberation of carbon dioxide from carbon atom 1 of the glucose. Therefore the contribution of the pentose phosphate cycle under these conditions was not determinable. Bernstein[84] demonstrated that growing cells of *E. coli* formed most of the ribose required for ribose nucleic acid synthesis from glucose after the loss of carbon atom 1. It is clear from these experiments that the pentose phosphate cycle occurs in *E. coli* and contributes to the formation of ribose from glucose. However, very little can be said regarding the quantitative aspects of the contribution of the cycle to the total oxidation of glucose. Cochrane and his colleagues[85, 86] have examined the oxidative metabolism of several species of the genus *Streptomyces*. The enzymes of the pentose cycle as well as the Embdem-Meyerhof pathway were found in these organisms, and studies with glucose-1-C^{14} indicated that both pathways occurred. No conclusion could be made concerning the extent of operation of either cycle.

Heath and Koffler[87] compared the fate of glucose-U-C^{14} (uniformly labeled) and glucose-1-C^{14} during short intervals of growth of *Penicillium chrysogenum*. Short intervals were chosen since it was recognized that continuous recycling by both pathways and mixing of common intermediates in the pools of the cells would obscure the results. It was concluded that approximately two-thirds of the glucose was utilized through a mechanism involving the primary oxidation of the first carbon atom to carbon dioxide. The mechanism was considered to be the pentose phosphate cycle.

The aerobic organism *Acetobacter suboxydans* does not ferment glucose; on the other hand, it can aerobically oxidize glucose with the evolution of carbon dioxide. In addition, the reactions of the TCA cycle have not been demonstrated.[88] These observations suggest that other pathways than the Embden-Meyerhof pathway and the TCA cycle account for the oxidation of glucose. Cheldelin and co-workers[89] have investigated this problem employing glucose and gluconate which were isotopically labeled with C^{14} in specific carbon atoms. Glucose-1-C^{14}, -2-C^{14}, -3,4-C^{14}, -6-C^{14}, and glucose-U-C^{14} were used. The gluconate had the same numerical labeling. A kinetic study of the oxidation of the variously isotopically labeled glucose and gluconate molecules by nonproliferating cells of *Acetobacter suboxydans* showed that carbon atoms 1 and 2 were rapidly and successively eliminated as carbon dioxide, while there was a slow and delayed release of carbon atom 6. Approximately 50 % of the added glucose carbon atoms appeared in the respiratory carbon dioxide; the remainder was retained in the medium. Most of the activity which was retained was attributable to carbon atom 6 of glucose. From these and other results the authors concluded that the pentose phosphate cycle accounted for most of the respiratory carbon dioxide. Carbon atoms 3 and 4 produced less but significant amounts of carbon dioxide, a result which unfortunately complicated the calculation and concrete interpretation of the results.

The elucidation of a mechanism such as the pentose phosphate cycle for the synthesis of cellular constituents, (i.e., ribose nucleic acid), and for oxidation of carbohydrates represents a very important advance in our knowledge regarding the metabolism of cells. In most instances the discovery of such mechanisms has been greatly facilitated by *in vitro* studies for which our present-day techniques are adequately suited. The ultimate goal, however, is to determine the participation of the mechanism in the integrated metabolism of the intact cell. Unfortunately, as with the pentose phosphate cycle, the data obtained from *in vivo* studies with our present inadequate methods and techniques cannot be definitely interpreted.[90] These methods and techniques are rapidly improving and without doubt we shall see advancement in this important area in the near future.

XIV. Summary and Conclusions

At the present time there are only two mechanisms employed by microorganisms for the *complete* oxidation of foodstuffs to carbon dioxide and water which have been well established. They are the TCA cycle and the oxidative pentose phosphate cycle. We have seen the experimental difficulties which had to be overcome merely to establish the existence of these cycles, without necessarily demonstrating their quantitative importance to the cell. To establish the latter the experimenter must always be aware of the possible existence of unknown mechanisms either related or unrelated to the mechanism in question. If the mechanisms are related, there are usually common components, and to differentiate these within the cell with our present methods taxes the ingenuity of the investigator. In some instances the differentiation is almost impossible. If the mechanisms are unrelated, there is always the possibility that the second one will not even be detected. The investigations which so recently demonstrated that anaerobic dissimilation of carbohydrates can occur by many more pathways than was previously thought possible serve as a warning against any confidence we may have concerning our complete knowledge about oxidative cyclic mechanisms. Our final hope is to determine all the metabolic sequences within the whole cell. However, the study of quantitative biology under *in vivo* conditions is exceedingly difficult. In all of biology there probably are no more adaptable forms than microorganisms. This property places the microbiologist in an admirable position, for by manipulation of the experimental design more information can be acquired than with less adaptable forms of life. On the other hand, this extreme adaptability has its shortcomings, particularly if the experimenter is not aware of these adaptive patterns. Each year more and more is being learned about the effect of conditions of growth upon the metabolic activities of the microbial cell. For example, we now know that under certain conditions the cell is not called upon to express the phenotypic property of synthesizing certain enzyme systems, since the conditions of growth are such that these enzymes are superfluous. Nevertheless, the capability exists in the cell, and by a thorough understanding of these growth conditions more metabolic sequences can be elucidated and their relationship to the cell may be evaluated.

Because of our increasing knowledge of microbial genetics, the improvement of our microbial and biochemical techniques, and the increasing interest in microbiology by young investigators, progress during the next few years in the exciting field of physiology of microorganisms will be substantial and rapid.

ACKNOWLEDGEMENTS

The author expresses his appreciation to Drs. H. J. Saz and H. E. Swim for permission to make extensive use of their data in the composition of this chapter. Gratitude is also extended to Drs. L. L. Campbell and J. Spizizen for their helpful discussions and criticisms.

REFERENCES

[1] A. Harden and W. J. Young, *Proc. Roy. Soc.* **B77**, 405 (1906).
[2] A. Szent-Györgyi, *Z. physiol. Chem.* **236**, 1 (1935).
[3] C. Martius and F. Knoop, *Z. physiol. Chem.* **246**, I (1937).
[4] C. Martius and F. Knoop, *Z. physiol. Chem.* **247**, 104 (1937).
[5] H. A. Krebs and W. A. Johnson, *Enzymologia* **4**, 148 (1937).
[6] F. Lipmann, *Bacteriol. Revs.* **17**, 1 (1953).
[7] F. Lynen, *Federation Proc.* **12**, 683 (1953).
[8] S. Ochoa, *Advances in Enzymol.* **15**, 183 (1954).
[9] I. C. Gunsalus, *Federation Proc.* **13**, 715 (1954).
[10] D. E. Green, *Biol. Revs. Cambridge Phil. Soc.* **29**, 330 (1954).

[11] H. Wieland and R. Sonderhoff, *Ann.* **499,** 213 (1932).
[12] C. R. Brewer and C. H. Werkman, *Enzymologia* **6,** 273 (1939).
[13] H. A. Krebs and L. V. Eggleston, *Biochem. J.* **34,** 442 (1940).
[14] C. H. Werkman and H. G. Wood, *Advances in Enzymol.* **2,** 135 (1942).
[15] H. G. Wood and C. H. Werkman, *J. Bacteriol.* **30,** 332 (1935); *Biochem. J.* **30,** 48 (1936).
[16] E. A. Evans, Jr., *Biochem. J.* **34,** 829 (1940).
[17] H. G. Wood and C. H. Werkman, *Biochem. J.* **32,** 1262 (1938).
[18] H. A. Krebs and L. V. Eggleston, *Biochem. J.* **34,** 1383 (1940).
[19] E. A. Evans, Jr. and L. Slotin, *J. Biol. Chem.* **136,** 301 (1940).
[20] H. G. Wood, C. H. Werkman, A. Hemingway, and A. O. Nier, *J. Biol. Chem.* **139,** 483 (1941); **142,** 31 (1942).
[21] T. Thunberg, *Skand. Arch. Physiol.* **40,** 1 (1920).
[22] G. R. Seaman and M. D. Naschke, *J. Biol. Chem.* **217,** 1 (1955).
[23] R. H. Vaughan, J. T. Osburn, G. T. Wedding, J. Tabachnick, C. G. Beisel, and T. Braxton, *J. Bacteriol.* **60,** 119 (1950).
[24] H. J. Saz and L. O. Krampitz, *J. Bacteriol.* **69,** 288 (1955).
[25] S. J. Ajl, *J. Bacteriol.* **59,** 499 (1950).
[26] H. E. Swim, Thesis, p. 96. Western Reserve University, Cleveland, Ohio (1952).
[27] H. J. Saz and L. O. Krampitz, *J. Bacteriol.* **67,** 409 (1954).
[28] S. J. Ajl, M. D. Kamen, S. L. Ranson, and D. T. O. Wong, *J. Biol. Chem.* **189,** 859 (1951).
[29] H. E. Swim and L. O. Krampitz, *J. Bacteriol.* **67,** 419 (1954).
[30] S. J. Ajl and D. T. O. Wong, *Arch. Biochem. Biophys.* **54,** 474 (1955).
[31] R. Sonderhoff and H. Thomas, *Ann.* **530,** 195 (1937).
[32] F. Lynen and N. Neciullah, *Ann.* **541,** 203 (1939).
[33] F. Lynen, *Ann.* **554,** 40 (1943).
[34] S. Weinhouse and R. H. Millington, *J. Am. Chem. Soc.* **69,** 3089 (1947).
[35] H. A. Krebs, S. Gurin, and L. V. Eggleston, *Biochem. J.* **51,** 614 (1952).
[36] J. A. DeMoss and H. E. Swim, *J. Bacteriol.* **74,** 445 (1957).
[37] H. A. Krebs, *Biochem. J.* **31,** 2905 (1937).
[38] H. E. Swim and L. O. Krampitz, *J. Bacteriol.* **67,** 426 (1954).
[39] R. Y. Stanier, *J. Bacteriol.* **54,** 339 (1947).
[40] J. L. Karlsson and H. A. Barker, *J. Biol. Chem.* **175,** 913 (1948).
[41] M. Suda, O. Hayaishi and Y. Oda, *Symposia on Enzyme Chem. (Japan)* **1,** 79 (1949).
[42] R. W. Stone and P. W. Wilson, *J. Bacteriol.* **63,** 605 (1952).
[43] R. W. Stone and P. W. Wilson, *J. Bacteriol.* **63,** 619 (1952).
[44] J. J. R. Campbell and F. N. Stokes, *J. Biol. Chem.* **190,** 853 (1951).
[45] F. J. S. Lara and J. L. Stokes, *J. Bacteriol.* **63,** 415 (1952).
[46] J. T. Barret, A. D. Larson, and R. E. Kallio, *J. Bacteriol.* **65,** 187 (1953).
[47] J. T. Barret and R. E. Kallio, *J. Bacteriol.* **66,** 517 (1953).
[48] C. Gilvarg and B. D. Davis, *J. Biol. Chem.* **222,** 307 (1956).
[49] J. J. R. Campbell, R. A. Smith, and B. A. Eagles, *Biochim. et Biophys. Acta* **11,** 594 (1953).
[50] R. A. Smith and I. C. Gunsalus, *J. Am. Chem. Soc.* **76,** 5002 (1954).
[51] H. J. Saz and E. P. Hillary, *Biochem. J.* **62,** 563 (1956).
[52] J. A. Olson, Nature, **174,** 695 (1954).
[53] D. T. O. Wong and S. J. Ajl, *Nature* **176,** 970 (1955).
[54] R. A. Smith and I. C. Gunsalus, *J. Biol. Chem.* **229,** 305 (1957).
[55] L. L. Campbell, Jr., *J. Bacteriol.* **68,** 598 (1954).
[56] D. T. O. Wong and S. J. Ajl, *J. Am. Chem. Soc.* **78,** 3230 (1956).

[57] D. T. O. Wong and S. J. Ajl, *Science* **126,** 1013 (1957).

[58] H. L. Kornberg and N. B. Madsen, *Biochim. et Biophys. Acta* **24,** 651 (1957).

[59] H. L. Kornberg and H. A. Krebs, *Nature* **179,** 988 (1957).

[60] E. H. Sayama, H. Fukumi, and R. Nakaya, *Jap. J. Med. Sci. & Biol.* **6,** 523 (1953).

[61] R. A. Altenbern and R. D. Housewright, *Arch. Biochem. Biophys.* **36,** 345 (1952).

[62] D. S. Goldman, *J. Bacteriol.* **71,** 732 (1956).

[63] M. Santer and S. J. Ajl, *J. Bacteriol.* **67,** 379 (1954).

[64] M. A. Eisenberg, *J. Biol. Chem.* **203,** 815 (1953).

[65] E. A. Delwiche and S. F. Carson, *J. Bacteriol.* **65,** 318 (1953).

[66] R. B. Roberts, P. H. Abelson, D. B. Cowie, E. T. Bolton, and R. Britten, "Studies of Biosynthesis in *Escherichia coli*." Carnegie Institute of Washington, Washington, D. C., 1955.

[67] G. Ehrensvärd, L. Reio, E. Saluste, and R. Stjernholm, *J. Biol. Chem.* **189,** 93 (1951).

[68] J. W. Foster, *Texas Repts. Biol. and Med.* **16,** 79 (1958).

[69] E. P. Goldschmidt, I. Yall, and H. Koffler, *J. Bacteriol.* **72,** 436 (1956).

[70] S. H. Hutner and A. Lwoff, "Biochemistry and Physiology of Protozoa," Vol. 1. Academic Press, New York, 1951.

[71] M. R. Bovarnick and J. C. Miller, *J. Biol. Chem.* **184,** 661 (1950).

[72] B. L. Horecker, *Brewers Dig.* **28,** 214 (1953).

[73] E. Racker, *Advances in Enzymol.* **15,** 141 (1954).

[74] I. C. Gunsalus, B. L. Horecker, and W. A. Wood, *Bacteriol. Revs.* **19,** 79 (1955).

[75] O. Warburg, W. Christian, and A. Griese, *Biochem. Z.* **282,** 157 (1935).

[76] F. Dickens, *Nature* **138,** 1057 (1936).

[77] F. Lipmann, *Nature* **138,** 588 (1936).

[78] F. Dickens, *Biochem. J.* **32,** 1626 (1938).

[79] D. B. M. Scott and S. S. Cohen, *J. Biol. Chem.* **188,** 509 (1951).

[80] B. L. Horecker and P. Z. Smyrniotis, *J. Biol. Chem.* **193,** 371 (1951).

[81] Z. Dische, *Naturwissenschaften* **26,** 252 (1938).

[82] F. Schlenk and M. J. Waldvogel, *Arch. Biochem.* **12,** 181 (1947).

[83] S. S. Cohen, *Nature* **168,** 746 (1951).

[84] I. A. Bernstein, *J. Biol. Chem.* **221,** 873 (1956).

[85] V. W. Cochrane, H. D. Peck, Jr., and A. Harrison, *J. Bacteriol.* **66,** 17 (1953).

[86] V. W. Cochrane and P. L. Hawley, *J. Bacteriol.* **71,** 308 (1956).

[87] E. C. Heath and H. Koffler, *J. Bacteriol.* **71,** 174 (1956).

[88] F. King and V. H. Cheldelin, *J. Bacteriol.* **66,** 581 (1953).

[89] P. A. Kitos, C. H. Wang, B. A. Mohler, T. E. King, and V. H. Cheldelin, *J. Biol. Chem.* **233,** 1295 (1958).

[90] H. G. Wood and J. Katz, *J. Biol. Chem.* **233,** 1279 (1958).

Suggested Supplementary Reading

Ajl, S. J., *Bacteriol. Revs.* **15,** 211 (1950).

Ajl, S. J., *Physiol. Revs.* **38,** 196 (1958).

Cochrane, V. W., "Physiology of Fungi." Wiley, New York, 1958.

Gunsalus, I. C., *Federation Proc.* **13,** 715 (1954).

Gunsalus, I. C., *in* "The Mechanism of Enzyme Action" (W. D. McElroy and B. Glass, eds.), p. 545. Johns Hopkins Press, Baltimore, Maryland, 1954.

Gunsalus, I. C., Horecker, B. L., and Wood, W. A., *Bacteriol. Revs.* **19,** 79 (1955).

Horecker, B. L., *Brewers Dig.* **28,** 214 (1953).

Kornberg, H. L., and Krebs, H. A., *Nature* **179,** 988 (1957).

Krebs, H. A., *Advances in Enzymol.* **3,** 191 (1943).

Krebs, H. A., *Harvey Lectures, Ser.* **44,** 165 (1950).

Lipmann, F., *Bacteriol. Revs.* **17,** 1 (1953).

Lynen, F., *Federation Proc.* **12,** 683 (1953).

Novelli, G. D., *Federation Proc.* **12,** 675 (1953).

Ochoa, S., *Advances in Enzymol.* **15,** 183 (1954).

Racker, E., *Advances in Enzymol.* **15,** 141 (1954).

Racker, E., *Harvey Lectures, Ser.* **51,** 143 (1957).

Roberts, R. B., Abelson, P. H., Cowie, D. B., Bolton, E. T., and Britten, R.,'' Studies of Biosynthesis in *Escherichia coli*.'' Carnegie Institute of Washington, Washington, D. C., 1955.

Utter, M. F., and Wood, H. G., *Advances in Enzymol.* **12,** 41 (1951).

Wong, D. T. O., and Ajl, S. J., *Science* **126,** 1013 (1957).

Wood, H. G., *Physiol. Revs.* **36,** 198 (1946).

Wood, W. A., *Bacteriol. Revs.* **19,** 222 (1955).

CHAPTER 5

The Dissimilation of High Molecular Weight Substances

H. J. ROGERS

I. Introduction

Under most conditions other than those artificially created in the laboratory, the amount of readily diffusible carbonaceous and nitrogenous
material of low molecular weight which is available to bacteria, or for that
matter to most animals, is strictly limited. The majority of the nutrients
will be in the form of large molecules, often bound together to give almost
completely insoluble substances. Teleologically the need for living forms,
including bacteria, to develop some system for hydrolyzing such large
molecules to smaller utilizable ones is clear. Moreover, the argument is not
all in favor of the bacteria. The scavenging action of organisms is vital both
to prevent the surface of the globe becoming one vast pyre of dead matter
and to conserve and recycle carbon, nitrogen, and other elements. Every-
thing living must on death be in some way destroyed and its carbon and
nitrogen returned for reutilization. As a consequence some system usually
in organisms must be capable of hydrolyzing and eventually oxidizing and
reducing all the component molecules to carbon dioxide and assimilable
nitrogen. This, of course, is equally true for not only plant and animal life

but for the bacteria and fungi themselves; otherwise the world would long ago have grown a thick coat of microorganisms. The choice between being buried either by undecomposed trees or by dead *Bacillus subtilis* or *Aspergillus niger* seems somewhat dubious. It is, therefore, logical to suppose that if one chooses the right place and the right way to look one will always find some organisms which can decompose any chosen naturally occurring substance, however intractable it may appear at first sight. This hypothesis has been many times tested and found to be true. For example, organisms, usually bacteria or fungi, have been found which utilize substances as diverse as cellulose, chitin, pneumococcal capsular polysaccharide, collagen, alginic acid, and bacterial cell walls. The present article is an attempt to bring together some of the information that has been gained during the course of these searches, and the studies that have been made of the mechanisms developed by microorganisms to deal with large molecules.

For insoluble substances, if not for other high molecular weight substances which seem rather unlikely to be able to diffuse into the cell, one might assume that the most obvious way to deal with them would be for the cell itself to elaborate some diffusible enzyme which could reach the substrate and break it down. This some organisms do, but it is by no means universal. Although, with a few exceptions, extracellular or freely diffusible enzymes elaborated by bacteria are specifically directed toward substrates of high molecular weight, the reverse is not always true. In some examples we shall consider, very large molecules organized into insoluble substances are reduced to assimilable and therefore presumably small molecules without any extracellular enzyme ever being demonstrable, the very contact between the substrate and the organism seems to be enough. Although the ability of bacteria to break down large molecules by various methods is vital both to the life of higher forms and to the bacteria themselves, it has its more sinister aspect. Bacteria are no choosers and a precious fabric may as likely form food for cellulose-decomposing organisms as the fibers of a dead plant. For example, in the days before adequate protective measures could be taken, destruction of raw cotton coming into England amounted to 10–15 %[1] owing to bacterial action during storage under damp conditions; another graphic example is the observation that the useful life of an unprotected sand bag lying on the ground under tropical conditions is about eleven days.[2] Likewise when organisms are growing in living host tissues, either plant or animal, their ability to hydrolyze vitally important substances often contributes to their maintenance and may on occasion be vital to them, always at the expense of the host. Pathogenic bacteria have the ability to destroy many substances of great biological importance to animals and plants; for example, collagen, nucleic acids, mucopolysaccharides, proteins, and pectin, to mention only a few.

There seems little need to elaborate further the importance of the subject. Sufficient has been said to emphasize this and also to indicate its breadth. In an article of this length it is obvious that drastic limitations will have to be imposed.

Firstly the term "high molecular weight substance" ought to be defined. In a sense a more logically acceptable but impossibly broad survey would be that of the utilization of substances which cannot penetrate the membrane of the microorganisms. Fortunately or unfortunately, according to the point of view, such a logical approach could not be justified in the light of our knowledge of the penetrability of the bacterial cell. It is, therefore, proposed to continue talking about high molecular weight substances but to remain disarmingly vague, with an indication that the term is to mean substances such as proteins, nucleic acids, and polysaccharides, and any others which may be relevant to the argument. The second limitation is of a more mechanical kind. It is clearly impossible to deal in detail with all the work on all the substances, even within the few groups specifically mentioned. An excellent book, for example, devoted exclusively to the microbial breakdown of cellulose is already available.[2] Therefore some plan of campaign had to be designed and it was thought most useful to give in detail only those examples which had been pursued thoroughly over a number of years, even though neat conclusions have not yet been reached. For example, it did not seem worthwhile to attempt a brief survey of all the work which has been done on the utilization of proteins by bacteria, even supposing this were possible; but a considerable amount of continuous work has been done on the proteases and peptidases of *Clostridium histolyticum*, and of streptococci and on subtilisin from *B. subtilis*. This does not, however, mean that very good work has not been done on the proteases of other organisms, but simply that a limitation had to be made somewhere. Occasionally, this approach has led to difficulties because although much may be known about the sort of bacteria that can do a certain job, the way in which they do it may still be wrapped in mystery. At the same time hints may suggest that the process is similar to one already studied in fungi, for example. Attention has thus been given to the fungal process with the implicit suggestion that, when adequately investigated, it may be found that bacteria accomplish the same task in a similar manner. Should the bacterial process prove to be vastly different the author will shelter behind the interest and amusement that later readers may take in comparing the beauty of reality with the stupidity of the picture drawn in the review.

Lastly this article will not attempt to review work which has already been recently reviewed. As far as I know no other article with just this title has been written before, but specific subjects in it have been repeatedly reviewed; references will be given to some of these reviews.

II. Methods of Study

A. The Recognition and Isolation of Organisms Utilizing High Molecular Weight Substances

Whether or not any known microorganism is recognized as being able to attack and utilize a substrate seems to be to some extent a matter of chance. For example, it is improbable that any considerable proportion of even the known bacterial species has been thoroughly tested for ability to hydrolyze cellulose or deoxyribonucleic acid. This rather haphazard state of affairs has resulted from the two major approaches that have been used in studying the breakdown of high molecular weight substances. The one is isolation by enrichment technique in which a medium consisting of a solution of essential inorganic salts, supplemented with the particular substrate under study, is inoculated with a naturally occurring mixture of organisms such as occurs in soil, sea mud, or decaying vegetable matter. The other is by deduction from the behavior of an organism in a particular habitat that certain substances are being destroyed; this hypothesis can then be tested. The former approach has been favored particularly in the study of the decomposition of insoluble substrates such as cellulose and chitin, but has also been used to find organisms destroying pneumococcal capsular polysaccharides and blood group substances. The second type of approach has found particular favor in studying animal and plant pathogens; thus, for example, were the investigations of *Clostridium perfringens* collagenase and deoxyribonuclease and *C. histolyticum* proteinase started; the properties of organisms causing food spoilage or showing other types of economically disadvantageous behavior have often been deduced from the type of damage.

1. Isolation by Enrichment Technique

As has been said, the essential of this technique is that an inorganic salt medium containing the particular substrate as a sole source of carbon and nitrogen be inoculated with a mixed culture of microorganisms derived from some source in which it is likely that active destruction of the particular substrate has been proceeding. Since most substances eventually reach either the ground, lake, or sea bottom, the commonest sources for the inoculum have been soils and muds. When growth and partial or total destruction of the substrate in the primary culture have been obtained, further cultures are carried out in the same medium. A pure culture rarely results, however, and the subsequent isolation of a single organism has frequently been very difficult. In the isolation[3] of the organism destroying the capsular polysaccharide of pneumococci, for example, the salt–substrate medium was inoculated with material from the cranberry bogs of New

Jersey. Dilutions of the enrichment cultures were then made such that each was likely to contain only one or a few organisms. These dilutions were inoculated into fresh medium and the cultures which then grew were plated on a selective medium containing a concentration of gentian violet previously found not to interfere with substrate decomposition in the enrichment cultures. Finally cultures derived from single colonies were heated to kill nonspore formers. By this mixture of techniques a pure culture, very active in destroying the pneumococcal polysaccharide, was isolated. When the isolation of organisms that can destroy insoluble substrates such as chitin or cellulose is the object of the work, it is usual to incorporate the substances into an agar plate and thus visualize the ability of individual colonies derived from enrichment cultures to hydrolyze them. Either a clear zone of destruction of some width or an area of partial clearing under and immediately around the colony may occur.

In some earlier work reliance was placed on a single technique such as enrichment alone, or selection of colonies showing zones of substrate destruction. Later work, however, has frequently shown that the resultant cultures were not, in fact, pure. That they were mixtures appears to explain satisfactorily such a phenomenon as that of irreversible adaptation which has been repeatedly observed. McBee[4] studied this phenomenon in the thermophilic cellulose-decomposing organisms. The claim had been made by many earlier workers that cellulose must be constantly present if the culture were to maintain its cellulolytic properties. If, for example, the organisms were grown on glucose then the resulting culture was found to have lost permanently its cellulose-destroying property. McBee proved in a number of instances that when pure cultures were isolated the cellulolytic property could be maintained satisfactorily on any medium giving growth. The previous observations were undoubtedly due to overgrowth of the cellulose-decomposing organisms by other contaminants also present. This sometimes provides a valuable criterion for the purity of cultures.

Enrichment technique is an exceedingly efficient way of isolating organisms that will actively destroy the particular substrate but it is highly selective in other ways. The nutritional requirements of the successful organism must necessarily be relatively simple and its growth rapid relative to other organisms in the mixture which can also decompose the substrate. It must also be able to grow better than the other organisms with similar powers under the particular physical conditions (e.g., temperature, aeration, ionic strength) chosen. Thus only the best-adapted (in the biological sense of the word) microorganisms will be selected. For this reason it is probably not valid to regard the cellulose- or chitin-decomposing organisms as representative of organisms with particular abilities, since many of them have been obtained by enrichment techniques which select on the basis of many characteristics besides substrate decomposition. Many other organisms with less powerful ability to destroy the substrates or with different physiological characteristics may exist unrecognized.

2. Deduction of Enzyme Formation from the Behavior of Organisms

The only purpose of a short section with this subtitle is to point out again how little we know about the potentialities of most organisms. The method by which the ability of some organisms to destroy a particular substrate has been recognized is often dependent on some quite different characteristic. For example, it is known that *C. perfringens* produces an enzyme which rather specifically hydrolyzes collagen (cf. Section IV, C, 3). Originally it was observed[5] that in tissue sections taken from the muscles of animals which had received *C. perfringens* toxin the collagen fibers had been destroyed. The toxin, however, is likely to be toxic not because it contains a collagenase but because of its lecithinase[6] action. How many other organisms, not possessing a toxic lecithinase or some other tissue-destroying mechanism to attract attention, also form collagenase? Likewise, hyaluronidase is known to be formed by several pathogenic microorganisms and many more such have been examined, largely because hyaluronidase has been thought to have some possible relation to the pathogenic process. Recently, two observations[7, 8] have shown that a strain of *Bacillus subtilis* and a flavobacterium are active hyaluronidase producers. How many other groups of organisms without pathogenic potentialities may contain hyaluronidase-producting representatives? These arguments might be greatly extended and they all point to the caution that, although we may know about the abilities of certain microorganisms to act on certain substrates, and although we may even know which organisms are likely to carry out certain processes under natural conditions, we know very little about which organisms are *capable* of carrying out specific tasks when tested under optimal conditions.

B. Methods for Studying the Breakdown of High Molecular Weight Substances

The complexity of structure and size of the molecules we are considering necessarily means that a variety of different methods can be used to study the breakdown of any given substance. For purposes of convenience the methods used will be divided into two groups: those satisfactory for the qualitative recognition of a process and those more useful for studying its detailed biochemistry.

1. Qualitative Methods

Where the substrate is insoluble, as with cellulose or chitin, by far the commonest methods of study are either to put a strip of the material into the medium and study its disintegration or to incorporate a powder in a solid medium, such as agar, and to look for zones of destruction around the colonies.

Both of these methods have their advantages, purposes, and limitations. The strip method is useful for enrichment cultures since relatively early stages in disintegration can be observed. However, the exact meaning of these very early stages may be questioned. For example, some "cellulose-destroying" organisms are said to "pulp filter paper or weaken it sufficiently so that fibers separate on slight agitation;"[9] exactly whether the cellulose molecule itself has been attacked or whether some other structure in the complex fibrous material (see Section IV, A, 1) has been broken down is not clear. Another advantage of the strip method is that it provides for a rather wide range of cultural conditions inasmuch as the bottom of the strip will be deep under the medium and almost anaerobic, whereas its top may project clear of the medium and allow very aerobic growth on its damp surface. The importance of allowing the strip to project has been noted, for example, by Benton[10] in his study of the isolation of chitin-destroying organisms. The total surface of substrate supplied by this method is, of course, very limited. In general with a better understanding of the physiology of organisms and adequate methods for aeration, I should think that the addition of powders to the enrichment culture would be the method of choice even though only more drastic breakdown might be recognizable.

The method of growing the organisms on the surface of a solid (usually agar) medium with powdered substrate incorporated is perhaps the commonest method for the study of the breakdown of insoluble substrates, after primary enrichment cultures have been made. In general this method can give a good deal of not only qualitative but even semiquantitative information. If wide, clear zones are found around colonies on a plate containing powdered cellulose or chitin, then it seems reasonable to deduce that a cellulase or chitinase has diffused away from the colony and hydrolyzed the substrate. These particular substances are so resistant to ordinary chemical attack that any other explanation seems unlikely. It may be just worthwhile, however, to point out that very beautiful zones of clearing can be obtained around colonies of the lactic acid bacteria growing on solid media containing glucose and powdered calcium carbonate. The production of zones around colonies is certainly not proof of enzymic action irrespective of the chemical properties of the substrate and the physiological behavior of the organism. The deduction can also probably be drawn with safety that, when wide zones of clearing are produced around colonies growing on a medium containing a chemically resistant substrate, the organisms are forming a truly extracellular enzyme. Here again proof is not absolute since enzyme may be liberated from autolyzing cells within the colony. Generally, however, when wide zones of clearing on solid media have been observed it has been possible to demonstrate the production of extracellular enzymes in liquid cultures by other means.

If sufficient care is taken in standardizing the conditions for examining zones of substrate lysis, certain very limited quantitative conclusions are likely to be valid. The size of the zone is largely controlled by the amount of enzyme formed and its rate of diffusion under the chosen conditions. Therefore a comparison of the zone diameters around colonies in a pure culture can give indications of the enzyme-forming ability of the cells within the colonies and variants may be recognized. When the behaviors of different species of organisms are compared, this method is less likely to be valid since there is no guarantee that the molecular weights of the enzymes will be the same and hence the different rates of diffusion will influence the size of the zones. For the most part, however, the method has been used in a purely qualitative manner.

2. METHODS FOR QUANTITATIVE STUDY

Once an organism which actively breaks down a particular substrate has been isolated in pure culture, little further progress can be made in understanding mechanisms until suitable methods for estimating the enzymes involved have been designed. This is equally true whether the aim is to understand the physiology of formation of the enzyme or the mechanism of hydrolysis of the substrate. The principles of the method that is devised are controlled, of course, very largely by the properties of the substrate. The methods that have found particular favor are based on: (a) special properties of the substrate, such as solubility, presence of anionic groups, absorption of ultraviolet light; (b) the viscosity of dilute solutions; (c) estimation of the liberation of parts of the large molecule, such as free reducing groups from polysaccharides, or primary amino groups from proteins.

a. Methods Dependent on Special Properties. Here are to be found methods for estimating the rate of breakdown of most of the substances bearing strong charges such as mucopolysaccharides, nucleic acids, and pectinic acids. Hyaluronidase, for example, can be measured by the rate at which it destroys the ability of hyaluronic acid to combine with proteins in acid solution to give insoluble products. The method may either be designed to give a so-called mucin clot[11] or a turbidity[12] the density of which can be measured optically. Pectinase can be estimated[13] by measuring the disappearance of insoluble Ca-pectinate, and the breakdown of deoxyribonucleic acid, ribonucleic acid,[14] and casein[15] have been measured by making use of the insolubility of the undegraded molecule in acid solution. The turbidity of the suspension of undegraded substrate can be measured optically or the precipitate dried and weighed. Another method for the measurement of nuclease[16] activity depends upon the different absorptions of the whole nucleic acid molecule and the products of hydrolysis at 260 mμ. The method relates enzyme activity to the shift in extinction at 260 mμ occurring during incubation under standard conditions.

Insolubility itself has been used as a criterion for quantitative estimation of enzymes such as cellulase and chitinase. The enzyme preparation is simply allowed to act on powdered cellulose or chitin and the remaining insoluble material centrifuged or filtered off and weighed. The difficulties involved in two-phase systems of this type are considerable if any knowledge of the kinetics of the process is required. The rate of enzyme action will clearly be dependent, among other factors, upon particle size, penetrability of the particles, and amount of agitation.[17] Further difficulties are introduced by the complex nature of the substances themselves (see Section IV, A, 1) and attempts have been made more recently to avoid these methods by using partially degraded and substituted soluble materials.

Another substrate property which has been employed particularly for the study of mucoprotein breakdown is the immunological reaction characteristic of the particular substance. In the studies of the blood group substances and pneumococcal polysaccharides, for example, this was the principal method of investigation (cf. Section IV,B,4,5). The labor involved in making some of these methods quantitatively exact is rather large and they have frequently been used in a semiquantitative fashion.

Among the methods that depend upon special properties of the substrate must be mentioned the common method used for estimating the action of amylase. This depends upon the ability of starch, particularly its amylose component, to form a blue color with solutions of iodine. The enzyme is allowed to act on starch under suitably standardized conditions and then a solution of iodine and a sample of the hydrolyzate mixed: the blue color formed can be measured colorimetrically and related to the remaining concentration of reactive starch. Many modifications of the technique have been suggested; that of Smith and Roe[18] is a good example.

b. The Viscosity Method. This method has been used to estimate the activity of enzymes attacking a wide variety of the substances dealt with in this article, for example, for hyaluronic acid,[19] deoxyribonucleic acid,[20] collagen,[21] mucoproteins,[22] and cellulose derivatives.[2] In essence the method is simple enough. The enzyme and substrate are brought together in a viscometer, usually of the Ostwald type, which is maintained in a bath with precise temperature control. The rate of diminution of viscosity is then observed over some chosen period of time. The results, as with the methods discussed above, must be expressed in arbitrary units. For example, unity may be regarded as the time required to reduce the viscosity to half its initial value[23] or a standard enzyme preparation may be set up and given an arbitrary value; the activities of other preparations are then compared with the standard.

The disadvantage of this method and of those dealt with in the previous section is that being purely empirical they give little precise indication of the underlying chemical changes. In most cases the best that can be said is that the molecule is made smaller. This state of affairs is not so serious when well-defined chemical substances are involved as substrates, but could be misleading with complicated substances. To give an extreme but possible example, much attention has recently been paid to the mode of combination of mucopolysaccharides in tissues. Chondroitin sulfate, for example, can be isolated in the form of a protein-mucopolysaccharide complex. The viscosity of solutions of this complex is very high and can be lowered by the action of proteases;[24, 25] presumably, it could also be lowered by chondroitin sulfatase. Thus, if organisms were found producing enzymes which lowered the viscosity of a solution of chondroitin sulfate, the composition of the substrate would have to be examined very carefully before the conclusion that a chondroitin sulfatase was at work. Moreover, if the chondroitin sulfate protein complex (perhaps in ignorance of its nature, called "native" chondroitin sulfate) and purified chondroitin sulfate were both used as substrates, the conclusion might be drawn that two kinds of chondroitin sulfatases were produced by microorganisms, one of which hydrolyzes the native product and the other of which hydrolyzes both the native and the purer "partially degraded substrate"—whereas, of course, the "native substrate" could be hydrolyzed either by a protease or a chondroitin sulfatase and the other by the polysaccharidase only. This fictitious example is given because it can be stated in understandable chemical terms. In many cases similar explanations might apply to less well understood systems, for example, where the action of enzymes on native cellulose, determined by solubilization of the material, is compared with the viscosity-lowering effect on solutions of carboxymethyl cellulose.

c. Liberation of Lower Molecular Weight Breakdown Products. Perhaps the commonest method for the measurement of the enzymic breakdown of natural polymers is either to measure directly the liberation of some characteristic reactive group that has been unmasked by the action of the enzyme, or to precipitate the unhydrolyzed substrate and less hydrolyzed fragments and measure the concentration of small molecular weight substances left in solution. The former approach is well represented by the measurement of the liberation of reducing sugars from polysaccharides and mucopolysaccharides. In this method the enzyme is allowed to act under standard conditions, the reaction is stopped, any protein precipitated, and the amount of reducing sugar present over and above that in the original solutions of substrate and enzyme measured by the use of the orthodox reagents for such purposes. Certain precautions must be taken in interpreting the results obtained. For example, different enzymes may cleave the molecule at different points as do α- and β-amylases, giving different rates of liberation of various oligosaccharides which may themselves differ in their reactions with the reducing sugar reagents. Likewise, substrates of imperfectly known structure may consist of two types of polysaccharide just as starch contains unbranched amylose and branched amylopectin. Enzymic attack on these two substrates may leave oligosaccharides with different reducing power. Finally, if more than one enzyme is responsible for the ultimate breakdown of the polymer to its component monomer units, the measurement of reducing group liberation is likely to be the summation of the action of enzymes. The hydrolysis of proteins has commonly been measured by the liberation of amino groups from peptide linkage. Such a method, of course, measures not only the hydrolysis of peptide bonds in the whole protein but also the liberation from all the peptides down to free amino acids. An alternative to this method which avoids confusion by peptidase activity has been to precipitate the larger fragments after enzymic action with a protein precipitant such as trichloracetic acid and to measure the soluble material either as total nitrogen, or as tyrosine by the color given by the Folin-Ciocalteu reaction, or as total aromatic amino acids by the absorption in ultraviolet light at 280 mμ wavelength. Nuclease action has also been measured by a precisely analogous method, making use of the absorption of ultraviolet light at 260 mμ wavelength, or by measuring either the amount of total phosphorus remaining in solution or deoxyribose or ribose according to whether deoxyribonucleic acid or ribonucleic acid has been used as substrate.

III. Primary Attack on High Molecular Weight Substances

A. LIBERATION OF EXTRACELLULAR ENZYMES

Undoubtedly many of the organisms that are capable of utilizing substances of high molecular weight do so by liberating into the medium enzymes which break the substrate down to very small assimilable molecules. At first sight it might seem vital for the organism to do so since it seems rather unlikely that molecules of some 100,000 molecular weight would be able to penetrate the cell membrane. This argument is two-edged, however, since it is equally difficult to understand how an extracellular enzyme of high molecular weight can get out of the cell unless, of course, it is formed somewhere near to the cell surface, as has been suggested elsewhere.[26, 27]

It may be that some enzymes are sufficiently effective remaining in place without diffusing away from the cell. Such an explanation might be the most satisfactory for the breakdown of even insoluble substances such as cellulose, by some bacteria, in the apparent absence of extracellular enzymes.

The criteria for deciding whether or not any given enzyme is extracellular are peculiarly difficult to formulate, but such problems will be discussed later in this treatise (in particular see Chapter 11, Vol. IV, by M. R. Pollock). While some enzymes start to be liberated early in the logarithmic growth phase of the culture, subsequently increase in activity approximately in parallel with the mass growth, and cease to increase when growth stops (e.g., the proteases of C. histolyticum[28] and the deoxyribonuclease of streptococci,[14] the appearance of others such as hyaluronidase, the lysozyme of staphylococci, and of Bacillus subtilis lags behind growth under some conditions and then rapidly increases.[29-32] In yet other systems little enzyme may appear in the culture fluid until growth has ceased as with amylase formation by B. subtilis.[33] Yet no evidence could be found for an early accumulation of any of these enzymes within the cells which might account for a later release into the medium by autolysis of the cells. Also, increasing the osmotic pressure of the medium by the addition of polyethylene glycol, which reduces the hazard of protoplast lysis greatly increased the amount of amylase formed, whereas if lysis accounted for enzyme liberation the reverse state of affairs might have been expected. Moreover, the appearance of amylase was stopped by the presence of agents inhibiting protein synthesis (eg., chloramphenicol). It was not stopped by some amino acid analogs.[34]

Apart from difficulties of interpretation as in the above examples, the kinetics of the formation of many so-called extracellular enzymes has not been examined or at any rate reported. Many workers have been content to examine resting phase cultures and to call the enzymes found in the fluid extra-cellular, or, if they have found zones produced on agar containing the substrate, they have been satisfied.

B. Liberation of Intracellular Enzymes by Cell Lysis

Although the liberation of a potent soluble enzyme may appear to be the most efficient method for dealing with a large molecule when the fate of individual cells is considered, equally efficient from the point of view of allowing survival of a population as a whole may be the sacrifice of a proportion of the individuals in the cause of the life of their compatriots. If potent enzymes are liberated when a proportion of the cells lyse, the assimilable substances produced by these enzymes may allow the remainder to live. Just as it is difficult to find rigorously defined examples of the certain formation of extracellular enzymes, it is equally difficult to find examples in which the source of the enzyme in the fluid phase of cultures is certainly due to partial cell lysis. An early example which probably illustrates the point is the study of enzymes in cultures of pneumococci by Avery and Cullen,[35, 36] who observed that whereas there were active invertase, amylase, inulase, and esterases in the culture filtrates from overnight cultures of pneumococci, these could not be detected in the fluid phase from 5-hour cultures. If, however, the cells from the young cultures were disrupted by freezing and thawing, then the enzymes could be found in the lysate. It thus seems likely, although not certain in the absence of precise quantitative data, that the appearance of the enzymes in the fluid phase of the older cultures is due to cell lysis.

The liberation of peptidases by *C. histolyticum*[37] appears to be another example of the lysis or partial lysis of cells. Weil and Kochalaty's work has the advantage of including in it a study of the liberation of true extracellular enzymes, the proteases. The ability of the cultures to hydrolyze gelatin was similar before and after filtration and reached a maximum in the culture at the same time as the number of live bacteria, i.e., at 24 hours. The ability of the culture fluid to hydrolyze DL-leucylglycylglycine, however, increased slowly over a period of 6 days. An attempt at the direct demonstration of the aminopeptidase in the cells from the young cultures, however, failed. This attempt was made by incubating a suspension of cells under toluene. Later, the authors[28] were able to demonstrate the peptidases within the bacteria by sonically disrupting cells from young cultures. This would appear to be a satisfactory demonstration of the likely appearance of soluble enzyme by cell lysis, a conclusion supported by other work.[38] A certain mystery exists, however, since this problem has been reinvestigated[39] with 82 strains of *C. histolyticum*; the liberation of peptidases was reported as exactly parallel with that of the proteases, both being detectable as soon as growth started, i.e., at 7 hours. This disagreement is unresolved and may, when further studied, tell us more about the conditions which decide whether a given enzyme is intracellular or extracellular.

C. Breakdown by Cell Contact

In a certain number of instances one is driven to the conclusion that high molecular weight substances can be broken down by close contact between the organism and the substrate. One of the most carefully studied instances is that of cellulose breakdown by the *Cytophaga*.[40] When these organisms are grown on the surface of media containing incorporated cellulose, unlike some other organisms living on the recalcitrant material, no zones are produced. The cellulose is only partially cleared immediately under the area of extensive growth. When fibers are examined microscopically from such areas they are seen to be closely encrusted with micro-

organisms; moreover, the pattern of their arrangement is such as to suggest that they have followed the underlying cellulose micelles. In other
words, they seem to have arranged themselves in the most intimate possible
contact with the glucose chains. This extremely orderly arrangement was
noticed as long ago as 1929 by Winogradsky[41] and no doubt results from
the ability of the *Cytophaga* to condition their movements by the ultra-
structure of the surface on which they are growing. An impressive demonstration of the speed with which cellulose can be used by these *Cytophaga*
cells when in place on the fibers was then reported. Stanier[40] compared the
oxygen uptake of lightly centrifuged *Cytophaga* cultures when supplied
with glucose, cellobiose, and cellulose itself. It will be seen from Fig. 1 that
the rate of oxidation of the cellulose is only slightly less than that of the
monomer glucose and about the same as that of cellobiose. Since the
respiratory systems of the organisms were intact it is rather unlikely that
extensive autolysis of the cells had taken place to liberate intracellular
cellulase; no extracellular cellulase has been demonstrated. Thus it seems
probable that the cellulose was being broken down and oxidized by some
extremely active surface enzyme. Some other cellulose-decomposing bacteria are reported as not forming extracellular enzymes; it would be of

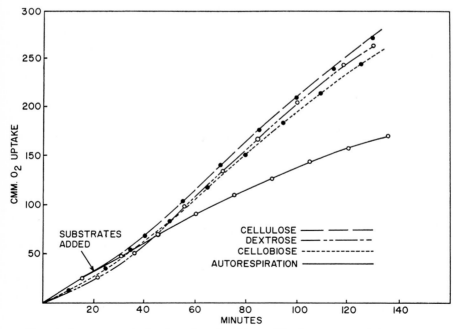

Fig. 1. Oxygen uptake by *Cytophaga hutchinsonii* in the presence of glucose, cellobiose, and cellulose and in the absence of any substrate. From Stanier.[40]

great interest to see whether these too can carry out an equally rapid oxidation of this large molecular weight substance. A further possible example of a similar utilization of a substance by surface-located enzymes is to be found in some work[42] on the hydrolysis of ribonucleic acid by *Pasteurella pestis*. In this study it was shown that a washed suspension of living organisms, a suspension of cells killed by phenylmercuric nitrate—by which the selective permeability properties of the cells would presumably be destroyed—and a cell-free preparation made by sonic disintegration, all hydrolyzed the substrate at the same rate. In order to appraise this situation thoroughly, of course, more would have to be known about the size of the ribonucleic acid, the permeability of the cell to it and the extent of adsorption of any extracellular ribonuclease to the cells.

D. Induction of Enzymes

Whether or not the enzyme or enzyme system concerned with the breakdown of substances is extracellular, intracellular, or residing on the surface, it may still be either inducible (adaptive) or constitutive. The meaning of these terms is now well understood and does not need fresh emphasis here. It may be well to point out, however, that as a result of the considerable amount of work done during the last few years the experimental conditions under which true induction can be demonstrated have been made very much more rigorous and it is rarely sufficient simply to show that more enzymic activity per unit weight of cells is present when the organism is grown in the presence of the substrate than in its absence. Many reviews of the subject have appeared recently and it will be sufficient to say that comparatively few enzymes of the type of specificity involved in this article have been examined sufficiently rigorously to be able to claim that they are certainly inducible.

Among the enzymes which have been shown to have greatly increased activity by the presence of the substrate are hyaluronidase formed by *Streptococcus hemolyticus* Lancefield groups A and C,[43, 44] and *C. perfringens* type A.[23, 45] Hyaluronidase formation by staphylococci, on the other hand, is not increased by the presence of the substrate.[43] Chitinase formation by a strain of *Streptomyces* has been shown to be increased by chitin[46] and pectinase formation by *Pseudomonas prunicola* is increased by the presence of pectin as well as galacturonic acid in the growth medium.[47] Amylase formation by *Clostridium acetobutylicum*[48a, b] and by *Pseudomonas saccharophila* is increased by the presence of starch and dextrins. The enzymes hydrolyzing heparin and β-heparin are not detectable unless the substrates are present in the growth media for a strain of flavobacterium;[7, 49] similarly, the presence of the capsular polysaccharides in the medium is necessary for the formation of appreciable quantities of the enzymes destroying them.[3]

Claims have been made that cellulase is both constitutive[50] and inducible.[51] In the light of the experience with the formation of other enzymes this is almost certainly a reflection of the different physiology of formation of the enzyme system by different organisms. The list could be greatly lengthened but sufficient has been said to show that many of these enzymes are probably inducible.

IV. Attack on Specific Groups of Substances

A. Polysaccharides

1. Cellulose

Of the subjects considered here the destruction of cellulose is perhaps the most practically important when we consider that the physical properties we associate with wood, cotton, rope, and plant tissues are largely determined by the integrity of the cellulose they contain.

a. The Nature of Cellulose. Essentially simple in chemistry cellulose has been defined[52] as "long-chain molecules of D-glucopyranose linked 1–4β [see below] with a molecular weight of at least 1.5×10^6 which represents a degree of polymerisation of 9200."

In cotton, for example, it seems to be generally agreed that the glucose units are linked together to give a somewhat kinked but rather rigid chain about 20,000 A. long and 7.5 A. wide. This structure alone, however, is not sufficient to account for the physical properties of cellulose fibers such as their strength and insolubility. The individual fibrils of glucose chains must be linked together in such a way as to obscure the hydrophilic groups and give rigidity to the structure. Various suggestions have been put forward,[2] such as glycosidic cross-linkages in various positions between the glucose chains and, more vaguely, by van der Waals' forces. From X-ray diffraction analysis the chains of glucose molecules are seen to be organized three-dimensionally and fibers show definite crystal structure. Analysis of natural fibers, such as cotton, by X-rays and dichroism shows that the degree of organization or crystallinity varies in different places;[55, 54] there are areas showing a high degree of crystallinity but others where the chains appear to be more randomly disposed. In Ramie fibers for example, the regions of three-dimensional order are about 600 A. long and 60–70 A. in diameter containing 100–150 molecular chains. In these areas of crystallinity the fibrils of organized cellulose chains are disposed at an angle to the fiber axis and the whole fiber has the form of a flattened twisted tube with about 150–300 convolutions to the inch. The degree of organization of the fibrils within the fiber depends to some extent on age.[2] The fiber itself consists of a primary very thin wall or cuticle, containing pectin and waxes with cellulose fibrils interwoven in it, an inner secondary wall, and a lumen. The secondary wall constitutes the bulk of the fiber and is built up of a succession of laminae with the cellulose fibrils aligned in a spiral fashion along the longitudinal axis.

It is important, in interpreting work on the biological breakdown of cellulose, to bear in mind this complicated structure. It is true that the cotton fiber, for example, contains up to 96 % cellulose but the remaining 4 %, even if it were far less in bulk, might be vitally important in determining whether or not the cellulose can be hydrolyzed, should it be disposed as a protective sheath between the majority of the cellulose fibrils and the enzyme. In order to make the cellulose more accessible to enzymes, workers have used a variety of chemical and physical treatments of natural fibers. Among the chemicals used have been cuprammonium, phosphoric acid, NaOH, lithium chloride, calcium thiocyanate, and many other treatments including deliberate partial hydrolysis by acid and substitution of various groups on to the molecule.[53] One of the actions of the former type of treatment is to swell the inner or secondary layers and burst the outer cuticle, thus allowing free physical access to the bulk of the cellulose in the secondary wall. However, the exact effects of the various treatments on the chemistry of the fiber components and their organization is by no means wholly clear. It is not perhaps surprising that different results for enzymic attack on "cellulose" should be claimed according to whether "cellulose" is regarded as whole untreated cotton fibers, cotton fibers dissolved and the "cellulose" reprecipitated, cotton fibers partially hydrolyzed with acid, or the cellulose they contain purified, partially hydrolyzed with acid, and then a variety of groups such as —COOH or —C_2H_5 substituted on to the 6-position of a variable proportion of the glucose molecules. It is perhaps more of a wonder that organisms can produce a sufficient diversity of enzymes, or enzymes of a wide enough range of action to accomplish all the tasks required eventually to reduce the chain of glucose molecules to monomer.

b. Organisms Breaking Down Cellulose. In 1942 Norman and Fuller[55] wrote: "An adequate system of classification and nomenclature for the cellulose bacteria is urgently needed. At present the situation is chaotic and is becoming worse. . . ." As with the affairs of men, little improvement can be seen by the biochemist writing this article, although noble duty has been done by such as McBee[56] and Hungate[57] in devising and describing adequate methods and criteria for the purification and study of the physiology of some of the anaerobic, thermophilic, and mesophilic cellulose-destroying organisms. Their work also established likely criteria by which the impurity of other workers' strains could be recognized. For example, pure cultures should maintain their ability to ferment cellulose even when they are grown on noncellulose-containing media. Previously, loss of cellulose-fermenting ability had been attributed to some form of irreversible deadaptation. Representatives of the named strains *C. thermocellum, C. terminosporus, C. thermocellulolyticus,* and *Bacillus cellulosae dissolvens* (now recognized[9] as *C. dissolvens*) were examined in detail, along with two unnamed strains received from other authors. They all gave active growth on cellulose, cellobiose, xylose, and hemicelluloses. They all failed to ferment glucose itself or fructose. This latter fact is one of great interest and importance in view of Stanier's[40] observations on another group of cellulose-destroying organisms, the *Cytophaga*. Before Stanier's work it had been claimed that these organisms also could not grow on glucose or indeed any reducing sugar and somewhat elaborate theories had been devised to account for this fact. In a delightfully simple experiment, however, Stanier showed that the true explanation resided in the well-known lability of glucose. If the glucose solutions were not heated in order to sterilize them the organisms grew well on media containing this carbohydrate. With this example in mind McBee,[4] in an equally beautiful experiment, eliminated toxic heat-produced breakdown products as a cause of the failure of his organisms to utilize glucose. The following experiment (see Table I) demonstrates that although no growth occurs when glucose alone is used as carbon source, the addition of glucose to either cellulose or cellobiose in no way impairs the utilization of these substrates but the glucose is not used. Thus we are driven in these, and some other examples, to the conclusion that while some organisms can use cellobiose and presumably cellulose via either cellobiose or some other small oligosaccharide, they cannot for some reason use the monomer glucose itself.

A list of some 150 cellulolytic organisms has been given by Siu,[2] of which the latest edition of Bergey[9] recognizes 54. These organisms for the most part divide themselves among the genera *Bacillus, Bacterium, Cellulomonas, Clostridium, Cytophaga, Pseudomonas,* and *Vibrio*. Unfortunately a number of these groups such as *Bacterium* and *Pseudomonas* are notoriously ill-defined. This list, of course, does not include the many unnamed cellulose-destroying organisms which have been isolated and studied. Many of the

TABLE I

THE INFLUENCE OF GLUCOSE ON THE UTILIZATION OF CELLOBIOSE AND
CELLULOSE BY A PURE CULTURE OF A
CELLULOSE-UTILIZING ORGANISM[a]

Carbohydrate in medium		Growth	Copper reduction value (expressed as glucose, mg./ml.)	
			Initial	Final
Glucose	0.1%	None	1.41	1.41
Glucose + cellulose	0.05% 0.05%	Good	0.68	0.65
Glucose + cellobiose	0.05% 0.05%	Good	1.41	0.63
None		None	0.14	0.16

[a] From McBee.[4]

recognized cellulolytic organisms have been isolated by primary enrichment technique from soil, sewage, the rumen, various forms of decaying vegetable matter, and other such likely sources. For the reasons pointed out earlier, they do, of course, represent a rather artificially selected group. A study by Clark and Tracey[58] primarily devoted to the decomposition of chitin by microorganisms but which also examined cellulose decomposition by a series of rather well-defined organisms may point a finger of fact, as well as logic, against supposing that cellulose decomposition defines a unique group of organisms. These authors found, for example, that all the strains of *Klebsiella pneumoniae*, *K. ozaenae*, and *K. rhinoscleromatis* which they tested produced cellulase. A wider examination of well-known species might be profitable in correcting any tendency to think of cellulose decomposition as defining a group of organisms any more satisfactorily than would starch fermentation.

c. *The Enzymic Hydrolysis of Cellulose.* Although cellulose is perhaps the most insoluble, intractable, and least diffusible of the substrates with which we are involved in this article, and one for which it would seem quite essential that extracellular enzymes should be deployed by the cell, the evidence is, as has already been mentioned, by no means conclusive that this is always true. Some organisms, for example, the Gram-negative coccal strains isolated by Hungate[59] from the rumen, produced wide zones of clearing in cellulose agar and therefore may be presumed to produce an extracellular enzyme. In other instances,[40, 59] however, it is equally clear that very intimate contact between the fiber and the organisms is required.

The most obvious way to break down cellulose would be for the glycosidic linkages to be hydrolyzed in a nonspecific manner until only glucose was left; the glucose could then be metabolized by the cell in the usual manner. Much evidence now suggests that, when extracellular enzymes are formed, this general course of events is the one usually followed, although more than one enzyme is often required. A radically different theory, which is still occasionally quoted, was originally proposed by Winogradsky,[60] namely, that the breakdown was an oxidative one leading to the initial formation of oxycellulose rather than a hydrolytic one. This was based on the results of a chemical examination of mucilage formed from filter paper consisting of partially hydrolyzed cellulose together with the bodies of the microorganisms growing on the fibers. Siu[2] has pointed out that the rich coating with bacterial bodies may explain the detection of uronic acids by several workers, since they may arise from the bacterial mucilage rather than from the cellulose. This theory is fully and critically discussed by Siu.[2]

As early as the beginning of this century,[61] the presence of cellobiose in enzymic hydrolyzates of cellulose was recognized. The technique at this time was to inoculate media containing well-washed filter paper with mud containing cellulose-destroying organisms or with cultures of various microorganisms, and to allow growth to take place, but before all the cellulose had disappeared to shake the culture with toluene or other bactericidal agents and continue incubation. The production of substances reducing alkaline copper reagents, such as Fehling's solution, was observed and both glucose and cellobiose could be isolated as osazones. The identity of the cellobiose as a β-linked disaccharide was established by the action of preparations which contain β-glucosidase, such as emulsin. On the basis of these experiments it was deduced that an extracellular cellulase was produced which hydrolyzed cellulose as far as the 1–4 β-linked disaccharide cellobiose and that a second enzyme might be responsible for hydrolysis of the disaccharide. The early evidence and discussion of this problem is summarized by Norman and Fuller[55] in their review of 1942. Although much work has since been done on the enzymic hydrolysis of cellulose, the problem of the number of steps and enzymes involved is still far from clear. The problem was examined quantitatively by Levinson et al.[62] using filtrates from cultures of five species of fungi. They followed the formation of glucose during the action of the filtrates on cellulose sulfate by the use of glucose oxidase, and the production of cellobiose by the action of a β-glucosidase preparation. They also examined the cellobiase content of the filtrates. All but one of the filtrates had only very slight action on cellobiose. During action on cellu-

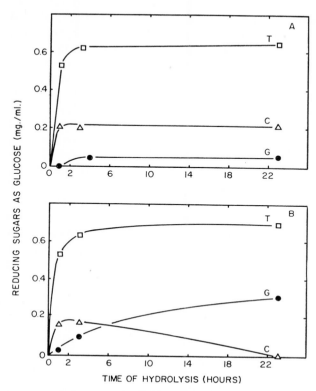

FIG. 2. Appearance of glucose and cellobiose during hydrolysis of cellulose sulfate by a filtrate of *Trichoderma viride*. A: No β-glucosidase added. B. β-Glucosidase added at the beginning of hydrolysis. (T) Total reducing value (mg./ml. glucose). (C) Cellobiose (mg./ml.). (G) Glucose (mg./ml.). From Levinson *et al.*[62]

lose sulfate with the cellobiase poor filtrates, cellobiose accumulated with the later formation of small amounts of glucose (Fig. 2). If some of the filtrate rich in cellobiase was also included, the cellobiose concentration reached a peak value and then disappeared with the formation of more glucose. These results were confirmed in a direct manner by paper chromatography. Only glucose and cellobiose were formed by the action of the filtrates on pure cotton linters, viscose rayon, or alkali-treated cellulose; several other spots appeared on the paper chromatograms of hydrolyzates of carboxymethyl cellulose, cellulose sulfate, and cellulose dextrins. With cellulose sulfate the sum of the glucose and cellobiose formed accounted for only about 40 % of the total reducing substances; using cellulose dextrin as substrate, only about 70 %. The additional substances traveled more slowly than cellobiose on the chromatograms and were presumed to be higher oligosaccharides of glucose. Kooiman *et al.*[63] later detected a range of sugars from glucose to cellohexose in such hydrolyzates. A possible explanation of the presence of these oligosaccharides has been provided by Aitken *et al.*,[64] who showed that cellulase preparations from *Myrothecium verrucaria* can build oligosaccharides from cellobiose by transglycosidation

These results give some support to the idea of a separate cellulase which carries hydrolysis as far as a disaccharide and a cellobiase which completes hydrolysis but which may form higher oligosaccharides by transglycosidation. Further evidence for the presence of a separate cellobiase in some cellulase preparations has been produced by Festenstein,[65, 66] who prepared the crude enzyme from rumen organisms either by extraction with butanol or by grinding with alumina. He showed that glucono-1,4-lactone, which is known to inhibit β-glucosidases and in particular the *o*-nitrophenyl β-glucosidase present in the rumen microorganism preparations, was able, almost but not quite completely, to prevent the production of glucose from carboxymethyl cellulose (CMC) while it inhibited the hydrolysis of CMC to cellobiose by only 60 %. It may be noted that cellobiose did not accumulate in the presence of the lactone. Likewise there seems strong evidence for the presence of a cellobiase in cellulolytic preparations from the wood rotting fungus *Poria vaillanttii*. It is claimed[66a] that no glucose is formed from cellulose if the cellobiase in the preparations is first inactivated.

Evidence contrary to the presence of separate cellobiase and cellulase enzymes in filtrates from the fungus *Myrothecium verrucaria* was produced by Whitaker,[67a, b] who purified cellulase from *Myrothecium verrucaria* by fractionation with ammonium sulfate and ethanol and obtained a preparation which gave only a single peak when examined in the ultracentrifuge and at three different pH values by electrophoresis. When tested against a variety of cellulose or substituted cellulose substrates and cellobiose the ratios of enzymic activity had not been changed from those in the crude filtrate, thus suggesting a single enzyme had been purified which rapidly hydrolyzed cellulose and slowly hydrolyzed cellobiose. However it must be noted that the extent as distinct from the rate of hydrolysis of the substrates was very low, being only of the order of 2 %. An observation by this author that high concentrations of cellobiose inhibit the action of cellobiase may possibly suggest that cellobiose may accumulate in enzymic hydrolyzates of cellulose because the disaccharide inhibits action of a single enzyme; the rate of hydrolysis of cellobiose is relatively very low compared with that of cellotriose. This suggestion does not necessarily conflict with the greater inhibition of the hydrolysis of cellobiose than of carboxymethyl cellulose by glucono-1,4-lactone. That hydrolysis of cellulose to glucose can be carried out by a single enzyme without intermediation of cellobiose[66] does not, of course, exclude the possibility that a separate cellobiase may well be formed by some bacteria and sometimes play a role in the over-all process. Evidence, for example, presented by McBee[4] makes it seem highly probable that hydrolysis of cellulose by his cultures of thermophilic bacteria involves a cellobiase. When he grew his cultures in the presence of excess cellulose and transferred them to a temperature of 68°C. at a time when active fermentation was still going on, growth stopped but cellulose hydrolysis continued and the osazone of cellobiose was isolated, whereas from cultures at 55°C. only glucosazone could be isolated. It therefore seemed probable that a cellobiase active at 55°C. but not at 68°C. was present and that this normally hydrolyzed the cellobiose to glucose. Similarly Aitken et al.[64] found that the ability of *Myrothecium verrucaria* filtrates to hydrolyze cellobiose could be abolished by heating them to 60°C. for 10 minutes. When this was done and the filtrates were then allowed to act on either insoluble or soluble cellulose or on carboxymethylcellulose, the amount of glucose formed was reduced by about 70 % while cellobiose formation was scarcely affected. Some glucose, however, was still formed, which argues again that cellulase or the cellulases present in the filtrates can themselves partially hydrolyze the polysaccharide to glucose without the intervention of cellobiase. Since the heated filtrates were inactive on cellobiose, the glucose presumably did not arise in these experiments via the 1–4 β-disaccharide. This result is similar to that obtained by Festenstein[65, 66] when cellobiase was inhibited by glucono-1,4-lactone.

Although it seems likely that cellobiase is often present, it seems unlikely that it always plays a necessary role in the enzymic hydrolysis of cellulose to glucose, and it is clear that a further type of complexity is present in preparations of cellulase. In an endeavor to overcome the difficulties of using insoluble substrates, a variety of partially hydrolyzed and substituted celluloses have been used. During their investigations of fungal and bacterial cellulases Reese et al.[51] examined the hydrolysis of carboxymethyl cellulose by filtrates from a variety of organisms, of which some of the *Aspergillus* species were not able to hydrolyze native cellulose. It was found that they were all able to hydrolyze carboxymethyl cellulose, irrespective of the chain length of the polymer within the limits of 125–200 glucose units long, providing the degree of substitution was not above 1.0 (i.e., not more than one carboxymethyl group for each repeating unit of glucose must be present); below this the rate of hydrolysis varied inversely with the degree of substitution. Likewise all the filtrates could hydrolyze hydroxyethyl cellulose but none could attack methyl cellulose to yield reducing sugars. Examination of some of the properties of the activity responsible for the hydrolysis of carboxymethylcellulose, such as pH optimum and stability to pH and temperature, showed that they were similar to those of the activity against native cellulose. On the basis of these experiments Reese et al.[51] proposed the presence of an enzyme, C_x, in the filtrates which hydrolyzed shorter anhydroglucose chains to "soluble small molecules capable of diffusion into the cell," later shown to be cellobiose and glucose,[62] but proposed that another enzyme, C_1, must also be present before native cellulose could be attacked. Festenstein[65] has since claimed that enzyme preparations can readily be prepared from rumen organisms which will hydrolyze substituted short-chain celluloses such as CMC without being able to hydrolyze native cellulose. Likewise Halliwell[17] has found evidence for differences in the enzymic attack on native cellulose and CMC. Again the evidence produced by Whitaker[67a] does not entirely agree with the suggestion that more than one enzyme is always involved in the hydrolysis of native cellulose. He tested both his enzyme, which showed only a single peak during electrophoresis, and the initial crude culture filtrate from which it had been derived against unswollen cotton linters, ground cotton linters, and carboxymethyl cellulose having the low degree of substitution of 0.5, and found that the relative enzymic activities against the three substrates had not changed significantly during purification. It may possibly be significant that whereas Reese *et al.*[51] grew these organisms on media containing carboxymethyl cellulose, Whitaker[67a] grew his on media containing cotton linters, but whether this difference had any influence is unknown. That the enzymic attack on carboxymethyl cellulose and presumably cellulose itself may be carried out by a number of "cellulases" is suggested by the work of Grimes *et al.*[68] and Miller and Blum.[69] Both groups of workers examined concentrated filtrates from *Myrothecium verrucaria*; the former by convection electrophoresis, the latter by electrophoresis on a starch block. Both sets of authors found that enzymic activity against soluble cellulose derivatives was scattered through several peaks. Miller and Blum,[69] using carboxymethyl cellulose as enzyme substrate, found as many as eight peaks; Grimes *et al.*[68] by more indirect methods recognized three components active against cellulose sulfate. The striking similarity of these observations to that of Wannamaker's[70] for the multiplicity of deoxyribonucleases formed by streptococci is to be noted. Thomas and Whitaker,[70a] however, have suggested that the apparent multiplicity of cellulases may be due to complex formation, possibly with polysaccharides. These authors found only a single spot of cellulase activity during electrophoresis of preparations of this enzyme on paper.

2. STARCH

Like cellulose, starch consists essentially of glucose joined by 1–4 linkages, except that the optical specificity of the linkage is α in starch instead of the β-linkage in cellulose. A further complexity is introduced into consideration of starch and the enzymes which act on it by the fact that almost all starches contain two polymers—one with the glucose units joined head to tail in a straight line to give amylose, while in the other, amylopectin, a ramifying structure like glycogen, is built up by the presence of branching points at the 6-positions in some of the glucose molecules. Apart from the so-called waxy starches from sorghum, rice, millet, barley, and certain kinds of corn, most starches contain 15–27 % amylose and the rest is amylo-pectin;[71] the waxy starches are almost entirely composed of amylopectin. The separation and description of the properties of amylose and amylo-pectin have been given by Schoch.[72] The nature of the starch grain itself is again, like the cellulose-containing fiber, complex. A review of this sub-ject and of the properties of the components is given by Greenwood.[71] In brief, the granule is surrounded by a thin layer of protein and in some instances a thin cellulose-containing outer wall is present. Within the wall the granule appears to be built in layers around a focal point which has been called the hilum. In most laboratory studies the starch granules have been treated in some way to break up this complicated structure and render the polyglucosans soluble.

Just as starch consists of two polysaccharides, two enzymes are known that can hydrolyze both types of molecules; a β-amylase which can hydro-lyze amylose completely to maltose, but which stops at the $6 \rightarrow 1$ branch-ing points in amylopectin, leaving a residual unhydrolyzed dextrin, and an α-amylase of very much more complex action. The mammalian and plant α-amylases have been discussed in a review by Caldwell[73] and en-zymic hydrolysis of starch generally by Whelan.[74] It seems certain that these enzymes act as endopolysaccharidases, producing a rapid drop in viscosity and discharge of the capability of amylose to give a blue color with iodine, but their exact mechanism of action is unknown. The bacterial enzymes, apart from those of *Bacillus macerans*, are α-amylases although comparatively little detailed work appears to have been done on the mode of action of the highly purified enzymes available.

a. *α-Amylase of Bacillus subtilis.* Meyer *et al.*[75] first succeeded in crystal-lizing an α-amylase from Biolase, a German commercial amylase prepara-tion. It is not clear from their short paper whether this preparation is made from *B. subtilis* or *B. mesentericus*. They say "L'enzyme est sécrétée par le *Bacillus subtilis* ou *mesentericus*"; it is, however, usually assumed that they were studying *B. subtilis* enzyme. The product obtained liberated 3.2 $\times$ 10^3 mg. of maltose per milligram of total nitrogen in the preparation during 3 min. incubation at 20°C. at the pH optimum of the enzyme. The crystals were homogeneous when solutions were examined electrophoretically. More recently Akabori *et al.*[76] have examined the amino acid composition of crystalline α-amylase from *Bacillus subtilis* N, which was prepared by the method of Hagihara[77] and compared the results with those for swine

TABLE II

AMINO ACID ANALYSES OF AMYLASES FROM DIFFERENT SOURCES[a]

Amino acid	Amount of amino acid found (g./100g. protein)			
	Swine pancreatic amylase	Human salivary amylase	Taka-α-amylase	*Bacillus subtilis* N.
Glycine	6.7	6.8	6.6	5.6
Alanine	6.9	4.4	6.8	6.0
Valine	7.8	6.9	4.7	5.5
Leucine	11.5	5.8	8.3	6.4
Isoleucine		5.8	5.2	4.0
Proline	3.6	3.6	4.2	4.1
Phenylalanine	10.1	7.2	4.2	5.8
Tyrosine	5.3	5.5	9.5	8.3
Tryptophan	6.7	7.2	4.0	6.2
Serine	4.1	7.8	6.5	6.2
Threonine	3.9	4.5	10.9	6.4
Cystine	2.3	4.4	1.6	0
Methionine	2.1	2.4	2.2	1.3
Arginine	5.8	8.7	2.7	6.8
Histidine	3.9	3.2	2.0	3.8
Lysine	4.9	6.3	5.9	7.3
Aspartic acid	14.5	19.3	16.5	15.0
Glutamic acid	10.5	9.6	6.9	13.5
Ammonia	1.6	—	1.5	1.3

[a] From Akabori *et al.*[76]

pancreatic,[78] human salivary,[79] and Taka-α-amylase.[80] This comparison is reproduced in Table II. The *subtilis* enzyme appears to be principally distinguished from the other enzymes by the complete absence of cystine. That the cystine content must be very small is confirmed by the finding that the total sulfur content of the protein was 0.23 % which agrees well with the expected amount of 0.27 % calculated from the methionine content. Mengi *et al.*[81] have reported a comparison between two α-amylases isolated from a commercial product from *B. subtilis*. Each had the same specific activity, each showed a pH optimum between 5.2 and 6.4, and they also agreed in their heat and pH stabilities. Junge *et al.*[81a] have examined two preparations of recrystallized α-amylase from *B. subtilis* and have confirmed that —SH and —S—S— groups are absent from the enzyme.

   b. α-Amylase of Pseudomonas saccharophila. This enzyme has been isolated and crystallized by Markovitz *et al.*[82] from cultures in which the source of carbon was maltose. The authors used the ingenious method designated by Thayer[83] for purification. In this the culture supernatant containing the enzyme is run through a column of starch and celite. The amylase remaining on the column is then eluted with increasing concentrations of either soluble starch or enzymic hydrolyzate of starch. The remaining part of the technique[82] involves orthodox ammonium sulfate and cold acetone fractionation. Final crystallization was from 75% saturated ammonium sulfate at pH 5.3. The crystalline product was homogeneous when examined at "various pH values between 5.5 and 8.0" by electrophoresis and in the ultracentrifuge and the sedimentation constant $S_{20,w}$ was calculated as 4.66. The specific activity measured in terms of the release of maltose from starch in 3 min. at 37°C. and pH 5.5 by the method of Noelting and Bernfeld[84] was 6×10^3 mg. maltose per milligram of total nitrogen in the preparation. Allowing for the difference of experimental conditions this value is not dissimilar from that found for the *subtilis* enzyme (i.e., 3×10^3 mg. of maltose per milligram of total nitrogen). The pH optimum in $M/30$ phosphate–$M/30$ succinate buffer was between 5.2 and 5.7; the Michaelis constant (K_m) was about 0.6 g. starch per liter as calculated from the slope of a Lineweaver and Burk type of plot. Thayer[83] compared the action upon soluble starch, amylopectin, and amylose of his purified amylase prepared from the culture fluid of *P. saccharophila*, with a cell-bound amylase. He measured the decrease in the color given by the hydrolyzates when iodine was added, using light of two different wavelengths. The actions of the two enzymes in liberating reducing sugars were also compared. He claimed that "the extracellular enzyme is dextrogenic (an α-amylase) and that the intracellular enzyme is saccharogenic (β-amylase) mixed with other enzymes which contribute to the activity observed." If this claim were proved to be true it would be of considerable importance, since to date no other β-amylase of bacterial origin has been reported.

c. *The Amylase of Clostridium acetobutylicum.* When maltose is present as principal carbon source for this organism only maltase and no amylase is formed,[48a] an interesting contrast with the behavior of *Pseudomonas saccharophila* which forms α-amylase under similar conditions. If, however, starch is added to medium for *C. acetobutylicum* both amylase and maltase are formed. Hockenhull and Herbert[48a] partially purified the amylase by adsorption on to starch from a solution containing 1% Na₂SO₄ and 50% ethanol of an ammonium sulfate precipitate from the culture supernatant. The enzyme was eluted by $0.04M$ phosphate buffer at pH 5.8. About 95% of the maltase was removed by their process. In some ways this amylase appears to differ from both α- and β-amylase. The rate of liberation of maltose from starch was rapid until 100% of the theoretical value had been reached; thereafter the rate of reducing sugar liberation was directly proportional to the maltase content of the preparations. This argues that unlike other amylases this enzyme can hydrolyze starch completely to maltose. Also unlike other amylases there was no activation by chloride ions.

d. *Bacillus macerans Amylase.* In 1904 Schardinger[85] isolated an organism which was contaminating a nutrient broth medium and which rapidly hydrolyzed starch to dextrins; he called this organism *B. macerans*. Further intensive chemical study of these dextrins has shown that they are quite different from those arising as a result of the action of α- or β-amylase. They consist of glucose molecules joined together by 1–4 α-linkages into rings of various sizes. This subject has recently been very thoroughly reviewed by Dexter French[86] and nothing further can yet be added. The enzyme preparations used to produce the cyclic dextrins are still relatively crude and no report of a homogeneous preparation is available.

3. Other Polysaccharides

a. Pectin. The substrate molecule consists of galacturonic acid molecules in which some of the carboxyl groups on the six positions of the galacturonopyranose structures are esterified with methyl groups. Two distinct enzymes exist: (a) a pectinesterase and (b) a polygalacturonidase. These two enzymes are, as one might expect, interrelated in action, a subject well-discussed by Lineweaver and Burk.[87] Although it is known that many bacteria have the ability both to remove the methoxy groups and to hydrolyze the polysaccharide chain, comparatively few studies have dealt with the enzymes concerned. Considerable evidence is available on the fungal, plant, and yeast enzymes.[13, 87]

Mills[47] studied the pectin esterase formed by *Pseudomonas prunicola*, showing that it was adaptively formed in response to pectin and, interestingly, galacturonic acid. Half maximal velocity was attained by the enzyme acting on pectin at a substrate concentration of 0.12%. It splits off about 75% of the methoxy groups. The crude preparation also hydrolyzed simple glycerides.

A survey of organisms that produce what the author calls pectinglycosidase (α, β, and γ) has been published together with an examination of the products formed from pectic materials during incubation with culture solutions from some of the active organisms.[87a] Two anaerobic pectinolytic organisms have been studied.[87b]

b. Alginic Acid. This substance obtained from seaweed consists of 1–4 linked chains of mannuronic acid. It is decomposed by a number of organisms first studied by Waksman *et al.*,[88] who described four organisms to which they gave specific names. The hydrolytic ability was considerable, 100 ml of culture destroyed up to 700 mg. of the polysaccharide in 21 days at 30°C. Other observations on alginic acid-destroying microorganisms have been made by Kåss *et al.*[89] and Thjotta and Kåss.[90] More recently[91] the hydrolysis of alginic acid by an unidentified organism was studied by paper circle chromatography of filtrates from cultures which had contained the polysaccharide. In 2-week-old cultures a series of oligosaccharide rings was obtained; but after 4 weeks' incubation only mannuronic acid itself remained. Enzyme preparations from the cultures were found to reduce rapidly the viscosity of alginic acid solutions. Cytophagas of marine origin are also known to hydrolyze alginic acid.[40] A strain of *Aerobacter aerogenes* has been claimed[91a] to form adaptively enzymes that hydrolyze alginic acid. Mannuronic acid and uronides were detected among the hydrolytic products.

B. MUCOPOLYSACCHARIDES AND MUCOPROTEINS

1. CHITIN

a. The Substrate. This substance forms the major part of the organic matrix upon which calcium carbonate is deposited to form the exoskeleton of many marine animals including crabs and lobsters. It also forms an important part of the cell walls of fungi. Thus it is of common origin and it has been calculated[92] that if the shells of the copepods, merely a subclass of crustaceous plankton, alone accumulated unhindered, many billions of tons would be deposited on the sea floor every year. As it is, however, many groups of organisms can produce active chitinases rendering the carbon and nitrogen available for further use.

The structure of chitin is like that of cellulose, a 1–4 β-linked chain of hexose molecules, but in place of glucose, N-acetylglucosamine occurs to give the following repeating unit:

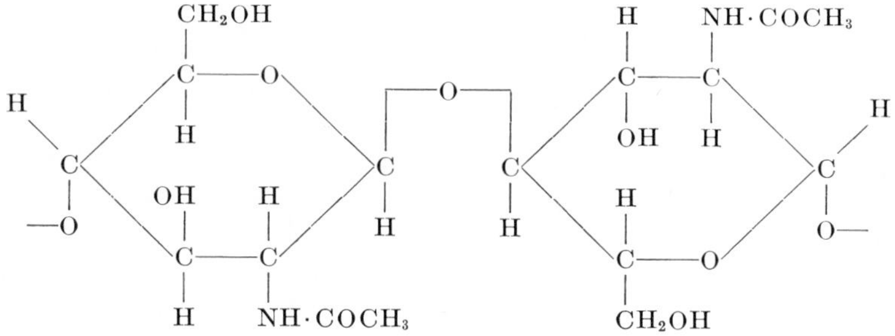

The shells of crustaceans from which chitin is usually prepared contain apart from calcium carbonate considerable protein and some lipid. The purification of chitin involves treatment of the shells with acid and alkali, and lipid solvent extractions.

b. The Organisms Hydrolyzing Chitin. Like the ability to hydrolyze cellulose and for that matter other polymers, the dissimilation of chitin appears to be a rather widespread property of bacteria. That they could use this intractable material was first recognized by Benecke,[93] who called the organism he isolated *Bacillus chitinovorus.* Many studies have since been devoted to the utilization of chitin; particularly, of course, have the sea and sea mud been fertile sources of organisms. Zobell and Rittenberg,[92] for example, state that from 0.1–1 % of all bacteria in sea water are active to some extent. From these studies it is clear that the property is not confined to one or even a few genera of microorganisms but is widespread throughout the microbiological kingdom. For example, Campbell and Williams[94] isolated three species of *Achromobacterium*, two of *Pseudomonas*, a *Flavobacterium*, and a *Micrococcus*. Benton[10] had isolated 17 different types of bacteria, none of which would fit into the Bergey classification of that time. Likewise Zobell and Rittenberg[93] isolated and gave some of the physiological characteristics of 14 "representatives of chitinoclastic bacteria most of which had been recovered two or more times from various marine materials." No attempt at classification was made but 31 different pure cultures were obtained some of which would grow on a mineral salts medium with only chitin present while others needed additional carbon sources and other organic nitrogen—possible evidence that organisms of different genera were involved. Some *Myxobacteria* can utilize chitin.[95, 96] A study by Clark and Tracey,[58] already referred to in connection with cellulose decomposition, again points to the danger of regarding the destruction of the material as in any way the hallmark of a distinct group of organisms. These authors, examining representative species from a fairly wide range of genera, most of the organisms not having previously been associated with chitin destruction, found that the following were in fact chitinovorous: *Chromobacterium ersayanum, C. indidum, C. prodigiosum (Serratia marcescens)*, one strain of *Klebsiella aerogenes, K. cloacae, K. ozaenae, K. pneumoniae, K. rhinoscleromatis, Pseudomonas hydrophilia, P. icthyosmia*, (two were unidentified pseudomonads), *C. septicum, C. perfringens* type A, two out of the three *Vibrio cholerae* subgroup I strains examined, *Vibrio* el Tor, another unidentified species of *Vibrio*, and an unidentified *Erwinea*; four strains of *Escherichia coli* tested were all negative.

In these experiments the organisms were cultivated in a peptone broth medium and then treated with toluene overnight. The presumably killed and partially autolyzed cultures were then tested for their chitinase or cellulase activity. Therefore, the positive results obtained are for constitutive enzymes only. Any organism producing the enzymes adaptively might be recorded as negative and the true distribution of chitinase and cellulase production may be even wider than is suggested on the face value of this work.

  c. *The Enzymic Decomposition of Chitin.* Enzymes destroying chitin were first recognized and studied in the digestive juices of snails (*Helix pomatia*) by Karrer and Hofmann[97] and Karrer and von François.[98] After 10 days' incubation at 36°C. and in phosphate buffer at pH 5.2 almost all of 100 mg. of the insoluble chitin had been dissolved and about 85 % could be accounted for as reducing sugar estimated as N-acetylglucosamine, which was isolated as a crystalline product. Zechmeister[99] and his colleagues, following these early observations, fractionated extracts from *Helix pomatia* gut on a column of bauxite recognizing one fraction which passed straight through the column and another which was adsorbed. By this means they showed that the hydrolysis by one enzyme system proceeded as far as the disaccharide chitobiose, and that a second enzyme chitobiase was capable of hydrolyzing the disaccharide to N-acetylglucosamine. Thus the situation is very similar to the classical idea of cellulose hydrolysis. Snail enzyme would appear at first sight to be a far cry from bacterial enzymes. Work, however, by Jenniaux[100] makes it plausible that in fact the earlier authors might conceivably have been studying enzymes formed by bacteria growing in the digestive tract of the animals. He found, for example, some 500,000–750,000 chitinolytic organisms per gram of the intestinal contents from *Helix pomatia*. Eleven different types of microorganism were isolated, all of them Eubacteriales. The abundance of chitinolytic true bacteria was, as the author pointed out, in contrast to the preponderance of chitinolytic Acetomycetales, Myxobacteriales and filamentous fungi which are such common chitin scavengers in other places, such as earth and sea, where chitin destruction is taking place. More recently the action of what may be truly extracellular chitinase has been examined by Reynolds,[46] who isolated two strains of *Streptomyces* and one "true bacterium" which would rapidly break down chitin powder added to a salts medium. The cultures were shaken to increase the accessibility of oxygen. Figure 3 shows the rate of breakdown by the three strains. The supernatant fluids from centri-

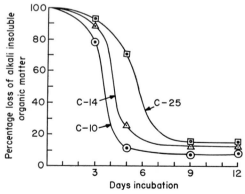

FIG. 3. Aerobic decomposition of chitin by three soil microorganisms growing in submerged but agitated cultures; C-10 and C-14 are species of *Streptomyces*; C-25 is a bacterium. From Reynolds.[46]

fuged cultures which had been grown for 5 days (*Streptomyces*) or 8 days (*Bacterium*), or filtrates from these cultures liberated reducing substances from powdered chitin when incubated for 48 hr. at 25°C. at pH 8.0. The presence of chitin in the culture medium was necessary if the fluids were to show chitinase activity; chitin could not be substituted by *N*-acetylglucosamine, or by glucose and asparagine. The time course of the production of extracellular chitinase is shown in Fig. 4. Having reached a maximum activity at about 7 days, further incubation of the culture led to destruction of the enzyme. The reducing substances obtained when the filtrates were allowed to react with chitin were examined by paper chromatography. The enzymic reaction was stopped before all the chitin had been solubilized. Two spots were obtained by paper chromatography in one direction with phenol/water/ammonia, or collidine/water and in two directions with the solvent systems phenol/water/ammonia and butanol/ethanol/water/ammonia. These spots corresponded in their rate of travel with markers of *N*-acetylglucosamine and *N*,*N*-diacetylchitobiose. In another experiment only the spot corresponding to *N*,*N*-diacetylchitobiose was detected in the hydrolyzate. These observations made it seem very probable that the enzymic hydrolysis of chitin followed the same course as that by other polysaccharidases, and that like hydrolysis by enzymes prepared from *Helix pomatia* two stages are carried out by a "chitinase" and a "chitobiase." In a later paper Berger and Reynolds[100a] confirmed the suggestion that a chitobiase was present in the filtrates from *Streptomyces* and also succeeded in separating two chitinases both having the same specificities for oligosaccharides prepared from chitin. This observation of more than one region possessing chitinase activity after gel-electrophoresis of preparations from *Streptomyces* filtrates, confirms earlier observations briefly reported by Jenniaux.[100b] The chitinases, free of chitobiase activity

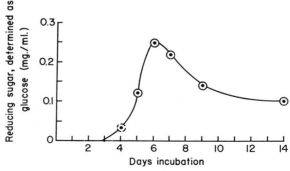

Fig. 4. The production of extracellular chitinase by *Streptomyces* sp. strain C-10 in submerged agitated culture in a chitin–mineral salts medium. From Reynolds.[46]

formed both N-acetylglucosamine and N,N'-diacetylchitobiose. Tracey,[101] however, examining the action of an enzyme prepared from the fungus *Lycoperdon*, found that no disaccharide accumulated and that the most effective inhibitor of the hydrolysis of chitosan (a partially acid-hydrolyzed chitin) was N-acetylglucosamine which may, as he points out, be evidence in favor of an unienzymic hydrolysis of the polysaccharide by chitinase from this organism.

2. HYALURONIC ACID

This mucopolysaccharide is found in mammalian synovial fluid, vitreous humor of the eye, Wharton's jelly of umbilical cord, skin generally, embryonic bone, and capsules of streptococci. In synovial fluid it exists[102] in the form of a protein complex which has the form of a long, randomly coiled, relatively easily penetrated skein. The mucopolysaccharide isolated from protein, which has been the form of the substrate chiefly used in enzymic studies, consists principally of an unbranched, or very little branched, polymer of the disaccharide 3-β-glucuronido-N-acetylglucosaminide which has the following structure:

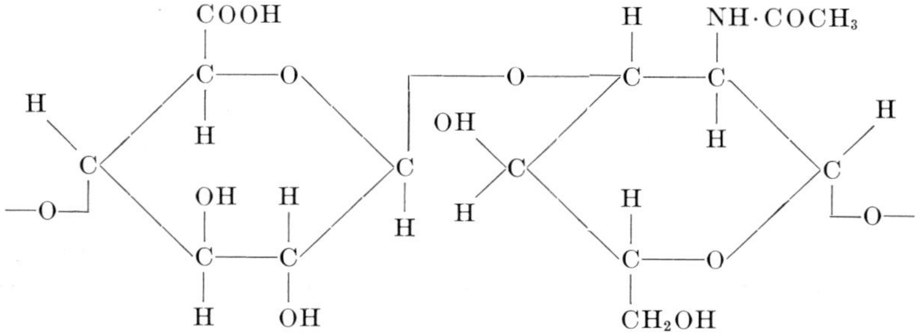

a. Organisms Hydrolyzing Hyaluronic Acid. i. Streptococcus hemolyticus. Representatives of almost all the types of Lancefield group A and many group B and C organisms have been shown to produce hyaluronidase, even many of those that have capsules of hyaluronic acid, the enzyme substrate.[103-108] As might be expected, the noncapsulated organisms form very much more potent enzymes than the capsulated ones. Hyaluronidase is formed adaptively at least by some strains of group A and group C streptococci[43, 44, 106, 109, 110a] and the organisms respond to the oligosaccharides in some enzymic hydrolyzates of hyaluronic acid, as well as to the whole mucopolysaccharide molecule.[43, 44] Hyaluronidase of streptococci appears to be extracellular;[44, 110b] group B organisms may form the enzyme constitutively

ii. Staphylococcus aureus. A very high proportion of coagulase positive staphylococci form hyaluronidase.[111, 112] It is not formed adaptively,[43, 111] that is, addition of hyaluronic acid to a variety of growth media has no influence on enzyme formation. The enzyme is extracellular[29] and its formation takes place in an accelerating fashion in relation to growth when the inoculum has been taken from a stationary phase culture.[29, 30] Some cultures consist of variants with different enzyme-forming ability.[112]

iii. Clostridium perfringens. Many strains of serological type A have been examined for hyaluronidase. For example, McClean et al.[113] examined 20 strains grown in hyaluronic acid-containing medium of which 12 were positive. Evans[114] examined 30 selected strains also growing them in the presence of hyaluronate and found 7 positive; Kass et al.[115] examined 94 freshly isolated strains and found 49 positive; and Oakley and Warrack[116] examined 14 strains in medium not containing hyaluronate and found 7 positive. The enzyme is formed adaptively by this organism.[23, 43-45, 115] Some strains may, of course, be different since Oakley and Warrack,[116] adding a low concentration (0.15 %) of hyaluronate of unspecified purity to rich media, failed to obtain an adaptive effect with their seven strains. Less is known about hyaluronidase formation by the other serological types of *C. welchii.* Table III summarized Oakley and Warrack's[116] examination of strains from B, C, D, E, and F types.

iv. Clostridium septicum. McClean et al.[113] examined 20 strains; of these 7 were positive.

v. Pneumococci. Humphrey [117] examined 81 strains of freshly isolated organisms belonging to 19 types; a rough estimate of the potentialities of the strains was obtained by measuring the enzymic activity in the culture supernatants from 24-hour cultures in hyaluronic acid containing broth. His results are shown in Table IV. Earlier in their classical work Meyer et al.[118, 119] had demonstrated hyaluronidase in preparations of cells grown with hyaluronic acid in the medium of types I, II, III, and IV.

TABLE III

HYALURONIDASE PRODUCTION BY DIFFERENT SEROLOGICAL
TYPES OF *Clostridium perfringens*[a]

Serological type	No. of strains examined	Positive	Negative
A	14	7	7
B	14	14	0
C	9	0	9
D	19	4	15
E	6	0	6
F	6	0	6

[a] From Oakley and Warrack.[116]

TABLE IV

HYALURONIDASE PRODUCTION BY SEROLOGICAL TYPES OF PNEUMOCOCCI[a, b]

Type of pneumococcus	Hyaluronidase production (units)				Total no. of strains
	1	1–10	10–100	100–500	
I	17	—	1	—	18
II	1	—	1	2	4
III	2	8	6	3	19
V	1	—	—	—	1
VII	—	1	—	2	3
VIII	1	2	2	2	7
IX	—	1	—	—	1
X	—	—	—	1	1
XII	—	1	—	—	1
XIII	—	—	—	1	1
XVII	1	—	—	—	1
XVIII	—	2	—	—	2
XIX	—	3	—	1	4
XX	—	—	3	—	3
XXI	—	—	—	1	1
XXIV	—	—	—	1	1
XXV	—	2	—	1	3
XXIX	—	1	—	—	1
XXXIII	—	2	—	—	2
Not I–XXXIII	2	1	2	2	7

[a] Expressed in mucin-clot prevention units of McClean.[11]
[b] From Humphrey.[117]

vi. Bacillus subtilis. Very recently a single strain has been shown to form an active hyaluronidase.[8]

vii. Flavobacterium Species. An organism isolated by Payza and Korn[7] has been shown to hydrolyze hyaluronic acid.[49, 120]

b. Mechanism of Action of Hyaluronidase. Hyaluronidases incubated with hyaluronic acid solutions lower their viscosity, destroy the ability to form acid-insoluble complexes with proteins and basic dyes, and liberate reducing sugars and substances, giving a positive test for N-acetylglucosamine.

Early work[43, 44, 121, 122] showed that the mammalian hyaluronidase and bacterial hyaluronidase gave rise to different hydrolytic products. Meyer[123] and his colleagues in a series of very beautiful papers have followed these early indications and shown that whereas the testicular enzyme produces a series of oligosaccharides which by prolonged incubation with high concentrations of enzyme is changed to a tetrasaccharide, and acts as a transglycosidase, crude enzyme preparations from streptococci, staphylococci,

C. perfringens and pneumococci appear to hydrolyze the mucopolysaccharide to a disaccharide. This disaccharide, however, differs from the repeating unit in the substrate molecule itself by having an unsaturated bond in the glucuronic acid between carbon atoms 4 and 5, giving the following structure.

$$
\begin{array}{l}
\text{COOH} \qquad\qquad\qquad \text{H} \quad \text{NH·COCH}_3 \\
\text{C---O} \qquad\qquad \text{O---C---C} \\
\text{H} \qquad\qquad \text{OH} \qquad\quad \text{H} \qquad \text{H} \\
\text{C} \qquad\qquad \text{C} \quad \text{C} \qquad\qquad \text{C} \\
\text{OH} \quad \text{H} \qquad \text{H} \qquad \text{H} \qquad\qquad \text{OH} \\
\text{H} \\
\text{C---C} \qquad\qquad\qquad \text{C---O} \\
\text{H} \quad \text{OH} \qquad\qquad\qquad \text{CH}_2\text{OH}
\end{array}
$$

Thus the evidence is that the scission carried out by the bacterial enzymes is not a hydrolysis in the ordinary sense in which water is added from the surrounding medium but one which involves a rather extraordinary shift of —H radicals within the molecule. Further work on this subject is obviously needed. Although a number of attempts at partial purification of the bacterial hyaluronidases has appeared, no claim has yet been made for a physically homogeneous product.

3. CHONDROITIN SULFATE

a. The Substrate. It is now known that chondroitin sulfate should be referred to in the plural sense rather than the singular since there are three different forms of the compound, called A, B, and C. It must be assumed from the methods used by most workers for obtaining the mucopolysaccharide that they were studying the breakdown of chondroitin sulfate A. The structure of this substance is a more or less coiled chain with the following repeating unit:

$$
\left[\begin{array}{l}
\text{COOH} \qquad\qquad\qquad \text{H} \quad \text{NH·COCH}_3 \\
\text{C---O} \qquad\qquad\quad \text{O---C---C} \\
\text{H} \qquad\quad \text{H} \qquad\quad \text{H} \qquad\quad \text{H} \qquad \text{H} \\
\text{C} \qquad\qquad\quad \text{C} \quad \text{C} \qquad\qquad\quad \text{C} \\
\text{O} \qquad \text{OH} \quad \text{H} \qquad \text{H} \quad \text{HO} \quad \text{H} \qquad\qquad \text{O---} \\
\text{C---C} \qquad\qquad\qquad\qquad \text{C---O} \\
\text{H} \quad \text{OH} \qquad\qquad\qquad \text{CH}_2\text{OSO}_3\text{H}
\end{array}\right]_n
$$

3-β-Glucuronido-6-sulfato-*N*-acetylgalactosaminide

So far as present evidence goes it seems unlikely that the protein-free molecule is extensively branched.

b. Enzymic Attack. Early work[124-126] showed that bacteria produced enzymes that would both remove the sulfate as free inorganic sulfate and liberate reducing substances from chondroitin sulfate. The bacteria concerned appeared to be strains of pseudomonads; their definition, however, is not very precise. Later, in a paper concerned with the enzymic hydrolysis of sulfated ketosteroids, Buehler *et al.*[127] mention very briefly that filtrates from cultures of *Pseudomonas nonliquefaciens*, and *Proteus vulgaris* liberate sulfate from chondroitin sulfate preparations. Very recently this subject has been tackled in a determined manner by Dodgson[128, 129] and his associates. The situation revealed is one of considerable interest to many besides those interested in the biochemistry of mucopolysaccharides. They failed to obtain active enzyme preparations from two strains of *Pseudomonas fluorescens* or from two of *Pseudomonas ovalis* and one of *Alcaligenes metalcaligenes*, but found that all the strains of *Proteus vulgaris* which they tested desulfated chondroitin sulfate. These preliminary tests were carried out by incubating cell suspensions with solutions of the polysaccharide and measuring the liberation of inorganic sulfate. The enzyme could be extracted relatively easily from the *Proteus vulgaris* cells to give an active preparation which was highly specific in that it did not attack some sixteen other sulfated substances including heparin, carrageenin, and a substance claimed[130] to be uridine diphosphate *N*-acetylgalactosamine sulfate. The preparation liberated both inorganic sulfate and reducing substances from chondroitin sulfate. Subsequently [129] the authors achieved a separation of these two activities by adsorption on to well-washed calcium phosphate gel and elution with successive small volumes of 2 *M* sodium acetate at pH 8.0. The later eluates contained sulfatase virtually free of ability to hydrolyze the glycosidic linkages (Fig. 5). A point of major interest is that the sulfatase is almost unable to remove sulfate groups from the whole polysaccharide, but if the chondroitin sulfate is first reduced to oligosaccharides, of the order of size of tetrasaccharide by the action of testicular hyaluronidase preparations, the sulfatase is then fully active. Contrariwise, however, the removal of sulfate groups does not appear to facilitate the action of the glycosidase—or as the authors call it, chondroitinase. A further study of this model might be rewarding from the viewpoint of understanding the mechanism of enzyme action. Later study[129a] of the chondroitinase from *Proteus vulgaris* has shown that after exhaustive digestion of chondroitin sulfate A with the enzyme, the principle product is a sulfated disaccharide; at intermediate stages oligosaccharides are formed. These substances appear to be similar or identical to those formed when hyaluronidase of mammalian origin acts on chondroitin

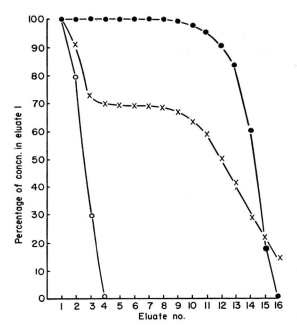

FIG. 5. Elutions of chondrosulfatase, chondroitinase, and protein from calcium phosphate gel; ● : chondrosulfatase, ○ : chondroitinase, × : protein. From Dodgson and Lloyd.[129]

sulfate. Bacterial hyaluronidases do not act on chondroitin sulfate, and from hyaluronic acid produce an unsaturated disaccharide (see IV,B,2).

4. Pneumococcal Polysaccharides

Several organisms have been isolated and studied[3, 131-136] which decompose in a highly specific manner the capsular polysaccharides of the pneumococci. The first was isolated from cranberry bogs in New Jersey.[3] The enzyme responsible for the destruction of the capsular polysaccharide of pneumococcus type III, which was measured by making use of the immunological properties of the substrate, was cell-bound and only liberated on autolysis of the cells. It was formed adaptively in response to the presence of either the whole pneumococcal polysaccharide or the aldobionic acid disaccharide repeating unit derived by partial acid hydrolysis; a wide range of other carbon sources was inactive. Likewise the action, as well as the formation of the enzyme, was highly specific. It was unable to affect polysaccharide from either type I or II pneumococci or that from Friedländer's organisms, nor was it able to attack gum arabic although this substance is sufficiently like pneumococcus type III polysaccharide to cross react with antisera against the latter. Later organisms were also isolated by a somewhat similar technique which would hydrolyze capsular polysaccharides from types I, II,[133, 135] and VIII[136] pneumococci. The only example of overlapping specificity[135] was the ability of the organism which attacked type I polysaccharide also to decompose the nonspecific pneumococcal polysaccharide; an organism specific for this substance alone was also isolated. It is interesting to note that the enzyme preparations which hydrolyzed the capsular polysaccharide of type III pneumococci were also capable of protecting animals against infection by the organism.[137]

Unfortunately no reports have been forthcoming on the purification or further study of the biochemistry of this interesting group of enzymes.

In contrast to the exacting specificity of the organisms already described an organism with more catholic tastes was described by Morgan and Thaysen.[138] This organism was originally isolated by enrichment technique on a medium containing the O-somatic polysaccharide from *B. dysenteriae*. Shiga and the authors opined that it was a species of *Myxobacterium*. Apart from the Shiga polysaccharide, this organism was able to destroy polysaccharides from *B. dysenteriae* Flexner, pneumococcus type II, tubercle, and also the blood group A substance.[139]

5. BLOOD GROUP SUBSTANCES

The study of organisms and enzymes prepared from them which will attack blood group substances has had a long and continuous history dating from 1934[139] up to the present time. Apart from the early paper to which reference has already been made, Chase[140] isolated an aerobic Gram-negative coccus from leaf mold which was able to destroy the immunological activity of preparations of a reacting substance prepared from human and horse saliva, and pig stomach. About the same time Schiff[141] described the activity of filtrates from a strain of *C. perfringens* which had been isolated from a case of lamb dysentery, and presumably of serological type B.[142] The blood group substance which he chose to study was that naturally present in the neopeptone used as a constituent of the growth medium for the organisms. The subject was reopened by Morgan[143] after World War II; he found that filtrates from type A *perfringens* cultures were able to destroy the isoagglutinating properties of his more purified A, B and, as it was then called, O substances. The enzyme was concentrated and partially purified from collagenase but still contained a very wide range of other enzymic activities. It was found that the activity destroying O substance was more resistant to heat than that which destroyed the A and B activities; the latter could be neutralized by the appropriate antibodies whereas the former could not. Some of the chemical changes induced by the enzyme in a physically homogeneous preparation, but which showed both A and O activities, suggested a rather extensive breakdown with the liberation of most of the amino acid carboxyl groups in the free form. In a subsequent study[144] rather more purified enzyme prepared from *C. perfringens* type B was used because this serological type was found to be more active in this respect than type A.[22] When this enzyme had acted on serologically specific H substance (previously defined as O activity) the hydrolysis products were fractionated through cellophane. The small molecular weight material which diffused freely contained the major part of the fucose in the original mucoprotein and some of the *N*-acetylglucosamine and galactose. Also present were a disaccharide and some small amino acid-containing residues. Even repeated treatment of the H substance with the enzyme preparation did not render it entirely diffusible. The original culture filtrates from the type B organisms, like the filtrates from type A, contained a heat-labile enzyme destroying blood group substance A. This enzyme had a pH optimum of activity 5.5, the heat-stable H-destroying enzyme had an optimum of pH 6.5. Further use of these enzymes may help to unravel the structure of this complicated group of substances.

An enzyme from a *Bacillus* species, probably *B. cereus*, which hydrolyzes O substance has been studied.[144a] Enzyme formation was increased by the presence of galactose, fucose, or melibiose in the medium but not by glucose, glucosamine, or lactose. The activity of the enzyme (by inhibition of hemagglutination) was inhibited by fucose (0.025 M), galactose, and galactosamine (0.1 M).

6. HEPARIN

Until very recently[7, 49, 120, 145] no very satisfactory enzyme preparations had been described that would rapidly hydrolyze the complex mucopolysaccharide, heparin. Despite the medical importance of heparin as an anticoagulant and the considerable amount of chemical work which has been done, its structure is still far from certain. It is known to contain approximately equimolar amounts of glucosamine and glucuronic acid, and one to three moles of sulfate per disaccharide unit. One of the sulfate groups is bound in an amide linkage to the amino group of glucosamine. The remainder of the linkages between the sugar molecules appear to be glycosidic in nature but their whereabouts on the molecule is uncertain.

Payza and Korn,[7] turning their attention to the problem of producing a bacterial heparinase, isolated an organism thought to be a species of *Flavobacterium* which appears to be a veritable "mucosolvent." The activity against heparin seems to be due to an adaptive[7] cell-bound enzyme system relatively easily extracted from the acetone-dried cells by dilute, alkaline (pH 8) phosphate buffer.[120] Extracts from the unadapted strain, however, will also hydrolyze hyaluronic acid and chondroitin sulfate A and C;

pectic acid, polygalacturonic acid, and chitin sulfate were also slowly hydrolyzed.[49, 120] If the cells are adapted to chondroitin sulfate B (i.e., β-heparin of Winterstein), the extracts will also hydrolyze this polysaccharide[49] which contains iduronic acid in place of the glucuronic acid of chondroitin sulfate A.

The hydrolysis of heparin was measured by the disappearance of the metachromatic color given when the mucopolysaccharide is mixed with the dye Azar A. Further examination of the reaction[7, 49] showed that reducing sugars, amino sugar, and periodate reactive groups were liberated and that an unsaturated disaccharide was formed which is said[49] to be different from that derived from the hyaluronic acid.

Examination[49] of the course of the hydrolysis of β-heparin by extracts from cells adapted to this mucopolysaccharide showed that the reaction was complicated. During the first stages the ultraviolet absorption band at 230 mμ appeared, which is characteristic of the unsaturated $\Delta 4,5$-glucuronic acid and the carbazole reaction for hexuronic acids increased. As the reaction proceeded, however, the ultraviolet absorption declined and it seems that free N-acetylgalactosamine was formed. Thus it is likely that a second enzyme system is present in the extracts which can hydrolyze the unsaturated di- or oligosaccharides, first formed, to free sugars. This second activity could be abolished by warming the extracts to 56°C. for 5 min.

The enzyme system hydrolyzing heparin itself is very sensitive to salt concentration as are many enzymes hydrolyzing polysaccharides. Phosphate activates when glycylglycine buffer is used but this effect does not appear to be in any way specific either to the cations or anions;[120] greater concentrations of salt are strongly inhibitory. The pH optimum of extracts from acetone powders is about 7.2.

C. PROTEINS

Inspection of a book dealing with the classification of microorganisms is sufficient to give some indication of their widespread ability to hydrolyze proteins such as gelatin, casein, and heat-denatured serum albumin. Tests for breakdown of these substances have long been part of the routine procedure for the classification of microorganisms and as a result we have much more thorough knowledge of the potentialities of microorganisms in this respect than we have when, say, cellulose or chitin hydrolysis is considered. Although thus more complete, our knowledge about the mechanism of action of the proteases and even about the properties of the enzymes themselves is remarkably poor. Very few have been purified and in most instances the specificity toward peptide bonds has not been tested, nor is it clear how many proteases or peptidases the organisms produce. This section will be confined to describing some instances of protease formation that have been examined in greater detail than others. Even here, however, great restriction has been made in that only a carefully selected amount of the total published work on each subject is quoted.

1. THE PROTEASES AND PEPTIDASES OF *Clostridium histolyticum*

In laboratory-induced infections with *C. histolyticum* the most outstanding symptom is the extensive digestion of the tissue proteins. Such are the powers of the organism that when it is injected into the thigh, the muscles of a guinea pig can be so digested that bare bone is left with threads of tissue hanging to it. It is, therefore, perhaps not surprising that considerable effort should have been devoted to studying the proteases produced by this organism. In 1937 Weil and Kochalaty[37] studied the course of production of an enzyme that hydrolyzed gelatin, clupeine, and casein. The enzyme or enzymes concerned increased rapidly and appeared to be extracellular. The gelatinase, measured by liberation of free —NH$_2$ groups, was somewhat activated by sulfhydryl compounds such as cysteine. On the other hand, activity against clupeine sulfate and casein was greatly activated by —SH, particularly if Fe^{++} ions were also present. Iron could be replaced by Mn^{++}, Ni^{++}, Cu^{++}, and Co^{++}. Iodoacetate did not inhibit the enzyme. Peptidases hydrolyzing DL-leucylglycylglycine were released slowly into the fluid phase of the culture, apparently from the autolyzing organisms.[28] Also associated with the bacteria as well as in the filtrates were small amounts of protease activity. A similar study[138] of this organism confirmed the rapid production of a very active gelatinase but showed that it was not activated at all by —SH reagents, whereas the clupeine enzyme required activation. This work also reported a casein-hydrolyzing enzyme which did not require activation. Maschmann also disagreed with Weil and Kochalaty in finding a slow release from cells in cultures rather than a fast appearance of activity against clupeine. Again peptidases were reported, and again according to this work they were only released very slowly into the culture fluid. Later[146] the peptidase both in intact and disrupted cells was claimed to be strongly activated by Mg^{++}. van Heyningen[15] abandoned gelatin as a substrate and the liberation of —NH$_2$ groups as a measure of protease action. He pointed out, quite rightly, the complications introduced by the possibility of peptidase action in this method, and came to the conclusion that two variants of the organism existed, one of which produced an extracellular protease inhibited by cysteine and an intracellular protease which was activated by —SH, and another variant which produced an extracellular proteinase activated by cysteine. Undoubtedly much confusion was introduced into this early work by the attempt to describe protease specificity by the type of protein hydrolyzed. Proteins, with a few exceptions, are too complex in structure and contain too great a variety of peptide bonds for enzyme specificity to be directed to the whole molecule. Recently a new approach has been made to the problem, using the available methods of protein separation and knowledge of protease specificity. De Bellis *et al.*[147] have fractionated culture filtrates by stepwise addition of $(NH_4)_2SO_4$. Four fractions were obtained and each was tested against a variety of substrates. They contained enzymes with the following specificities:

1. Hydrolyzed collagen, azocoll, and gelatin—presumably this can be said to contain a collagenase.

2. After cysteine activation, hydrolyzed benzoylarginine amide and arginine methyl ester, i.e., it showed esterase activity.

3. Hydrolyzed the peptides leucylglycine, leucyldiglycine, and valine decapeptide.

4. Hydrolyzed proteins generally, including azocoll, gelatin, casein, hemoglobin, egg albumin, fibrin, and bovine plasmin.

A similar separation between the collagenase activity and the cysteine-activated general protease has also been achieved[148] by different methods, and other confirming evidence has come from immunological studies.[149] Thus much of the early confusion over whether or not gelatin hydrolysis could be activated by —SH reagents seems comprehensible in terms of the production of two enzymes, one which is a general protease and one which is not but is a specific collagenase. Variants producing more or less of these two enzymes may well exist; whether the general protease activity is also due to more than one enzyme cannot yet be stated. If van Heyningen[15] was right it may be. The collagenase has since been shown to be activated by Ca^{++}.[21] A number of stimulating ideas are suggested by a study that has been made of what is claimed to be a homogeneous protein from the organisms.[150] The enzyme isolated from culture filtrates gave a single peak during electrophoresis at pH 5 and 8 and at three different ionic strengths at pH 7 but still hydrolyzed both gelatin and clupeine. It gave only negligible absorption of ultraviolet light of wavelengths from 250 to 290 mμ and, therefore, has presumably a very low content of aromatic amino acids thus resembling only gelatin and collagen among the known proteins. It contained no demonstrable —SH groups but was activated in its hydrolysis of gelatin and clupeine by cysteine and Fe^{++}. A study of the action of the nonactivated and activated enzyme on gelatin and clupeine showed that —SH reagents not only increased the rate of hydrolysis but also the extent of breakdown of the protein molecule (see Table V). If this is true then the specificity of the enzyme would appear to have been changed and the ratios of —NH_2 to —COOH groups liberated suggested to the authors that the nonactivated enzyme may be able to open only imido groups

TABLE V

HYDROLYSIS OF GELATIN BY *Clostridium histolyticum* PROTEINASE[a]

Incubation (hours)	Increase of free amino and carboxyl groups in 200 mg. gelatin (as ml. 0.1 N KOH)[b]					
	A Before addition of activator: initial enzyme		B Activator added when hydrolysis by initial enzyme was complete		C Enzyme and activator added simultaneously: fully activated enzyme	
	Amino[c]	Carboxyl[d]	Amino[c]	Carboxyl[d]	Amino[c]	Carboxyl[d]
1	0.47	0.64	0.86	0.98	1.35	1.95
4.5	0.65	1.28	1.21	1.29	1.79	2.64
6	0.65	1.28	1.22	1.30	1.79	2.68
Additional enzyme added	0.65	1.28	1.22	1.30	1.79	2.68

[a] *Reaction Mixture A:* 70 ml. acetone-purified enzyme (initial proteolytic activity = 0.89, full activity = 1.52 ml. 0.1 N KOH; no peptidase or polypeptidase activity), 30 ml. 6.6% gelatin solution adjusted to pH 7.

Reaction Mixture B: 20 ml. of A, completely hydrolyzed, and 2 ml. of Fe^{++}—SH activator (27.4 mg. $FeSO_4$ and 30 mg. cystine-HCl) adjusted to pH 7.

Reaction Mixture C: 70 ml. enzyme (same as for A), 30 ml. 6.6% gelatin solution, 2 ml. Fe^{++}—SH activator (27.4 mg. $FeSO_4$, 30 mg. cysteine-HCl) adjusted to pH 7 (from Kochalaty and Krejci[150]).

[b] These figures include the KOH added to compensate for the continuous drop in pH which begins immediately after addition of the substrate, and maintain a constant pH of 7.

[c] Determination in Van Slyke micro apparatus, using 2 ml. of reaction mixture.

[d] Titration with alcoholic KOH, using 5 ml. of reaction mixture.

in gelatin, whereas after activation other peptide bonds can be broken. Table V shows the type of results the authors obtained. Unfortunately the specificity of the enzyme preparation is not given but from its ability to hydrolyze clupeine and its activation by —SH reagents it probably corresponds to the general protease of De Bellis *et al.*[147] rather than to the specific collagenase. Other work,[150a] however, suggests that there are likely to be a number of proteases in *C. histolyticum* filtrates besides the collagenase and —SH activated enzyme.

Further study[150b] of collagenase from *C. histolyticum* has shown it to be a protein of molecular weight about 100,000 the enzymic activity of which is inhibited by sulfydryl compounds, by diisopropyl fluorophosphate and by sequestrating agents. Examination of[150c] the bond specificity of the enzyme has shown that out of many different kinds of synthetic peptides only those of the type -Pro-R-R'Pro-, or -hypro-R-R'-pro- are rapidly hydrolyzed. For example, Cbzy- hypro-gly-gly-pro-OCH₃ was split to give Cbzy-hypro-gly and gly-pro-OCH₃ . Similarly the peptide gly-pro-leu-gly-proNH₂ was hydrolyzed to give gly-pro-leu and gly-pro-NH₂ . This type of specificity demanding closely situated proline or hydroxyproline residues may well explain why only collagen or gelatin are hydrolyzed by collagenase.

A detailed examination of the peptidase fraction of De Bellis et al.[147] has been published by Mandl et al.[39] They claim no activation by metal ions but that the enzymes contain "metal-activators in tight linkage." Co⁺⁺ appeared to be inert with tripeptides as substrate but activated when dipeptidase was studied. Other metal ions such as Fe⁺⁺ inhibited at relatively high concentration, with the exception of Mg⁺⁺ which inhibited the hydrolysis of DL-leucylglycine even at a concentration of $5 \times 10^{-5} M$ whereas it was ineffective with L-leucylglycylglycine at 0.2 M. The preparations were inactivated by sodium ethylenediamine tetra-acetate ($10^{-3} M$) when tested against any of the substrates examined. It is on this basis that the authors deduced the presence of bound metal activators. Such discrepancy as exists between this work and earlier work about the activating effect of metal ions could possibly be explained by the presence in earlier workers' preparations of chelating agents such as nonhydrolyzed peptides or amino acids which would lower the concentration of ions available for combination with the enzymes.

The activity of several peptidase preparations made by fractionation of culture filtrates with ammonium sulfate was tested[39] against a number of peptides and a summary of some of the results is reproduced in Tables VI, VII, and VIII. Clearly several peptidases were present in the original filtrates.

2. SUBTILISIN—A PROTEASE FROM *Bacillus subtilis*

Linderstrøm-Lang and Ottesen,[151] "when working up slops of salt-free isoelectric ovalbumin solutions from half a year of experiments" observed a protein crystallizing as plates instead of "flat cigar-shaped needles." "A further perusal of our stock of old dialyzed ovalbumin solutions in the refrigerator revealed six samples, one to two years old, three of which had been stored with toluene, three without. Only the latter were infected, two with bacteria and one with moulds (and bacteria?) upon crystallization they gave a good (60 %) yield of plates." Thus began the history of a most interesting enzyme. It was found that *Bacillus subtilis* formed the enzyme, giving protein from ovalbumin which crystallized as plates. A soluble enzyme preparation could be obtained[152] by growing the organism in a casein digest glucose medium for 25–30 hr. when it appeared in the culture filtrate. Subsequently[153] it was crystallized in 64 % yield on the basis of enzymic

TABLE VI

RELATIVE ACTIVITIES OF VARIOUS AMMONIUM SULFATE FRACTIONS
PREPARED FROM *Clostridium histolyticum* FILTRATES
ON PEPTIDE SUBSTRATES[a]

Peptide	Ammonium sulfate fraction (% saturation)				
	27–28	26–30	28–30	35–40	32–40
DL-Leu-gly	0.07	0.22	0.11	0.34	0.77
L-Leu-L-ala	—	—	—	—	1.24
L-Leu-L-leu	0.17	0.20	0.18	0.20	0.50
L-Leu-L-try	0	0.09	0.03	0.39	1.10
L-Leu-L-tyr	0	0.40	0	0	1.20
L-Leu-NH₂	0	0	0	0	0.30
DL-Ala-gly	0.08	0	0.05	0.1	0.30
L-Ala-L-leu	0	0	0	0	0.19
DL-Ileu-gly	0	0	0	0.36	0.22
DL-Met-gly	0.24	0	0.22	0.16	0.17
L-Phe-gly	0.24	0	0.16	0.20	0.35
L-Pro-gly	0	0	0	0	0.08
DL-Val-gly	0.11	0	0	0.22	0.11
.Gly-L-ala	0.14	0.22	0.11	0.07	0.14
Gly-gly	0	0	0.62	0.70	0
Gly-L-leu	—	—	—	—	0
Gly-L-pro	0.14	0.05	0.10	0.05	0.20
.Gly-L-try	0	0.14	0.17	0.17	0.17
Gly-L-tyr	0	0.70	0	0	0.11
Gly-L-val	0	0	0	0	0.12

[a] The values given represent zero-order constants divided by enzyme concentration (from Mandl *et al.*[39]).

TABLE VII

HYDROLYSIS OF PEPTIDES BY SOME OF THE FRACTIONS
LISTED IN TABLE VI[a, b]

Hydrolyzed	Weakly or rarely split	Not hydrolyzed
Gly-L-leu-gly	Cl-acetyl gly-L-leu	L-Ala-L-glu (also LD and DL)
Gly-L-ala-gly	Gly-L-phe-NH₂ acetate	L-Glu-L-ala (also LD)
DL-Ala-DL-nor·val	L-Leu-L-phe-L-pro ester	L-Ala-L-glu-D-ala (also DLL and DLD)
L-Ala-L-phe	—	L-Glu-D-ala-L-ala
L-Phe-L-ala	—	L-Cys-gly-gly
L-Pro-L-val	—	—
L-Leu-L-phe	—	—
L-Leu-L-phe-L-pro		
L-Leu-L-phe-L-pro-L-val		

[a] From Mandl *et al.*[39]
[b] These tests were qualitative only.

TABLE VIII

PEPTIDES NOT SPLIT BY ANY OF THE PREPARATIONS
FROM *Clostridium histolyticum* FILTRATES[a]

Cl-acetyl-L-tyr	Gly-gly ester	L-Tyr ester
Bzl-L-ala	D-Leu-L-tyr	Gly ester
Cbzy[b]-gly-L-phe-NH₂	D-Leu-gly	DL-Val ester

[a] From Mandl *et al.*[39]
[b] Cbzy = carbobenzoxy group.

activity. At pH 5.3 and 6.5 the preparation gave a single symmetrical peak during electrophoresis with an isoelectric point of 9.4. Calculations suggested that the enzyme accounted for as much as one-third of the bacterial nitrogen. This amazingly high proportion of the organism appearing as a single enzyme is a matter of the very greatest physiological interest when it is considered that in one strain of staphylococci, for example, the total extracellular protein which contains several enzymes only amounts to about 3 % of the bacterial protein.[29]

The platelike protein formed from ovalbumin was called plakalbumin and the enzyme which forms it subtilisin. Subtilisin does not seem to be in any sense specific for ovalbumin since it can break down casein, hemoglobin, ovalbumin, gelatin,[153] and activate chymotrypsinogen.[154] During the course of hydrolysis of the proteins about the same number of peptide bonds are broken and the pH optimum is about the same[153] as for trypsin, although trypsin itself cannot form plakalbumin from ovalbumin.[151] Subtilisin is inhibited by triisopropyl fluorophosphate[153] and hydrolyzes methyl butyrate,[153] also in common with trypsin. The rate of activation of chymotrypsinogen is very much lower[153] than when trypsin is employed.

Plakalbumin itself was found not to be very much smaller in size than the original ovalbumin; nitrogen equivalent to six atoms was found as nonprotein nitrogen after enzyme action.[155] Analysis[156] of ultrafiltrates from the hydrolyzates suggested the presence of two or three peptides, one a dipeptide and either one tetra- or two tripeptides. Subsequent work[157, 158] showed that, in fact, three peptides were present, a dipeptide, a tetrapeptide and a hexapeptide. These peptides were separated and the amino acid sequence determined by a modification of the phenylisothiocyanate method[159] and it was concluded that they had the following structure: A. alanylglycylvalylaspartylalanylalanine; B. alanylglycylvalylaspartic acid; C. alanylalanine, B and C thus both being parts of A.

Thus, when the enzyme acts on ovalbumin, the bond split is likely to be that between aspartic acid and alanine. Acting on oxytocin,[160] it has also been found to split the —Glu(—NH₂)—aspartyl and the leucyl—glycyl(—NH₂) bonds. In other proteins, such as ribonuclease,[160a] subtilisin attacks a wide range of peptide bonds.

3. *Clostridium perfringens* PROTEINASES AND IN PARTICULAR COLLAGENASE

Early work[38, 161, 162] had shown that *C. perfringens* produced a very active gelatinase which was rather specific in that the filtrates would not attack ovalbumin, casein, or fibrin. Presumably on the basis of this specificity Maschmann suggested the name "collagenase" but later withdrew. With the increasing interest brought by the possibility of infected war wounds in the Second World War *C. perfringens* filtrates were intensively studied by a number of groups of workers. Macfarlane and MacLennan[163] observed that slices of rabbit and human muscle disintegrated when they were incubated with filtrates from *C. perfringens* cultures, but did not dissolve. When they were incubated with trypsin they became gelatinous, but the fibrous material still seemed to be intact. If both *C. perfringens* filtrate and trypsin were combined, complete solution of the slices could be achieved. The authors deduced that the filtrates were attacking the collagen in the slices, a supposition confirmed by orthodox histological study.[5] The muscle-disintegrating action of the filtrates was shown[164] to be distinct from the α-toxin (lecithinase), hemolysin, and hyaluronidase also present and designated as due to κ toxin of *C. perfringens*. There is, of course, no evidence that collagenase is toxic. Biochemical studies were then directed toward the study of this enzyme.[165-167] The first studies[165] were undertaken using commercial hide powder, coupled to form a dye complex and called "azocoll," as substrate. This formed a very convenient assay system since with the colored powder, enzymic activity could be assayed by measuring the amount of the dye solubilized. Unfortunately, collagen being exceedingly labile, the product was subsequently[166] shown to be attacked by nonspecific proteases which do not attack native collagen. Nevertheless, using this substrate considerable purification of collagenase was achieved, although the final product was far from being physically homogeneous. This partially purified product had no action on normal horse serum proteins or clupeine sulfate, and only a trace of activity against urea-denatured hemoglobin, casein, or heat-denatured serum albumin. It also failed to hydrolyze prolylglycine, *O*-acetyl-L-hydroxyproline, L-glycylproline, and hippuramide as other peptide materials relevant to collagen. Subsequent[116] study of preparations of this type revealed what appears to be either an interesting change in enzymic specificity or an activation. It was found that if the enzyme preparations were treated in alkaline solution at pH 10 and at 2°C., the activity against fresh collagen was labile and decreased, but far from inactivating the enzymes hydrolyzing "denatured" collagen alkali treatment made these more active. When the specificity of this enzyme, called the secondary enzyme, was tested, it was found not to hydrolyze casein, seracin, hemoglobin, or clupeine. This activity, apparently specific for partly damaged collagen, was also activated by heating at pH

7.0 at 50°C. in borate buffer, but was destroyed at 60°C. (10 min.). The activity against native collagen was destroyed in 10 min. at 56°C. Later[167] attention was turned to the protease production by other serological types of *C. perfringens*, all the previous work having been done with type A, that usually associated with wound infections in human beings. In filtrates from types B and D organisms another nonspecific protease was demonstrated[167,168] which hydrolyzes casein, hemoglobin, and seracin, but not native collagen; this enzyme was called λ. Thus, type D resembles *C. histolyticum*, producing collagenase as well as the nonspecific protease. Neither collagenase nor the nonspecific protease of type B was inhibited by soybean trypsin inhibitor, but the nonspecific protease was strongly (75 %) inhibited by 0.1 M citrate. Table IX summarizes the results obtained from these more recent studies of *C. perfringens* proteases.

4. AN AMINO POLYPEPTIDASE OF *Clostridium botulinum* TYPE B

A brief description of this enzyme seems justified in view of the evidence[169] that this organism produces only one protease. The organism was grown for 14–18 hr. at 34°C. and the enzyme isolated from the culture filtrate by fractionation with ammonium sulfate and ammonium sulfate plus sodium chloride. Examination of the solubility curve of the material in ammonium sulfate showed a single sharp break and only one peak could be seen during ultracentrifugation, indicating that only one major component was probably present. Again, like the purified protease from *C. histolyticum* obtained by Kochalaty and Krejci,[150] the enzyme showed no peak in the ultraviolet at 260 or 280 mμ after treatment with ribonuclease. It therefore presumably contained only a very low concentration of aromatic amino acids. Examination of the actions of the original supernatant and the purified enzyme on a number of substrates showed that they both acted at the same rate on the same substrates, as can be seen from the Table X. It would thus seem possible that this organism grown under these particular conditions liberates into the medium as an extracellular product, a single proteolytic enzyme with limited specificity.

5. STREPTOCOCCAL PROTEINASE

The origin of the study[170a, b, 171a] of this enzyme lay in work concerned with strains of streptococci which could not readily be classified by the Lancefield technique because no M protein[171b] could be extracted from them. It was observed[170a] that if the organisms were grown at room temperature instead of at 37°C. an active M preparation could be made; furthermore, the culture filtrate from cultures grown at 37°C. was able to destroy M substance, suggesting that an M-destroying enzyme was formed at 37°C. Since M substance is a protein capable of being destroyed by trypsin it

TABLE IX

COMPARISON OF THE PROPERTIES OF THE PROTEOLYTIC
ENZYMES PRODUCED BY *Clostridium perfringens*[a]

Observation	Collagenase	"Secondary" enzyme	λ-Enzyme
Occurrence in filtrates from different serological types	A, C, E, and some D	?	B, E, some D
Action on substrates[b]			
Native collagen	+	−	−
Hide powder and gelatin	+	+	+
Casein, hemoglobin	(−)	−	+
Seracin	(−)	(−)	+
Clupeine	−	−	−
Optimum pH	6.5 (collagen) 6.5–7.5 (hide powder)	5.0–7.5	6.0–7.5
Effect of acid	Unstable pH < ca. 5	Unstable at pH ca. 5	Unstable at pH < ca. 5
Effect of alkali	Unstable pH > ca. 8.5	Appears at pH 9–10.5. Unstable at pH > 10.5	Unstable pH > 9
Effect of heat	Destroyed 10 min. at 56°C.	Appears at 50°C.; destroyed 10 min. at 60°C. in borate buffer	95% Destroyed in 10 min. at 60°C.
Inhibition by[c]			
Cysteine	+	?	++
Cyanide	−	?	+
Citrate	−	−	+
Normal horse serum	−	−	+

[a] From Bidwell.[167]

[b] Symbols: + = hydrolyzed, − = not hydrolyzed, (−) = trace of activity.

[c] Symbols: + = inhibited, − = not inhibited.

seemed reasonable to suppose that when growing at 37°C. the organisms formed a protease. If the amount of filtrate used was much reduced it was able to solubilize M protein from organisms grown at room temperature without destruction. Crude enzyme preparations from the filtrates after treatment with reducing agents were able to hydrolyze other proteins such as casein, gelatin, and fibrin, and also benzoyl-L-arginineamide, although they were inactive toward the tripeptide L-leucylglycylglycine. Iodoacetate inhibited the action of the enzyme preparations. It was suspected, from the action of reducing agents, that the proteinase might be liberated from the organisms in the form of an inactive precursor. Later work[170b] confirmed this and showed that very small amounts of trypsin were able to activate the enzyme, thus providing a model for autocatalytic activation in normal cultures such as occurs with the trypsinogen–trypsin conversion. Chymotrypsin was not able to activate. Whether or not autocatalytic activation took place in the cultures depended[170b] upon the growth medium and conditions of growth; at 22°C. the precursor was not activated, which explains the original observation that M substance could be isolated from cells grown at room temperature.

Both the inactive precursor and the active enzyme have been crystallized[171a] and the results for activation by either reducing reagents or trypsin confirmed. Both were studied immunologically by the precipitin reaction and the interesting observation made that while only one antigen could be demonstrated in the active protease, two were found in the inactive precursor, one of which was identical with the active protease. Either the immunological test is very much more sensitive than the enzymological one, or some intermediate form between the protease and the precursor exists, which cannot be distinguished immunologically from active enzyme but nevertheless is not itself active.

D. NUCLEIC ACIDS

That nucleic acids are broken down when bacteria "autolyze" has been known for very many years,[180] but only within the last ten years have

TABLE X

A COMPARISON OF THE ACTION OF THE PURIFIED PROTEASE FROM
Clostridium botulinum TYPE B WITH THAT OF THE INITIAL
CULTURE FILTRATE[a]

Substrate	Rate of hydrolysis[b]		Ratio (b)/(a)
	Culture supernatant (a)	Purified enzyme (b)	
Casein	5.0	21.4	4.28
Denatured pepsin	4.5	20.1	4.46
Denatured egg albumin	1.8	8.0	4.40
Denatured serum albumin	0	0	—
Denatured egg albumin	0	0	—
DL-Ala-phe-gly	0.75	3.20	4.27
DL-Ala-gly-gly	0.63	2.75	4.36

[a] From Millonig.[169]
[b] Calculated from the initial slope of the hydrolysis curve.

specific bacterial nucleases been studied. Little work has been done as yet on the mode of action of these enzymes.

1. STREPTOCOCCAL DEOXYRIBONUCLEASE AND RIBONUCLEASE

The production of deoxyribonuclease (DNase) by streptococci was reported simultaneously by McCarty[14] and Tillet et al.[172] McCarty[14] examined the ability of 36 strains of Lancefield group A streptococci, one strain of *Bacillus subtilis*, one of *Escherichia coli*, and one of type II pneumococcus to liberate both deoxyribonuclease and ribonuclease (RNase) into the culture fluid. All the strains of streptococci were active in this respect, although the pneumococcal culture showed a trace of activity and the other two organisms were inactive. The deoxyribonuclease activity in the streptococcal cultures was very much greater than that of the ribonuclease, being equivalent to about one-third of that of a beef pancreas extract made with two to three volumes of $0.25 N H_2SO_4$. The ribonuclease action, on the other hand, was equivalent to only about $0.01 \mu g./ml.$ of crystalline pancreatic ribonuclease. The deoxyribonuclease activity was liberated rapidly into the culture fluid and appeared to be truly extracellular. The interesting observation was made during the course of this work, that deoxyribonucleic acid could not replace a supply of free purines in initiating the growth of small inocula, presumably either because insufficient enzyme is carried over with the inoculum or because the products of enzyme action cannot diffuse into the cell. Tillet et al.[172] also surveyed streptococci for formation of deoxyribonuclease and showed that Mg^{++} activated the enzyme. They found the following distribution of enzyme formation among the organisms examined: group A streptococci, 8/8 positive; group B, 1/1 positive; group C, 1/2 positive; group E, 1/1 positive; *Streptococcus viridans*, 6/6 negative; pneumococcus, one strain each of types I, II, VIII, and XIX, all negative. Within a year a report[173] appeared of a streptococcal preparation containing deoxyribonuclease being used to liquefy purulent pleural exudates. Subsequent surveys,[174] the results of one of which are reproduced in Table XI, have confirmed the universality of the production of both nucleases by group A streptococci. The production of deoxyribonuclease by washed suspensions of these organisms has been studied.[175a]

Deoxyribonuclease was partially purified by ammonium sulfate fractionation by McCarty[14] until it was about 2.5 times as active as the amorphous beef pancreas enzyme. This preparation did not show protease or streptokinase activity. Its action was shown[175b] to be inhibited by antisera prepared by injection of the enzyme into rabbits and by sera from human beings who had had certain streptococcal infections.

The bond specificity of streptococcal deoxyribonuclease has been found[175c] to be for the 3'-phosphate linkages in deoxyribonucleic acid leaving 5'-sub-

TABLE XI

THE PRODUCTION OF NUCLEASES BY SEROLOGICAL TYPES OF STREPTOCOCCI[a]

Group or species	No. of strains	No. of strains producing			
		RNase and DNase	RNase only	DNase only	Neither
Group A	42	42	0	0	0
Group B	73	20	1	0	52
Human C	7	0	0	6	1
Animal C	5	0	0	5	0
Streptococcus equi	1	0	0	1	0
Group F	6	0	0	3	3
Nonminute G	2	0	0	1	1
Minute G	2	0	0	1	1
Group L	2	0	0	2	0

[a] From Brown.[174]

stituted fragments of variable length, including traces of mononucleotides and dinucleotides. The pyrimidine-purine bonds appear to be preferentially split.

An important observation has been made by Wannamaker[70] who subjected ammonium sulfate-precipitated deoxyribonuclease prepared from five strains of group A streptococci to electrophoresis on a bed of starch at pH 9.0. He found that three components could be recognized with deoxyribonuclease activity. The relative proportions of these components varied according to the strain. When antisera were prepared against the components it was found that they were immunologically specific, antiserum to component A reacting with the enzyme in band A, and so on. Moreover the enzymes differed in their pH optima and the inhibition caused by citrate. The parallel between this observation of multiple bands of enzymic activity during electrophoresis of deoxyribonuclease with similar observations made on cellulase and chitinase (cf. Sections IV,A, 1 and B,1) is striking. It will be of the greatest interest eventually to see whether the enzymic activities are due to truly different proteins or to the same protein in loose complex with either other proteins or some other substances.

2. DEOXYRIBONUCLEASE OF *Staphylococcus aureus*

The enzyme formed by staphylococci[176] seems to differ from the strepotococcal enzyme principally in being activated by Ca^{++} and not Mg^{++}, which far from activating actually inhibited the viscosity-reducing action of a concentration of 0.01 M. It was optimally activated by a concentration of 0.01 M calcium chloride and its pH optimum was about 8.6. Other workers,[176a] however, have not been able to confirm the Ca^{++} activation of staphylococcal deoxyribonuclease and find that the addition of ethylene-diaminoacetic acid does not inhibit the enzyme. It is a remarkably heat-stable enzyme,[176] resisting a temperature of 95°C. for 15 min. when heated in the presence of bacterial cells. Partial purification of heated enzyme was achieved by ammonium sulfate, trichloroacetic acid and ethanol fractionation. The final preparation was about $\frac{1}{100}$ as active as crystalline pancreatic deoxyribonuclease.

An examination of the hydrolytic products formed by digestion of 200 mg. of deoxyribonucleic acid (DNA) with a total of 15,000 viscosity-reducing units of enzyme showed that 50–60 % of the secondary phosphoryl groups were released. This hydrolyzate was then fractionated on a column of Dowex-1. Four mononucleotides were isolated, the total yield of the four being equivalent to 28 % of the original DNA. Since phosphorus was not liberated from them by the 5'-nucleotidase of snake venom it was concluded that they were likely to be 3' substituted. Thus it appears probable that the micrococcal deoxyribonuclease differs from most of the other enzymes attacking DNA, both in its properties and in the extent and type of attack on the molecule. Comparative work on the biochemistry of this and the streptococcal enzyme should prove of interest.

In a further paper Weckman and Catlin[177] surveyed a large number of staphylococci and concluded that deoxyribonuclease formation was rather well correlated with coagulase formation. It should perhaps be pointed out that the formation of many active substances by staphylococci is also correlated with coagulase formation.[111]

3. Deoxyribonuclease of *Clostridium perfringens* and *Clostridium septicum*

Robb-Smith[5] first suggested that the damage to the nuclear material in polymorphonuclear leucocytes that he noticed when directly observing the action of toxic filtrates from *C. perfringens* cultures upon tissues might be due to a nuclease. Oakley and Warrack[116] then tested three type A strains, three type B, one type C, one type E, and two type F strains of *C. perfringens*. All the strains were positive. Unfortunately the authors used the so-called ACRA test[178] which depends upon the formation of a distinct "blob" when a drop of a mixture of an anionically charged polymer and congo red is dropped into acid ethanol; if the polymer has been broken down by enzymes a "blob" no longer forms. The activity of the enzyme can be calculated from the dilution at which the "blob" formed by the hydrolyzate just starts to spread. Such end point methods are excellent for measuring combination between antibody and enzyme but have disadvantages in the precise measurement of enzymic activity. It is, therefore, not yet possible to compare the activities of the enzymes formed by the clostridia with those of the enzymes formed by streptococci or staphylococci. In another paper Warrack et al.[179] found that deoxyribonuclease activity was also present in filtrates from *C. septicum*. In this work a viscosity method was used and a more direct comparison is possible which suggests that these filtrates were of the order of ten- or twentyfold less active than those handled by McCarty[14] from group A streptococci. The enzymes from both *C. perfringens* and *C. septicum* were specifically neutralized by their antibodies.

4. RIBONUCLEASE OF *Bacillus subtilis*

At least one strain of *B. subtilis* has been shown[179a] to produce a very active ribonuclease. This enzyme was like the amylase of this organism, formed after rapid bacterial growth had ceased. The maximum activity obtained in the culture supernatant was equivalent to about 20 μg./ml. of crystalline pancreatic ribonuclease. After preliminary purification by ammonium sulfate fractionation, examination of the material on columns of Amberlite IRC-50 equilibrated with 0.2 M sodium phosphate at pH 5.9 showed one major and one minor peak of ribonuclease activity. The specific activity of the material in the major peak was about the same as that of crystalline pancreatic ribonuclease. The optimum for enzymic activity was pH 7.5.

E. BACTERIAL CELL WALLS

That certain bacteria could be rapidly lysed by some component present in tissue secretions and particularly in egg white was first observed by Fleming.[180] He gave the name lysozyme to this entity. Subsequent work has shown[181] that lysozyme will also dissolve the isolated cell walls of sensitive organisms. Other enzymes and enzyme-like substances formed by bacteria which also have the same sort of action as lysozyme have now been recognized. No collective name has yet been found for these activities.

1. LYSIS BY *Bacillus subtilis*

Historically, *B. subtilis* was the first organism recognized[182] as having the ability to lyse other bacteria such as pneumococci and it has been subjected to a number of later studies. An autolysin was studied[183] in ammonium sulfate precipitates prepared from autolysates of the organism which could lyse isolated cell walls of *B. subtilis* itself; it also hydrolyzed a polysaccharide obtained by alkaline treatment of the cells. An enzyme-like substance formed extracellularly has been studied[31, 184] which will lyse either living cells or dissolve cell walls prepared from *Micrococcus lysodeikticus*, *Sarcina lutea*, *S. flava*, *B. megaterium*, and *B. subtilis* at about the same relative rates as can crystalline lysozyme from egg white. The pH optimum is higher for the bacterial than the egg white enzyme; the products formed by both from cell walls appear to be similar although the criteria at present available are rather vague.

2. OTHER *Bacillus* SPECIES

A number of organisms of this group, for example, *B. cereus, B. megaterium,* and *B. anthracis* spores, contain[185] active principles of enzymelike nature which are able to lyse vegetative cells both of the same and other species. Again soluble material of a mucopeptide nature (i.e., containing amino acids, amino sugars, and other sugars) was detected as a soluble product formed by the enzyme.

3. LYSIS BY *Staphylococcus aureus*

A logarithmically growing culture of these organisms diluted in distilled water shows cell lysis; diluted in hypertonic solutions, such as strong sucrose or salt solution, it shows the formation of protoplasts.[186] Lysates of the cells were able also to lyse *Micrococcus lysodeikticus*. One strain of this organism has now been shown[31] to form a potent extracellular activity against *Micrococcus lysodeikticus*. For example, 1 ml. of supernatant at the end of the logarithmic growth phase of a shaken broth culture contains the equivalent of 8–10 μg. of crystalline egg white lysozyme. This enzyme will not, however, lyse living staphylococcal cells but it will lyse cell walls prepared from them, liberating products similar to those obtained from *Micrococcus lysodeikticus* cells by the action of egg white lysozyme.

4. LYSIS BY *Streptomyces albus*

Welsch[187] found that many strains of actinomycetes produced a soluble substance which lysed many heat-killed Gram-negative organisms and living Gram-positive forms. This substance he called actinomycetin. Examination[188] of filtrates from one strain, *Streptomyces albus*, showed a principle very active against either cells or cell walls from *Streptococcus hemolyticus*. Solution of the walls appeared to be due to a polysaccharidase rather than to a protease which was also present.

In contrast, a system that appears to hydrolyze peptide bonds has been studied;[189, 190] this lyses a variety of organisms including staphylococci and dissolves cell walls prepared from them. The active principles have been purified and two enzymes with synergistic action recognized. During action on cell walls small dialyzable peptides are liberated and either alanine, glycine, or both, apparently according to the organism from which the cell walls have been prepared.

5. A Lysin Associated with *Streptococcus haemolyticus*

The ability of phage lysates of a Lancefield group C streptococcus to lyse streptococci of the same and other serological groups (A, C, and E) has been demonstrated.[191] As the author says, "It is not yet clear whether the lytic factor is produced by the phage alone or whether it is a streptococcal product that activates some substance liberated by the phage, it is, however, only demonstrable when phage lysis has taken place."

REFERENCES

[1] N. Fleming and A. C. Thaysen, *Biochem. J.* **14**, 25 (1920).
[2] R. G. H. Siu, "Microbiological Decomposition of Cellulose." Reinhold, New York, 1951.
[3] R. J. Dubos and O. T. Avery, *J. Exptl. Med.* **54**, 51 (1931).
[4] R. H. McBee, *J. Bacteriol.* **56**, 653 (1958).
[5] A. H. T. Robb-Smith, *Lancet* **249**, 362 (1945).
[6] M. G. Macfarlane and B. C. J. G. Knight, *Biochem. J.* **35**, 884 (1941).
[7] A. N. Payza and E. D. Korn, *J. Biol. Chem.* **223**, 853 (1956).
[8] M. Richmond, unpublished communication, 1958.
[9] R. S. Breed, E. G. D. Murray, and N. R. Smith, "Bergey's Manual of Determinative Bacteriology," 7th ed. Williams & Wilkins, Baltimore, Maryland, 1957.
[10] A. G. Benton, *J. Bacteriol.* **29**, 449 (1935).
[11] D. McClean, *Biochem. J.* **37**, 169 (1943).
[12] S. Tolksdorf, M. H. McCready, D. R. McCullagh, and E. Schwenk, *J. Lab. Clin. Med.* **34**, 74 (1949).
[13] Z. I. Kertesz, *in* "The Enzymes" (J. B. Sumner and K. Myrbäck, eds.), Vol. 1, Pt. 2, p. 745. Academic Press, New York, 1951.
[14] M. McCarty, *J. Exptl. Med.* **88**, 181 (1948).
[15] W. E. van Heyningen, *Biochem. J.* **34**, 1540 (1940).
[16] M. Kunitz, *J. Gen. Physiol.* **24**, 15 (1940).
[17] G. Halliwell, *J. Gen. Microbiol.* **17**, 153 (1957).
[18] B. W. Smith and J. H. Roe, *J. Biol. Chem.* **179**, 53 (1949).
[19] H. Gibian, *Ergeb. Enzymforsch.* **13**, 1 (1954).
[20] M. Laskowski and M. K. Seidel, *Arch. Biochem. Biophys.* **7**, 465 (1945).
[21] P. M. Gallop, S. Seifter, and E. Meilman, *J. Biol. Chem.* **227**, 891 (1957).
[22] M. V. Stack and W. T. J. Morgan, *Brit. J. Exptl. Pathol.* **30**, 470 (1949).
[23] D. McClean and C. W. Hale, *Biochem. J.* **35**, 159 (1941).
[24] M. B. Mathews, *Arch. Biochem. Biophys.* **61**, 367 (1956).
[25] H. Muir, *Biochem. J.* **69**, 195 (1958).
[26] H. J. Rogers and P. C. Spensley, *Biochem. J.* **60**, 635 (1955).
[27] H. J. Rogers, *Ann. N. Y. Acad. Sci.* **65**, 132 (1956).
[28] W. Kochalaty, L. Weil, and L. Smith, *Biochem. J.* **32**, 1685 (1938).
[29] H. J. Rogers, *J. Gen. Microbiol.* **10**, 209 (1954).
[30] H. J. Rogers, *J. Gen. Microbiol.* **16**, 22 (1957).
[31] M. Richmond, *Biochim. et Biophys. Acta.* **33**, 78 (1959).
[32] M. Richmond, *Biochim. et Biophys. Acta.* **31**, 564 (1958).
[33] M. Nomura, B. Maruo, and S. Akabori, *J. Biochem.* (Tokyo) **43**, 143 (1956).
[34] M. Nomura, J. Hosoda, B. Maruo and S. Akabori, *J. Biochem. (Tokyo)* **43**, 841 (1956).

[35] O. T. Avery and G. E. Cullen, *J. Exptl. Med.* **32**, 547, 583 (1920).

[36] O. T. Avery and G. E. Cullen, *J. Exptl. Med.* **32**, 571 (1920).

[37] L. Weil and W. Kochalaty, *Biochem. J.* **31**, 1255 (1937).

[38] E. Maschmann, *Biochem. Z.* **295**, 391 (1938).

[39] I. Mandl, L. T. Ferguson, and S. F. Zaffuto, *Arch. Biochem. Biophys.* **69**, 565 (1957).

[40] R. Y. Stanier, *Bacteriol. Revs.* **6**, 143 (1942).

[41] S. Winogradsky, *Ann. inst. Pasteur* **43**, 549 (1929).

[42] G. E. Woodward, *J. Biol. Chem.* **156**, 143 (1944).

[43] H. J. Rogers, *Biochem. J.* **39**, 435 (1945).

[44] H. J. Rogers, *Biochem. J.* **40**, 583 (1946).

[45] S. O. Byers, A. A. Tytell, and M. A. Logan, *Arch. Biochem. Biophys.* **22**, 66 (1949).

[46] D. M. Reynolds, *J. Gen. Microbiol.* **11**, 150 (1954).

[47] G. B. Mills, *Biochem. J.* **44**, 302 (1949).

[48a] J. D. Hockenhull and D. Herbert, *Biochem. J.* **39**, 102 (1945).

[48b] D. Scott and L. R. Hendrick, *J. Bacteriol.* **63**, 795 (1952).

[49] P. Hoffman, A. Linker, P. Sampson, K. Meyer, and E. D. Korn, *Biochim. et Biophys. Acta* **25**, 658 (1957).

[50] R. A. Hammerstrom, K. D. Claus, J. W. Coghlan, and R. H. McBee, *Arch. Biochem. Biophys.* **56**, 123 (1955).

[51] E. T. Reese, R. G. H. Siu, and H. S. Levinson, *J. Bacteriol.* **59**, 485 (1950).

[52] D. H. Northcote, *Biol. Revs. Cambridge Phil. Soc.* **33**, 53 (1958).

[53] R. F. Nickerson, *Advances in Carbohydrate Chem.* **5**, 103 (1950).

[54] R. L. Whistler and W. M. Corbett, *in* "The Carbohydrates," (W. Pigman, ed.), p. 662. Academic Press, New York, 1957.

[55] A. G. Norman and W. H. Fuller, *Advances in Enzymol.* **2**, 239 (1942).

[56] R. H. McBee, *Bacteriol. Revs.* **14**, 51 (1950).

[57] R. E. Hungate, *Bacteriol. Revs.* **14**, 1 (1950).

[58] P. H. Clark and M. V. Tracey, *J. Gen. Microbiol.* **14**, 188 (1956).

[59] R. E. Hungate, *J. Bacteriol.* **53**, 631 (1947).

[60] S. Winogradsky, *Ann. inst. Pasteur* **43**, 549 (1929).

[61] H. Pringsheim, *Z. Physiol. Chem., Hoppe-Seyler's* **78**, 266 (1912).

[62] H. S. Levinson, G. R. Mandel and E. T. Reese, *Arch. Biochem. Biophys.* **31**, 351 (1951).

[63] P. Kooiman, P. A. Roelofsen, and S. Sweeris, *Enzymologia* **16**, 237 (1953).

[64] R. A. Aitken, B. P. Eddy, M. Ingram, and C. Weurman, *Biochem. J.* **64**, 63 (1956).

[65] G. N. Festenstein, *Biochem. J.* **65**, 23P (1957).

[66] G. N. Festenstein, *Biochem. J.* **69**, 562 (1958).

[66a] B. C. Sison and W. J. Schubert, *Arch. Biochem. Biophys.* **78**, 563 (1958).

[67a] D. R. Whitaker, *Arch. Biochem. Biophys.* **43**, 253 (1953).

[67b] D. R. Whitaker, *Nature* **168**, 1070 (1951).

[68] R. M. Grimes, C. W. Duncan, and C. A. Hoppert, *Arch. Biochem. Biophys.* **68**, 412 (1957).

[69] G. L. Miller and R. Blum, *J. Biol. Chem.* **218**, 131 (1956).

[70] L. W. Wannamaker, *J. Exptl. Med.* **107**, 783 (1958).

[70a] R. Thomas and D. R. Whitaker, *Nature* **181**, 715 (1958).

[71] C. T. Greenwood, *Advances in Carbohydrate Chem.* **11**, 335 (1956).

[72] T. J. Schoch, *Advances in Carbohydrate Chem.* **3**, 247 (1945).

[73] M. L. Caldwell, *Advances in Carbohydrate Chem.* **5**, 229 (1950).

[74] W. J. Whelan, *Biochem. Soc. Symposia (Cambridge, Engl.)* **11**, 17 (1953).

[75] K. H. Meyer, M. Fuld, and P. Bernfeld, *Experientia* **3**, 411 (1947).

[76] S. Akabori, Y. Okada, S. Fujiwara, and K. Sugae, *J. Biochem. (Tokyo)* **43**, 741 (1956).

[77] S. Hagihara, *Ann. Rept. Sci. Works, Fac. Sci., Osaka Univ.* **2**, 35 (1954).

[78] M. L. Caldwell, E. S. Dickey, V. M. Hanrahan, H. C. Kung, J. T. Kung, and M. Misko, *J. Am. Chem. Soc.* **76**, 143 (1954).

[79] J. Muus, *J. Am. Chem. Soc.* **76**, 5163 (1954).

[80] S. Akabori, T. Ikenaka, H. Hanafuser, and Y. Okada, *J. Biochem. (Tokyo)* **41**, 803 (1954).

[81] R. Menzi, E. A. Stein and E. H. Fischer, *Helv. Chim. Acta* **40**, 534 (1957).

[81a] J. M. Junge, E. A. Stein, H. Neurath, and E. H. Fischer, *J. Biol. Chem.* **234**, 556 (1959).

[82] A. Markovitz, H. P. Klein, and E. Fischer, *Biochim. et Biophys. Acta* **19**, 267 (1956).

[83] P. S. Thayer, *J. Bacteriol.* **66**, 656 (1953).

[84] G. Noelting and P. Bernfeld, *Helv. Chim. Acta* **31**, 286 (1948).

[85] F. Schardinger, *Z. Untersuch. Nahr u. Genussm.* **6**, 865 (1904).

[86] D. French, *Advances in Carbohydrate Chem.* **12**, 189 (1957).

[87] H. Lineweaver and D. Burk, *Advances in Enzymol.* **11**, 267 (1951).

[87a] W. K. Smith, *J. Gen. Microbiol.* **18**, 33, 42 (1958).

[87b] G. W. Lanigan, *J. Bacteriol.* **77**, 1 (1959).

[88] S. A. Waksman, C. L. Carey, and M. C. Allen, *J. Bacteriol.* **28**, 213 (1934).

[89] E. Kåss, I. Lid, and J. Molland, *Avhandl. Norske Videnskaps-Akad. Oslo. I. Mat. Naturv. Kl.* **11**, 1–22 (1945).

[90] Th. Thjotta and E. Kåss, *Avhandl. Norske Videnskaps-Akad. Oslo. I. Mat. Naturv. Kl.* **5**, 1–20 (1945).

[91] P. Kooiman, *Biochim. et Biophys. Acta* **13**, 338 (1954).

[91a] I. Katsuhiro and Y. Ando, *Nippon Nôgei-Kagaku Kaishi* **30**, 742 (1956) (*Chem. Abstr.* **52**, 8270, 1958).

[92] C. E. ZoBell and S. C. Rittenberg, *J. Bacteriol.* **35**, 275 (1938).

[93] W. Benecke, *Botan. Ztg.* (1 Abb.) **63**, 227 (1905).

[94] L. L. Campbell and O. B. Williams, *J. Gen. Microbiol.* **5**, 894 (1951).

[95] R. Y. Stanier, *J. Bacteriol.* **53**, 297 (1947).

[96] H. Veldkamp, *Mededel. Landbouwhogeschool Wageningen* **55**, 127 (1955).

[97] P. Karrer and A. Hofmann, *Helv. Chim. Acta* **12**, 616 (1929).

[98] P. Karrer and G. von François, *Helv. Chim. Acta* **12**, 986 (1929).

[99] L. Zechmeister, G. Toth and M. Balint, *Enzymologia* **5**, 302 (1938).

[100] C. Jenniaux, *Arch. intern. physiol.* **58**, 350 (1950).

[100a] L. Berger and D. M. Reynolds, *Biochim. et Biophys. Acta* **29**, 522, (1958).

[100b] C. Jenniaux, *Arch. intern. physiol. et biochem.* **65**, 135 (1957); *Biochem. J.* **66**, 29P.

[101] M. V. Tracey, *Biochem. J.* **61**, 579 (1955).

[102] A. G. Ogston and J. Stanier, *Biochem. J.* **46**, 364 (1950); **49**, 585 (1951).

[103] V. Faber and K. Rosendal, *Acta Pathol. Microbiol. Scand.* **35**, 159 (1954).

[104] A. P. MacLennan, *J. Gen. Microbiol.* **14**, 134, 143; **15**, 485 (1956).

[105] N. Crowley, *J. Pathol. Bacteriol.* **56**, 27 (1944).

[106] R. M. Pike, *J. Infectious Diseases* **79**, 148 (1946); **83**, 1, 12 (1948).

[107] B. E. Russell and N. P. Sherwood, *J. Infectious Diseases* **84**, 81 (1949).

[108] R. G. E. Murray and R. H. Pearce, *Can. J. Research* **E27**, 254 (1949).

[109] D. McClean, *J. Pathol. Bacteriol.* **53**, 13 (1941).

[110a] E. W. Emmart and R. M. Cole, *J. Bacteriol.* **70**, 596 (1955).

[110b] B. Sallman, *J. Bacteriol.* **62**, 741 (1951).

[111] H. Schwabacher, A. C. Cunliffe, R. E. O. Williams, and C. J. Harper, *Brit. J. Exptl. Pathol.* **26**, 124 (1945).

[112] H. J. Rogers, *J. Pathol. Bacteriol.* **66**, 545 (1953).

[113] D. McClean, H. J. Rogers, and B. W. Williams, *Lancet* 355 (1943).

[114] D. G. Evans, *J. Pathol. Bacteriol.* **57**, 75 (1945).

[115] E. H. Kass, H. C. Lichstein, and B. A. Waisbreu, *Proc. Soc. Exptl. Biol. Med.* **58**, 172 (1945).

[116] C. L. Oakley and G. H. Warrack, *J. Pathol. Bacteriol.* **63**, 45 (1951).

[117] J. H. Humphrey, *J. Pathol. Bacteriol.* **56**, 273 (1944).

[118] K. Meyer, E. Chaffee, G. L. Hobby, and M. H. Dawson, *J. Exptl. Med.* **73**, 309 (1941).

[119] K. Meyer, G. L. Hobby, E. Chaffee, and M. H. Dawson, *J. Exptl. Med.* **71**, 137 (1940).

[120] E. D. Korn and A. N. Payza, *J. Biol. Chem.* **223**, 859 (1956).

[121] L. Habn, *Arkiv. Kemi Mineral Geol.* **19A**, 33, **21A**, 1 (1945); **22A**, 1, 2 (1946).

[122] H. J. Rogers, *Biochem. J.* **40**, 782 (1946); **42**, 633 (1948).

[123] M. M. Rapport, K. Meyer, and A. Linker, *J. Am. Chem. Soc.* **73**, 2416 (1951); B. Weissman, K. Meyer, P. Sampson, and A. Linker, *J. Biol. Chem.* **208**, 417 (1954); A. Linker, K. Meyer, and B. Weissman, *J. Biol. Chem.* **213**, 237 (1955); A. Linker, K. Meyer, and P. Hoffman, *J. Biol. Chem.* **219**, 13 (1956); P. Hoffman, K. Meyer, and A. Linker, *J. Biol. Chem.* **219**, 653 (1956); K. Meyer, A. Linker, and M. M. Rapport, *J. Biol. Chem.* **192**, 275 (1951).

[124] C. Neuberg and O. Rubin, *Biochem. Z.* **67**, 82 (1914).

[125] C. Neuberg and E. Hoffman, *Biochem. Z.* **234**, 345 (1931).

[126] T. Soda and F. Egami, *J. Chem. Soc. Japan, Pure Chem. Sect.* **59**, 1202 (1938).

[127] H. J. Buehler, P. A. Katzman, and E. A. Doisy, *Proc. Soc. Exptl. Biol. Med.* **78**, 3 (1951).

[128] K. S. Dodgson, A. G. Lloyd, and B. Spencer, *Biochem. J.* **65**, 131 (1957).

[129] K. S. Dodgson and A. G. Lloyd, *Biochem. J.* **66**, 532 (1957).

[129a] K. S. Dodgson and A. G. Lloyd, *Biochem. J.* **68**, 88 (1958).

[130] J. Strominger, *Biochim. et Biophys. Acta* **17**, 283 (1955).

[131] R. J. Dubos, *J. Exptl. Med.* **55**, 377 (1932).

[132] R. J. Dubos, *J. Exptl. Med.* **62**, 259 (1935).

[133] G. M. Sickles and M. Shaw, *J. Infectious Diseases* **53**, 38 (1933).

[134] G. M. Sickles and M. Shaw, *J. Bacteriol.* **28**, 415 (1934).

[135] G. M. Sickles and M. Shaw, *Proc. Soc. Exptl. Biol. Med.* **31**, 443 (1933–34).

[136] G. M. Sickles and M. Shaw, *Proc. Soc. Exptl. Biol. Med.* **32**, 857 (1935).

[137] K. Goodner, R. J. Dubos, and O. T. Avery, *J. Exptl. Med.* **55**, 393 (1932).

[138] W. T. J. Morgan and A. C. Thaysen, *Nature* **132**, 604 (1933).

[139] K. Landsteiner and M. W. Chase, *Proc. Soc. Exptl. Biol. Med.* **32**, 713 (1934–35).

[140] M. W. Chase, *J. Bacteriol.* **36**, 383 (1938).

[141] F. Schiff, *J. Infectious Diseases* **65**, 127 (1939).

[142] C. L. Oakley, *Bull. Hyg.* **18**, 781 (1943).

[143] W. T. J. Morgan, *Nature* **158**, 759 (1946).

[144] D. J. Buchanan, M. J. Crumpton, and W. T. J. Morgan, *Biochem. J.* **65**, 186 (1957).

[144a] S. Iseki and S. Tsumoda, *Proc. Japan Acad.* **28**, 370 (1952); Z. Yosizawa, *Tôhoku J. Exptl. Med.* **65**, 175 (1957); I. Naylor and H. Baer, *J. Bacteriol.* **77**, 771 (1959).

[145] E. D. Korn, *J. Biol. Chem.* **226**, 841 (1957).

[146] W. Kochalaty, L. Smith, and L. Weil, *Biochem. J.* **32**, 1691 (1938).

[147] R. De Bellis, I. Mandl, J. D. MacLennan, and E. L. Howes, *Nature* **174**, 1191 (1954).

[148] I. H. Lepow, S. Katz, J. Pensky, and L. Pillemer, *J. Immunol.* **69**, 435 (1952).

[149] C. L. Oakley and G. H. Warrack, *J. Gen. Microbiol.* **4**, 365 (1950).

[150] W. Kochalaty and L. E. Krejci, *Arch. Biochem. Biophys.* **18**, 1 (1948).

[150a] J. D. MacLennan, I. Mandl, and E. L. Howes, *J. Gen. Microbiol.* **18**, 1 (1958); C. L. Oakley and G. H. Warrack, *J. Gen. Microbiol.* **18**, 9 (1958); I. Mandl and S. F. Zaffuto, *J. Gen. Microbiol.* **18**, 13 (1958).

[150b] S. Seifter, P. M. Gallop, L. Klein, and E. Meilman, *J. Biol. chem.* **234**, 285 (1959).

[150c] Y. Nagai and H. Noda, *Biochim. et Biophys. Acta* **34**, 298 (1959); W. Grassman, H. Hörman, A. Nordwig, and E. Wunsch, *Z. physiol. Chem., Hoppe-Seyler's* **316**, 287 (1959).

[151] K. Linderstrøm-Lang and M. Ottesen, *Nature* **159**, 807 (1947).

[152] A. V. Güntelberg, *Compt. rend. trav. lab. Carlsberg. Ser. chim.* **29**, 27 (1953–56).

[153] A. V. Güntelberg and M. Ottesen, *Nature* **170**, 802 (1952) *Compt. rend. trav. lab. Carlsberg. Ser. chim.* **29**, 36 (1953–56).

[154] A. Abrams and C. F. Jacobsen, *Compt. rend. trav. lab. Carlsberg. Ser. chim.* **27**, 447 (1949–51).

[155] K. Linderstrøm-Lang and M. Ottesen, *Compt. rend. trav. lab. Carlsberg. Ser. chim.* **27**, 447 (1949–51).

[156] N. Eeg-Larson, K. Linderstrøm-Lang, and M. Ottesen, *Arch. Biochem. Biophys.* **19**, 340 (1948).

[157] M. Ottesen and C. Villee, *Compt. rend. trav. lab. Carlsberg. Ser. chim.* **27**, 421 (1951).

[158] M. Ottesen and A. Wollenberger, *Nature* **170**, 801 (1952).

[159] P. Edman, *Acta Chem. Scand.* **4**, 283 (1950).

[160] H. Tuppy, *Biochim. et Biophys. Acta* **11**, 449 (1953).

[160a] S. M. Kalman, K. Linderström-Lang, M. Ottensen, and F. M. Richards, *Biochim. et Biophys. Acta* **16**, 297 (1955).

[161] E. Maschmann, *Biochem. Z.* **295**, 1, 351 (1937–38).

[162] L. Weil, W. Kochalaty, and L. D. Smith, *Biochem. J.* **33**, 893 (1939).

[163] R. G. Macfarlane and J. D. MacLennan, *Lancet* **249**, 328 (1945).

[164] C. L. Oakley, G. H. Warrack, and W. E. van Heyningen, *J. Pathol. Bacteriol.* **58**, 229 (1946).

[165] E. Bidwell and W. E. van Heyningen, *Biochem. J.* **42**, 140 (1948).

[166] E. Bidwell, *Biochem. J.* **44**, 28 (1949).

[167] E. Bidwell, *Biochem. J.* **46**, 589 (1950).

[168] C. L. Oakley, G. H. Warrack, and M. E. Warren, *J. Pathol. Bacteriol.* **60**, 498 (1948).

[169] R. C. Millonig, *J. Bacteriol.* **72**, 301 (1956).

[170a] S. D. Elliot, *J. Expt. Med.* **81**, 573 (1945).

[170b] S. D. Elliot and V. P. Dole, *J. Exptl. Med.* **85**, 305 (1947).

[171a] S. D. Elliot, *J. Exptl. Med.* **92**, 201 (1950).

[171b] R. C. Lancefield, *Harvey Lectures, Ser.* **36**, 281 (1942).

[172] W. S. Tillett, S. Sherry, and L. R. Christensen, *Proc. Soc. Exptl. Biol. Med.* **68**, 184 (1948).

[173] W. S. Tillett and S. Sherry, *J. Clin. Invest.* **28**, 173 (1949).

[174] A. L. Brown, *J. Bacteriol.* **60**, 673 (1950).

[175a] A. W. Bernheimer and N. K. Ruffier, *J. Exptl. Med.* **93**, 399 (1951).

[175b] M. McCarty, *J. Exptl. Med.* **90**, 543 (1949).

[175c] J. L. Potter and M. Laskowski, *J. Biol. Chem.* **234**, 1263 (1959).

[176] L. Cunningham, B. W. Catlin, and M. P. de Garilhe, *J. Am. Chem. Soc.* **78**, 4642 (1956).

[176a] M. H. Fusillo and D. L. Weiss, *J. Bacteriol.* **78**, 520 (1959).

[177] B. G. Weckman and B. W. Catlin, *J. Bacteriol.* **73**, 747 (1957).

[178] F. M. Burnet, *Australian J. Exptl. Biol. Med. Sci.* **26**, 71 (1948).

[179] G. H. Warrack, E. Bidwell and C. L. Oakley, *J. Pathol. Bacteriol.* **63**, 293 (1951).

[179a] S. Nishimura and M. Nomura, *Biochim. et Biophys. Acta*, **30**, 430 (1958); *J. Biochem. (Tokyo)* **46**, 161 (1959).

[180] A. Fleming, *Proc. Roy. Soc.* **B93**, 306 (1922).

[181] M. R. J. Salton, *Nature* **170**, 746 (1952); *Biochim. et Biophys. Acta* **22**, 495 (1956).

[182] M. Nicolle, *Ann. inst. Pasteur* **21**, 613 (1907).

[183] M. Nomura and J. Hosoda, *J. Bacteriol.* **72**, 573 (1956).

[184] Y. Satomura, S. Okada, and J. Fukumoto, *Chem. Abstr.* **51**, 13998 (1957).

[185] R. E. Strange and F. A. Dark, *J. Gen. Microbiol.* **16**, 236 (1957).

[186] P. Mitchell and J. Moyle, *J. Gen. Microbiol.* **16**, 184 (1957).

[187] M. Welsch, "Phénomènes d'Antibiose chez les Actinomycètes. J. Ducolt, Geintloux (Belgium), 1947.

[188] M. McCarty, *J. Exptl Med.* **96**, 555, 569 (1952).

[189] J. M. Ghuysen, Thèse d'Agrégation de l'Enseignement Supérieur, Université de Liège, Liège, 1957.

[190] M. R. J. Salton and J. M. Ghuysen, *Biochim. et Biophys. Acta* **24**, 160 (1957).

[191] W. R. Maxted, *J. Gen. Microbiol.* **16**, 584 (1957).

CHAPTER 6

Survey of Microbial Electron Transport Mechanisms

M. I. DOLIN

I. Introduction

Three general processes are considered in the study of biological oxidation: (1) Dehydrogenation of a substrate, followed by transfer of the hydrogen, or electrons, to an ultimate acceptor. (2) Conservation, in a biologically available form, of the energy released in step 1. (3) Subsequent metabolism of the dehydrogenated (oxidized) substrate.

The present chapter is concerned with the enzyme mechanisms by which bacteria accomplish the first two of these processes. In biological oxidation the energy present in an organic substrate is released by successive dehydrogenations of the carbon chain. Reducing equivalents are removed, two at a time, and transferred to a final acceptor, which may or may not be oxygen, via a graded series of reversible oxidation-reduction systems. The occurrence of several reversible oxidation-reduction systems between the initial reductant and final oxidant makes for smoother release of energy and provides loci for energy conservation steps. (The conflict between the terms hydrogen and electron transport has been clarified by recent work, to be discussed in the next section. Quantitative treatment of electron transport is given in Section VII.)

In general, knowledge of bacterial electron transport mechanisms has lagged behind that of the mammalian systems. There are two reasons for this. First, the great diversity of metabolic types among bacteria makes for greater diversity in composition of the electron transport chain; even for a given organism, change in environmental conditions may alter the nature and concentration of the electron transport catalysts. Second, with bacteria one of the practical considerations has been, until recently, the problem of obtaining the large quantities of cells needed for enzyme purification work. An analytical difficulty common to the study of many biological respiratory systems stems from the fact that the catalysts comprising these systems may be bound to particulate structures.[1-3] This feature makes it difficult to investigate individual steps in the sequential series of oxidation-reduction reactions catalyzed by such preparations. The intact respiratory particle of animal systems, the mitochondrion, has now begun to yield individual subunits, which may be isolated and studied independently.[2] Bacterial respiratory particles, as they occur in disrupted cell preparations, are much smaller than mitochondria and appear to consist primarily of broken cytoplasmic membranes.[4, 5]

Although this chapter concerns only bacterial systems, reference will be made to other microorganisms and to animal systems for purposes of orientation. The bacteria to be considered here are the cytochrome-containing aerobes and facultative anaerobes. Respiratory enzymes of non-cytochrome-containing bacteria will be considered in more detail in Chapter 9.

II. The Respiratory Chain

A. COMPONENTS

The sequence of electron transport reactions, as presently understood, is shown in Fig. 1. Hydrogen from substrate is transferred via pyridine nucleotides to flavoprotein, which in turn donates electrons to the cytochrome system. The reduced cytochrome is reoxidized by cytochrome oxidase and the latter catalyzes the reduction of molecular oxygen to water. Cytochrome and cytochrome oxidase are iron-porphyrin enzymes, discussed in detail in Chapters 7 and 8. In intact animal mitochondria[3] the

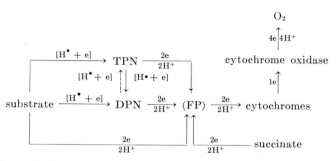

FIG. 1. Generalized electron transport chain. The number and nature of the flavo-protein (FP) and cytochrome components will depend upon the system under investi-gation. The formulation, [H· + e], indicates that the equivalent of a hydrogen atom plus an electron, or a hydride ion, is transferred. Transfer to and from flavoprotein is shown as a classic electron transport, for reasons discussed in the text.

reduction sequence for cytochrome is b, c, a, a_3 (cytochrome oxidase). The identity and number of cytochrome components involved in bacterial sys-tems has purposely been left unspecified, since components vary from species to species and with growth conditions[6] (Section VI, B). Further-more, bacterial pigments spectroscopically identical with mammalian cyto-chrome c, for instance, may have entirely different physicochemical and enzymic properties than the animal counterpart.[7] The electron transport catalysts, including diphosphopyridine nucleotide (DPN) in relatively in-tact preparations, may all be bound into an organized structure that per-mits efficient interaction between the various components.

In addition to the components mentioned, it becomes increasingly ob-vious that lipids and lipid soluble substances have a significant function in electron transport systems. Since this is a relatively new development there is as yet little information on lipid function in bacterial systems. In mam-malian respiratory preparations, lipids may act as a matrix in which the respiratory catalysts are imbedded,[8] although a more active role in catalysis has been suggested.[9] Among the fat-soluble substances, vitamin K_1 can react with the respiratory chain of mammalian systems[10, 11] and bacteria (*Mycobacterium phlei*).[12] Alpha-tocopherol appears to be associated with mammalian respiratory particles[13, 14] and can function as an activator of a soluble pyruvate oxidase derived from an acetate-requiring mutant of *Escherichia coli*.[15a]

Substituted *p*-benzoquinones (collectively designated the coenzyme Q group) have been isolated from beef heart mitochondria and various micro-organisms (*Azotobacter vinelandii, Torula, Saccharomyces cerevisiae*).[15b] The nucleus of these quinones is 2,3-dimethoxy-5-methyl-*p*-benzoquinone, with an isoprene polymer occupying carbon 6 of the quinone ring. The length of the isoprenoid chain differs depending upon the source of the quinone, and varies from a length of 10 units (Q_{10}) for the beef heart quinone to a length of 6 units (Q_6) for the quinone isolated from *S. cerevisiae*. It is suggested that coenzyme Q_{10} of mitochondria functions in electron transport from succinate to oxygen[15c] and that it may be involved in oxidative phosphorylation.[15d] Apparently similar quinones, isolated from a variety of animal tissues, have been designated ubiquinone.[15e]

Besides the components already noted, mammalian[2] and bacterial (*Azotobacter*)[16] respiratory particles contain nonheme iron and copper. A specific role for the latter metals has not been established.

It will be noted from Fig. 1 that the role of oxygen in a typical respiratory system is that of oxidizing the reducing equivalents removed from substrate. In these reactions, any oxygen that appears in the dehydrogenated substrate molecule is derived from water (i.e., through carbonyl oxidation systems and hydrases). There are enzymes, however, that catalyze the direct introduction of either one or two atoms of oxygen from molecular oxygen into substrate. These reactions, which among bacteria have been studied mainly in the genus *Pseudomonas*, are probably not respiratory processes, but mechanisms for preparing specific compounds. The subject has been thoroughly reviewed by Mason[17] and will not be considered here.

The point of entry of a substrate into the respiratory chain is governed by thermodynamic considerations and by the enzymic constitution of the particular system under investigation. Some substrates, for instance, have the potentiality of reacting at the pyridine nucleotide level and also higher up in the chain. Table I shows the entry point of various compounds into the respiratory chain and indicates those which can react at more than one site. Theoretical treatment is given in Section VII. Various enzyme systems have been described as "cytochrome-linked dehydrogenases" because they were thought to couple substrate dehydrogenation more or less directly with cytochrome reduction.[18] For two such systems, however, succinic dehydrogenase[19] and lactic dehydrogenase of yeast,[20, 21] it is now known that flavoprotein mediates the electron transport to cytochrome. These systems may be prototypes for other cytochrome-linked dehydrogenases (i.e., those for α-glycerophosphate, choline, or malate).

It should be stated at the outset that the formulations of Fig. 1 and Table I do not imply that a single flavoprotein is the electron acceptor for all the reactions shown.

B. REDUCTION AND REOXIDATION OF PYRIDINE NUCLEOTIDES

1. FORMATION OF DPNH AND TPNH

The bulk of hydrogen transport in main-line respiration passes through pyridine nucleotide coenzymes.[22] In this manner, reducing equivalents

TABLE I

SITE AT WHICH VARIOUS COMPOUNDS ENTER THE RESPIRATORY CHAIN[a]

Pyridine nucleotide	Flavoprotein	Unknown
Glyceraldehyde-3-PO$_4$	Succinate	Glucose (*Pseudomonas fluorescens,*
Isocitrate	Fatty acyl-CoA	*Acetobacter suboxydans*)
Pyruvate ⎫	H$_2$?	Gluconate (*Pseudomonas fluorescens*)
α-Ketoglutarate ⎭ via lipoic acid	Lactate (yeast)	Malate (yeast)
Malate	—	α-Glycerophosphate
Lactate	—	Choline
Alcohol	—	—
Aldehydes	—	—
Glucose, glucose-6-PO$_4$	—	—
α-Glycerophosphate	—	—
β-Hydroxybutyrate, β-hydroxy-butyryl-CoA	—	—
Formate	—	—
Glutamate	—	—

[a] See: this chapter as well as H. A. Krebs and H. L. Kornberg *Ergeb. Physiol., biol. Chem. u. exptl. Pharmakol.* **49,** 212 (1957), and T. P. Singer and E. B. Kearney, *in* "The Proteins" (H. Neurath and K. Bailey, eds.), Vol. 2, Part A, p. 123. Academic Press, New York, 1954.

drawn from a wide variety of substrates are funneled through a common pathway to oxygen. The structure of DPN is shown in Fig. 2; triphospho-pyridine nucleotide (TPN) differs only in having a phosphate group on carbon 2 of the ribose linked to adenine. Chemical or enzymic reduction and oxidation take place at the para position[23] and are accompanied by the appearance and disappearance, respectively, of an absorption band at 340 mμ. The absorption change permits spectrophotometric assay of pyridine nucleotide-linked reactions. Classically,[24] the reduction of DPN would be

$$AH_2 \rightarrow A + 2H^+ + 2e \qquad (1a)$$

$$DPN^+ + 2H^+ + 2e \rightarrow DPNH + H^+ \qquad (1b)$$
$$\text{Sum: } \overline{AH_2 + DPN^+ \rightarrow DPNH + A + H^+}$$

formulated as the electron transfer shown in equations (1a) and (1b).

However, a great deal of kinetic, isotopic and spectrophotometric evidence[25, 26] now indicates that the mechanism of pyridine nucleotide dehydrogenase activity involves H transfer within a ternary complex of enzyme, DPN, and substrate. A general formulation is shown in reactions (2a)–(2d). Experiments with deutero-labeled substrates or DPNH (i.e., DPND) have shown[27, 28a] that with many pyridine nucleotide-linked de-

$$E + DPN^+ \rightleftarrows E \cdot DPN^+ \tag{2a}$$

$$E \cdot DPN^+ + AH_2 \rightleftarrows E \cdot DPN^+ \cdot AH_2 \rightleftarrows E \cdot DPNH \cdot A + H^+ \tag{2b}$$

$$E \cdot DPNH \cdot A \rightleftarrows E \cdot DPNH + A \tag{2c}$$

$$\underline{E \cdot DPNH \rightleftarrows E + DPNH} \tag{2d}$$

$$\text{Sum: } DPN^+ + AH_2 \rightleftarrows DPNH + A + H^+$$

hydrogenases there occurs a direct and stereospecific transfer of hydrogen to and from DPN. That is, (1) the hydrogen transferred from substrate or pyridine nucleotide does not equilibrate with protons in the environment and (2) the enzyme catalyzing the transfer shows specificity for the α- or β-side of the pyridine ring. The reduction of DPN by deutero-labeled ethanol is illustrated in Fig. 3. The α and β specificities of a series of de-

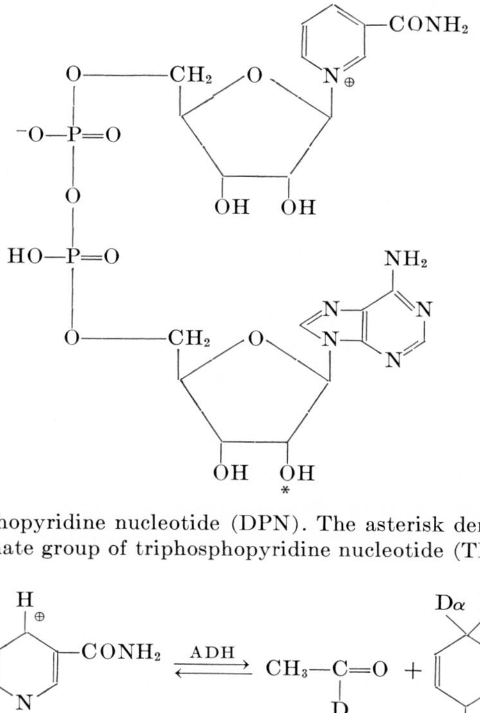

FIG. 2. Diphosphopyridine nucleotide (DPN). The asterisk denotes the position of the third phosphate group of triphosphopyridine nucleotide (TPN).

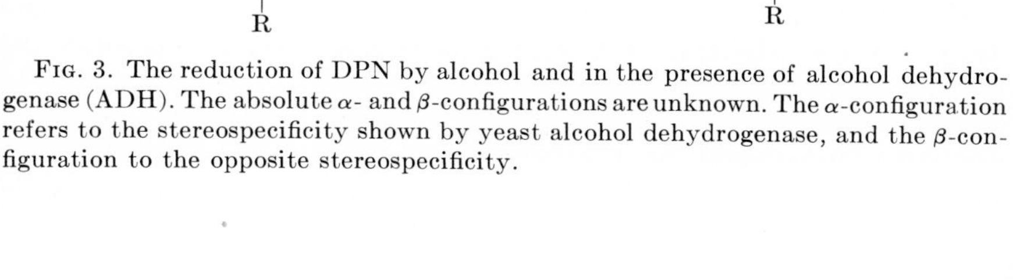

FIG. 3. The reduction of DPN by alcohol and in the presence of alcohol dehydrogenase (ADH). The absolute α- and β-configurations are unknown. The α-configuration refers to the stereospecificity shown by yeast alcohol dehydrogenase, and the β-configuration to the opposite stereospecificity.

hydrogenases have been summarized.[28a] These reactions are properly called hydrogen transfer, since the equivalent of one H atom plus one electron [H· + e] or [H:]⁻ is transferred from donor to acceptor, and equations (1a) and (1b) do not accurately represent the "activation" of either the electron donor or acceptor by the enzyme. If, however, hydrogen transfer from donor to acceptor is mediated by an enzyme-bound, reduced intermediate that has an appreciable acid dissociation, activation of substrate may, in a formal sense,[24] conform to equation (1a). Flavoprotein enzymes such as cytochrome c reductase, succinic dehydrogenase (see below), and dihydroorotic dehydrogenase[28b] may offer examples of the latter mechanism.

2. INTERCONVERSION OF DPNH AND TPNH

Soluble enzymes have been prepared (pyridine nucleotide transhydrogenases) from *Pseudomonas fluorescens*, *P. aeruginosa*, and *Azotobacter* sp.[26] which catalyze the following reactions:

$$TPNH + DPN^+ \rightleftarrows TPN^+ + DPNH \tag{3a}$$

$$DPNH + {}^*DPN^+ \rightleftarrows DPN^+ + {}^*DPNH \tag{3b}$$

The reversal of reaction (3a) requires 2′-adenylic acid; reaction (3b) was demonstrated with nicotinamide-labeled DPN. By means of reaction (3a), TPN-specific dehydrogenases can be linked to DPNH formation. Since evidence from animal systems indicates that TPNH and DPNH may be reoxidized by different pathways, with only DPNH oxidation resulting in oxidative phosphorylation, transhydrogenases may be of importance in regulating energy metabolism.[29] It has also been suggested that transhydrogenase enzymes may be required for the reduction of particle-bound DPN by free DPNH.[26] Transhydrogenase enzymes of animal origin are particle-bound and have somewhat different properties from the bacterial enzymes.[30] Bacterial transhydrogenase catalyzes direct and stereospecific H transfer. A soluble transhydrogenase from placenta[31a] which catalyzes reaction (3a) in a freely reversible manner requires small amounts of a steroid hormone as cofactor, a finding which has obvious implications for metabolic control mechanisms. The transhydrogenase activity of mitochondria, however, does not appear to be a steroid-dependent reaction.[31b]

3. OXIDATION OF DPNH BY MOLECULAR OXYGEN

Particulate systems for the oxidation of DPNH by oxygen are assumed to have the general composition [(DPN)–flavoprotein–cytochromes–cytochrome oxidase]. These oxidases have been studied extensively in animal systems (reviewed by Chance[3]) and beginnings have been made with bacteria. The over-all reaction conforms to equation (4), and involves a

$$2DPNH + 2H^+ + O_2 \rightarrow 2DPN^+ + 2H_2O \qquad (4)$$

$$4H^+ + 4e + O_2 \rightarrow 2H_2O \qquad (5)$$

four-electron transfer, as shown in equation (5). This balance has been documented for animal systems[32, 33] and is presumed to express the stoichiometry for apparently similar bacterial systems, although balances are not always presented. Particulate cytochrome-containing DPNH oxidases have been reported in *Azotobacter vinelandii*,[16, 34, 35] *Escherichia coli*,[36] *Pseudomonas fluorescens*,[37] *Mycobacterium tuberculosis*,[38a] *Alcaligenes faecalis*,[38b] and *Mycobacterium phlei*.[39] Other reports of particulate preparations (yeast, *Proteus*, *Aerobacter*),[40] *Serratia marcescens*,[41] and *Bacillus megaterium*[5] do not mention DPNH oxidation specifically; however, the fact that these preparations catalyze the oxidation of several Krebs cycle intermediates and other pyridine nucleotide-linked substrates suggests that DPNH oxidases of the type under consideration here may be present in the latter organisms. It should be emphasized, however, that conclusions regarding specific mechanisms should not be drawn merely from the fact that bacterial and mammalian DPNH oxidases resemble each other in gross composition.

III. Subdivision of the Respiratory Chain

A. Reduction of Cytochrome System by Reduced Pyridine Nucleotides

1. Relation to Flavin

The sequence in which the bound catalysts operate in mammalian mitochondrial preparations has been deduced in several ways[3] (oxidation-reduction potential of components; inhibitor studies; kinetics of oxidation and reduction of individual components, using sensitive spectrophotometric techniques; studies of partial reactions, catalyzed by soluble components, or by mixtures of soluble and particulate preparations). Since relatively few components have been put into true solution, the classic techniques of enzyme chemistry, which involve studies of single steps, each catalyzed by a separate enzyme, are not fully applicable. The concept has arisen[2, 42] that particulate systems can be fragmented in specific ways to give particle subunits of relatively constant composition and enzyme activity. Ideally, fragmentation would result in the preparation of truly soluble components: (a) enzymes catalyzing the reduction of one or more cytochromes, (b) a series of soluble cytochrome components, and (c) a terminal (cytochrome) oxidase. According to current concepts, therefore, the soluble respiratory catalysts that have been isolated are presumed to have arisen from particulate oxidases. Strict application of this concept, especially to bacterial systems, may not be warranted, however. The question of the origin of a given enzyme may be difficult to deduce and should be carefully evaluated for each system. It is possible, for instance, that some of the bacterial respiratory systems will require the participation, at one or more points, of enzymes that are "normally" soluble.

Among the animal systems, cytochrome c and cytochrome c reductases[3] have been obtained in soluble form; among the microorganisms, various cytochrome reductases (Table II) and a series of soluble cytochromes (Chapters 7 and 8) have been prepared.

Enzyme-bound flavin was first implicated in the early steps of electron transport to oxygen or to iron carriers by the work of Warburg and Christian[43] and of Theorell.[44] This work will be considered in more detail in Chapter 9. The structure of riboflavin and reduced riboflavin is shown in Fig. 4. In its functional form, riboflavin occurs either as FMN (flavin mononucleotide) or FAD (flavin adenine dinucleotide). FMN has a phosphate group on the 5′-ribityl moiety of riboflavin; in FAD, 5′-adenylic acid is combined in a pyrophosphate linkage with FMN. The discovery and chemistry of these compounds have been reviewed.[45, 46]

Many flavoproteins are now known.[46] The bacterial flavoproteins not concerned primarily with cytochrome reduction are discussed in Chapter 9. Proof of flavoprotein catalysis requires either (a) isolation of the pure enzyme in amounts sufficient to demonstrate the flavin component, or (b) demonstration of reversible inactivation of the enzyme by removal and readdition of the flavin component.[45] The latter approach is not always possible since some flavoproteins may be inactivated at the acid pH needed for removal of the bound flavin or, in some cases, because the reformation of active enzyme appears to require special conditions.[47] Flavoproteins vary widely in the tenacity with which they bind the flavin moiety and vary from nitrate reductase of *Neurospora*,[48] in which the flavin dissociates spontaneously during enzyme purification, to succinic dehydrogenase,[19] in which the flavin is combined with the protein by strong, presumably covalent, linkages. The absorption spectra of free flavins are shown in Fig. 5. On chemical reduction by hydrosulfite, the yellow color of the flavin is discharged and the absorbance of the 450-mμ band decreases approximately 90%. Similar results are obtained with various flavoproteins;[46] however, with some flavoprotein enzymes, addition of substrate results in incomplete reduction of the 450-mμ band and formation of a new band in the long wavelength region.[49, 50] The latter changes indicate the formation of enzyme substrate complexes which in some systems may have a free radical nature.[49, 51]

Evidence that flavoproteins are concerned in the reduction of cytochrome c came from the demonstration that highly purified cytochrome c reduc-

TABLE II

CELL-FREE PYRIDINE NUCLEOTIDE-CYTOCHROME REDUCTASE SYSTEMS FROM MICROORGANISMS

Organism	Reductant	Cytochrome	Prosthetic group or cofactors	TON[a] Crude enzyme	TON[a] Purified enzyme	Reference
Azotobacter vinelandii[b]	DPNH	Azotobacter $c_4 + c_5$	—	—	—	61
Mycobacterium phlei (1)	DPNH	Mammalian c	$FAD,^d FMN^e$	—	—	62
Mycobacterium phlei (2)	DPNH	Mammalian c	Menadione	—	—	62
Pseudomonas denitrificans	DPNH	P. denitrificans c	—	—	—	63
Micrococcus denitrificans	DPNH	M. denitrificans or horse heart c	—	—	—	63
		M. denitrificans b_1				
Escherichia coli	DPNH	Mammalian c	FAD	~0.15	—	63
Acetobacter peroxidans	TPNH	Mammalian c	—	—	4.5	64
Achromobacter fischeri	DPNH	Mammalian c	FMN + menadione	—	—	65
Streptococcus faecalis	DPNH	Mammalian c	FAD	0.20–0.40	—	66
Lactobacillus delbrueckii	DPNH	Mammalian c		0.03	—	—[f]
Clostridium perfringens[c]	DPNH	Mammalian c	FAD + unidentified flavin	0.30	11.5 (3700)	67–69
Clostridium kluyveri	DPNH	Mammalian c	—	—	—	70
Rhodospirillum rubrum	DPNH	Mammalian or R. rubrum c	—	—	—	71
Rhodopseudomonas spheroides	DPNH	Mammalian c	—	—	—	71
Chromatium						
Chlorobium limicola						
Streptomyces fradiae	DPNH	S. fradiae b	—	—	—	72
	TPNH					72
Yeast	TPNH	Mammalian c	FMN	~0.015	8.65 (650)	52
Neurospora crassa	TPNH	Mammalian c	FAD, FMN	—	—	73

[a] TON = μmoles of reduced pyridine nucleotide oxidized per minute per milligram protein, under similar experimental conditions (initial rates). Values in parentheses are μmoles of reduced pyridine nucleotide oxidized per minute per μmole of bound flavin.

[b] Particulate enzyme.

[c] This enzyme is also a DPNH oxidase. See Chapter 9.

[d] FAD (flavin adenine dinucleotide).

[e] FMN (flavin mononucleotide).

[f] M. I. Dolin, unpublished.

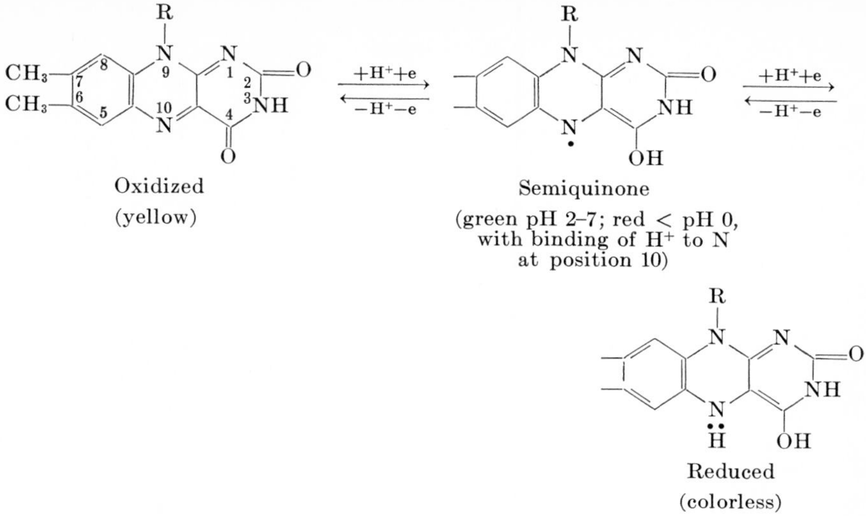

CH_3- ... N ... N ... O
CH_3- ... NH
Oxidized
(yellow)

$\xrightarrow{+H^++e}$ $\xleftarrow{-H^+-e}$

R ... N ... N ... O
... NH
$\overset{\bullet}{N}$
OH
Semiquinone
(green pH 2–7; red < pH 0,
with binding of H^+ to N
at position 10)

$\xrightarrow{+H^++e}$ $\xleftarrow{-H^+-e}$

R ... N ... N ... O
NH
$\overset{..}{\underset{H}{N}}$ ... OH
Reduced
(colorless)

FIG. 4. Reduction of riboflavin. After L. Michaelis, M. P. Schubert, and C. V. Smythe, *J. Biol. Chem.* **116,** 587 (1936).

KEY: For riboflavin, $R = -CH_2-(CHOH)_3-CH_2OH$.
For FMN, $R = -CH_2-(CHOH)_3-CH_2OPO_3H_2$.

For FAD, $R = -CH_2-(CHOH)_3-CH_2O-\overset{\overset{O}{\|}}{\underset{OH}{P}}-O-\overset{\overset{O}{\|}}{\underset{OH}{P}}-O-$adenosine.

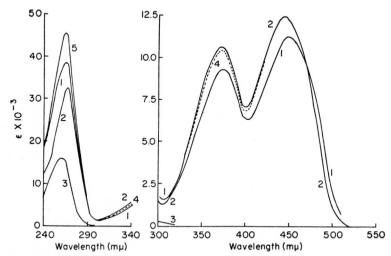

FIG. 5. Absorption spectra of flavins and of AMP. 1, FAD; 2, riboflavin; 3, AMP; 4, FMN (interrupted line); 5, theoretical spectrum of AMP + FMN; between 290 and 510 mμ the theoretical spectrum is the same as the spectrum of FMN. From L. G. Whitby, *Biochem. J.* **54,** 437(1953).

tases[46, 52, 53] (enzymes that catalyze cytochrome c reduction, but that do not react at any appreciable rate with oxygen) contain flavin prosthetic groups. The reaction catalyzed by these enzymes can be formulated as follows:

$$PNH + H^+ + FP \rightarrow FPH_2 + PN^+ \tag{6a}$$

$$FPH_2 + 2 \text{ cyt. c } (Fe^{+++}) \rightarrow FP + 2 \text{ cyt. c } (Fe^{++}) + 2H^+ \tag{6b}$$

Sum: $PNH + 2 \text{ cyt. c } (Fe^{+++}) \rightarrow PN^+ + 2 \text{ cyt. c } (Fe^{++}) + H^+$

This reaction sequence is not intended to show the mechanism, but merely to indicate over-all stoichiometry. It is with reactions of this type that the link between two-electron and one-electron transport takes place, since two reducing equivalents from reduced flavoprotein are transferred to one-electron acceptors. It has been postulated[54] that such transfers to one-electron acceptors are specifically catalyzed by metalloflavoproteins (those that contain a metal in addition to a flavin prosthetic group, i.e., the iron-containing cytochrome c reductase of pig heart.[55] Ordinary flavoproteins were thought to catalyze only two-electron transport. However, it is now known that various flavoproteins which do not contain significant amounts of metals[49, 50] are capable of catalyzing efficient one-electron transfer reactions. Recent spectrophotometric[56] and potentiometric[57] evidence extends and confirms the theory of Michaelis[58a] that oxidation and reduction of flavin (as well as other redox dyes) involves the formation of a semiquinone, as shown in Fig. 4. This one-electron intermediate is presumed to facilitate the link between two- and one-electron transfer reactions. (It has been pointed out, however,[58b] that the occurrence of a one-electron intermediate does not necessarily implicate it in the mechanism of electron transfer. The sequiquinone may form through dismutation of one fully reduced and one fully oxidized molecule.) Beinert has presented spectrophotometric evidence that semiquinoid intermediates may form not only with free flavin[56] but also with enzyme-bound flavin.[59] Another mechanism for linking flavoprotein oxidation to cytochrome reduction would require the binding of two cytochrome molecules to one molecule of cytochrome reductase.

The reaction between reduced pyridine nucleotide and cytochrome c reductase appears to be stereospecific. With DPNH-cytochrome c reductase of pig heart it has been shown that both the oxidation of DPNH by cytochrome c and an exchange reaction that takes place between DPNH and D_2O are specific for the βH of the pyridine ring.[60] The exchange reaction suggests that the "activation" of DPNH by cytochrome reductases may be represented formally by the reversal of equation (1b).

2. Soluble Cytochrome Reductases from Microorganisms

The first cytochrome reductase obtained in highly purified form was isolated from yeast[52] (mol. wt. 75,000 on basis of 1 bound flavin per mole enzyme). FMN is the bound flavin and TPNH the reductant. Although many cytochrome c reductase *activities* have been reported in bacteria, few enzymes have been extensively purified and the latter have been obtained in relatively dilute solution. The difficulties involved in preparing large amounts of purified enzyme from bacterial sources has been mentioned. Table II lists various pyridine nucleotide-cytochrome c reductase activities that have been found in microorganisms. These reactions were demonstrated with cell-free enzymes and soluble cytochrome components. Turnover numbers are recorded for the purified enzymes (yeast, *E. coli*, *Clostridium perfringens*); it will be noted that the activity of the bacterial enzymes compares very favorably with that of the yeast reductase. In fact, on a protein or flavin basis, the turnover of the enzyme obtained from the obligate anaerobe *C. perfringens* exceeds that of the yeast enzyme. The activity of the *Clostridium kluyveri* enzyme is also reported to be high.[26] Since clostridia and *Streptococcus faecalis* do not contain cytochromes, the presence in these organisms of potent cytochrome c reductases indicates that the occurrence of such enzymes in any given system does not, in itself, furnish evidence for the existence of a functional cytochrome-linked respiratory system. The relation of these findings to the physiology of cytochrome-free facultative and obligate anaerobes will be considered in Chapter 9.

Mammalian cytochrome c, which is readily available, has been used as the oxidant for most of the reactions shown in Table II. Results obtained in this way can be misleading, however, since bacteria may show preferential activity toward their own cytochromes.[7] Some of the recently isolated soluble bacterial b and c cytochromes have been tested, as shown, but little information about the nature of the reductases is available.

3. Artificial or Model Cytochrome Reductases

In addition to the enzymes which resemble the original yeast reductase, various artificial cytochrome reductases can be reconstructed. These reactions depend upon the fact that cytochrome c can be reduced nonenzymically by reduced compounds, such as hydroquinone,[74] reduced menadione,[66] free reduced flavins,[75, 76] reduced phospho- or silicomolybdate,[77] and slowly by ferrous citrate chelates.[78] Therefore, enzymes which can catalyze the reduction of these compounds, with reduced pyridine nucleotide as electron donor, can also cause pyridine nucleotide-dependent cytochrome reduction. Such enzymes are the quinone and menadione reductases of *E. coli*,[79] the menadione reductase of *M. phlei*,[62] and the flavin-dependent menadione reductases of *S. faecalis*[80] and *Achromobacter fischeri*.[66] Quinones, in general, may act as electron acceptors for a variety of flavoproteins.[81] Free flavin can serve as acceptor for DPNH oxidation in crude extracts of *C. perfringens*[67, 82] and *C. kluyveri*.[70] Various flavoproteins, including the diaphorase of *P. fluorescens*, can catalyze the reduction of ferric citrate chelates.[78] (Aldehyde dehydrogenase can use phospho- or silicomolybdates as electron acceptors and thereby cause cytochrome c reduction;[77] pyridine nucleotide-dependent reduction, in such a system, has not been reported.) Reduction of noncytochrome iron (Fe^{+++}, methemoglobin, ferric 8-hydroxy-quinoline chelate)[76] and ferric citrate[78] can also be achieved through free reduced flavin and therefore through enzymes that can reduce free flavin. Pig heart diaphorase (recently identified as lipoic dehydrogenase[83]) catalyzes cytochrome c reduction by DPNH in the presence of lipoic acid. The lipoic dehydrogenase reaction (Chapter 9) yields reduced lipoic acid which, presumably in a spontaneous reaction, reduces cytochrome c.

As an example of one model reaction, the menadione-dependent reduction of cytochrome c[62, 66, 81] is shown in equations (7a) and (7b).

$$DPNH + H^+ + \text{menadione} \rightarrow DPN^+ + \text{menadione} \cdot H_2 \qquad (7a)$$

$$\text{menadione} \cdot H_2 + 2 \text{ cytochrome c } (Fe^{+++}) \rightarrow$$

$$\underline{\qquad\qquad\qquad \text{menadione} + 2 \text{ cytochrome c } (Fe^{++}) + 2H^+} \quad (7b)$$

$$\text{Sum: } DPNH + 2 \text{ cytochrome c } (Fe^{+++}) \rightarrow$$

$$DPN^+ + 2 \text{ cytochrome c } (Fe^{++}) + H^+ \qquad (7c)$$

The artificial reactions, in general, show low activity compared to the purified cytochrome reductases; some of the menadione reductases, however, support rapid cytochrome reduction.

These reactions may have no physiological significance, except as possible bypasses (Sections IV, C and VI, A), although it is tempting to think that menadione (vitamin K_3) may act in some cases as a water-soluble model for vitamin K, and not merely as a nonspecific quinone. Vitamin K is found in many bacterial species[84] and has been directly implicated in the respiratory chain of *M. phlei*.[12, 39] The site of action has not yet been established, however, with a mammalian respiratory chain preparation, reduced menadione apparently reacts at the flavoprotein level[85] and does not spontaneously reduce bound cytochromes.

The biological consequence of some of these model reactions is illustrated by the luminescent system of *A. fischeri*. Compounds which reoxidize reduced flavin spontaneously (cytochrome c, Fe^{+++}, methemoglobin) inhibit luminescence by competing with the luciferase for $FMNH_2$.[76]

4. Other Components of Cytochrome Reductase

Purified pig heart cytochrome c reductase[55] contains nonheme iron; α-tocopherol has been identified in solubilized beef heart DPN-cytochrome c reductase.[86] There is no information on the occurrence of bound metals or fat-soluble vitamins in the purified bacterial reductases.

B. Terminal Oxidases

Reducing equivalents from flavoprotein are transferred through the cytochrome system in a series of one-electron steps. These reactions, which comprise true electron transport, involve a ferri-ferro cycle for each of the intermediate cytochrome components. The oxidation-reduction reactions can be followed by spectrophotometric observation of the characteristic cytochrome bands (see Chapter 7). Chance[87] believes that thermal collisions between neighboring cytochromes can account for the observed kinetics of electron transport in this region of the respiratory chain. The ultimate

$$4 \text{ cyt. c (Fe}^{++}) + O_2 + 4H^+ \xrightarrow{\text{cyt. oxidase}} 4 \text{ cyt. c (Fe}^{+++}) + 2H_2O \qquad (8)$$

cytochrome component (cytochrome c oxidase in mammalian and yeast systems)[6] can react with oxygen and catalyze the four-electron reduction of O_2 to $2H_2O$, as shown in equation (8).

Possible mechanisms for reaction (8) have been considered.[3, 17, 88] Briefly, these require either (a) a series of 4 one-electron steps with free radical forms of oxygen as intermediates, (b) a two-electron reduction of oxygen to a peroxide, followed by a two-electron reduction of the peroxide to $2H_2O$—higher valence states of the iron, i.e., Fe^{4+}, may occur in this reaction, (c) participation of a tetraheme cytochrome c oxidase in a simultaneous four-electron reduction of oxygen.

Cytochrome c oxidase from mammalian sources has not been obtained in true solution, although the enzyme can be "solubilized" in deoxycholate and various particulate preparations have been studied.[89] Particulate preparations with cytochrome oxidase activity have also been obtained from yeast[6] and bacteria; "soluble" or at least small particle preparations have been described for P. aeruginosa and Azotobacter vinelandii (Table III).

Table III summarizes the characteristics of various bacterial cytochrome c oxidase preparations. It is rather difficult at present to assess the significance of these reactions since the turnover of some, at least, of these enzyme preparations appears to be too low to account for the respiration of the intact organism. The discrepancies may, in part, be traced to technical difficulties in the assay procedure. If it is assumed that the oxidase reactions that have been demonstrated constitute a major physiological pathway and that the enzymes have not been damaged in preparation, low activity

TABLE III

CYTOCHROME c OXIDASES OF BACTERIA

Organism	Enzyme preparation	Reduced substrate	Inhibitors	Spectral identification	TON[a]	Reference
Azotobacter vinelandii	Particulate preparation (WLP)	A. vinelandii cyt. c_4 (not mammalian cyt. c)	—	Cyt. a_2 + CO binding pigment of Chance et al.[?6]	0.33 (c_4)	71, 61, 35
Azotobacter vinelandii	Soluble extract, 5-fold purified	Azotobacter cyt. c_4 + c_5 (horse heart cyt. c is ⅛ as active)	CN, azide, CO (CO inhibition reversed by light)	—	0.05–0.26 ($c_4 + c_5$)	90
Pseudomonas aeruginosa	Cyt.$_{GB}$, soluble purified enzyme	P. aeruginosa cyt. 551 and "blue protein" (low activity on mammalian and yeast cyt. c)	CN, CO (partial reversal of CO inhibition by light)	An "a" type cytochrome? a_1 or a_2 ?	—	91
Pseudomonas denitrificans	Extract of organism	P. denitrificans cyt. c	CN	—	—	63
Micrococcus denitrificans	Extract of organism, purified 16-fold (particulate)	M. denitrificans cyt. c, horse heart cyt. c	CN, azide, CO (light reversal of CO inhibition)	? No cyt. a_3 absorption in purified enzyme	0.12	63, 92
Rhodospirillum rubrum	Extract of organism (particulate)	Mammalian cyt. c, R. rubrum cyt. c	CN, azide	—	0.015	71
Rhodopseudomonas spheroides	Extract of organism	Mammalian cyt. c	—	—	0.04	71
Chromatium	Extract of organism	Mammalian cyt. c	—	—	0.002	71
Chlorobium limicola	Extract of organism	Mammalian cyt. c	—	—	0.004	71

[a] TON = μmoles of O_2 reduced to H_2O per minute per milligram protein. These values may be approximate since different cytochrome c concentrations were used in the assays reported. Also, turnovers may not be accurate if cytochrome c is inhibitory (see text). Letters in parentheses in this column represent the reduced cytochrome used as substrate. In other cases, reduced mammalian cytochrome c was used.

may be explicable on the following grounds. (*a*) The specific substrate for the oxidase may not always be available (specificity for bacterial cytochromes is illustrated in Table III). The absence in a variety of cytochrome-containing bacteria[6] of oxidases for reduced mammalian cytochrome c may be understandable on this basis. (*b*) If bacterial cytochrome oxidases resemble the mammalian counterpart, the reactions will show first-order kinetics for all reasonable concentrations of cytochrome c; however, the rate constant will decrease with increasing cytochrome c (reduced or oxidized) concentration.[93] The inhibition reaction makes it difficult to extrapolate back to the situation in intact cells and to calculate the "true" turnover characteristic of the bound cytochrome and cytochrome oxidase components. (*c*) If some of the bacterial cytochrome oxidases that have been prepared resemble the relatively intact mammalian respiratory particle, special "opening" techniques[2] may have to be used in order to facilitate contact between an exogenous cytochrome component and the bound cytochrome oxidase.

It has been pointed out[7] that even when cytochrome oxidase activity is demonstrable, the reaction may not be direct (as shown in equation 8), but may consist of a series of model reactions in which some autoxidizable component other than the classic cytochrome oxidase is the terminal catalyst.

Artificial substrates such as *p*-phenylenediamine or *p*-phenylenediamine plus α-naphthol (Nadi reagent) are sometimes used as reductants of the cytochrome c-cytochrome oxidase system; however, the nonspecificity of this reaction, when used as a criterion for cytochrome oxidase activity, has been emphasized.[6]

"Typical" cytochrome c oxidases are inhibited by CN, azide, and CO.[3, 6] Classically, the spectrophotometric identification of a terminal oxidase is made by examining the action spectrum for reversal of CO inhibition[87] by light. If the latter corresponds with the photochemical dissociation spectrum of the CO-inhibited system, the spectrum is that of the CO compound of the oxidase. Although many bacterial oxidases are inhibited by typical cytochrome oxidase inhibitors, there is much variability in inhibition pattern and in the extent of CO inhibition and its reversibility by light.[6] Spectrophotometric techniques[6] have demonstrated that: (*a*) Yeast contains a cytochrome of the classic a_3 type. (*b*) *Bacillus subtilis* contains a cytochrome closely resembling cytochrome a_3, but the organism has no oxidase activity for reduced mammalian cytochrome c. It is questionable whether any bacteria yet examined contain the classic cytochrome a_3. (*c*) The terminal oxidase of *Acetobacter pasteurianum* appears to be cytochrome a_1. (*d*) A variety of bacteria may use an enzyme similar to the *Rhodospirillum* heme protein (RHP)[7, 94] as a terminal oxidase. The latter enzyme has been obtained in soluble, purified form from *R. rubrum* and appears to be an autoxidizable variant of cytochrome c.[94] RHP can be reduced by mammalian cytochrome c reductase; however, the physiological reductant is unknown. Apparently it is an open question whether autoxidation of RHP results in the formation of water or peroxide.[7] Since the enzyme does not form complexes with CN or azide, it cannot account for the cyanide sensitive terminal oxidase activities that have been reported.

Several autoxidizable CN-insensitive cytochrome b components have been found in bacteria[63, 72] but the extent to which they may be able to function as terminal oxidases is not known. The possible function of flavoproteins as direct oxidases for reduced pyridine nucleotide will be considered in Section VI.

C. SUBSTRATES AS REDUCTANTS OF THE RESPIRATORY CHAIN

1. SUCCINATE OXIDATION

One member of the citric acid cycle, succinate, enters the cytochrome chain at the flavoprotein level (Fig. 1). Succinate oxidation has been studied extensively with various particulate preparations;[3] however, Singer and Kearney showed that the primary dehydrogenase (assayed with phenazine methosulfate as electron acceptor) can easily be isolated in soluble form from many sources.[19] The enzyme, highly purified from beef heart or yeast[19] is an iron-flavoprotein (mol. wt. $\sim$200,000; 4 nonheme iron atoms and 1 mole of flavin per mole enzyme). The flavin (FAD or derivative thereof) is covalently linked to the protein. Succinic dehydrogenase (animal and yeast) also functions as a fumarate reductase. With the proper reductants (e.g., $FMNH_2$ or various leuco dyes) the enzyme catalyzes fumarate reduction to succinate. Catalysis is more rapid, however, in the direction of succinate oxidation. Particulate heart preparations will, under anaerobic conditions, catalyze a fumarate-stimulated, nonstereospecific exchange between the methylene hydrogens of succinate and deuterium of D_2O.[95a] This exchange is probably best explained by the reversibility of the succinic

$$\text{succinate} + E \rightleftarrows \text{fumarate} + E \cdot H_2 \qquad (9)$$

dehydrogenase reaction, as shown in equation (9), since reduced enzyme could exchange protons with water (see discussion Gutfreund[95b]).

Succinic dehydrogenase has also been purified from the obligate anaerobe *Micrococcus lactilyticus*.[96, 97] The enzyme is an iron-flavoprotein containing 1 mole of FAD and 40 atoms of nonheme iron per 460,000 g. of protein (mol. wt. several million). The flavin, unlike that of the yeast and animal enzymes, is easily removed on heating. Reversibility of the bacterial succinic dehydrogenase can be demonstrated with $FMNH_2$ or leucomethylviologen as reductants and, in fact, the reaction is more rapid in the direction of fumarate reduction. A soluble succinic dehydrogenase from the facultative anaerobe, *Propionibacterium pentosaceum*,[98] falls between the aerobic and anaerobic systems with regard to ease of reversibility The interesting suggestion has been made [96, 98, 99] that the ratio of succinic dehydrogenase to fumarate reductase activity varies from one succinic dehydrogenase to another in accordance with the physiological requirements of the system from which the enzyme is obtained. Aerobes catalyze predominantly succinate oxidation; anaerobes, fumarate reduction. The latter reaction is important since fumarate can serve as electron acceptor for many anaerobic dehydrogenations.[100]

There is at present no evidence for a catalytic role for nonheme iron in the purified succinic dehydrogenases.[97, 101] The physiological electron acceptor for the primary dehydrogenase is unknown, although by analogy to the particulate animal systems[3] a heme protein of the cytochrome b type might be implicated in an early step. Studies with various bacterial enzyme preparations (*Corynebacterium diphtheriae*,[102] *Bacterium tularense*,[103] and *Propionibacterium pentosaceum*)[98] also suggest the participation of a b-type cytochrome in succinate oxidation.

Succinate oxidation has been studied in particulate preparations obtained from many different bacteria, among them *Salmonella aertrycke*,[104] *C. diphtheriae*,[102] *Mycobacterium avium*,[105] *M. tuberculosis*,[38a] *E. coli*[36, 99] and *Azotobacter vinelandii*.[16, 35] Soluble dehydrogenases have been isolated from *Proteus vulgaris*,[106] *A. vinelandii*,[107] and *B. tularense*.[103] The primary dehydrogenase of these systems has not been purified.

2. YEAST LACTIC DEHYDROGENASE

Yeast lactic dehydrogenase catalyzes the oxidation of lactate to pyruvate, with cytochrome c as electron acceptor. Thus the enzyme is quite different from the pyridine nucleotide-linked lactic dehydrogenases derived from many animal and bacterial sources.[46] The yeast enzyme, which has been highly purified[21] and crystallized[20] from bakers yeast resembles succinic dehydrogenase in being an iron-flavoprotein; however, the lactic enzyme, unlike succinic dehydrogenase, contains bound cytochrome b_2 in addition to nonheme iron. Highly purified lactic dehydrogenase[21] contains, per 230,000 g. protein, 1 mole of FMN, 1 mole of cytochrome b_2, and 8 atoms of nonheme iron. This composition suggests that the enzyme represents a solubilized portion of the respiratory chain. The yeast enzyme, with its bound flavin and heme acceptors, is poised mainly for unidirectional lactate oxidation; however, some reversibility can be shown with $FMNH_2$ as reductant.[21] With the pyridine nucleotide-linked lactic dehydrogenases, on the other hand, the equilibrium at neutral pH favors pyruvate reduction by DPNH, although easy reversibility can be demonstrated at alkaline pH.

From a teleological point of view, the two types of dehydrogenase were designed for different purposes (see Section VII).

3. Oxidation of Glucose, Gluconate, Pyruvate

There is at present no evidence for the existence of enzymes which directly transfer electrons from organic compounds to a cytochrome component. As mentioned previously, it is possible that the succinate and lactate oxidations discussed above are models for the mechanism by which dehydrogenations that are not pyridine nucleotide-dependent are coupled to the cytochrome chain. The link between substrate and cytochrome may be mediated by flavin, or perhaps by as yet undiscovered carriers. These considerations may apply to the following reactions.

A soluble, extensively purified enzyme that catalyzes the oxidation of gluconic acid to 2-ketogluconic acid has been isolated from *P. fluorescens*.[108] The purified enzyme contains a cytochrome b-like pigment and utilizes one-electron acceptors such as cytochrome c and ferricyanide as oxidants. Glucose oxidation to gluconic acid has been studied in particulate preparations from *P. fluorescens*[37, 108] and in a deoxycholate "solubilized" cytochrome-containing enzyme preparation from *Acetobacter suboxydans*.[109]

Bacterial pyruvate oxidase systems of the classic animal type are DPN-linked;[110] however, a non-DPN-linked pyruvic dehydrogenase has been isolated from *Proteus vulgaris*.[111] This enzyme couples pyruvate oxidation to the reduction of a particulate, autoxidizable cytochrome system. Reduction of endogenous cytochrome by substrate can be demonstrated for the *Pseudomonas*, *Acetobacter* and *Proteus* systems. The mediator(s) between substrate and cytochrome are unknown.

Escherichia coli contains, in addition to the animal type of pyruvate oxidase system, a soluble pyruvic dehydrogenase which can couple the oxidation of pyruvate to the reduction of a particulate, cytochrome-containing system.[110] With an acetate-requiring mutant of *E. coli*, the soluble dehydrogenase has been shown to be a flavoprotein. This system is described in Chapter 9, Section VI,B.

D. Inorganic Reductants of the Respiratory Chain

1. Hydrogen Gas

Hydrogen gas is used as a reductant by a wide variety of autotrophic and heterotrophic bacteria. The literature is much too extensive to be reviewed here (see the reveiw of Gest[112] and paper of Peck *et al.*[113] for a review of hydrogen activation mechanisms). Hydrogenase is the enzyme presumed to function in the evolution or utilization of H_2, as shown in equation (10).

$$H_2 \rightleftarrows 2\ H^+ + 2e \qquad (10)$$

The enzyme appears to be particulate in several aerobes and facultative anaerobes and soluble in various clostridia. There is as yet no general agreement as to what constitutes a valid assay for the primary hydrogenase enzyme (the immediate activator of H_2 or acceptor of electrons from hydrogen gas). The exchange between D_2O and H_2 or the ortho- to parahydrogen conversion, both of which are enzyme-catalyzed reactions, have been suggested as primary assays. For several of the soluble hydrogenases, there are reports that the primary enzymes may be metallo-flavoproteins.[114-117] The acceptors that function subsequent to the primary step vary with the nature of the system under consideration—that is with the kinds of coupling reactions that exist between hydrogenase and the ultimate oxidant. Flavins, pyridine nucleotides, exogenous and endogenous cytochromes, fumarate, and nitrate will act as electron acceptors for one or another of the enzyme systems. Oxygen will serve as an ultimate oxidant for the hydrogen bacteria, *Azotobacter* and *E. coli*. One- or two-electron dyes are routinely used as oxidants in assay systems.

2. THIOSULFATE, SULFITE, NITRITE

It appears from recent work that the respiratory catalysts involved in the oxidation and reduction of sulfur and nitrogen-containing inorganic compounds may be entirely analagous to those that function in organic metabolism. Thus, work with the autotroph *Thiobacillus denitrificans* indicates that a cytochrome of the c-type is part of the respiratory chain that functions in the oxidation of thiosulfate or sulfite.[118] The cytochrome has been isolated and purified. Experiments with intact cells of *Nitrobacter* suggest that a cytochrome absorbing at 551 mμ is involved in nitrite oxidation.[119] Nitrite-oxidizing ability of the cells is directly proportional to their content of the cytochrome component. Inorganic sulfur and nitrogen containing oxidants of the cytochrome chain will be considered in Section IV,B.

IV. Oxidants of the Respiratory Chain Other Than O_2

A. HYDROGEN PEROXIDE

There is evidence that hydrogen peroxide may serve as the ultimate oxidant of the cytochrome chain in bakers yeast,[120, 121] *Acetobacter peroxidans*,[122-124] and *Pseudomonas fluorescens*.[125] The first evidence on this point came when a peroxidase for reduced cytochrome c was isolated and highly purified from yeast.[120] The enzyme, which contains an iron protoporphyrin prosthetic group, was reported to be rather specific for cytochrome c as substrate. Chance,[126] however, reports that typical peroxidase substrates, such as p-phenylenediamine, can be oxidized by the enzyme and, further, that the classic peroxidases of plant and animal origin also have high activity with reduced cytochrome c as substrate. In addition, he has shown that in intact respiring yeast, exogenous H_2O_2 is utilized even more rapidly than oxygen for the oxidation of reduced endogenous cytochrome c.[121]

Acetobacter peroxidans[122-124] can use H_2O_2 as the oxidant for several substrates, including H_2. A cytochrome peroxidase mechanism may be present in these cells.[123] A cytochrome c peroxidase has been isolated from *P. fluorescens*;[125] the partially purified enzyme contains a cytochrome c pigment, however, the prosthetic group of the peroxidase itself is unidentified. Since *P. fluorescens* appears to contain a flavoprotein DPNH oxidase, it has been suggested that the following sequence of reactions describes the respiratory system of the organism.

$$DPNH + H^+ + O_2 \rightarrow H_2O_2 + DPN^+ \text{ (DPNH oxidase)} \tag{11a}$$

$$DPNH + 2 \text{ cyt. c } (Fe^{+++}) \rightarrow$$
$$DPN^+ + 2 \text{ cyt. c } (Fe^{++}) + H^+ \text{ (cyt. c reductase)} \tag{11b}$$

$$2 \text{ cyt. c } (Fe^{++}) + 2H^+ + H_2O_2 \rightarrow$$
$$\underline{\qquad\qquad 2 \text{ cyt. c } (Fe^{+++}) + 2 H_2O \text{ (cyt. c peroxidase)}} \tag{11c}$$

Sum: $2 DPNH + 2H^+ + O_2 \rightarrow 2H_2O + 2DPN^+$

This scheme, which may be taken as a model for peroxidase-mediated respiration, illustrates one difficulty involved in trying to assess the physiological significance of iron-porphyrin peroxidases, namely, in order for the enzyme to function, a source of peroxide must be present. As shown in the scheme, the source is generally attributed to the autoxidation of flavoproteins. The question which has not yet been satisfactorily answered for any of the cytochrome-containing organisms is the extent to which such autoxidation reactions may fulfill the requirement of a peroxide-generating system. In yeast[121] it is believed that flavoproteins are *not* autoxidized rapidly enough to play the role required by equations (11a)–(11c). Even if a bypass to oxygen via flavoprotein does exist in a given system, the reaction need not yield peroxide.[47,50,67-69] The physiological role of these interesting peroxidases remains to be clarified. The role of H_2O_2 in the respiratory systems of cytochrome-free bacteria will be considered in Chapter 9.

B. NITRATE, NITRITE, SULFATE, ETC.

Various lines of evidence have implicated: (*a*) cytochromes of the b-type in the reduction of nitrate by *P. denitrificans*,[63] *M. denitrificans*,[63] and *E. coli*,[127, 128] and (*b*) cytochromes of the c-type in the reduction of nitrate by *M. denitrificans*[128] and *A. fischeri*[129] and in the reduction of nitrate and nitrite by *P. aeruginosa*.[130] A c-type cytochrome is implicated in sulfate, thiosulfate, and sulfite reduction in the anaerobe *Desulfovibrio desulfuricans*.[131, 132a] A general formulation of such reactions is shown in Fig. 6.

$$DPN \rightarrow FP \rightarrow \text{cytochrome(s)} \rightarrow \begin{cases} \text{nitrate reductase} \longrightarrow NO_3^- \\ \text{nitrite reductase} \longrightarrow NO_2^- \\ \text{nitric oxide reductase} \rightarrow NO \end{cases}$$

$$[2H]\cdots \qquad \rightarrow \text{cytochrome(s)} \rightarrow \begin{cases} \text{sulfate reductase} \longrightarrow SO_4^= \\ \text{thiosulfate reductase} \rightarrow S_2O_3^= \\ \text{etc.} \end{cases}$$

FIG. 6. Reduction of inorganic nitrogen and sulfur compounds. The true substrate for the cell-free sulfate reductase of *Desulfovibrio desulfuricans* is adenosine-5'-phosphosulfate.[132c]

(Evidence for pyridine nucleotide and flavin mediation has been reported for the nitrate reductases,[127, 129] and for nitrite and nitrous oxide reduction,[132b] but not for the sulfur reactions.)

Evidence for the existence of nitrate,[127, 129] nitrite,[130] thiosulfate, sulfite, and tetrathionate reductases[131, 132a] has been presented. Although the chemical nature of the reductases is unknown, they have a function similar to that of the classic cytochrome oxidase, that is, they transfer electrons from cytochrome to an ultimate electron acceptor. Sato[128] has suggested that schemes such as that shown in Fig. 6 account for the "nitrate respiration" of various organisms (*E. coli*, *Pseudomonas*, *S. aureus*) that are able to grow anaerobically with nitrate as an electron acceptor. According to this view, flavoproteins that utilize nitrate as the immediate oxidant[48] may be specifically involved in the nitrate assimilation reactions, but not in "nitrate respiration."

There is some question whether specific reductases are always needed for the reoxidation of reduced cytochrome by inorganic nitrogen compounds. Cytochrome c_3 of *Desulfovibrio*, for instance, is reoxidized nonenzymically by NH_2OH.[133] It is possible that the reoxidation of *M. denitrificans* cytochrome b by nitrate is a spontaneous reaction.[63]

C. ARTIFICIAL ELECTRON ACCEPTORS

Electron flow may be diverted to artificial acceptors such as oxidation-reduction dyes,[134, 135] quinones,[81] and iron compounds such as ferricyanide.[136] These acceptors are useful when the natural physiological acceptor is unknown or not easily available. Dyes which undergo color change on reduction (bleaching of methylene blue, or 2,6-dichlorophenol-indophenol) are especially useful. The methylene blue technique,[137] for instance, was of great practical importance in early studies of bacterial enzymes. Enzymes studied (anaerobically) with such acceptors were operationally defined as dehydrogenases since the reactions presumably involved transfer of (2H) from substrate to artificial acceptor, and did not require the participation of oxygen. A dehydrogenase, defined in this way, may consist of a complex of enzymes and intermediate carriers. Since artificial acceptors are not specific for a given locus, the composition of a particular "dehydrogenase" system cannot be deduced solely from the observation that one or another acceptor may function as oxidant. For instance, various oxidation-reduction dyes, such as methylene blue or 2,6-dichlorophenol-indophenol,[46, 47] or quinones[81] may act as oxidants for flavoprotein. In the succinic oxidase system, however, methylene blue does not function at the primary dehydrogenase (flavoprotein) site, but farther along in the chain.[138, 139] Ferricyanide may oxidize reduced flavoproteins[19, 47] or spontaneously oxidize reduced cytochrome.[140] 2,6-Dichlorophenol-indophenol at pH 5.5 rapidly oxidizes DPNH in a spontaneous reaction;[47] various quinones can oxidize DPNH spontaneously.[141] Other nonenzymic oxidations of DPNH have been demonstrated and the rates tabulated.[142] Although artificial electron acceptors are not diagnostic reagents, they are specific to the extent that they will not act as stoichiometric acceptors unless their oxidation-reduction potential is higher than that of the electron donor system (see Section VII, A).

It should be mentioned here that when an autoxidizable acceptor is used,

$$AH_2 + \text{oxidant} \rightarrow \text{oxidant} \cdot H_2 + A \quad \text{(dehydrogenation)} \qquad (12a)$$

$$\underline{\text{oxidant} \cdot H_2 + O_2 \rightarrow \text{oxidant} + H_2O_2 \quad \text{(autoxidation)}} \qquad (12b)$$

$$\text{Sum:} \quad AH_2 + O_2 \rightarrow H_2O_2 + A$$

(methylene blue, some quinones, free flavins) the "dehydrogenase" can be coupled to oxygen, and an artificial "oxidase" thus created.[134] Peroxide is the product of such reactions.[135]

V. Catalase and Peroxidase

Catalase and peroxidase are iron-porphyrin enzymes that catalyze reactions (13) and (14), respectively.[17]

$$H_2O_2 + H_2O_2 \rightarrow 2H_2O + O_2 \qquad (13)$$

$$H_2A + H_2O_2 \rightarrow A + 2H_2O \qquad (14)$$

At low peroxide concentrations, catalase is also able to carry out reaction (14), the two-electron reduction of H_2O_2 by a series of electron donors (H_2A). Typical of the nonspecific substrates for peroxidases are aromatic amines, phenols, and various aromatic acids. Catalase may utilize some of these substrates as well as several alcohols, formaldehyde, formate, nitrite, etc. (see Mason[17] for a list of catalase and peroxidase substrates). In general, catalase activity (O_2 evolution) has been demonstrated in most cytochrome-containing aerobes and facultative anaerobes. Anaerobes and lactic acid bacteria are usually catalase-negative, although recently activity has been reported in various lactobacilli[143] in members of the genus *Pediococcus*[144, 145] and in certain anaerobes.[146a] The catalase activity of *Pediococcus cerevisiae*[146b] has been obtained in a cell-free, heat-labile enzyme preparation. The enzyme, which may be a prototype for the "catalases" of lactic acid bacteria and anaerobes, differs from classic catalase in being resistant to high concentrations of azide and cyanide. It is possible, therefore, that the *Pediococcus* enzyme is not a metallo-porphyrin. A monograph on bacterial catalase appeared in 1947.[147]

Two of the bacterial catalases have been thoroughly characterized—those of *M. lysodeikticus*[148a] and *Rhodopseudomonas spheroides*.[148b] These enzymes, which like erythrocyte catalase contain four iron-protoporphyrin prosthetic groups, also resemble erythrocyte catalase in their mechanism and substrate specificity.[148b, 149] The catalase of *M. lysodeikticus* has been crystallized.[148a]

Apparently the only data regarding the "physiological" occurrence of peroxide during oxidations carried out by cytochrome-containing bacteria has also been obtained with *M. lysodeikticus*. In intact cells, respiring on glucose, in the absence of exogenous peroxide, Chance[150] has demonstrated the formation of a catalase·H_2O_2 complex (complex-I). The complex serves as oxidant for endogenous electron donor(s) and for added formate or nitrite. Further evidence that bacterial catalases are iron-protoporphyrin enzymes comes from work with heminless (cytochrome- and catalase-free) mutants of *E. coli*[151] and *S. aureus*.[152] With the *E. coli* mutant, catalase may be re-formed on the addition of hemin to a cell-free extract of the organism —the first example of *in vitro* catalase formation from apoenzyme and hemin. In *S. aureus*, the analagous resynthesis of catalase takes place only in whole cells.[153]

There is as yet no evidence that any bacteria contain enzymes analagous to the typical animal and plant peroxidases (*Pseudomonas* cytochrome c peroxidase appears to be specific for *Pseudomonas* cytochrome c).[125] Most assays of peroxidase in bacteria have been performed qualitatively, with typical nonspecific peroxidase substrates. It is not always clear whether the reactions are distinguishable from the heat-stable peroxidase activities that have been demonstrated in a wide variety of bacterial species[154-157] or from the peroxidase activity of catalase.[17] The bacterial catalysts responsible for these reactions have not been isolated or identified. The heat-stable reactions, as pointed out by Keilin,[158] can be given by cytochrome. Peroxidase activity is also exhibited by many hematin compounds.[159] No explanation is as yet available for the heat-stable peroxidase activity reported for various streptococci.[157] Streptococci do contain a heat-labile flavoprotein DPNH peroxidase,[50] which will be described in Chapter 9. Whether hydroperoxidases (catalase and porphyrin-containing peroxidases) have a physiological function as protective agents (against peroxide toxicity) or as oxidative catalysts is still an open question (see, for instance, Chance[160]).

VI. Determination of Respiratory Type

A. Determination of Reaction Sequences

Broad division of bacterial species into obligate aerobes, facultative anaerobes, and obligate anaerobes is made on obvious physiological grounds. Figure 7, which summarizes the reaction pathways discussed in this chapter as well as in Chapters 7 and 8, is an attempt to correlate gross physiological characteristics with enzymic constitution. It is recognized, of course, that such syntheses cannot be completely accurate in detail. In general, these pathways have been inferred by using a variety of approaches, including inhibition studies, isolation of partial reactions, spectrophotometric studies, deductions made from oxidation-reduction potential of the components and from analogies to known systems. Direct spectrophotometric observation, in intact cells, of the partial reactions of cytochrome reduction and reoxidation are considered in Chapter 7, which also deals with the

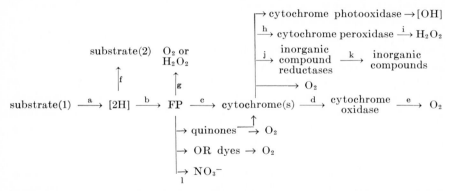

Fig. 7. Tentative scheme for electron transport systems used by various microorganisms, including physiological and nonphysiological bypasses. [2H], depending upon the pathway under consideration, may represent (1) reducing equivalents, (2) reduced pyridine nucleotides, or (3) reduced flavoprotein. Cytochrome photooxidase is used by photosynthetic bacteria (see Chapter 8).

Obligate aerobes: Cannot grow in absence of O_2 ; presumably no functional fermentative metabolism. Pathways of electron transport: a, b, c, d, e.

Facultative anaerobes: Can grow in presence or absence of O_2 (in absence of O_2 use fermentative pathways). (1) Without cytochrome (e.g., lactic acid bacteria). Pathways of electron transport: Aerobic, a, b, g. Anaerobic, a, f (may be sole pathway for some representatives of this class). (2) Containing cytochrome (e.g., coliforms). Pathways of electron transport: Aerobic, a, b, c, d, e; a, b, g? Anaerobic, a, f; a, b, c, j (NO_3^- reduction); a, b, l.

Obligate anaerobes: Cannot grow aerobically. (1) Without cytochrome (e.g., clostridia). Pathways of electron transport: a, f; a, b, g (not used under physiological conditions). (2) Containing cytochromes (e.g., *Desulfovibrio desulfuricans*). Pathways of electron transport: a, b, c, j (reduction of sulfur anions—step c not demontrated).

relevant inhibitor techniques. At present, it will merely be noted that by-passes around metallo-porphyrin systems are usually not sensitive to the classic cytochrome oxidase inhibitors (CN, CO, azide). For some organisms, by passes around oxygen (e.g., H_2O_2 reduction in yeast,[121] nitrate reduction in *M. denitrificans*[63, 92] and *P. aeruginosa*[91, 130] may be found along with a cytochrome oxidase pathway. The direct oxidation of reduced flavoprotein by oxygen may or may not yield peroxide (see Chapter 9), but the extent to which this reaction occurs during normal respiration in cytochrome containing bacteria is still unknown (see below).

It should be emphasized that not all of the reactions shown in Fig. 7 branch from the same flavoprotein nor do all of the reactions occur in a given system. The pathways indicated are probably correct in their main outlines, but complete and detailed reaction sequences are not known. In all probability not all of the catalysts are as yet recognized. It would be desirable to analyze respiratory systems by stepwise reconstruction from isolated and purified components, but the particulate nature of many of the catalysts has so far prevented full exploitation of this approach. Some promising results have been obtained, however. For example, succinic dehydrogenase can be removed from the succinic oxidase system of heart muscle sarcosomes.[139] The succinic oxidase system can then be reconstructed by addition of cytochrome c and soluble, purified succinic dehydrogenase to the "resolved" sarcosomes.[139] With *P. aeruginosa*[91] the cytochrome components and "blue protein" (see Chapter 8) have been isolated and purified and the electron transport sequence of the intact cell deduced from the potential of the individual components and the specificity of their interaction.

A note of caution regarding reconstruction studies should be sounded. When compared with a more highly organized system, a partially degraded electron transport preparation from heart muscle[161] is reported to show alteration in both the electron transport sequence between flavoprotein and cytochromes and in the site of action of inhibitors. It appears that partial disorganization of a particulate system may permit interactions that are not possible in a native respiratory particle. The possibility that even in the intact respiratory system there may be more than one reaction sequence between DPNH and oxygen must also be recognized.[162] With bacterial systems, a further complication is introduced because the nature and concentration of respiratory catalysts may change as growth conditions are altered.

B. Variation in Respiratory Chain with Change in Environmental Conditions

The literature on this subject cannot be reviewed in detail. Briefly, in yeast there appears to be a direct correlation between respiratory activity and cytochrome content;[163] no such simple relation exists among the bacteria.[6] In anaerobically grown baker's yeast, the cytochrome oxidase and cytochrome c content and the respiratory activity are very low. Adaptation of cells to oxygen leads to restoration of respiratory activity and of the cytochrome oxidase and cytochrome c content.[163] Streptomycin-resistant mutants of E. coli[151] and S. aureus[152] lack cytochromes and have little respiratory activity. In these three organisms, therefore, there appears to be a direct relation between cytochrome content and respiratory activity (O_2 uptake). However, this correlation does not seem to hold for all cytochrome-containing microorganisms. Cytochrome deficiency produced by anaerobic growth of B. cereus[164] or by growth of Aerobacter indologenes in iron-deficient media[165] does not impair the respiratory activity (oxygen uptake) of these organisms with glucose as substrate and the respiration remains as cyanide-sensitive as in normal cells.

Growth of P. fluorescens with nitrate, as a substitute for oxygen, as the ultimate electron acceptor, leads to greater synthesis of cytochrome c and cytochrome peroxidase than does growth in the presence of oxygen.[166a, 166b] For A. aerogenes,[167] it appears that there is an optimum oxygen concentration for the synthesis of cytochrome a_2 ; yields decrease markedly on either side of the optimum. For B. subtilis, the type of cytochrome system present may depend on the rate of growth[168] or the nutrition.[169]

With regard to a bypass to oxygen at the flavoprotein level, the correlation between cytochrome content and respiratory activity in yeast and in the E. coli and S. aureus mutants mentioned above suggests that in these organisms direct flavoprotein respiration does not take place to a significant extent. However, flavoprotein oxidases for reduced pyridine nucleotide are thought to function in P. fluorescens[166b] under conditions of both high and low cytochrome c content, and in the cytochrome-containing organisms, M. denitrificans[92] and P. tularensis.[170] Unlike normal yeast, yeast adapted to growth in CN appear to use a CN-resistant respiratory system, possibly flavoprotein in nature.[171]

Among microorganism therefore, the interrelations between environmental growth conditions, respiratory capacity, and content of respiratory catalysts are not yet resolved. The potential for variation must be kept in mind when electron transport pathways are evaluated. In spite of the great variety of specific reactions described, it remains true, however, that a few reaction *types* are sufficient to correlate the many diverse findings, as stressed by Kluyver and van Niel.[172a]

VII. Electron Transport in Fermentation and Oxidation

A. Some Thermodynamic Considerations

The reaction $AH_2 \rightarrow A + H_2$ may be regarded as the sum of two half-cell reactions, each operating at its characteristic potential. If the electrode

$$AH_2 \rightarrow A + 2H^+ + 2e \qquad (15a)$$

$$\frac{2H^+ + 2e \rightarrow H_2}{\text{Sum: } AH_2 \rightarrow A + H_2} \qquad \begin{matrix}(15b)\\(15c)\end{matrix}$$

potential of the hydrogen half-cell under defined conditions is used as a standard, then any other reversible oxidation-reduction system may be compared with it. More electronegative systems (lower oxidation-reduction potential) will reduce the hydrogen half-cell and cause reaction (15c) to proceed from left to right; whereas more electropositive systems will oxidize the hydrogen half-cell and reaction (15c) will proceed from right to left. The equilibrium constant and free energy change of reaction (15c) are therefore related to the voltage difference between the two oxidation-reduction systems. These relations are given by the following thermodynamic formulas. (Only brief treatment of the subject can be given here. Detailed treatments are given in standard texts, such as Clark.[24])

$$\Delta F^\circ = -nF\Delta E_0 \qquad (16)$$

In equation (16) ΔF° = the free energy change (cal./mole) in the standard state (25°C., and unit activities—1 molal activity for solutes, 1 atm. pressure for gases); n = number of electrons transferred; ΔE_0 = potential difference in volts, F = the faraday (23,063 cal. per volt equivalent).

$$\Delta F^\circ = -RT \ln K_{eq.} \qquad (17)$$

In equation (17) R = the gas constant and T the absolute temperature. At 25°C., $\Delta F^\circ = -1364 \log K_{eq.}$. The free energy change, ΔF°, is the maximum amount of work that can be obtained from a reaction when unit activity of reagents are converted to unit activity of products. The general equation describing the free energy change for *any* activity of reactants is:

$$\Delta F = \Delta F^\circ + RT \ln \frac{(C)^c \times (D)^d}{(A)^a \times (B)^b} \qquad (18)$$

For unit activities, therefore, $\Delta F = \Delta F^\circ$. Under standard conditions, except for hydrogen ion concentration, which is controlled at some fixed pH, ΔF° is replaced by the symbol $\Delta F'$. When ΔF° is negative (exergonic or spontaneous reaction) the equilibrium point of a reaction favors product formation; when ΔF° is positive, at equilibrium there is a preponderance of starting reagents over products. If ΔF° is zero, the reaction is at equilibrium (at unit activities). The magnitude of the free energy change indicates the extent to which the reaction will proceed in either direction. A large negative ΔF° indicates that the reaction will run toward completion, a large positive ΔF° that the reaction will proceed only very slightly toward completion. If ΔF° is zero, the $K_{eq.}$ is 1. The free energy change is an important quantity since it indicates the potential amount of energy that may be available to a biological system from a given reaction.

The electrode potential of a half-cell is given by the formula

$$E_{h} = E_0 + \frac{RT}{nF} \ln \frac{(ox.)}{(red.)} \qquad (19)$$

At 25°C. and a specified pH,

$$E_{h} = E_0' + \frac{0.0592}{n} \log \frac{(ox.)}{(red.)} \qquad (20)$$

Oxidation-reduction potentials are reported as E_0', the standard potential of the half-reduced system [i.e., (ox.)/(red.) = 1] on a scale in which the potential of the standard hydrogen half-cell at pH 0 is taken as zero. At pH 7, E_0' at 25°C. for the hydrogen couple is −0.414 v.

Table IV lists the standard potentials of a variety of biologically important systems. In only a few instances have the values for the enzymically catalyzed reactions been checked by potentiometric methods (succinate-fumarate; several of the pyridine nucleotide dehydrogenases; DPNH-DPN).[173, 174] Results for the succinate-fumarate system and the DPN[174] couple agree well with equilibrium data. Because of the relation between E_0, $\Delta F°$ and $K_{eq.}$, the oxidation-reduction potential, or at least the *theoretical* oxidation-reduction potential may be calculated from the equilibrium constant of a reaction or from the free energy change derived from thermal and ancillary data.[175] The particular virtue of expressing results as electrode potentials is that it becomes possible to predict at a glance the direction and extent (but not the rate) of the reaction that results from the coupling of any two half-cells. In the presence of the appropriate catalyst, electron flow will take place from the system of lower potential (more negative) to the system of higher potential (more positive). The greater the voltage difference, the farther the reaction will go toward completion (reduction of the electropositive system).

After dehydrogenation of a substrate, two reducing equivalents pass through the components of the electron transfer chain. The latter forms a transport sequence in which there occurs a stepwise increase in potential from that of the DPNH couple to that of the oxygen electrode (Table IV, Fig. 8). The fate of the carbon skeleton left after the dehydrogenation is a problem separate from that of electron transport. The structure of the dehydrogenated product does determine, however, the potential at which the next dehydrogenation will take place, and therefore the kinds of carriers that may be involved (Fig. 8). Among the substrate systems, the carbonyl to carboxyl oxidations are the most potent electron donors and the succinate fumarate system (probably paraffin to olefin in general, i.e., fatty

TABLE IV

SOME ELECTRODE POTENTIALS OF BIOLOGICAL INTEREST

Couple	E_0' (volts at pH 7)	Reference[a]
$2H_2O \rightleftarrows O_2 + 4H^+ + 4e$	$+0.816$	
$NO_2^- + H_2O \rightleftarrows NO_3^- + 2H^+ + 2e$	$+0.421$	
$H_2O_2 \rightleftarrows O_2 + 2H^+ + 2e$	$\sim +0.295$	
Cyt. $a_3^{2+} \rightleftarrows$ cyt. $a_3^{3+} + 1e$ (pH 7.4)	$+0.285$	172b
Cyt. $a^{2+} \rightleftarrows$ cyt. $a^{3+} + 1e$ (pH 7.4)	$+0.29$	
Cyt. $c^{2+} \rightleftarrows$ cyt. $c^{3+} + 1e$	$+0.25$	
Succinate $\rightleftarrows$ fumarate $+ 2H^+ + 2e$	$+0.031$	
Leucomethylene blue $\rightleftarrows$ methylene blue $+ 2H^+ + 2e$	$+0.011$	172c
$H_2 \rightleftarrows 2H^+ + 2e$ (pH 0)	0.0	
Cyt. $b^{2+} \rightleftarrows$ cyt. $b^{3+} + 1e$ (pH 7.4)	-0.04	
Old yellow enzyme (reduced) $\rightleftarrows$ old yellow enzyme (oxidized) $+ 2H^+ + 2e$	-0.122	
Lactate $\rightleftarrows$ pyruvate $+ 2H^+ + 2e$	-0.19	
Leucoriboflavin $\rightleftarrows$ riboflavin $+ 2H^+ + 2e$	-0.20	
$FADH_2 \rightleftarrows FAD + 2H^+ + 2e$	-0.22	57
$FMNH_2 \rightleftarrows FMN + 2H^+ + 2e$	-0.22	57
$DPNH + H^+ \rightleftarrows DPN^+ + 2H^+ + 2e$	-0.32	
$TPNH + H^+ \rightleftarrows TPN^+ + 2H^+ + 2e$	-0.324	
$H_2 \rightleftarrows 2H^+ + 2e$	-0.414	
Glyceraldehyde-3-phosphate $+ H_2O \rightleftarrows$ 3-phosphoglycerate $+ 3H^+ + 2e$	-0.57	Calculated from data given in ref. 22
α-Ketoglutarate $+ H_2O \rightleftarrows$ succinate $+ CO_2$ (gas) $+ 2H^+ + 2e$	-0.673	
Pyruvate $+ H_2O \rightleftarrows$ acetate $+ CO_2$ (gas) $+ 2H^+ + 2e$	-0.699	

[a] Except where noted, values are taken from K. Burton in appendix to reference 22.

acyl-CoA to α,β-unsaturated acyl-CoA) the most potent electron acceptors.

By comparing the potential for dehydrogenation of various typical groups, a rationale can be given to the coenzyme specificities and to the point at which substrates enter the respiratory chain. Substrates usually react with carriers having potentials in the vicinity of (or higher than) the potential for the substrate dehydrogenation. Succinate and fatty acid de-

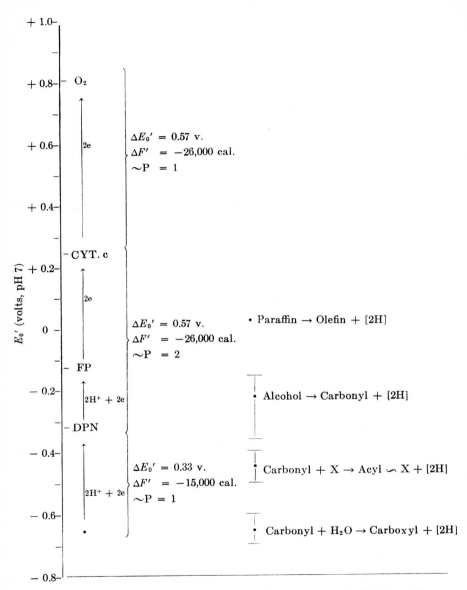

Fig. 8. Comparison of electrode potentials of coenzyme and substrate systems. The yield of ∼P for the partial reactions was determined in experiments with mammalian mitochondria (text). For the substrate systems, the average potential and variation in potential for each type of reaction is shown (calculated from the data of reference 22). The succinate → fumarate reaction was used for the potential of paraffin → olefin. Figure is drawn to scale.

hydrogenases, for instance, would be expected to use flavin coenzymes, and not pyridine nucleotides, as the immediate hydrogen acceptor. The paraffin to olefin dehydrogenation in general seems to be a flavin-linked reaction as evidenced by the fact that the dehydrogenases for succinate, fatty acyl-CoA and dihydroorotic acid[28b] are flavoproteins.

The formulation shown in Table IV is not meant to indicate that the mechanism of dehydrogenation involves reversible liberation of $2H^+ + 2e$ from the substrate. In some cases it is known that the formulation does not represent the dehydrogenation mechanism. For instance, oxidative decarboxylation of pyruvate, with DPN as acceptor is catalyzed by a multienzyme system[110] in which several coenzymes are involved. Electron transfer for a portion of the voltage span to DPN may take place ionically by transfer of the acyl anion

from one to another coenzyme. Thus, (a) the reaction occurs in several steps and (b) the electrons transferred are carried by a moiety derived from the substrate. The direct H transfers, discussed in Section II, B, also do not conform to the reversible half-cell reactions shown in Table IV. Indeed, in all potentiometric determinations of the dehydrogenation potential of substrate systems, an electroactive mediator (oxidation-reduction dye of suitable potential) must be added in order for the system to behave reversibly at an inert electrode. Nevertheless, for the purposes of thermodynamic calculations, it is possible to proceed as if the formulations of Table IV were correct. If the potentials (or theoretical potentials) are accurate, the free energy change and equilibrium constant for the over-all reaction, calculated from two half-cell potentials, will be accurate, regardless of the mechanism.

Certain precautions should be noted. (1) The values given in Table IV apply when (ox.)/(red.) is unity. When the ratio increases, the potential becomes more positive, when it decreases the potential becomes more negative [see equation (20)]. As far as the respiratory chain is concerned, this variable may not introduce as much difficulty as previously thought. Chance and Williams have shown[3] that during steady state oxidation carried out by mitochondria, the ratio (ox.)/(red.) for DPNH, flavoprotein, and cytochromes b, c, and a is close enough to unity so that little error is involved in using standard potentials for calculations.

(2) The potential of electron transfer coenzymes may change on binding of these compounds to protein. The potential of the old yellow enzyme, for instance, is about 0.1 v. higher than that of free flavins (Table IV). It is probable that both lower and higher potentials will be found for other

flavoprotein enzymes. The general phenomenon of change in potential with binding is important in that it allows the formation of efficient oxidation-reduction catalysts for a specific reaction. A theoretical treatment of the binding phenomenon (in terms of the dissociation constants of the reduced and oxidized compounds from the protein) has been given by Clark[24] for iron-porphyrins and applied to DPN and DPNH binding to alcohol dehydrogenase by Theorell and Bonnichsen.[176]

(3) Free energies, calculated from the data in Table IV, will apply to the standard state (molal activities, except for [H+]). To convert to other conditions, formula (18) may be used. When correcting to a different pH, allowance must be made for the free energy of dissociation of the various ionic species that may be present. It has often been pointed out that there may be great difficulties involved in trying to estimate the concentrations (activities) of compounds in the physiological state.

(4) A reaction that is thermodynamically possible may not take place rapidly enough (even in the presence of suitable catalysts) to be physiologically useful.

B. QUANTITATIVE ASPECTS OF ELECTRON TRANSPORT

As an example of the predictions that can be made by using free energy data, it can be stated that the one-step dehydrogenation of succinate to fumarate to yield hydrogen gas is a thermodynamically impossible reaction (i.e., it will not proceed to any significant extent, before equilibrium is reached). Inspection of Table IV shows that the succinate-fumarate couple will oxidize the hydrogen couple and that the reverse reaction will be very unfavorable, but it is possible to calculate exactly how unfavorable

$$2H^+ + 2e \rightleftarrows H_2 \qquad\qquad E_0' = -0.414 \text{ v.} \qquad (21)$$
$$\underline{\text{succinate} \rightleftarrows \text{fumarate} + 2H^+ + 2e \qquad E_0' = +0.03 \text{ v.} \qquad (22)}$$
$$\text{Sum: succinate} \rightarrow \text{fumarate} + H_2 \qquad E_0' = -0.444 \text{ v.}$$

the reaction is. The voltage difference between the two systems (subtracting the potential of the reducing system—in this instance the succinate-fumarate couple—from that of the oxidizing system) gives $\Delta E_0' = -0.444$ v. Using formula (16), $\Delta F' = -46,126 \times -0.444 = +20,400$ cal. The reaction is endergonic by a wide margin. The equilibrium constant, from equation (17), is

$$20,400 = -1364 \log K$$

$$\frac{(\text{fum.})(\text{H}_2)}{(\text{succ.})} = K = 1 \times 10^{-15}$$

That is, for $P_{H_2} = 10^{-4}$ atm. (partial pressure of H_2 in the atmosphere) the fumarate/succinate ratio at equilibrium is 10^{-11}. The reduction of fumarate to succinate, however is obviously a very favorable reaction. Similar calculations for the reaction between the succinate-fumarate couple and the pyridine nucleotide system yield an equilibrium constant of 6×10^{11} for the reduction of fumarate. The succinate-fumarate system is known to serve as the physiological oxidant for many anaerobic dehydrogenations.[100] Although succinate oxidation to fumarate does not furnish molecular hydrogen, the dehydrogenation of pyruvic acid does. The dehydrogenation of pyruvic acid is a major source of H_2 in bacterial fermentations.[177] Table V shows the free energy changes in the oxidative decarboxylation of pyruvic acid when the oxidation is coupled with electron acceptors of increasingly higher potential. (The theoretical potential for dehydrogenation of pyruvate is obtained from free energy data, and as discussed previously, is not to be interpreted as a reversible electrode potential. The processes considered may be termed electron transport, but the reaction route is not specified.)

When electron flow from the pyruvate system is intercepted by the hydrogen half-cell, over-all reaction (1) (in Table V) occurs. This reaction

TABLE V

ELECTRON TRANSPORT FROM "PYRUVIC DEHYDROGENASE COMPLEX" TO VARIOUS ACCEPTOR SYSTEMS

Reducing couple	Oxidizing couple	Over-all reaction	$\Delta E_0'$ (pH 7)	$\Delta F'$ (cal./mole)
1. Pyruvate + $H_2O \rightarrow$ acetate + CO_2 + $2H^+$ + 2e (E_0' = −0.70 v.)	$2H^+ + 2e \rightarrow H_2$ (E_0' = −0.414 v.)	Pyruvate + $H_2O \rightarrow$ acetate + CO_2 + H_2	0.286	−13,200
2. (a) No. 1	$DPN^+ + 2H^+ + 2e \rightarrow$ $DPNH + H^+$ (E_0' = −0.32 v)	Pyruvate + H_2O + $DPN^+ \rightarrow$ acetate + CO_2 + $DPNH$ + H^+	0.38	−17,500
(b) $DPNH + H^+ \rightarrow$ $DPN^+ + 2H^+ +$ 2e	Pyruvate + $2H^+$ + 2e $\rightarrow$ lactate (E_0' = −0.19 v.)	Pyruvate + DPNH + $H^+ \rightarrow$ lactate + DPN^+	0.13	−6,000
(c) No. 1	Pyruvate + $2H^+$ + 2e $\rightarrow$ lactate	Sum (2a) + (2b): 2 pyruvate + $H_2O \rightarrow$ lactate + acetate + CO_2	0.51	−23,500
3. No. 1	$O_2 + 2H^+ + 2e \rightarrow$ H_2O_2 (E_0' = +0.295 v.)	Pyruvate + H_2O + $O_2 \rightarrow$ acetate + CO_2 + H_2O_2	1.0	−46,000
4. No. 1	$1/2\,O_2 + 2H^+ + 2e \rightarrow$ H_2O (E_0' = 0.816 v.)	Pyruvate + $\frac{1}{2}\,O_2 \rightarrow$ acetate + CO_2	1.52	−70,000

is carried out by many clostridia;[177] the free energy release is theoretically large enough to cover the formation of a "high-energy" bond (Section VIII) and experimentally the reaction has been observed to yield acetyl-phosphate.[177] This reaction represents one method by which anaerobes are able to carry out energy-coupled oxidation-reduction reactions. In a sense, the hydrogen couple is the oxidant. Similar considerations apply to the reaction in which formate, rather than hydrogen and CO_2, is produced, since formate is thermodynamically equivalent to a mixture of hydrogen and CO_2 (i.e., the oxidation-reduction potential for dehydrogenation of formate to $CO_2 + 2H^+ + 2e$ is approximately the same as that of the hydrogen couple).

When a more electropositive system (lactate-pyruvate) serves as oxidant, reaction (2) of Table V is obtained. The over-all reaction, a so-called pyridine nucleotide-linked dismutation, is shown in reactions (2a), (2b), and (2c). DPN, reduced by the pyruvic dehydrogenase complex, dissociates from the last component of the system and combines with lactic dehydrogenase (Section II, B) to cause the reduction of pyruvate to lactate. In some systems a portion of the energy released in the oxidation of pyruvate by DPN is conserved in an "energy-rich" bond.[110] In reactions (1) and (2c), the free energy released per mole of pyruvate utilized is approximately the same. These reactions may serve as prototypes for electron transport in fermentation reactions. In a general case, the reducing equivalents removed from a substrate at one potential are accepted by the same, or another, substrate at a higher potential. The total voltage span, however, is much smaller than that involved in the oxidation of 2H by oxygen; consequently, only a small portion of the energy potentially available is released when substrate systems serve as the terminal H acceptors.

Coupling of pyruvate oxidation with the reduction of oxygen to peroxide is illustrated in reaction (3), Table V. This reaction may serve as a model for flavoprotein-mediated oxidations that result in peroxide formation. The free energy released is lower than for the reaction in which oxygen is reduced to water. In *Lactobacillus delbrueckii* the oxidation is catalyzed by a "direct" flavoprotein oxidase, whereas in *S. faecalis* the DPN-linked pyruvic dehydrogenase complex is coupled to oxygen via a flavoprotein-DPNH oxidase (see Chapter 9). A second molecule of pyruvate is oxidized spontaneously to acetate and CO_2 by peroxide; in the *S. faecalis* system peroxide is decomposed by a flavoprotein-DPNH peroxidase.[47, 50]

In reaction (4), Table V, the dehydrogenation of pyruvate is coupled to the four-electron reduction of oxygen to water. Electron transport through such a system may involve all the components of a typical respiratory chain, including the cytochromes. Other mechanisms are, however, possible. For instance, in the flavoprotein reactions discussed above, either the chemical reduction of peroxide by pyruvate (*L. delbrueckii* system) or the enzymic reduction of peroxide catalyzed by DPNH peroxidase (*S. faecalis* system) makes the over-all oxidation conform to reaction (4) of the table. The *S. faecalis* reaction is, however, the more useful of the two (see Chapter 9 for details of these and other mechanisms). The formulations of Table V emphasize the previous statement that the free energy released in a given dehydrogenation depends upon the oxidizing system to which the dehydrogenation is coupled. The higher the potential of the oxidant, the greater the energy released. How much of the energy can be made accessible to a biological system depends upon the mechanism of the oxidation (i.e., the number of sites at which mechanisms exist for coupling electron transport to the synthesis of "energy-rich" compounds).

VIII. Coupled Oxidative Phosphorylation

A. YIELD OF "ENERGY-RICH" PHOSPHATE ($\sim$P)

In order to serve the energy requirements of the cell, energy released in oxidative reactions must be conserved in some biologically available form. Equation (23) is a general formulation for the coupling between oxidation and energy-trapping reactions. In this reaction, the free energy of the oxida-

$$AH_2 + B + nADP + nPO_4 \rightarrow A + BH_2 + nATP + nH_2O \qquad (23)$$

tion, or a portion of it, is conserved in the "high-energy" bond of adenosine triphosphate (ATP).* The mechanisms of ATP utilization cannot be reviewed here. The reader is referred to the review of Krebs and Kornberg.[22]

The yield of $\sim$P in equation (23) depends upon the ΔF of the reaction (voltage span between AH_2 and B) and upon the number of energy conservation steps that may be available between AH_2 and B. When B is O_2, results are usually reported as P/O ratios, that is, equivalents of phosphate esterified per atom of oxygen taken up (i.e., per 2H oxidized). The integral value of the ratio is sometimes taken as the number of points at which mechanisms for phosphate esterification exist. Figure 8 shows the probable yield of $\sim$P, based on experiments with animal mitochondria,[22, 179] for electron transport between various members of the respiratory chain [various pairs of AH_2 and B in equation (23)]. Comparison of the respiratory chain sequence with the dehydrogenation potentials of various substrate

---

* The term "high-energy bond" has been criticized as being misleading.[178] The free energy released on hydrolysis of a "high-energy" compound is not contained in any one bond, but is a statistical property of the system, being defined by equation 18. In the text, the symbol $\sim$P is used for convenience. At pH 7, $\Delta F'$ for the hydrolysis of ATP is approximately -7900 cal., whereas under the conditions used in oxidative phosphorylation studies, the best approximation for $\Delta F'$ at pH 7 is probably $-12,000$ cal.[178a]

systems indicates the total amount of phosphate esterification that may theoretically be expected for the one-step oxidation (one pair of hydrogens transferred) of typical substrates. Oxidation of carbonyl groups to carboxyl groups, with DPN as electron acceptor, can be coupled with the formation of an energy-rich bond (without need for further hydrogen transfer reactions). During glucose oxidation via the glycolytic pathway and the tricarboxylic acid cycle, this reaction occurs upon the reduction of DPN by glyceraldehyde-3-phosphate, pyruvate, and α-ketoglutarate.[22] The oxidation of pyruvate and α-ketoglutarate by various bacteria[110] and of acetaldehyde by *C. kluyveri*[180] offer further examples of this energy-coupled oxidation. This reaction is usually termed "substrate-linked phosphorylation," to distinguish it from the respiratory chain phosphorylation that accompanies the reoxidation of DPNH. Substrate-linked phosphorylation is not sensitive to dinitrophenol, whereas respiratory chain phosphorylation is uncoupled by this reagent (i.e., phosphorylation is abolished, but oxygen uptake is either not affected or somewhat stimulated). The mechanism of substrate-linked phosphorylation is reasonably well understood; several acyl esters may occur as intermediates.[22]

Phosphate esterification coupled to true electron transport through the respiratory chain is a characteristic property of mitochondria.[3] With animal mitochondrial systems, the reoxidation of DPNH, with oxygen as acceptor yields, experimentally, $3 \sim P$ for a two-electron transfer (Fig. 8). Two of the phosphorylations can be obtained with cytochrome c as acceptor and one in the reoxidation of cytochrome c by oxygen.[22, 179] Theoretically, one might expect that the step from DPNH to cytochrome c would yield one $\sim P$ between DPNH and flavoprotein, and a second $\sim P$ in the reoxidation of reduced flavoprotein by cytochrome c. Such partial reactions have not been demonstrated to date. The oxidation of succinate by O_2 yields two $\sim P$, in keeping with the predictions that would be made from schemes such as that of Figure 8. In spite of much work, the intimate mechanism of respiratory chain phosphorylation is still not understood. There is, however, increasing evidence that vitamin K_1 functions in both electron transport and oxidative phosphorylation in bacterial[12, 39] and mammalian systems.[10, 11, 85] It has also been suggested that α-tocopherol may function in oxidative phosphorylation.[14] Mechanisms for the mediation of phosphate transfer to ADP via vitamin K_1[181, 182] and α-tocopherol[14] have been suggested.

The free energy of DPNH oxidation, with oxygen as acceptor, is $-52,000$ cal. Since, under the experimental conditions used for P/O determinations, the ΔF for ATP hydrolysis (pH 7) is approximately $-12,000$ cal.,[178] the efficiency of DPNH oxidation, as carried out by animal mitochrondria, is approximately 70 %.

B. BACTERIAL SYSTEMS

Respiratory particles capable of catalyzing coupled oxidative phosphorylation have been isolated from several bacterial species including *Alcaligenes faecalis*,[38b] *M. phlei*[12, 183] and *Azotobacter vinelandii*.[35, 184, 185] The *Azotobacter* and *A. faecalis* systems differ somewhat from mammalian mitochondria in (1) being less sensitive to dinitrophenol and (2) exhibiting lower P/O ratios for the oxidation of typical substrates. With *M. phlei* succinate oxidation results in P/O ratios approaching those found for mammalian systems and the phosphorylation is sensitive to typical uncoupling agents. DPNH oxidation by preparations from *Azotobacter*, *A. faecalis*, or *M. phlei* yields P/O ratios approaching 1, whereas with mammalian mitochondria the probable ratio is 3 and directly observed values as high as 2.6 have been obtained.[179] It is not clear whether this situation reflects a real difference between bacterial and mammalian systems (i.e., whether some bacterial respiratory particles have fewer loci for coupled oxidative phosphorylation) or whether optimum conditions have not as yet been found for the demonstration of oxidative phosphorylation with DPNH as substrate in bacterial systems.

A promising feature of several of the bacterial systems is the finding that oxidative phosphorylation can be shown to require soluble proteins in addition to the respiratory particles.

In *M. phlei*, a soluble protein seems to be the dinitrophenol-sensitive component of the phosphorylation system.[186a] The over-all reaction has also been shown to require a naphthoquinone.[12] Irradiation of particles and soluble supernatant components at 3600 A. leads to inactivation of both oxidation and phosphorylation; these activities are restored to the normal level by the physiologically occurring naphthoquinone that has been isolated from *M. phlei*.[186b] Vitamin K_1 is less effective.[12] FMN can restore the oxidation but not the ability to couple oxidation to phosphorylation. Similar ultraviolet inactivations, reversible by vitamin K_1, have been demonstrated for animal mitochondria.[11] Stimulation of oxidation and phosphorylation by soluble proteins has also been demonstrated for *A. vinelandii*[35] and *A. faecalis*.[38b] In the latter system, there appears to be an additional requirement for a polynucleotide of the RNA type. Little information is available concerning phosphorylation coupled to electron transport in bacteria which use inorganic electron donors or acceptors. With intact cells, phosphate turnover studies suggest that oxidative phosphorylation may occur when nitrate is the electron acceptor for formate oxidation by *E. coli*[187] or when oxygen serves as acceptor for the oxidation of sulfur compounds by thiobacilli.[188]

In several bacteria, high-molecular weight polyphosphates (metaphosphate) previously identified histologically as metachromatic granules or volutin granules[1, 189] appear to be storage forms for "high-energy" phos-

phate generated in oxidative phosphorylation. Chemical identification of
the volutin granules as polyphosphate has been made in *A. aerogenes*, *C.
diphtheriae*, mycobacteria, and *S. cerevisiae*.[1] The formation of metaphosphate from ATP in *E. coli*[190] and probably *C. diphtheriae*[190] and yeast[191]
takes place as follows:

$$n\text{ATP} \rightleftarrows n\text{ADP} + (\text{PO}_3{}^-)n \tag{24}$$

The *E. coli* enzyme has been purified and, with substrate concentration of
reactants, has been shown to catalyze reaction (24) in a reversible manner.
Polyphosphate is formed solely from the terminal phosphate of ATP.

REFERENCES

[1] M. Alexander, *Bacteriol. Revs.* **20**, 67 (1956).

[2] D. E. Green, R. E. Basford, and B. Mackler, *in* "Inorganic Nitrogen Metabolism"
(W. D. McElroy and B. Glass, eds.), p. 628. Johns Hopkins Press, Baltimore,
Maryland, 1956.

[3] B. Chance and G. R. Williams, *Advances in Enzymol.* **17**, 65 (1956).

[4] R. Y. Stanier, *in* "Cellular Metabolism and Infections" (E. Racker, ed.), p. 3.
Academic Press, N. Y., 1954.

[5] R. Storck and J. T. Wachsman, *J. Bacteriol.* **73**, 784 (1957).

[6] L. Smith, *Bacteriol. Revs.* **18**, 106 (1954).

[7] M. Kamen, *Bacteriol. Revs.* **19**, 250 (1955).

[8] S. W. Edwards and E. G. Ball, *J. Biol. Chem.* **209**, 619 (1954).

[9] G. V. Marinetti, D. J. Scaramuzzino, and E. Stotz, *J. Biol. Chem.* **224**, 819 (1957).

[10] C. Martius and D. Nitz-Litzow, *Biochim. et Biophys. Acta* **13**, 152, 289 (1954).

[11] R. D. Dallam and W. W. Anderson, *Biochim. et Biophys. Acta* **25**, 439 (1957).

[12] A. F. Brodie, M. M. Weber, and C. T. Gray, *Biochim. et Biophys. Acta* **25**, 448
(1957).

[13] K. O. Donaldson and A. Nason, *Proc. Natl. Acad. Sci. U. S.* **43**, 364 (1957).

[14] J. Bouman and E. C. Slater, *Biochim. et Biophys. Acta* **26**, 624 (1957).

[15a] L. P. Hager, *J. Am. Chem. Soc.* **79**, 5575 (1957).

[15b] R. L. Lester, F. L. Crane, and Y. Hatefi, *J. Am. Chem. Soc.* **80**, 4751 (1958).

[15c] F. L. Crane, C. Widmer, R. L. Lester, and Y. Hatefi, *Biochim. et Biophys. Acta*
31, 476 (1959).

[15d] Y. Hatefi and F. Quiros-Perez, *Biochim. et Biophys. Acta* **31**, 502 (1959).

[15e] R. A. Morton, *Nature* **182**, 1764 (1958).

[16] J. H. Bruemmer, P. W. Wilson, J. L. Glenn and F. L. Crane, *J. Bacteriol.* **73**, 113
(1957).

[17] H. S. Mason, *Advances in Enzymol.* **19**, 79 (1957).

[18] W. H. McShan, *in* "Respiratory Enzymes" (H. A. Lardy, ed.), p. 101. Burgess
Publ. Co., Minneapolis, Minnesota, 1949.

[19] T. P. Singer, E. B. Kearney, and V. Massey, *Advances in Enzymol.* **18**, 65 (1957).

[20] C. A. Appleby and R. K. Morton, *Nature* **173**, 749 (1954).

[21] E. Boeri and L. Tosi, *Arch. Biochem. Biophys.* **60**, 463 (1956).

[22] H. A. Krebs and H. L. Kornberg, *Ergeb. Physiol., biol. Chem. u. exptl. Pharmakol.*
49, 212 (1957).

[23] M. E. Pullman, A. San Pietro, and S. P. Colowick, *J. Biol. Chem.* **206**, 129 (1954).

[24] W. M. Clark, "Topics in Physical Chemistry." Williams & Wilkins, Baltimore,
Maryland, 1952.

[25] H. R. Mahler, *Ann. Rev. Biochem.* **26,** 17 (1957).

[26] N. O. Kaplan, *Bacteriol. Revs.* **19,** 235 (1955).

[27] B. Vennesland and F. H. Westheimer, *in* "The Mechanism of Enzyme Action" (W. D. McElroy and B. Glass, eds.), p. 357. Johns Hopkins Press, Baltimore, Maryland, 1954.

[28a] H. R. Levy and B. Vennesland, *J. Biol. Chem.* **228,** 85 (1957).

[28b] H. C. Friedemann and B. Vennesland, *J. Biol. Chem.* **233,** 1398 (1958).

[29] N. O. Kaplan, M. N. Swartz, M. E. Frech, and M. M. Ciotti, *Proc. Natl. Acad. Sci. U. S.* **42,** 481 (1956).

[30] N. O. Kaplan, S. P. Colowick, and E. F. Neufeld, *J. Biol. Chem.* **205,** 1 (1953).

[31a] P. Talalay, and H. G. Ashman-Williams, *Proc. Natl. Acad. Sci. U. S.* **44,** 15 (1958).

[31b] M. A. Stein and N. O. Kaplan, *Science* **129,** 1611 (1959).

[32] A. L. Lehninger, *J. Biol. Chem.* **190,** 345 (1951).

[33] R. W. Estabrook and B. Mackler, *J. Biol. Chem.* **229,** 1091 (1957).

[34] R. Repaske and J. J. Josten, *Bacteriol. Proc. (Soc. Am. Bacteriologists)* p. 115 (1955).

[35] A. Tissières, H. G. Hovenkamp, and E. C. Slater, *Biochim. et Biophys. Acta* **25,** 336 (1957).

[36] R. E. Asnis, V. G. Vely, and M. C. Glick, *J. Bacteriol.* **72,** 314 (1956).

[37] W. A. Wood, *Bacteriol. Revs.* **19,** 222 (1955).

[38a] I. Millman and R. W. Darter, *Proc. Soc. Exptl. Biol. Med.* **91,** 271 (1956).

[38b] G. B. Pinchot, *J. Biol. Chem.* **229,** 1, 11, 25 (1957).

[39] M. M. Weber and A. F. Brodie, *Bacteriol. Proc. (Soc. Am. Bacteriologists)* p. 105 (1958).

[40] P. M. Nossal, D. B. Keech, and D. J. Morton, *Biochim. et Biophys. Acta* **22,** 412 (1956).

[41] A. W. Linnane and J. L. Still, *Biochim. et Biophys. Acta* **16,** 305 (1955).

[42] H. R. Mahler, *in* "Currents in Biochemical Research" (D. E. Green, ed.), p. 251. Interscience, New York, 1956.

[43] O. Warburg and W. Christian, *Biochem. Z.* **266,** 377 (1933).

[44] H. Theorell, *Nature* **138,** 687 (1936).

[45] H. Theorell, *in* "The Enzymes, Chemistry and Mechanism of Action" (J. B. Sumner and K. Myrbäck, eds.), Vol. II, Part 1, p. 335. Academic Press, New York, 1951.

[46] T. P. Singer and E. B. Kearney, *in* "The Proteins" (H. Neurath and K. Bailey, eds.), Vol. 2, Part A, p. 123. Academic Press, New York, 1954.

[47] M. I. Dolin, *Arch. Biochem. Biophys.* **55,** 415 (1955).

[48] A. Nason and H. J. Evans, *J. Biol. Chem.* **202,** 655 (1953).

[49] H. Beinert and E. Page, *J. Biol. Chem.* **225,** 479 (1957).

[50] M. I. Dolin, *J. Biol. Chem.* **225,** 557 (1957).

[51] E. Haas, *Biochem. Z.* **290,** 291 (1937).

[52] E. Haas, B. L. Horecker, and T. R. Hogness, *J. Biol. Chem.* **136,** 747 (1940).

[53] B. L. Horecker, *J. Biol. Chem.* **183,** 593 (1950).

[54] H. R. Mahler and D. E. Green, *Science* **120,** 7 (1954).

[55] H. R. Mahler and D. G. Elowe, *J. Biol. Chem.* **210,** 165 (1954).

[56] H. Beinert, *J. Am. Chem. Soc.* **78,** 5323 (1956).

[57] H. J. Lowe and W. M. Clark, *J. Biol. Chem.* **221,** 983 (1956).

[58a] L. Michaelis, *in* "The Enzymes, Chemistry and Mechanism of Action" (J. B. Sumner and K. Myrbäck, eds.), Vol. II, Part 1, p. 1. Academic Press, New York, 1951.

[58b] F. H. Westheimer, *in* "The Mechanism of Enzyme Action" (W. D. McElroy and B. Glass, eds.), p. 321. Johns Hopkins Press, Baltimore, Maryland, 1954.

[59] H. Beinert, *J. Biol. Chem.* **225**, 465 (1957).

[60] G. R. Drysdale and M. Cohen, *Biochim. et Biophys. Acta* **21**, 397 (1956).

[61] A. Tissières, *Biochem. J.* **64**, 582 (1956).

[62] M. M. Weber and A. F. Brodie, *Biochim. et Biophys. Acta* **25**, 447 (1957).

[63] L. P. Vernon, *J. Biol. Chem.* **222**, 1035 (1956).

[64] A. F. Brodie, *J. Biol. Chem.* **199**, 835 (1952).

[65] S. W. Tanenbaum, *Biochim. et Biophys. Acta* **21**, 335 (1956).

[66] M. J. Cormier and J. R. Totter, *J. Am. Chem. Soc.* **76**, 4744 (1954).

[67] M. I. Dolin, *J. Bacteriol.* **77**, 383 (1959).

[68] M. I. Dolin, *J. Bacteriol.* **77**, 393 (1959).

[69] M. I. Dolin, *Bacteriol. Proc.* (Soc. Am. Bacteriologists) p. 105 (1958).

[70] M. M. Weber and N. O. Kaplan *Bacteriol. Proc.* (*Soc. Am. Bacteriologists*) p. 96 (1954).

[71] M. D. Kamen and L. P. Vernon, *J. Biol. Chem.* **211**, 663 (1954).

[72] Y. Birk, W. S. Silver, and A. H. Heim, *Biochim. et Biophys Acta* **25**, 227 (1957).

[73] S. C. Kinsky and W. D. McElroy, *Arch. Biochem. Biophys.* **73**, 466 (1958).

[74] E. Stotz, A. E. Sidwell, and T. R. Hogness, *J. Biol. Chem.* **124**, 733 (1938).

[75] T. P. Singer and E. B. Kearney, *J. Biol. Chem.* **183**, 409 (1950).

[76] M. J. Cormier, J. R. Totter, and H. H. Rostorfer, *Arch. Biochem. Biophys.* **63**, 414 (1956).

[77] J. L. Glenn and F. L. Crane, *Biochim. et Biophys. Acta* **22**, 111 (1956).

[78] M. M. Weber, H. M. Lenhoff, and N. O. Kaplan, *J. Biol. Chem.* **220**, 93 (1956).

[79] W. D. Wosilait and A. Nason, *J. Biol. Chem.* **208**, 785 (1954).

[80] M. I. Dolin, *Biochim. et Biophys. Acta* **15**, 153 (1954).

[81] H. R. Mahler, A. S. Fairhurst, and B. Mackler, *J. Am. Chem. Soc.* **77**, 1514 (1955).

[82] M. I. Dolin, *Bacteriol. Proc.* (*Soc. Am. Bacteriologists*) p. 110 (1957).

[83] V. Massey, *Biochim. et Biophys. Acta.* **30**, 205 (1958).

[84] H. R. Rosenberg, "Chemistry and Physiology of the Vitamins," p. 481. Interscience, New York, 1945.

[85] J. P. Colpa-Boonstra and E. C. Slater, *Biochim. et Biophys. Acta* **27**, 122 (1958).

[86] F. Vasington, K. O. Donaldson, and A. Nason, *Federation Proc.* **17**, 327 (1958).

[87] B. Chance, *Federation Proc.* **16**, 671 (1957).

[88] J. E. LuValle and D. R. Goddard, *Quart. Rev. Biol.* **23**, 197 (1948).

[89] W. W. Wainio and S. J. Cooperstein, *Advances in Enzymol.* **17**, 329 (1956).

[90] E. C. Layne and A. Nason, *J. Biol. Chem.* **231**, 889 (1958).

[91] T. Horio, *J. Biochem.* (*Tokyo*) **45**, 267 (1958).

[92] L. P. Vernon and F. G. White, *Biochim. et Biophys. Acta* **25**, 321 (1957).

[93] L. Smith, *Arch. Biochem. Biophys.* **63**, 403 (1956).

[94] R. G. Bartsch and M. D. Kamen, *J. Biol. Chem.* **230**, 41 (1958).

[95a] S. England and S. P. Colowick, *J. Biol. Chem.* **221**, 1019 (1956).

[95b] H. Gutfreund, *in* "The Enzymes" (P. D. Boyer, H. Lardy, and K. Myrbäck, eds.), 2nd ed., Vol. 1, p. 249. Academic Press, New York.

[96] M. G. P. J. Warringa, O. H. Smith, A. Giuditta, and T. P. Singer, *J. Biol. Chem.* **230**, 97 (1958).

[97] M. G. P. J. Warringa and A. Giuditta, *J. Biol. Chem.* **230**, 111 (1958).

[98] T. P. Singer, *Abstr. Meeting Am. Chem. Soc.* p. 41c, Sept. (1957).

[99] H. D. Peck, O. H. Smith, and H. Gest, *Biochim. et Biophys. Acta* **25**, 142 (1957).

[100] H. Krebs, *Biochem. J.* **31**, 2095 (1937).

[101] V. Massey, *J. Biol. Chem.* **229**, 763 (1957).

[102] A. M. Pappenheimer, Jr., and E. D. Hendee, *J. Biol. Chem.* **180,** 597 (1949).
[103] C. L. Wadkins and R. C. Mills, *Federation Proc.* **15,** 377 (1956).
[104] E. Kuhn and L. G. Abood, *J. Biol. Chem.* **180,** 813 (1949).
[105] M. Kusunose, S. Nagai, E. Kusunose, and Y. Yamamura, *J. Bacteriol.* **72,** 754 (1956).
[106] E. B. Kearney and T. P. Singer, *J. Biol. Chem.* **219,** 963 (1956).
[107] R. Repaske, *J. Bacteriol.* **68,** 555 (1954).
[108] B. C. Hertlein and W. A. Wood, *Bacteriol. Proc. (Soc. Am. Bacteriologists)* p. 105 (1958).
[109] T. E. King and V. H. Cheldelin, *J. Biol. Chem.* **224,** 579 (1957).
[110] I. C. Gunsalus, *in* "The Mechanism of Enzyme Action" (W. D. McElroy and B. Glass, eds.), p. 545. Johns Hopkins Press, Baltimore, Maryland, 1954.
[111] H. S. Moyed and D. J. O'Kane, *J. Biol. Chem.* **218,** 831 (1956).
[112] H. Gest, *Bacteriol. Revs.* **18,** 43 (1954).
[113] H. D. Peck, A. San Pietro and H. Gest, *Proc. Natl. Acad. Sci. U. S.* **42,** 13 (1956)
[114] A. L. Shug, P. W. Wilson, D. E. Green, and H. R. Mahler, *J. Am. Chem. Soc.* **76,** 3355 (1954).
[115] H. R. Whitely and E. J. Ordal, *in* "Inorganic Nitrogen Metabolism" (W. D. McElroy and B. Glass, eds.), p. 521. Johns Hopkins Press, Baltimore, Maryland, 1956.
[116] L. Packer and W. Vishniac, *Biochim. et Biophys Acta* **17,** 153 (1955).
[117] H. D. Peck and H. Gest, *J. Bacteriol.* **73,** 569 (1957).
[118] G. Milhaud, J.-P. Aubert, and J. Millet, *Compt. rend. acad. sci.* **246,** 1766 (1958).
[119] H. Lees and J. R. Simpson, *Biochem. J.* **65,** 297 (1957).
[120] A. M. Altschul, R. Abrams, and T. R. Hogness, *J. Biol. Chem.* **136,** 777 (1940).
[121] B. Chance, *in* "The Mechanism of Enzyme Action" (W. D. McElroy and B. Glass, eds.), p. 399. Johns Hopkins Press, Baltimore, Maryland, 1954.
[122] H. Wieland and H. J. Pistor, *Ann.* **535,** 205 (1938).
[123] S. W. Tanenbaum, *Biochim. et Biophys. Acta* **21,** 335 (1956).
[124] D. E. Atkinson, *J. Bacteriol.* **72,** 189 (1956).
[125] H. M. Lenhoff and N. O. Kaplan, *J. Biol. Chem.* **220,** 967 (1956).
[126] B. Chance, *in* "Enzymes and Enzyme Systems" (J. T. Edsall, ed.), p. 93. Harvard Univ. Press, Cambridge, Massachusetts, 1951.
[127] S. Taniguchi, R. Sato, and F. Egami, *in* "Inorganic Nitrogen Metabolism" (W. D. McElroy and B. Glass, eds.), p. 87. Johns Hopkins Press, Baltimore, Maryland, 1956.
[128] R. Sato, *in,* "Inorganic Nitrogen Metabolism" (W. D. McElroy and B. Glass, eds.), p. 163. Johns Hopkins Press, Baltimore, Maryland, 1956.
[129] J. C. Sadana and W. D. McElroy, *Arch. Biochem. Biophys.* **67,** 16 (1957).
[130] W. Verhoeven and Y. Takeda, *in* "Inorganic Nitrogen Metabolism" (W. D. McElroy and B. Glass, eds.), p. 159. Johns Hopkins Press, Baltimore, Maryland, 1956.
[131] J. R. Postgate, *J. Gen. Microbiol.* **14,** 545 (1956).
[132a] M. Ishimoto, J. Koyama, T. Yagi, and M. Shiraki, *J. Biochem. (Tokyo)* **44,** 413 (1957).
[132b] V. A. Najjar and C. W. Chung, *in* "Inorganic Nitrogen Metabolism" (W. D. McElroy and B. Glass, eds.), p. 260. Johns Hopkins Press, Baltimore, Maryland, 1956.
[132c] H. D. Peck, *Proc. Natl. Acad. Sci. U. S.* **45,** 701 (1959).
[133] J. C. Senez and F. Pichinoty, *Biochim. et Biophys. Acta* **28,** 355 (1958).
[134] O. Meyerhof, *Arch. ges. Physiol. Pflüger's* **169,** 87 (1917).

[135] C. Oppenheimer and K. G. Stern, "Biological Oxidation." Interscience, New York, 1939.

[136] J. H. Quastel and A. H. M. Wheatley, *Biochem. J.* **32,** 936 (1938).

[137] T. Thunberg, *Skand. Arch. Physiol.* **40,** 1 (1920).

[138] A. Giuditta and E. B. Kearney, *Federation Proc.* **17,** 229 (1958).

[139] D. Keilin and T. E. King, *Nature* **181,** 1520 (1958).

[140] L. Smith, *in* "Methods in Enzymology" (S. P. Colowick and N. O. Kaplan, eds.), Vol. II, p. 732. Academic Press, New York, 1955.

[141] W. D. Wosilait and A. Nason, *J. Biol. Chem.* **206,** 255 (1954).

[142] K. A. Schellenberg and L. Hellerman, *J. Biol. Chem.* **231,** 547 (1958).

[143] J. C. Dacre and M. E. Sharpe, *Nature* **178,** 700 (1956).

[144] E. A. Felton, J. B. Evans, and C. F. Niven, Jr., *J. Bacteriol.* **65,** 481 (1953).

[145] R. R. Gutekunst, E. A. Delwiche, and H. W. Seeley, *J. Bacteriol.* **74,** 693 (1957).

[146a] A.-R. Prévot and H. Thouvenot, *Ann. inst. Pasteur* **83,** 443 (1952).

[146b] E. A. Delwiche, *Bacteriol. Proc.* (*Soc. Am. Bacteriologists*) p. 117 (1959).

[147] J. Molland, *Acta. Pathol. Microbiol. Scand. Suppl.* **66,** 9 (1947).

[148a] D. Herbert and J. Pinsent, *Biochem. J.* **43,** 193 (1948).

[148b] R. K. Clayton, *Biochim. et Biophys. Acta* **36,** 40 (1959).

[149] B. Chance and D. Herbert, *Biochem. J.* **46,** 402 (1950).

[150] B. Chance, *Science* **116,** 202 (1952).

[151] Mirko Beljanski and Monique Beljanski, *Ann. inst. Pasteur* **92,** 396 (1957).

[152] J. Jensen and E. Thofern, *Z. Naturforsch.* **8b,** 604 (1953).

[153] J. Jensen, *J. Bacteriol.* **73,** 324 (1957).

[154] A. B. Callow, *Biochem. J.* **20,** 247 (1926).

[155] O. F. Edwards and L. F. Rettger, *J. Bacteriol.* **34,** 489 (1937).

[156] W. Frei, L. Reidmüller, and F. Almasy, *Biochem. Z.* **274,** 253 (1934).

[157] M. A. Farrell, *J. Bacteriol.* **29,** 411 (1935).

[158] D. Keilin, *Proc. Roy. Soc.* **B98,** 312 (1925).

[159] R. Lemberg and J. W. Legge, "Hematin Compounds and Bile Pigments." Interscience, New York, 1949.

[160] B. Chance, *Advances in Enzymol.* **12,** 153 (1951).

[161] R. W. Estabrook, *J. Biol. Chem.* **227,** 1093 (1957).

[162] A. E. Reif and V. R. Potter, *Arch. Biochem. Biophys.* **48,** 1 (1954).

[163] P. Slonimski, *Proc. Intern. Congr. Biochem., 3rd Congr., Brussels,* **1955** p. 243 (1956).

[164] P. Schaeffer, *Biochim. et Biophys. Acta* **9,** 261 (1952).

[165] W. S. Waring and C. H. Werkman, *Arch. Biochem.* **4,** 75 (1944).

[166a] H. M. Lenhoff and N. O. Kaplan, *J. Biol. Chem.* **220,** 967 (1958).

[166b] H. M. Lenhoff, D. J. D. Nicholas, and N. O. Kaplan, *J. Biol. Chem.* **220,** 983 (1956).

[167] F. Moss, *Austral. J. Exptl. Biol. Med. Sci.* **34,** 395 (1956).

[168] P. Chaix and J. F. Petit, *Biochim. et Biophys. Acta* **25,** 481 (1957).

[169] N. D. Gary and R. C. Bard, *J. Bacteriol.* **64,** 501 (1952).

[170] G. Rendina and R. C. Mills, *J. Bacteriol.* **74,** 572 (1957).

[171] L. B. Pett, *Biochem. J.* **30,** 1438 (1936).

[172a] A. J. Kluyver and C. B. van Niel, "The Microbe's Contribution to Biology." Harvard Univ. Press, Cambridge, Massachusetts, 1956.

[172b] W. W. Wainio, *J. Biol. Chem.* **216,** 593 (1955).

[172c] L. Anderson and G. W. E. Plaut, *in* "Respiratory Enzymes" (H. A. Lardy, ed.), p. 71. Burgess Publ. Co., Minneapolis, Minnesota, 1949.

[173] References on the substrate systems and evaluation of potential vs. equilibrium data given in K. Burton and T. H. Wilson, *Biochem. J.* **54,** 86 (1953).

[174] F. L. Rodkey, *J. Biol. Chem.* **213**, 777 (1955).

[175] G. S. Parks and H. M. Huffman, "The Free Energies of Some Organic Compounds." Reinhold, New York, 1932.

[176] H. Theorell and R. Bonnichsen, *Acta. Chem. Scand.* **5**, 1105 (1951).

[177] S. R. Elsden, *in* "The Enzymes, Chemistry and Mechanism of Action" (J. B. Sumner and K. Myrbäck, eds.), Vol. 2, Part 2, p. 791. Academic Press, New York, 1952.

[178] R. J. Gillespie, G. A. Maw and C. A. Vernon, *Nature* **171**, 1147 (1953).

[178a] K. Burton, *Nature* **181**, 1594 (1958).

[179] A. L. Lehninger, *Harvey Lectures Ser.* **49**, 176 (1955).

[180] R. M. Burton and E. Stadtman, *J. Biol. Chem.* **202**, 873 (1953).

[181] K. Harrison, *Nature* **181**, 1131 (1958).

[182] V. M. Clark, G. W. Kirby, and A. Todd, *Nature* **181**, 1650 (1958).

[183] A. F. Brodie and C. T. Gray, *J. Biol. Chem.* **219**, 853 (1956).

[184] I. A. Rose and S. Ochoa, *J. Biol. Chem.* **220**, 307 (1956).

[185] P. E. Hartman, A. F. Brodie, and C. T. Gray, *J. Bacteriol.* **74**, 319 (1957).

[186a] A. F. Brodie and C. T. Gray, *Biochim. et Biophys. Acta* **19**, 384 (1956).

[186b] A. F. Brodie, B. R. Davis, and L. F. Fieser, *J. Am. Chem. Soc.* **80**, 6454 (1958).

[187] H. Takahashi, S. Taniguchi, and F. Egami, *J. Biochem.* (*Tokyo*) **43**, 223 (1956).

[188] W. Vishniac and M. Santer, *Bacteriol. Proc.* (*Soc. Am. Bacteriologists*) **21**, 195 (1957).

[189] G. Schmidt, *in* "Phosphorus Metabolism" (W. D. McElroy and B. Glass, eds.), Vol. I, p. 443. Johns Hopkins Press, Baltimore, Maryland, 1951.

[190] S. R. Kornberg, *Biochim. et Biophys. Acta* **26**, 294 (1957).

[191] O. Hoffmann-Ostenhof, J. Kenedy, K. Keck, O. Gabriel, and H. W. Schönfellinger, *Biochim. et Biophys. Acta* **14**, 285 (1954).

CHAPTER 7

Cytochrome Systems in Aerobic Electron Transport

LUCILE SMITH

I. The Nature of the Cytochrome Pigments

The cytochrome pigments are hemoproteins. This means that they are composed of an iron-porphyrin prosthetic group attached by one or more linkages to the protein part of the molecule.[1,2] In the different hemoproteins the porphyrin or the protein part may differ, or there may be different kinds of bonds between the porphyrin and the protein parts. The cytochromes are rapidly reversible redox systems, and the valence of the iron appears to change on oxidation and reduction.[3a] When the cytochromes are in the reduced (ferrous) form, they show sharp bands in the absorption spectrum in the region from 500 to 650 mμ; in the oxidized form (ferric) only broad diffuse bands are apparent in this region of the spectrum. In both the oxidized and reduced forms the absorption spectra of the cytochromes show intense bands in the so-called "Soret" region of the spectrum (400 to 450 mμ), these absorption bands being related to the presence of an intact porphyrin ring. When oxidized cytochromes are reduced, there is a shift of 7 to 20 mμ in the position of the Soret band toward longer wave-

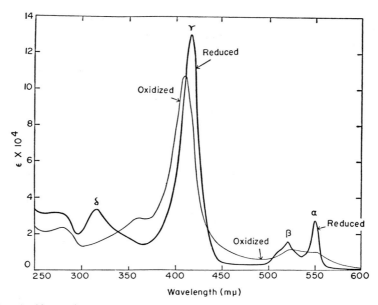

FIG. 1. Absorption spectra of mammalian cytochrome c in the oxidized and reduced forms.[3b] Data are reprinted through the courtesy of the British Medical Bul-
letin.

lengths. Figure 1 shows the absorption spectra of purified cytochrome c
from horse heart in both oxidized and reduced forms.[3b]

The characteristic changes of absorption spectra of the cytochrome
pigments during oxidation and reduction led to the recognition of their
involvement in cellular respiration. By observations of many kinds of cells
with a spectroscope, Keilin[4] saw the cytochrome absorption bands appear
and disappear as conditions changed from anaerobic to aerobic. All the
known functions of the cytochrome pigments are based on their capacity
readily to undergo oxidation-reduction reactions. As discussed below, it
now appears that some of the cytochromes function in aerobic oxidations
by forming part of a chain of enzymes that transport hydrogen or electrons
from the substrate being oxidized to molecular oxygen. It is these respiratory chain cytochromes which will concern us in this chapter. Other cyto
chromes have been characterized that perform other functions in cells, but
these either have not been found in bacteria or are discussed in Chapter 8.

II. Nomenclature of the Cytochromes

From his original observations of the cytochromes involved in reaction
with oxygen, Keilin[4, 5] recognized that there were at least three such pig-

ments present, which he designated components a, b, and c. Further work has indicated that these different components have a number of properties which distinguish them, and as additional components have been found, they have often been named as cytochromes of type a, b, or c, according to the following characteristics:

(1) Cytochromes of type a have absorption bands in the reduced form in the red region of the spectrum, that is, from about 590 to 635 mμ. The absorption spectra of reduced cytochromes a and a$_3$ are different from those of b- or c-type cytochromes in that the former have only one band in the visible region of the spectrum, while the latter have two. The porphyrin rings of the prosthetic groups of the a-type cytochromes have been shown to be different from those of types b and c.[6, 7] The compound of the heme of cytochromes a, a$_1$, and a$_3$ with pyridine (known as the pyridine hemochromogen) has absorption bands at 587 and 430 mμ in the reduced form. Some of the a-type cytochromes react rapidly with oxygen and will form compounds with carbon monoxide.

(2) Cytochromes of type b show absorption spectra in the reduced form similar to that characteristic of a protohemin hemochromogen, which is a compound formed by linkage of nitrogenous compounds to the iron of the hemin nucleus.[8] These have α-, β-, and γ-absorption bands around 560, 530, and 430 mμ. The b-type cytochromes can be easily split into heme and protein parts by treatment with alkali. Then after splitting, a characteristic hemochromogen, such as that with pyridine, can be prepared as a means of identifying protohemin as the prosthetic group.

(3) The c-type cytochromes are characterized by somewhat greater stability to heat and to acid and alkali than those of type a or b. The prosthetic group is protohemin with additional linkages on the two vinyl groups to cysteine residues in the protein part.[9] It is more difficult to hydrolyze the heme-protein linkages in cytochromes of type c, but some of these can be split with alkali so that characteristic hemochromogens can be formed with pyridine or cyanide. The c-type cytochromes are very slowly autoxidizable, if at all.

Numerous cytochromes have been discovered and designated according to this system of nomenclature. There have now been described cytochromes a through a$_4$, b through b$_7$, and c through c$_5$. Cytochromes f and h do not occur in bacteria and thus do not concern us here.

Another type of cytochrome nomenclature has been suggested by Scarisbrick.[10] Following this system the pigment is named according to the source of the cytochrome and the wavelength of the alpha absorption band of the reduced pigment. Thus *Azotobacter vinelandii* cytochrome 554 would refer to a pigment in *Azotobacter vinelandii* having an alpha absorption band at 554 mμ. This pigment is usually referred to as cytochrome c$_5$.

Recently another system of nomenclature of the cytochromes has been suggested by Egami et al.,[11] and a committee of the International Union of Biochemists is at present working on still another. However the cyto-chromes are named, the difficulty remains that the physiological reactions of most of these pigments are not known, and the nomenclature rests mainly upon characteristics of the absorption spectra.

III. Methods of Studying the Respiratory Chain Pigments

A. OBSERVATIONS OF ABSORPTION SPECTRA

The cytochrome pigments and also the pyridine nucleotides and fla-voproteins which make up the respiratory chain all show changes of ab-sorption spectrum on oxidation or reduction; thus they can be studied by observing these changes. The changes in absorption spectra of the cyto-chrome pigments, but not the pyridine nucleotides or the flavoproteins, can be followed by observations with a spectroscope. After the original work of Keilin, numerous observations were made of the cytochrome ab-sorption bands in different kinds of bacteria.[12-14] In making these direct spectroscopic observations of cells, it is important to have a good source of illumination. The spectroscopic technique has been reviewed by Hartree.[15]

The absorption spectra of the cytochromes have also been investigated with spectrophotometers. The cytochrome content of most cells is rather low, and spectrophotometric measurements of the absorption spectra of cytochromes in intact cells are difficult because of the considerable light scattering and the presence of other pigments. Thus special precautions must be observed to eliminate these interferences and to ensure that enough light is transmitted through the turbid suspension to be able to maintain a narrow band width. A spectrophotometer has been specially designed for this purpose;[16] it can measure small changes in absorption spectra which occur when aerobic bacteria exhaust the oxygen in solution by their respira-tion. If there are no changes in light scattering during this period, the difference spectra obtained result from oxidation-reduction changes of the enzymes which are involved in the reaction with oxygen. Actually it has always been possible to eliminate effects on absorption spectrum resulting from changes in light-scattering properties of bacteria or from other non-specific reactions;[17] with the specially designed spectrophotometers it has been possible to measure anaerobic minus aerobic difference spectra of many kinds of microorganisms,[18] as well as difference spectra obtained on reaction of pigments with reagents such as carbon monoxide, cyanide, or azide. The recent development of double-beam spectrophotometers has greatly minimized interference by nonspectral changes in signal.

There is one report of a difference spectrum of bacteria made in an ordinary spectrophotometer;[19] the organism, *Nitrobacter*, appears to have an unusually high cytochrome content. In a number of instances difference spectra have been obtained in ordinary spectrophotometers with particulate preparations derived from bacteria, in which the light scattering is less than in whole cells.[20-23]

Another method sometimes used to decrease interference from light scattering is to increase the refractive index of the suspending medium. Weibull[24] and Stanier *et al.*[25] used glycerol for this purpose in measuring the absorption spectra of insoluble particulate fractions of *Bacillus megaterium* and *Pseudomonas fluorescens*. Although Barer[26] found high concentrations of proteins successful in decreasing light scattering, no cytochrome absorption spectra have been determined in this way.

There has been one report of measurements of cytochromes of intact *Escherichia coli* by collection of the scattered light in an absorbing sphere with diffusely reflecting walls.[27]

Keilin and Hartree[28] devised a method of examining cytochrome absorption bands at the temperature of liquid air, where the absorption bands of the cytochromes will be intensified and sharpened and will sometimes split into two or more bands. It is only in this manner that the α-absorption bands of cytochromes c and c_1 can be seen separately. Using this method, Tissières could identify two c-type cytochromes in *Azotobacter vinelandii* with absorption bands which overlapped at room temperature.[22] In *Acetobacter suboxydans*[28, 29] and *Bacillus subtilis*[29, 30] a large single α-absorption band seen at room temperature splits into several bands at the temperature of liquid air.

B. MEASUREMENTS OF REACTION WITH OXYGEN

Since the cytochromes are part of the chain of enzymes carrying out aerobic oxidation of substrates, the measurement of oxygen uptake in the presence of various substances is sometimes used to test for the presence of this system of enzymes. Since a whole chain of enzymes is involved in the reaction of substrates with oxygen (see below), the observed rates of oxygen uptake will depend upon a number of factors, but most directly will be a measure of the rate-limiting reaction in the chain and thus may not demonstrate the full capacity of the cytochromes present.

The part of the cytochrome chain which reacts with oxygen can also oxidize a number of dyes and other redox systems with oxygen (for example, *p*-phenylenediamine or hydroquinone), and this type of reaction is sometimes used as a measure of "cytochrome oxidase" activity. Either the oxygen uptake or the oxidation of the dye can be measured. It should be pointed out that the method is a quite nonspecific one and should be used only in conjunction with other data.[15, 31]

C. Use of Inhibitors

One approach to the study of the respiratory chain enzymes involves the use of inhibitory substances which act at different points along the chain to interrupt the electron transport. For example, cytochrome oxidase activity is inhibited by cyanide, azide, and carbon monoxide. As discussed below, light-reversible carbon monoxide inhibition of respiration is the most specific test for cytochrome oxidases. The respiration of many bacteria and of cell-free extracts is inhibited by 0.001 M cyanide,[13, 32, 33] but in bacterial extracts azide sometimes appears to be a less effective inhibitor.[20, 33, 34a,b] There is evidence that some bacterial extracts contain cyanide-insensitive reduced diphosphopyridine nucleotide (DPNH) and reduced triphosphopyridine nucleotide (TPNH) oxidases.[34a, 35]

Narcotics inhibit the reduction of the cytochromes, possibly by affecting the mutual accessibility of the enzymes in the chain.[36] In the mammalian respiratory chain antimycin A reacts with an unidentified factor to interrupt electron transfer.[37] This inhibitor has no effect upon the respiratory chains of bacteria,[17, 20, 38] but some quinoline N-oxime derivatives appear to have inhibitory effects in bacteria similar to that of antimycin A in mammalian cells.[38]

There are a number of difficulties involved in inhibitor studies. These have been reviewed[15, 39, 40] and can be summed up as follows:

(1) With intact cells, there may be a permeability barrier to the inhibitor. This is true of azide, which penetrates some cells only in the form of the undissociated acid.

(2) Some inhibitors may be bound in an inactive form by substances present in cells or extracts. For example, keto acids react rapidly with cyanide to form cyanohydrins and proteins will bind antimycin A.[41]

(3) The inhibitor may not react with the member of the enzyme chain which is the rate-limiting step. In this case, considerable inhibition of the enzyme will not affect the rate of the over-all reaction.

IV. Functions of the Cytochromes

The respiratory chain of mammalian tissues has been much more extensively studied than the corresponding system of microorganisms. The components and sequence of reactions in the mammalian respiratory chain is usually given as follows:[42]

$$succinate$$
$$\searrow$$

substrates → DPN- or TPN-linked dehydrogenases → flavoprotein →

cytochrome b → cytochrome c_1 →

cytochrome c → cytochrome a → cytochrome a_3 → oxygen

where the arrows indicate the direction of passage of hydrogen or electrons. In intact cells or with cellular extracts, the pigments which become rapidly oxidized at low oxygen tension and are rapidly reduced as the oxygen tension is decreased to a value near zero are considered to participate in the respiratory chain. All cytochrome oxidases, including the mammalian enzyme and those of bacteria, react rapidly with oxygen and have very high affinities for oxygen;[43, 44] the concentration of oxygen giving half of the maximum rate of respiration is of the order of 10^{-7} to 10^{-6} M oxygen.

In intact mammalian liver and heart mitochondria, this chain of hydrogen and electron transport is coupled in at least three places to enzyme systems which can bring about the phosphorylation of adenosine diphosphate (ADP) to adenosine triphosphate (ATP). Thus the ultimate function of the enzyme chain which brings about the aerobic oxidation of substrates is to furnish a source of energy for the cells, since ATP can be used in energy-requiring reactions.

A. OXIDASES

As indicated in the above scheme, cytochrome a_3 is the component in mammalian tissues and in yeast that reacts rapidly with oxygen.[45, 46] It then reacts with cytochrome a, which then oxidizes cytochrome c, etc. Together cytochromes a and a_3 comprise the combination of pigments which can rapidly oxidize reduced cytochrome c with oxygen. This can be demonstrated with added cytochrome c, which is one of the cytochromes that has been obtained in purified form. The mixture of cytochromes a and a_3 is thus often referred to as cytochrome c oxidase.

The classic method for demonstrating which enzyme in the chain is the terminal oxidase is based upon the fact that carbon monoxide competes with oxygen for reaction with the oxidase, and the carbon monoxide compound can be decomposed by light. The pigment with which carbon monoxide and oxygen compete for combination is the one that reacts directly with oxygen, and the absorption spectrum of the carbon monoxide compound of this pigment can be determined from the action spectrum, that is, from measurements of the relief of inhibition of the respiration by light of different wavelengths.[47, 48] The action spectrum can then be compared with the absorption spectrum measured in the presence of carbon monoxide and with the photochemical dissociation spectrum (absorption spectrum of the carbon monoxide compounds dissociated by light).[49] From measurements of this kind on a number of bacteria,[46, 48, 50] some information has been gleaned about the nature of the terminal oxidases present. This is summarized in Table I.

Although some bacteria contain a cytochrome with spectroscopic properties similar to those of mammalian cytochrome a_3 (for example, *B.*

LUCILE SMITH

TABLE I

TERMINAL RESPIRATORY ENZYMES OF BACTERIA[a]

Terminal oxidase	Organisms	Peaks of absorption spectrum of carbon monoxide compound (mμ)	Peaks in absorption spectrum of reduced oxidase (mμ)	Turnover number at 25° C. (sec.$^{-1}$)
Cytochrome a$_3$	Bacillus subtilis Sarcina lutea	590-91, 547-50, 430-31	605, 445	76 (in B. subtilis oxidizing glucose)
Cytochrome a$_1$	Only terminal oxidase in: Acetobacter pasteurianum One of several oxidases in: Proteus vulgaris Azotobacter vinelandii	585-92, 548, 427-28	About 590, about 440	620 (in A. pasteurianum oxidizing alcohol)
Cytochrome a$_2$	One of several oxidases in: Escherichia coli Proteus vulgaris Aerobacter aerogenes	636-37	628-630	—
"Carbon-monoxide binding pigment" (cytochrome o)	Only terminal oxidase in: Micrococcus pyogenes var. albus Acetobacter suboxydans One of several oxidases in: Escherichia coli Proteus vulgaris Aerobacter aerogenes Azotobacter vinelandii	567-68, 535-37, 416-18	430, ? ?	—

[a] The identity of the terminal oxidases has been established in a number of bacteria by measurement of the carbon monoxide action spectra of the organisms. In some instances the photodissociation action spectra have also been measured. This information has been obtained only for the organisms listed in the table. Terminal respiratory enzymes are those that react with oxygen.[46, 48-50, 57]

subtilis), the bacterial cytochrome a_3 is not identical with the mammalian enzyme.[46, 51] The bacterial cytochromes a plus a_3 do not rapidly oxidize mammalian cytochrome c.[52] In fact, most bacterial extracts will oxidize mammalian cytochrome c only very slowly, if at all.[52-54] Extracts of *Micrococcus denitrificans* appear to oxidize mammalian cytochrome c,[34a] but it has not been established whether the rate is as high as with the mammalian oxidase.

The specificity of the bacterial oxidases for the cytochrome substrates also extends to the c-type cytochromes. For example, two purified c-type cytochromes from *Azotobacter vinelandii* are rapidly oxidized by oxidases of these bacteria, but not by the mammalian oxidase or by those of a number of other species of bacteria.[55] Although the c-type cytochrome isolated from *M. denitrificans* is oxidized by mammalian cytochrome c oxidase,[34a, 54] the rate appears to be low.

Great caution must be executed in deciding whether a given reaction observed *in vitro* has physiological importance for the cells until quantitative measurements are made to ascertain that the reaction is rapid enough to fulfill the required function. In the case of the cytochrome oxidases, as pointed out by Kamen,[56] a somewhat autoxidizable cytochrome that can couple with mammalian cytochrome c would appear to simulate cytochrome c oxidase activity.

Several different cytochrome oxidases are found among the bacteria. The pigment designated cytochrome a_1 of *Acetobacter pasteurianum* has been shown to be the terminal oxidase of this bacterium[48] and is the only pigment in the strain studied that combines with carbon monoxide.[57] Cytochrome a_1 has an absorption peak at 590 mμ in the reduced form. Evidence for a high concentration of a spectroscopically similar pigment is seen in the difference spectrum of *Nitrobacter*.[19] It is also found in a number of other bacteria in combination with one or more other cytochromes that can react with carbon monoxide; it is often seen in combination with cytochrome a_2, which can also act as a terminal oxidase.[50] Cytochrome a_2 has so far never been found as the only terminal oxidase present in a bacterium. Castor has shown[50] that the concentration of cytochrome a_2 is low in cells in the logarithmic phase of growth. In preparing cell-free extracts the cytochrome a_2 of the cells is sometimes lost,[22, 58] but the respiration is still active in its absence, because of the presence of another oxidase.

The terminal oxidase of some bacteria is a pigment which, unlike the other oxidases, is not an a-type cytochrome.[48, 49] It is found in quite a number of bacteria,[50] sometimes as the only oxidase (for example in *M. pyogenes* var. *albus* and *Acetobacter suboxydans*) and sometimes in combination with cytochromes a_1 and a_2 (in *Aerobacter aerogenes*, *E. coli*, *Azotobacter vinelandii*). The carbon monoxide compound of this pigment is similar to that of a pigment from photosynthetic bacteria[59] which seems to have a prosthetic group like that of cytochrome c, but some of the linkages between the iron and the protein part are missing. It thus appears that different kinds of hemins may act as prosthetic groups of oxidases. The new type of oxidase has so far been referred to as the "carbon monoxide binding pigment," but will in the future be named cytochrome o.[50]

To sum up, several cytochromes have been characterized as terminal oxidases of bacteria: cytochromes a_1, a_2, a_3, and the "carbon monoxide binding pigment." Some bacteria have only one oxidase, others may have two or three. Castor has shown[50] that when more than one oxidase is present, any one of these may act as the terminal oxidase. It has not yet been possible to show to what extent the different oxidases are operative under different conditions. The respiration of some bacteria, such as *E. coli* and *Azotobacter*, is less sensitive to inhibition by carbon monoxide than that of others, and the inhibition is relieved only by relatively strong illumination. It may be that in these bacteria, which have several oxidases, there is a relatively greater excess of oxidase activity.

Although there are other oxidases in cells besides the cytochrome oxidases, the affinity of the other oxidases for oxygen is usually much lower. Studies with inhibitors and kinetic studies show that in mammalian cells and in most bacteria which contain a cytochrome system, the bulk of the respiration goes via the cytochrome pathway.

B. FUNCTIONS OF b- AND c-TYPE CYTOCHROMES

The cytochromes described above as terminal oxidases pass electrons directly to molecular oxygen. From our present knowledge it appears that the rest of the respiratory chain cytochromes serve as a pathway for electron transport between flavoproteins and the terminal oxidases. Thus they are assumed to undergo alternate oxidation and reduction during the oxidation of the substrates and somehow to link these oxidations to the formation of ATP. Unfortunately the mechanism of electron transport through this chain of enzymes, which are all anchored to cellular particles, although often discussed, is still not known.

Several c-type cytochromes of bacteria have been isolated and purified (see Section VIII). The cytochrome c_2 of the photosynthetic bacteria is not a member of the respiratory chain of these bacteria.[60] But the other purified bacterial c-type cytochromes are rapidly oxidized and reduced by particulate preparations from the corresponding bacteria; thus they can act as intermediary electron carriers.[34a, 54, 55] It has been suggested that a c-type cytochrome of *Nitrobacter* is reduced directly by nitrite,[19] since no cytochrome b was seen in these organisms. However, the presence of a small amount of cytochrome b could be masked by a large amount of cytochrome c in spectrophotometric observations, so that observations of the absorption spectrum at liquid air temperature would be necessary to rule out the presence of cytochrome b.

Only two bacterial cytochromes of type b have been isolated.[35] Both were rapidly reduced by extracts of the corresponding bacteria in the presence of succinate or DPNH. The cytochromes b_2 of yeast and b_5 of mammalian microsomes show lactate and DPNH cytochrome c reductase activities, respectively.[61, 62] There is so far no evidence in bacteria for the presence of cytochromes which are not a part of the respiratory chain, such as the cytochrome b_5 found associated with mammalian microsomes.

Bacterial cytochromes have also been shown to react in oxidation-reduction reactions that pass electrons to other oxidants than molecular oxygen, such as nitrate, sulfate, the oxidant formed on illumination of photosynthetic cells, and possibly an oxidant formed during the fixation of nitrogen. In some nitrate-reducing bacteria the same cytochrome chain can react with either nitrate or oxygen.[63, 64] These reactions are discussed in Chapter 8.

V. The Particulate Nature of the Bacterial Respiratory System

The remarkable multienzyme system which mediates respiration and the associated ATP formation appears to be attached to insoluble particulate material within the cell in an orderly arrangement that allows rapid reactions to take place.[36, 42] In mammalian liver, the enzyme systems of oxidative phosphorylation are a part of the mitochondria, as are the enzymes of the tricarboxylic acid cycle. This has been established by the examination of mitochondria isolated in a relatively intact form. When mammalian cells are broken up in such a way that the structure of the mitochondria is not maintained, fragments of the mitochondria can be separated because of their insolubility. For example, the succinoxidase preparation of Keilin and Hartree[65] is a suspension of small, insoluble particles derived from the disintegration of the mitochondrial membrane.[66] These particles are not capable of phosphorylation of ADP, and only succinate and DPNH are oxidized at an appreciable rate.

Examination of broken-cell extracts of bacteria has not revealed the presence of particles with all of the biochemical properties of mammalian or plant mitochondria. When the cell-free extracts are centrifuged, several fractions can be separated by their ease of sedimentation. Usually all fractions possess similar enzymic activities,[25, 31, 67-70] the particles differing only in size.

The cytochrome system has always been found to be associated with particulate matter in bacterial extracts. Usually the absorption spectrum of the cytochromes seen in the particulate fractions is the same as that observed in the intact cells;[25, 33, 71-73] the one exception is the low level or absence of cytochrome a_2 in the particulate material. The particle-bound cytochromes can also become reduced on addition of an oxidizable substrate and then are reoxidized by aeration.[25, 55, 67]

The bacterial particulate matter also contains some dehydrogenases. Washed, insoluble particles from *Azotobacter vinelandii*[55, 67] were observed to oxidize succinate or DPNH, while preparations from *Aerobacter aerogenes* could oxidize in addition lactate.[74, 75] Fractions from other bacteria were also able to oxidize formate[7] and α-glycerophosphate[33] or malate.[25, 69, 70, 76] However, when the particulate fractions were supplemented with nonsedimentable fractions, additional substrates could be oxidized,[71, 75, 77, 78] although it was not possible to demonstrate complete oxidation of substrates of the tricarboxylic acid cycle to CO_2 and H_2O.[67] Linnane and Still[79] subjected suspensions of *Serratia marcescens* in sucrose to rapid shaking with glass beads for varying time intervals in the shaker designed by Nossal.[80] Some of the dehydrogenases and the tricarboxylic acid cycle enzymes—isocitric and malic acid dehydrogenases and aconitase and fumarase—were very easily dissociated from the particles during the shaking procedure. In contrast, succinic, lactic, formic, and α-ketoglutaric acid dehydrogenases, like the cytochrome system, remained firmly bound to the insoluble material, even with increased periods of shaking. The hydrogenase of *Hydrogenomonas facilis* is attached to insoluble particles if the bacteria are given only brief treatment in a sonic oscillator, but can be released in soluble form by increased periods of exposure to sonic oscillation.[81] It thus appears that the cytochrome system is more firmly bound to the particulate material than the dehydrogenases, except those for succinic, malic, and lactic acids. The dehydrogenases which remain bound to the particles will depend to some extent upon the method of breaking the bacteria. When the dehydrogenases are released from the particles into the soluble fraction, they are still able to interact with the particulate enzymes.

When Schachman, Pardee, and Stanier[82] centrifuged extracts of several kinds of bacteria broken in a number of different ways, they could distinguish in all of the extracts fractions with sedimentation constants around 40, 29, and 5 S. As discussed above, the cytochrome system and other oxidizing enzymes have been found to be present in fractions sedimenting at varying centrifugal fields. Although fractions from a number of bacteria which contained the 40 S particles were often observed to exhibit considerable succinoxidase activity, [70, 75, 77] the activity was never localized in these fractions. Sometimes the smaller particulate fractions showed greater oxidizing activity, expressed in terms of the protein content.[67-70] Tissières *et al.*[67] even found that they could increase the specific activity of a larger particulate fraction from *Azotobacter vinelandii* to that of a smaller fraction by exposing the former briefly to sonic oscillation. In some instances the smallest particulate material obtained could be sedimented only after several hours centrifugation at 140,000 g.[25, 33, 68, 76] Thus in cell-free extracts of bacteria there exists a whole range of particle sizes, all of which show similar oxidative activities and some of which are very small. The smallest particles have usually been obtained from extracts made by breaking the bacteria by exposure to sonic oscillation.[33, 68, 83] Electron micrographs of actively oxidizing particulate preparations also show a heterogeneous mixture of particles.[25, 76, 77] In a coarse particulate fraction obtained from *Pseudomonas fluorescens*[25] the particles ranged in diameter from 10 to 100 mμ. As calculated by Tissières,[75] particles with a diameter of 150 A. would have a volume only one-millionth that of a liver mitochondrion.

More recent work has shown that particles with a sedimentation constant around 40 S and which are high in ribonucleic acid (RNA) content can be separated from the particles containing the oxidative enzymes by starch electrophoresis[76] or by ultracentrifugation.[84] On breaking *Azotobacter vinelandii* in a sonic oscillator the RNA particles and a soluble dehydrogenase were released at the same rate as the rupture of the cells;[85] thus the RNA-containing particles are assumed to exist as such in the cytoplasm. The rate of release of the oxidizing enzymes and the phospholipids was, however, slower and similar to the decrease of turbidity, suggesting that these particles are derived from the breakdown of a larger structure, probably the cell envelope. On brief exposure to sonic oscillation large fragments remained which were called "hulls" and were thought to contain cell wall and possibly an adhering membrane.[85] Separation of the RNA particles from the oxidizing particles by starch electrophoresis[76] showed that the former fraction contained particles of diameter 30 mμ which contained 50% RNA and 50% protein and no enzymic activities. The main component of this fraction had a sedimentation constant of 42 S. The other particles, which represented a very heterogeneous fraction, contained all of the enzymic activities and were high in phospholipid. Exposure of the isolated hulls to more extensive sonic oscillation produced the oxidizing particles of irregular size and shape.

Weibull[86, 87] digested the cell wall of *Bacillus megaterium* with lysozyme in the presence of a sucrose concentration which prevented the osmotic lysis of the protoplasts formed. When the protoplasts were lysed osmotically, a "ghost" fraction was derived from the cytoplasmic membrane plus possible adhering particles. This ghost fraction could be separated by low centrifugal force and was found to contain all of the cytochrome system of the cell. Treatment of this fraction in a sonic oscillator gave rise to insoluble particulate material like that usually obtained on rupture of the bacteria. Militzer *et al.*[88, 89] appear to have obtained a ghost fraction with similar properties by treatment of thermophilic bacteria with lysozyme.

Thus there is now good evidence that the particles of broken-cell extracts of bacteria which show respiratory activity are particles of varying sizes which are derived from a larger structure. This structure seems to be the cytoplasmic membrane, possibly with some attached structures. The respiratory particles do not exist as such in the intact cells, in contrast to the RNA-containing particles which exist preformed in the cytoplasm. In this respect, it is interesting that the respiratory particles of the bacteria resemble in activity either the succinoxidase particles obtained by extensive disruption of heart muscle[45] or the small particles derived from liver or heart mitochondria which can oxidize a limited number of substrates and can carry out some oxidative phosphorylation.[90-92]

Storck and Wachsman[93] found that the ghost fraction obtained by lysis of B. megaterium protoplasts represents 15 % of the total lysate; this would seem to be high if it comprises only the cytoplasmic membrane. They did not obtain a clear-cut localization of the various oxidizing capacities either in the ghost fraction or in the supernatant obtained from centrifuging down the ghosts, but the succinic, lactic, and α-ketoglutaric acid dehydrogenases were concentrated in the ghost fraction. The supernatant fraction contained some structures which looked like pieces of ghosts. These experiments appear to demonstrate how easily the ghost fraction is disrupted into smaller pieces.

One difficulty yet to be explained is the considerable loss of respiratory activity sometimes observed on rupturing the cells.[75, 78, 94] This is not always the case. Broken-cell extracts of Azotobacter vinelandii in buffer[95] or in sucrose or lactose[69, 70] are about as active metabolically as the original organisms. Although Linnane and Still[79] found that the amount of some dehydrogenases released from the particles during shaking with glass beads depended somewhat upon the concentration of sucrose in the suspending medium, it has usually been observed that the activities of the particles prepared from ruptured bacteria are the same irrespective of the medium in which they are broken.[67, 96, 97] This is in contrast to the situation in preparing intact animal mitochondria, where hypertonic sucrose solutions must be used. These observations agree with the suggestion that the particles derived from the bacteria do not represent cell structures.

Attempts to increase the specific activities of the oxidizing systems of isolated bacterial particles have so far met with only limited success.[20, 21, 68, 98] Also no separation of the particles into subfractions with a separation of the oxidative activities has been obtained.[20, 68]

VI. Oxidative Phosphorylation

In some broken-cell suspensions of bacteria the formation of ATP from ADP has been obtained during the oxidation of substrates by oxygen.

Usually the ratio of ATP formed to O_2 consumed was found to be low compared with similar ratios obtained with mammalian or plant mitochondria. In bacterial extracts, P:O ratios of 0.4 to 1 have been obtained with fractions of *Proteus vulgaris*,[74] *Corynebacterium creatinovorans*,[99] *Azotobacter vinelandii*,[67, 72, 99-101] *Micrococcus denitrificans*,[34a] and *E. coli*.[102] In experiments with *Alcaligenes faecalis*,[103, 104] *Aerobacter aerogenes*,[74] and *Mycobacterium phlei*,[96, 97, 105] P:O ratios greater than 1 have been reported. However, in some cases the values for the inorganic phosphate disappearing did not agree with the ATP formed (measured as acid-labile phosphate).

The bacterial systems studied differ in a number of properties from the system of intact liver mitochondria which carries out oxidative phosphorylation. For one thing, the bacterial systems were found to be relatively insensitive to the inhibitor dinitrophenol,[74, 99, 100, 104, 106, 107] which acts in low concentrations (10^{-5} M) to "uncouple" the phosphorylation from the oxidative reactions in mammalian mitochondrial systems. The *M. phlei* system seems to be different from the other bacterial systems, being completely uncoupled by 5×10^{-5} M dinitrophenol, even when α-ketoglutarate was the substrate.[105] In mammalian systems, there is one substrate-linked phosphorylation with this substrate that is insensitive to the inhibitor.[108a] The bacterial systems also differ from the mammalian ones in that the bacterial preparations do not show "respiratory control." In mammalian mitochondria this respiratory control means that respiration is inhibited unless there is a phosphate acceptor system present so that phosphorylation can proceed. It is not known whether this difference between the bacterial and mammalian systems is due to the presence of an endogenous phosphate acceptor system in the bacterial preparations or to a different type of coupling between the respiration and the phosphorylation. As discussed above, the particles derived from broken-cell extracts of bacteria represent pieces derived from the breakdown of a larger structure, while isolated liver mitochondria represent intact structures in the cytoplasm.

Evidence has been reported for the separation of the enzyme systems carrying out oxidative phosphorylation in *A. faecalis*[103, 104] and *M. phlei*[97] into several components, one of which is in the soluble fraction. Both Tissières *et al.*[106] and Rose and Ochoa[100] obtained oxidative phosphorylation with washed particles from *Azotobacter vinelandii*. However, when the supernatant fraction from centrifugation at 120,000 g for 90 minutes was added to the washed particles, more rapid phosphorylation was observed than expected from the separate activities of the particles and the supernatant fraction.[106] The effect of the soluble fraction was not so pronounced with the particles from *Azotobacter* as with those from *A. faecalis* or *M. phlei*.

Two fractions of particles can be separated by centrifugation from *Azo-*

tobacter vinelandii extracts prepared by grinding the bacteria with powdered glass. The smaller particles have the greatest phosphorylating activity, expressed on a dry weight basis, but qualitatively the two kinds of particles seem to be identical.[67] These data agree with the above suggestions about the source of the bacterial particles. Also the same phosphorylating activity was obtained when bacteria were broken in water, buffer, or sucrose.

Finally, no experiments similar to those done with liver mitochondria[42] have been carried out with phosphorylating bacterial particles to show the oxidation-reduction reactions of the respiratory chain enzymes accompanying initiation or cessation of phosphorylation. This will be difficult to accomplish in the bacterial systems because of the lack of respiratory control.

VII. Bacterial Cytochromes

As discussed in previous sections, the bacteria have been shown to possess a-, b-, and c-type cytochromes plus cytochrome o. As far as is known, these cytochromes have properties similar to the cytochromes of yeast and mammalian tissues, which are often referred to as the "typical" cytochrome system. The anaerobic minus aerobic difference spectrum of some mammalian cells, pictured in Fig. 2, shows the changes in absorption spectrum of the pigments which react with oxygen. The α-, β-, and γ-cytochrome peaks are marked accordingly. Several difference spectra of bacteria are plotted in Figs. 3 through 7. The qualitative observations on absorption spectra of bacterial cytochromes can be summarized as follows:

(1) Some bacteria show cytochrome absorption bands at the same wave-

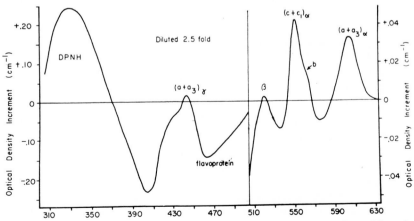

Fig. 2. Difference in absorption spectrum between anaerobic and aerobic guinea pig liver mitochondria. Different dilutions of the suspension were used for the two wavelength regions and the optical density scales are also different.

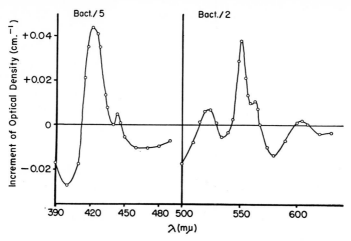

Fig. 3. Anaerobic minus aerobic difference spectrum of *B. subtilis.*[31] The bacterial suspension was diluted 2-fold for measurements between 500 and 600 mμ and 5-fold for measurements between 390 and 490 mμ.

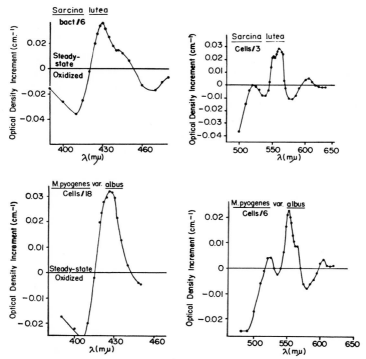

Fig. 4. Anaerobic minus aerobic difference spectra of *Sarcina lutea* and *Micrococcus pyogenes* var. *albus.*[17]

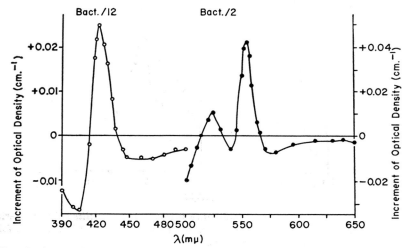

FIG. 5. Anaerobic minus aerobic difference spectrum of *Acetobacter suboxydans*.[31]

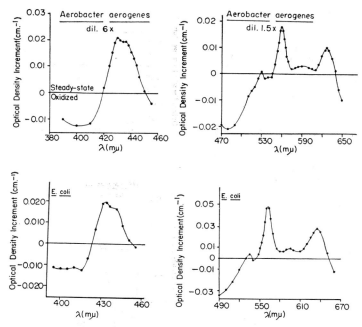

FIG. 6. Anaerobic minus aerobic difference spectra of *Aerobacter aerogenes* and *Escherichia coli*.[17] The *E. coli* suspension was diluted 2-fold for measurements between 490 and 670 mμ and 6-fold for measurements in the Soret region of the spectrum.

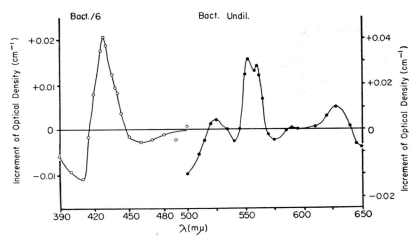

FIG. 7. Anaerobic minus aerobic difference spectrum of *Azotobacter chroococcum*.[132]

lengths as those of yeast and heart muscle; examples are *B. subtilis* and *Sarcina lutea*. As discussed in Section IV, these cytochromes are not identical with their mammalian equivalents. *M. pyogenes* var. *albus* shows a difference spectrum between 500 and 650 mμ similar to the typical one, but the peak of cytochrome a_3 in the Soret region is missing. Thus these bacteria contain cytochrome a, but no cytochrome a_3.

(2) A number of bacteria lack the cytochrome a peak which may be replaced by cytochrome a_1 (in *Acetobacter pasteurianum*) or by a mixture of cytochromes a_1 plus a_2 (*E. coli, Aerobacter aerogenes, Azotobacter chroococcum*). There is no evidence of an a-type cytochrome in *Acetobacter suboxydans* or *Rhodospirillum rubrum*.

(3) Several bacterial species contain the α-absorption band of cytochrome b_1 in place of the similar band of cytochrome b. This is sometimes the only α-band seen in the spectral region characteristic of b- and c-type cytochromes even at liquid air temperature (example: *E. coli, A. aerogenes*). In other bacteria, cytochrome b_1 is seen in combination with c-type absorption bands (example: *Azotobacter*). In some strains of *B. subtlis*, Keilin and Hartree[28] found that at liquid air temperature the cytochrome b_1 absorption band split into three bands corresponding to cytochromes b, c, and c_1. Chaix and Petit[30] observed four absorption bands.

(4) Two strains of *Acetobacter* show the difference spectra at room temperature with a large α-absorption band at 554 mμ. At the temperature of liquid air, this band is found to have one main and two smaller components, the former resembling cytochrome c_1 and the latter at positions corresponding to cytochromes c and b.[28, 29]

(5) Numerous assortments of the various cytochromes may be seen in different bacteria. The data are summarized in Tables II and III.

To sum up, the cytochrome systems of various bacteria may include pigments like the "typical" cytochromes a, a_3, b, c, and c_1. Or, these together with cytochromes a_1, a_2, a_4,[108b] b_1, b_4, c_3, c_4, and c_5 may be present in various combinations. The latter group of cytochromes has so far only been observed in bacteria. In spite of the great variety of cytochromes found among the bacteria, there is no evidence that they perform functions different from those of mammalian tissues. The main difference between the bacterial and the mammalian cytochrome systems seems to be the presence of several oxidases in some bacteria.

The studies of the bacterial cytochrome systems, with their great variety of pigments, have given some insight into the cytochrome requirements for an electron transport chain.

(1) The combination of cytochromes a and a_3 is not necessary, and the ratios of the two differ with the organism.

(2) The ratio of cytochromes c and c_1 varies over a wide range.

(3) At least one organism has failed to show evidence of a c-type cytochrome.

TABLE II

PEAKS IN DIFFERENCE SPECTRA OF BACTERIAL CYTOCHROMES[a]

Bacteria	Visible[b]					Soret[b]	
	α				β	γ	
Bacillus subtilis		604	564	552	523	444	422
Micrococcus pyogenes var. albus		604	565	552	523	—	427
Sarcina lutea		605	562	552	523	444	430
Micrococcus lysodeikticus		600		552	520	440	432
Aerobacter aerogenes	628	592	560		530	435	430
Escherichia coli	630	593	560		533	437	432
Proteus vulgaris	630	595	560		533	440	430
Azotobacter chroococcum	628	590	560	552	530	440?	428
A. chroococcum after several transfers		590		552	522	440?	427
Acetobacter pasteurianum		588		554	523	445	428
Acetobacter suboxydans				554	525	—	422
Pseudomonas fluorescens		580	560	552	523	—	424
Streptococcus faecalis	No cytochrome peaks						
Yeast		605	563	552	525	445	426
Heart muscle particles		605	563	552	525	445	426

[a] See Smith.[31]

[b] Wavelengths in millimicrons.

TABLE III

COMBINATIONS OF CYTOCHROMES OCCURRING IN BACTERIA[a]

Bacterium	Cytochrome components
Bacillus subtilis	a, a_3 , b, c, c_1
Sarcina lutea	a, a_3 , b, c^b
Micrococcus pyogenes var. *albus*	a, b, c,[b] o
Acetobacter suboxydans	b, c, c_1 , o
Acetobacter pasteurianum	a_1 , b, c, c_1
Acetobacter peroxydans	a_1 , a_2 , a_4 ,[c] b, c, c_1
Azotobacter vinelandii	a_1 , a_2 , b_1 , c_4 , c_5 , o
Aerobacter aerogenes	a_1 , a_2 , b_1 , o
Escherichia coli	a_1 , a_2 , b_1 , o
Proteus vulgaris	a_1 , a_2 , b_1 ,[b] o

[a] The table represents a compilation of information from a number of sources. Complete data on cytochrome components are obtained only by examination of the absorption spectra both at room temperature and at liquid air temperature plus tests for the oxidases present by measurements of carbon monoxide difference spectra or action spectra. Complete data have been obtained for only a relatively small number of bacteria. The purpose of the table is to illustrate the various combinations of cytochromes which occur in bacteria.

[b] The absorption spectra of these bacteria have not been examined at liquid air temperature.

[c] Cytochrome a_4 has only been observed in these bacteria;[108b] its function has not been investigated.

(4) All cytochrome-containing bacteria studied show several of these pigments. These presumably make up the organism's electron transport chain. No requirement for a given combination of types can yet be discerned. This may suggest that the only requirement may be a combination of cytochromes with enough difference in redox potential to give the energy for ATP synthesis.

The possible pathways observed among the different bacteria are summarized in Fig. 8.

Bacteria like *Acetobacter* and *Azotobacter* contain relatively high concentrations of cytochrome pigments. More pertinent is a measurement of the turnover numbers of the bacterial cytochromes. Table IV lists

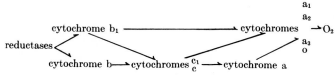

FIG. 8. Possible pathways of electron transport in bacterial cytochrome systems.

TABLE IV

Rate of Turnover of Bacterial Cytochromes

Organism	Substrate	O_2 uptake (μM/sec.) / ΔOD^a main Soret peak (424–430 mμ)	O_2 uptake (μM/sec.) / ΔOD^a Soret peak of cytochrome a_3 or a_1 (445 or 440 mμ)	Turnover number[b] of cytochrome a_3 or a_1 (sec.$^{-1}$)
Yeast	Alcohol	—	186	65
Heart muscle particles	Succinate	—	80	29
Acetobacter pasteurianum	Alcohol	1291	4500	620
Aerobacter aerogenes	Lactate	160	218	—
Azotobacter chroococcum	Glucose	185	—	—
Micrococcus pyogenes var. *albus*	Glucose	89	—	—
Sarcina lutea	Succinate	847	2130	—
Escherichia coli	Succinate	411	454	—
Micrococcus lysodeikticus	Lactate	853	—	—
Acetobacter suboxydans	Alcohol	1530	—	—
Bacillus subtilis	Glucose	82	760	76
Pseudomonas fluorescens	Glucose	209	—	—

[a] Difference in OD between anaerobic and aerobic states.

[b] (O_2 uptake)/(Δ OD) $\times$ 4 $\times$ Δ extinction coefficient for cytochrome a_3 or a_1.

the ratios of oxygen uptake to cytochrome peaks in the difference spectra for yeast, heart muscle particles, and a number of bacteria. This ratio is an expression of the turnover numbers of the bacterial cytochromes, and can be calculated as turnover numbers for those cytochromes where the difference in extinction coefficients between the oxidized and reduced forms is known. The data show that some of the bacterial cytochromes have quite high rates of turnover.

VIII. Soluble Bacterial Cytochromes

Recently a number of bacterial cytochromes have been obtained in soluble form, purified to varying degrees, and some of the chemical and physical properties studied. It is not surprising that most of the bacterial cytochromes which have been obtained in soluble form are those of type c, since these are the most stable. Sometimes methods used for the isolation of cytochrome c from mammalian tissues were unsuccessful in work with the bacterial pigments; consequently several other types of extraction procedure have been developed.[22, 35, 54, 109, 110]

The first cytochrome to be isolated from bacteria was one from a photosynthetic bacterium, *Rhodospirillum rubrum*.[111] This cytochrome appears to be involved in light-induced reactions in these bacteria.[112] Cytochrome pigments have also been isolated from other photosynthetic bacteria and from anaerobic sulfate and from nitrate-reducing organisms. These bacteria all have an oxidative metabolism, although the oxidant is not oxygen. The cytochromes of anaerobic metabolism are described in Chapter 8.

Cytochromes of type c have been isolated from *Azotobacter vinelandii*,[22, 55] *Micrococcus denitrificans*,[35, 54] *Pseudomonas aeruginosa*,[63, 109] *Pseudomonas denitrificans*,[35, 54] an unidentified pseudomonad,[113] and from *Pseudomonas fluorescens*.[114] As discussed in Section IV, there is considerable specificity in the interaction between the c-type cytochromes and the cytochrome oxidases. Of the c-type cytochromes isolated, only that from *M. denitrificans* was observed to be oxidized by mammalian cytochrome c oxidase, and this reaction appeared to have a rather low rate.[54] In all cases where observations were made, the bacterial c-cytochromes were rapidly oxidized and reduced by oxidases and reductases on particles prepared from the corresponding bacteria.[22, 35, 54, 63] The purified cytochromes from *Azotobacter vinelandii* were not oxidized by particulate preparations from *E. coli* or *Acetobacter peroxydans*.[22] The preparation of cytochrome c from *Pseudomonas fluorescens* contains a peroxidase which will oxidize the reduced cytochrome c on addition of H_2O_2.[114] The relationship between the cytochrome c peroxidase and the cytochrome c oxidase of these bacteria is not clear.

Two c-type cytochromes were isolated from *Azotobacter vinelandii*[22] and *Pseudomonas aeruginosa*,[109, 115] and there is evidence for two in an unidentified pseudomonad.[113] These are reminiscent of the mixture of cytochromes c and c_1 in mammalian and yeast cells. As with cytochromes c and c_1, the wavelengths of the α-absorption peaks of the two c-type cytochromes are so close that only one fused peak is observed in the mixture at room temperature. Thus they are recognized as separate entities only by physical separation or by observations of the absorption spectra at the temperature of liquid air.[22] In *Pseudomonas aeruginosa* it is claimed that electron transport has been observed between the two c-type cytochromes.[115]

Some of the properties of the isolated c-type bacterial cytochromes are summed up in Table V (the cytochromes of the photosynthetic bacteria are excluded). In all cases these cytochromes were shown to have absorption spectra, chemical reactions, and stability similar to mammalian cytochrome c and to form the same pyridine and cyanide hemochromogens. They thus have the same prosthetic group as mammalian cytochrome c. The isoelectric points are usually quite different from that of the mammalian pigment, indicating a different protein moiety. Kamen and Takeda[110] showed the amino acid composition of the cytochrome c from *Pseudomonas aeruginosa* to be quite different from that of mammalian cytochrome c.

TABLE V

PROPERTIES OF SOLUBLE BACTERIAL CYTOCHROMES

Cytochrome[a]	Bacteria from which cytochrome isolated	Activity	Chemical and physical properties	Peaks in absorption spectrum of reduced pigment
c-Type cytochrome (63, 110, 115)	Pseudomonas aeruginosa	Intermediate electron carrier	$E_0' = 0.25$ volts at pH 7; not autoxidizable; hemin like cytochrome c	551, 521, 416 mμ
c$_1$-Type cytochrome (63, 110, 115)	Pseudomonas aeruginosa	Intermediate electron carrier	$E_0' = 0.225$ volts at pH 7; not autoxidizable; hemin like cytochrome c	554, 525, 416 mμ
c-Type cytochrome (35, 54)	Micrococcus denitrificans	Intermediate electron carrier can be oxidized by mammalian cytochrome c oxidase	$E_0' = 0.25$ volts at pH 7; isoelectric point at acid pH; not autoxidizable; hemin like cytochrome c	550, 522, 416 mμ
c-Type cytochrome (35, 54)	Pseudomonas denitrificans	Intermediate electron carrier	$E_0' = 0.32$ volts at pH 7; hemin like cytochrome c	551-52, 523, 417 mμ
c-Type cytochrome (114)	Pseudomonas fluorescens	Preparation of the cytochrome contains a peroxidase which oxidizes the cytochrome in the presence of H_2O_2	—	550, 520, 415 mμ
c-Type cytochrome (113)	Unidentified pseudomonad	Intermediate electron carrier	$E_0' = 0.26$ volts at pH 7; isoelectric point at acid pH; hemin like cytochrome c	550, 520, 416 mμ
c$_1$-Type cytochrome (113)	Unidentified pseudomonad	Intermediate electron carrier	$E_0' =$ about 0.20 volts; isoelectric point at alkaline pH; slowly oxidized in air	553, 523, 419 mμ

Cytochrome c_4 (22, 55)	Azotobacter vinelandii	Intermediate electron carrier; not oxidized by oxidases of mammalian tissues or E. coli or Acetobacter peroxydans	$E_0' = 0.32$ volts at pH 7; not autoxidizable; does not combine with cyanide or carbon monoxide; relatively stable to heat or alkali, denatured in acid; hemin like cytochrome c; isoelectric point at acid pH; contains 0.46% iron; mol. wt. around 12,000	551, 522, 416 mμ (mM extinction coefficients are 23.8, 17.6, 157.2)
Cytochrome c_5 (22, 55)	Azotobacter vinelandii	Intermediate electron carrier; not oxidized by oxidases of mammalian tissues or E. coli or Acetobacter peroxydans	$E_0' = 0.30$ at pH 7; not autoxidizable; does not combine with cyanide or carbon monoxide; relatively stable to heat or alkali, denatured in acid; hemin like cytochrome c; isoelectric point at acid pH	555, 526, 420 mμ
Cytochrome b_4 (117)	Halotolerant bacteria	—	Preparation is probably a mixture, the predominant pigment being a c-type cytochrome	554, 521, 418 mμ
b_1-Type cytochrome (35)	Micrococcus denitrificans	Oxidized by nitrate; reduced by cellular reductases in the presence of succinate or DPNH; autoxidizable; does not combine with cyanide	Protohemin is the prosthetic group; not reduced by ascorbate or ferrocyanide; isoelectric point at alkaline pH	559, 528, 426 mμ
b_1-Type cytochrome (35)	Pseudomonas denitrificans	Oxidized by nitrate; reduced by cellular reductases in the presence of succinate or DPNH; autoxidizable	Protohemin is the prosthetic group; not reduced by ascorbate or ferrocyanide; isoelectric point at alkaline pH	559, 528, 426 mμ

a In this column, numbers in parentheses refer to references.

The redox potentials of the bacterial c-cytochromes vary considerably, some being even more oxidizing than that of mammalian cytochrome c. The cytochrome from *M. denitrificans* has a potential very similar to the mammalian pigment, and is slowly oxidized by the mammalian oxidase.[54]

An *Azotobacter* cytochrome has been obtained in crystalline form.[116]

The two c-type cytochromes isolated from *Azotobacter vinelandii* have been given the special names cytochrome c_4 and c_5 ; they do not interact with oxidases of mammalian tissues or other species of bacteria. So far the c-type cytochromes isolated from other bacteria have not been given special names. If further work shows similar species specificity, a new system of nomenclature will certainly be necessary. Thus far it seems likely that the c-type cytochromes described here all perform similar functions.

Cytochromes of type b have been isolated from *M. denitrificans* and *Pseudomonas denitrificans*.[35] These were found to be autoxidizable and did not combine with cyanide. These cytochromes were reduced by particulate preparations from the corresponding bacteria in the presence of succinate or DPNH.

The cytochrome isolated from halotolerant bacteria[117] and named cytochrome b_4 appears to be a mixture of more than one pigment,[118] the predominant one being a c-type rather than a b-type cytochrome.

The pigment isolated from *Pseudomonas aeruginosa* and called cytochrome GB (for green-brown)[109, 115] has such an unusual absorption spectrum that it seems to be a fraction containing more than one pigment. This fraction shows some oxidase activity for one of the c-type cytochromes from these bacteria.

IX. The Effect of Environmental Factors during Growth on the Cytochrome Content of Bacteria

A. Effect of Oxygen Tension

The cytochromes of yeast grown under anaerobic conditions are qualitatively different from those of aerobically grown yeast.[119, 120] Similar experiments with bacteria have shown quite different effects with different species.

In a number of kinds of bacteria, there was no change observed in the positions of the cytochrome absorption bands when the organisms were grown aerobically as compared with those grown under anaerobic conditions; however, there was a decrease in the intensities of the absorption bands in the anaerobically grown cells.[121-123] On the other hand, Moss[124] observed that the cytochrome a_2 content of *E. coli* and of *Aerobacter aerogenes*[125] was greater when the bacteria were grown at lower oxygen tensions. When *Aerobacter aerogenes* were grown with measured oxygen tensions,[125] the absorption band of cytochrome a_2 was found to be greatest at an oxygen concentration of 10^{-6} M. The content of cytochrome b remained relatively constant when the oxygen concentration was varied between 10^{-6} and 10^{-3} M. Particles prepared from *E. coli* grown anaerobically were found to be lacking in cytochrome a_2, while the pigment was present on particles prepared from cells grown with aeration.[33] The observation of Castor[50] that cytochrome a_2 was present only in cells harvested in the logarithmic growth phase may be related to effects of oxygen tension. Lenhoff and Kaplan[114, 126] found that the content of cytochrome c in *Pseudomonas fluorescens* decreased when the bacteria were grown under strong aeration. In the case of *Pseudomonas fluorescens*, nitrate was present during growth. Since the bacteria are nitrate reducers, this is a more complicated case. Verhoeven and Takeda[63] found similar effects of air in other denitrifying organisms, as well as on one that could not reduce nitrate. *Pseudomonas denitrificans* also fits this pattern of effect of oxygen tension; but no change in cytochrome content of *Micrococcus denitrificans* with changes in oxygen tension was observed during growth.[54] Vernon[34a] found that the relative amounts of the two c-type cytochromes of a nitrate-reducing pseudomonad were different when the cells were grown in the presence or absence of air.

Faced with so many different effects, it is impossible to make any generalizations about the relationship between oxygen tension during growth and cytochrome content of the bacteria. It is even more difficult to explain why variations of oxygen tension make a difference in some species and have no effect in others. More careful and extensive studies are indicated.

B. Effect of Growth Rate

Chaix and Petit[29, 127] examined the cytochrome absorption bands of *B. subtilis* at the temperature of liquid air and observed changes in the relative intensities of the bands which appear to be influenced by the growth rate. These observations were made under conditions where oxygen was stated not to be limiting.

C. Effect of the Iron Content of the Medium

Growth of *Aerobacter indologenes* in an iron-deficient medium[128] resulted in a loss of all of the cytochrome bands. Under similar conditions, the cytochromes of *Aerobacter aerogenes* also decreased, with the cytochrome a_2 decreased to a greater extent than the others.[34b] *Corynebacterium diphtheriae* grown within a certain range of iron concentration in the medium, showed on addition of iron an increase of the cytochrome content of the cells. The changes in cytochrome content could not always be correlated with changes in respiratory activity. Lenhoff *et al.*[129] found that the iron content of the medium affected the growth rate of *Pseudomonas fluorescens* only when the cells were grown anaerobically, since the cytochrome content was low when the bacteria were grown in the presence of air.

D. OTHER EFFECTS

Changes in the cytochrome content of bacteria have been observed under apparently constant conditions of culture. Tissières[34b] described pronounced differences in the cytochrome a_2 content of cultures of *Aerobacter aerogenes* grown under similar conditions. Keilin[130] found that the cytochrome a_2 of *Acetobacter pasteurianum* varied with the culture medium as well as the age of the organism. Effects of composition of the growth medium on the cytochrome content have been observed in other instances.[131, 132] In a strain of *Azotobacter chroococcum* which originally showed a substantial absorption peak of cytochrome a_2, this absorption peak disappeared after several transfers, with no measurable change in the respiratory activity.[17]

Although the work on changes in cytochrome content of bacteria has not been helpful so far in delineating the functions of the different cytochromes, it has pointed to the need for well-regulated conditions in experiments with bacterial cytochromes.

X. Summary

As in mammalian and plant cells and yeast, a series of cytochrome pigments forms part of the respiratory chain of many bacteria. The cytochrome pigments are at the end of the chain where reaction with oxygen takes place, some of the cytochromes being able to react rapidly with molecular oxygen. Although the cytochromes appear to perform similar functions in all respiratory chain systems, the cytochromes of bacteria often differ from those of plant and animal tissues in absorption spectra and other physical and chemical characteristics and always in specificity. Two interesting aspects of the bacterial systems are: the variety of cytochromes which may be present, and the existence of more than one oxidase in some cells. The cytochromes of the bacterial systems, which are linked to insoluble particulate matter within the cells, can have very high turnover rates. The bacterial respiratory chain systems have also been shown to be able to link the oxidation reactions with the formation of ATP.

In recent years considerable success has been achieved in isolating and purifying cytochromes from bacteria. This type of progress should soon lead to an increase in our knowledge of the reactions of these pigments.

In some instances the wide variety met among the cytochromes of bacteria has been useful in elucidating relationships among the different cytochromes. For example, *M. pyogenes* var. *albus* with cytochrome a but no a_3 and *B. subtilis* with a different ratio of cytochrome a to a_3 from that in mammalian tissues were valuable material for studying the reactions of these two cytochromes.[51] A study of the combinations of cytochrome components of different bacteria leads to the conclusion that the only requirement is for a mixture of several cytochromes with appropriately separated redox potentials.

Finally, it must be noted that some bacteria do not have any cytochrome pigments.[31, 133] Examples of these are not only the obligately anaerobic bacteria with no oxidative metabolism, such as clostridia, but also some facultative anaerobes like streptococci or pneumococci. Some bacteria may respire by means of a flavoprotein oxidase (see Chapter 9). All of the obligately aerobic bacteria studied have relatively high concentrations of cytochromes.

REFERENCES

[1] J. Wyman, Jr., *Advances in Protein Chem.* **4**, 407 (1948).

[2] R. Lemberg and J. W. Legge, "Hematin Compounds and Bile Pigments," p. 337. Interscience, New York, 1949.

[3a] H. Theorell, *Advances in Enzymol.* **7**, 265 (1947).

[3b] D. Keilin and E. C. Slater, *Brit. Med. Bull.* **9**, 89 (1953).

[4] D. Keilin, *Proc. Roy. Soc.* **B98**, 312 (1925).

[5] D. Keilin, *Erg. Enzymforsch.* **2**, 239 (1933).

[6] R. Lemberg, B. Bloomfield, P. Caiger, and W. H. Lockwood, *Australian J. Exptl. Biol. Med. Sci.* **33**, 435 (1955).

[7] J. Barrett, *Biochem. J.* **64**, 626 (1956).

[8] R. Hill, *Proc. Roy. Soc.* **B100**, 419 (1926).

[9] H. Theorell, *Biochem. Z.* **298**, 242 (1938).

[10] R. Scarisbrick, *Ann. Rept. Progr. Chem.* **44**, 226 (1947).

[11] F. Egami, M. Ishimoto, T. Mori, Y. Ogura, K. Okunuki, and R. Sato, *J. Biochem. (Tokyo)* **44**, 619 (1957).

[12] W. Frei, L. Reidmüller, and F. Almasy, *Biochem. Z.* **274**, 253 (1934).

[13] A. Fujita and T. Kodama, *Biochem. Z.* **273**, 186 (1934).

[14] S. Yamagutchi, *Botan. Mag. (Tokyo)* **51**, 457 (1937).

[15] E. F. Hartree, *Advances in Enzymol.* **18**, 1 (1957).

[16] B. Chance, *Rev. Sci. Instr.* **22**, 619 (1951).

[17] L. Smith, *Arch. Biochem. Biophys.* **50**, 299 (1954).

[18] B. Chance, *Science* **120**, 767 (1954).

[19] H. Lees and J. R. Simpson, *Biochem. J.* **65**, 297 (1957).

[20] J. H. Bruemmer, P. W. Wilson, J. L. Glenn, and F. L. Crane, *J. Bacteriol.* **73**, 113 (1957).

[21] T. E. King and V. H. Cheldelin, *J. Biol. Chem.* **224**, 579 (1957).

[22] A. Tissières, *Biochem. J.* **64**, 582 (1956).

[23] G. Rendina and R. C. Mills, *J. Bacteriol.* **74**, 572 (1957).

[24] C. Weibull, *J. Bacteriol.* **66**, 696 (1953).

[25] R. Y. Stanier, I. C. Gunsalus, and C. F. Gunsalus, *J. Bacteriol.* **66**, 543 (1953).

[26] R. Barer, *Science* **121**, 709 (1955).

[27] J. B. Bateman and G. W. Monk, *Science* **121**, 441 (1955).

[28] D. Keilin and E. F. Hartree, *Nature* **164**, 254 (1949).

[29] D. Keilin and L. Smith, Unpublished observation.

[30] P. Chaix and J. F. Petit, *Biochim. et Biophys. Acta* **22**, 66 (1956).

[31] L. Smith, *Bacteriol. Revs.* **18**, 106 (1954).

[32] S. Yamagutchi, *Acta Phytochim. (Japan)* **8**, 157 (1934).

[33] R. E. Asnis, V. G. Vely, and M. C. Glick, *J. Bacteriol.* **72,** 314 (1956).

[34a] L. P. Vernon and F. G. White, *Biochim. et Biophys. Acta* **25,** 321 (1957).

[34b] A. Tissières, *Biochem. J.* **50,** 279 (1951).

[35] L. P. Vernon, *J. Biol. Chem.* **222,** 1035 (1956).

[36] D. Keilin and E. F. Hartree, *Biochem. J.* **44,** 205 (1949).

[37] V. R. Potter and A. E. Reif, *J. Biol. Chem.* **194,** 287 (1952).

[38] J. W. Lightbown and F. L. Jackson, *Biochem. J.* **63,** 130 (1956).

[39] R. Hill and E. F. Hartree, *Ann. Rev. Plant Physiol.* **4,** 115 (1953).

[40] L. Smith and B. Chance, *Ann. Rev. Plant Physiol.* **9,** 449 (1958).

[41] A. E. Reif and V. R. Potter, *J. Biol. Chem.* **205,** 279 (1953).

[42] B. Chance and G. R. Williams, *Advances in Enzymol.* **17,** 65 (1956).

[43] G. D. Ludwig and S. A. Kuby, *Federation Proc.* **14,** 247 (1955).

[44] I. S. Longmuir, *Biochem. J.* **57,** 81 (1954).

[45] D. Keilin and E. F. Hartree, *Proc. Roy. Soc.* **B127,** 167 (1939).

[46] B. Chance, *J. Biol. Chem.* **202,** 397 (1953).

[47] F. Kubowitz and E. Haas, *Biochem. Z.* **255,** 247 (1932).

[48] L. N. Castor and B. Chance, *J. Biol. Chem.* **217,** 453 (1955).

[49] B. Chance, L. Smith, and L. N. Castor, *Biochim. et Biophys. Acta* **12,** 289 (1953).

[50] L. N. Castor, Unpublished observations.

[51] L. Smith, *J. Biol. Chem.* **215,** 847 (1955).

[52] L. Smith, *Arch. Biochem. Biophys.* **50,** 315 (1954).

[53] L. P. Vernon and M. D. Kamen, *J. Biol. Chem.* **211,** 663 (1954).

[54] M. D. Kamen and L. P. Vernon, *Biochim. et Biophys. Acta* **17,** 10 (1955).

[55] A. Tissières and R. H. Burris, *Biochim. et Biophys. Acta* **20,** 436 (1956).

[56] M. D. Kamen, *Bacteriol. Revs.* **19,** 250 (1955).

[57] B. Chance, *J. Biol. Chem.* **202,** 383 (1953).

[58] A. Tissières, *Nature* **169,** 880 (1952).

[59] R. G. Bartsch and M. D. Kamen, *J. Biol. Chem.* **230,** 41 (1958).

[60] L. Smith, *in* "Research in Photosynthesis," p. 179. Interscience, New York, 1957.

[61] S. J. Bach, M. Dixon, and L. G. Zerfas, *Biochem. J.* **40,** 229 (1946).

[62] B. Chance and G. R. Williams, *J. Biol. Chem.* **209,** 945 (1954).

[63] W. Verhoeven and Y. Takeda, *in* "Inorganic Nitrogen Metabolism" (W. D. McElroy and B. Glass, eds.), p. 159. Johns Hopkins Press, Baltimore, Maryland, 1956.

[64] R. Sato, *in* "Inorganic Nitrogen Metabolism" (W. D. McElroy and B. Glass, eds.), p. 163. Johns Hopkins Press, Baltimore, Maryland, 1956.

[65] D. Keilin and E. F. Hartree, *Proc. Roy. Soc.* **B129,** 277 (1940).

[66] K. W. Cleland and E. C. Slater, *Biochem. J.* **53,** 547 (1953).

[67] A. Tissières, H. G. Hovenkamp, and E. C. Slater, *Biochim. et Biophys. Acta* **25,** 336 (1957).

[68] T. G. G. Wilson and P. W. Wilson, *J. Bacteriol.* **70,** 30 (1955).

[69] M. Alexander and P. W. Wilson, *Proc. Natl. Acad. Sci. U. S.* **41,** 843 (1955).

[70] M. Alexander and P. W. Wilson, *J. Bacteriol.* **71,** 252 (1956).

[71] H. S. Moyed and D. J. O'Kane, *J. Biol. Chem.* **218,** 831 (1956).

[72] L. A. Hyndman, R. H. Burris, and P. W. Wilson, *J. Bacteriol.* **65,** 522 (1953).

[73] J. W. Legge, *Australian J. Biol. Sci.* **7,** 504 (1954).

[74] P. M. Nossal, D. B. Keech, and D. J. Morton *Biochim. et Biophys. Acta* **22,** 412 (1956).

[75] A. Tissières, *Nature* **174,** 183 (1954).

[76] E. H. Cota-Robles, A. G. Marr, and E. H. Nilson, *J. Bacteriol.* **75,** 243 (1958).

[77] M. Alexander, *Bacteriol. Revs.* **20,** 67 (1957).

[78] H. E. Swim and H. Gest, *J. Bacteriol.* **68,** 755 (1954).

[79] A. W. Linnane and J. L. Still, *Biochim. et Biophys. Acta* **16,** 305 (1955).

[80] P. M. Nossal, *Australian J. Exptl. Biol. Med. Sci.* **31,** 583 (1953).

[81] D. E. Atkinson and B. A. McFadden, *J. Biol. Chem.* **210,** 885 (1954).

[82] H. K. Schachman, A. B. Pardee, and R. Y. Stanier, *Arch. Biochem. Biophys.* **38,** 245 (1952).

[83] R. Repaske, *J. Bacteriol.* **68,** 555 (1954).

[84] A. Tissières, *Intern. Symp. Hematin Enz.* In press.

[85] A. G. Marr and E. H. Cota-Robles, *J. Bacteriol.* **74,** 79 (1957).

[86] C. Weibull, *J. Bacteriol.* **66,** 688 (1953).

[87] C. Weibull, *J. Bacteriol.* **66,** 696 (1953).

[88] W. Militzer, T. B. Sonderegger, and L. C. Tuttle, *Arch. Biochem.* **24,** 75 (1949).

[89] W. Militzer, T. B. Sonderegger, L. C. Tuttle, and C. E. Georgi, *Arch. Biochem.* **26,** 299 (1950).

[90] C. Cooper and A. L. Lehninger, *J. Biol. Chem.* **219,** 489 (1956).

[91] W. W. Kielley and J. R. Bronk, *J. Biol. Chem.* **230,** 521 (1958).

[92] D. E. Green, R. L. Lester, and D. M. Ziegler, *Biochim. et Biophys. Acta* **23,** 516 (1957).

[93] R. Storck and J. T. Wachsman, *J. Bacteriol.* **73,** 784 (1957).

[94] D. E. Atkinson, *J. Bacteriol.* **72,** 195 (1956).

[95] W. E. Magee and R. H. Burris, *J. Bacteriol.* **71,** 635 (1956).

[96] A. F. Brodie and C. T. Gray, *J. Biol. Chem.* **219,** 853 (1956).

[97] A. F. Brodie and C. T. Gray, *Science* **125,** 534 (1957).

[98] C. Widmer, T. E. King, and V. H. Cheldelin, *J. Bacteriol.* **71,** 737 (1956).

[99] A. F. Brodie and C. T. Gray, *Biochim. et Biophys. Acta* **19,** 384 (1956).

[100] I. A. Rose and S. Ochoa, *J. Biol. Chem.* **220,** 307 (1956).

[101] P. E. Hartman, A. F. Brodie, and C. T. Gray, *J. Bacteriol.* **74,** 319 (1957).

[102] D. F. Hersey and S. J. Ajl, *J. Gen. Physiol.* **34,** 295 (1951).

[103] G. B. Pinchot, *J. Am. Chem. Soc.* **77,** 5763 (1955)

[104] G. B. Pinchot, *Biochim. et Biophys. Acta* **23,** 660 (1957).

[105] A. F. Brodie an C. T. Gray, *Biochim. et Biophys. Acta* **17,** 146 (1955).

[106] A. Tissières and E. C. Slater, *Nature* **176,** 736 (1955).

[107] G. B. Pinchot, *J. Biol. Chem.* **205,** 65 (1953).

[108a] E. C. Slater and F. A. Holton, *Biochem. J.* **56,** 28 (1954).

[108b] C. H. Chin, *Congr. intern. biochim. 2e Congr., Paris, 1952. Résumés Communs.* p. 277.

[109] T. Horio, *J. Biochem. (Tokyo)* **45,** 195 (1958).

[110] M. D. Kamen and Y. Takeda, *Biochim. et Biophys. Acta* **21,** 518 (1956).

[111] L. P. Vernon, *Arch. Biochem. Biophys.* **43,** 492 (1953).

[112] L. Smith and J. Ramírez, *Arch. Biochem. Biophys.* **79,** 233 (1959).

[113] L. P. Vernon, *J. Biol. Chem.* **222,** 1045 (1956).

[114] H. M. Lenhoff and N. O. Kaplan, *J. Biol. Chem.* **220,** 967 (1956).

[115] T. Horio, *J. Biochem. (Tokyo)* **45,** 267 (1958).

[116] N. P. Neumann and R. H. Burris, *Federation Proc.* **17,** 282 (1958).

[117] F. Egami, M. Itahashi, R. Sato, and T. Mori, *J. Biochem. (Tokyo)* **40,** 527 (1953).

[118] R. Sato, Personal communication.

[119] P. Slonimski, *Actualités biochim.* **17,** (1955).

[120] C. H. Chin, *Nature* **165,** 926 (1950).

[121] P. Schaeffer, *Biochim. et Biophys. Acta* **9,** 261 (1952).

122 E. Englesberg, J. B. Levy, and A. Gibor, *J. Bacteriol.* **68,** 178 (1954).
123 J. Jensen and E. Thofern, *Z. Naturforsch.* **8b,** 599 (1953).
124 F. Moss, *Australian J. Exptl. Biol. Med. Sci.* **30,** 531 (1952).
125 F. Moss, *Australian J. Exptl. Biol. Med. Sci.* **34,** 395 (1956).
126 H. M. Lenhoff and N. O. Kaplan, *Nature* **172,** 730 (1953).
127 P. Chaix and J. F. Petit, *Biochim. et Biophys. Acta* **45,** 481 (1957).
128 W. S. Waring and C. H. Werkman, *Arch. Biochem.* **4,** 75 (1944).
129 H. M. Lenhoff, D. J. D. Nicholas, and N. O. Kaplan, *J. Biol. Chem.* **220,** 983 (1956).
130 D. Keilin, *Nature* **132,** 783 (1933).
131 N. D. Gary and R. C. Bard, *J. Bacteriol.* **64,** 501 (1952).
132 L. Smith, Unpublished observations.
133 M. A. Farrell, *J. Bacteriol.* **29,** 411 (1935).

Chapter 8

Cytochrome Systems in Anaerobic Electron Transport*

Jack W. Newton† and Martin D. Kamen‡

I. Introduction

The division of the bacteria into aerobes and anaerobes constitutes an important nutritional criterion in bacteriology. It is well known from comparative biochemistry, however, that this division cannot be rigidly maintained.

The oxidoreduction mechanisms of chemosynthetic and photosynthetic bacteria can be considered analogous, although many diverse bacterial genera exist grading from obligate anaerobes to aerobes. Among the chemosynthetic bacteria, those which reduce compounds of sulfur in various oxidation states are anaerobes, those which reduce nitrogen compounds in various oxidation states are facultative anaerobes, and those oxidizing reduced sulfur and nitrogen compounds are obligate aerobes. These bacteria grow either by using energy derived from the oxidation of reduced sub-

* The term "electron transport" is used in this chapter in its general sense without reference to any specific oxidoreduction mechanism.[1]

† Present address: Pioneering Laboratory for Microbiological Chemistry, Northern Utilization Research and Development Division, U. S. Dept. of Agriculture, Peoria, Ill.

‡ Researches by the authors referred to in this chapter have been supported by grants form the National Science Foundation, the C.F. Kettering Foundation, and the National Institutes of Health. This chapter is Communication No. 44 in the series, *Publications of the Graduate Department of Biochemistry, Brandeis University*. General reviews of interest which further elaborate topics discussed in this chapter are cited in the list of references.

strates with preformed electron acceptors or by oxidation of preformed electron donors with specific exogenous oxidants.

Among the photosynthetic bacteria there are obligate anaerobes, such as the green and purple sulfur bacteria and the facultative photoheterotrophic nonsulfur purple bacteria. Again, the photosynthetic bacteria can oxidize reduced substrates only by means of specific photooxidants generated by the absorption of light energy.

All of these bacteria differ basically from the strictly fermentative anaerobes in that they cannot form electron acceptors solely by dismutation of substrate. They require that both electron acceptors and donors be exogenously supplied. In the interaction between donor and acceptor, electron transport systems are required which contain a variety of hematin compounds, that is, heme proteins which are analogous to, but apparently not identical with, those found in aerobic tissues. Little similarity is found with fermentative microorganisms such as the clostridia, which appear to lack electron carrier systems containing heme proteins.

Virtually all of our knowledge concerning the electron transport mechanisms of these "oxidative anaerobes," as the chemosynthetic and photosynthetic bacteria might be called, has only been obtained recently. However, sufficient data are now available to permit a discussion of some of the characteristic properties of cytochrome systems which occur in these groups of bacteria.

II. General Characteristics of Electron Transport in Anaerobes

A. Thermodynamic Considerations

It is informative to estimate the maximum energy available for biochemical use in the electron transport systems which may be encountered in anaerobes. In the example of mammalian aerobic respiration a theoretical limit is set by the effective potential (E_0') of the oxidized-reduced diphosphopyridine nucleotide (DPN) couple and those for typical substrates (approximately -0.4 to -0.32 volt) and that of the oxygen electrode (approximately $+0.8$ volt). The flow of electrons between these two end points is mediated by a series of oxidoreduction systems involving pyridine nucleotides, dehydrogenases, flavin enzymes, and cytochromes. The storage of energy released in this process is effected by coupled phosphorylation of inorganic phosphate, the biochemically useful energy appearing eventually as adenosine triphosphate (ATP). For each electron transferred across the transport chain to oxygen, three phosphate esterifications can occur. Because the energy equivalent of approximately 1.2 electron volts is generated by each electron transferred, and because each polyphosphate bond formed requires nearly 0.35 electron-volt equivalents, practically all of the energy liberated by electron transport can be transformed into phosphate-bond energy.

With the exception of the particles derived from photosynthetic bacteria, there have been no demonstrations of phosphorylations coupled to electron transport in the anaerobic bacteria, although some preliminary attempts have been made with cells of nitrate reducers[2] and clostridial extracts.[3, 3a] If it is assumed that the starting potential for nitrate reduction is near the DPN-DPNH system and that the potential of the nitrate-nitrite couple is +0.5 volt,[4] then the total potential change is reduced to approximately 0.9 volt, thus "shortening" the assumed electron transport chain and reducing the possible yield of ester phosphate, as ATP, per single electron transfer. However, as will be discussed later, it is not clear for what hydrogen donor nitrate serves as terminal oxidant. The available evidence indicates that several pathways exist in different organisms for electron transport to nitrate. Therefore, the point of insertion of the nitrate-nitrite system in the chain will determine the ester phosphate/NO_3^- obtained. Subsequent experiments may show that this ratio does in fact vary from one carrier system to another.

It is possible to demonstrate a phosphorylation coupled to the aerobic oxidation of ferrocytochrome c by mammalian preparations, thereby proving the availability for coupling to phosphorylating systems of electron transport above the cytochrome c level.[5] The theoretical maximum potential drop would be about 0.5 volt, the actual drop depending, of course, on the exact nature of the oxidant. The c-type cytochrome isolated from *Pseudomonas denitrificans* has a potential at pH 7 of +0.32 volt,[6] and consequently, if coupled to the nitrate-nitrite system, could barely provide a one-step potential change adequate for synthesis of a pyrophosphate bond. As an oxidant for a cytochrome b, however, the nitrate system could provide an electron span adequate for one phosphorylation, assuming an oxidation potential of about zero volts for b cytochromes.[7-9]

When considering the sulfate system as oxidant, some special problems arise. *Desulfovibrio desulfuricans* contains a cytochrome "c" (so-called "cytochrome c_3") with an E_0' of -0.205 volt, which can act as a carrier in the reduction of sulfite, thiosulfate, and tetrathionate or dithionite by hydrogen.[10] Since hydrogen, or substrates at or near the same electrode potential as hydrogen, can serve as electron donors for growth, it is apparent that the usable potential span extends only from $E_0' = -0.4$ volt to $E_0' \simeq -0.188$ volt. With only approximately 0.2 volt per electron available as a potential drop, insufficient energy is provided to produce one pyrophosphate linkage even with the whole span utilized. It is necessary to assume that at least two electrons are transferred. It should be noted, as we will see in a later section, that cytochrome c_3 contains two heme moieties per mole. An alternative mechanism—that of substrate level phosphorylation such as encountered in the oxidation steps of glycolysis—may also be operative in addition to coupling through electron transport.

Active phosphorylating preparations are readily obtained from photosynthetic anaerobes.[11-14] All of the preparations obtained thus far require light, but otherwise are substrate-independent. It is generally assumed that an oxidant is formed in the light which oxidizes the terminal electron acceptor and draws electrons through a "respiratory" chain coupled to phosphorylation. In this system it is still not established whether the electrons are donated by bound substrates, or by photoreductant derived from water directly. The amount of phosphate which can be esterified in the absence of added substrates favors the latter alternative. This system is an anaerobic variant—it might be called "fermentation of water"— since the water is apparently providing both electron donor and acceptor systems. So far, no quantum yield has been determined for photophosphorylation by extracts of purple bacteria, but data which will be discussed later suggest that it may be a fairly efficient process.[15]

Pyridine nucleotides, flavin, and large amounts of cytochrome have been detected in particles from photosynthetic bacteria which carry out light-induced phosphorylation.[16] Therefore, the minimum requirements of an electron transport system are present. A light-dependent oxidation of the particle-bound cytochrome has been demonstrated, both in whole cells and isolated particles,[17-26] and evidence for the involvement of pyridine nucleotide and flavin has recently been obtained.[26a, b]

The anaerobic photosynthetic bacteria also appear to contain a "compressed" electron transport system. For, if the electron transport chain of *Chromatium*, for example, begins at the level of reduced pyridine nucleotide, and ends at the bacterial cytochrome c ($E_0' = -0.040$ volt),[27] virtually all of the chain is required for synthesis of only one pyrophosphate bond. It is possible that the photooxidant provides an acceptor at a much more oxidizing potential, however, as is most probably the case with the facultative photoheterotroph, *Rhodospirillum rubrum* (see Table I).

From this discussion it should be clear that it is not possible to extrapolate directly from mammalian respiratory systems to those found in the microorganisms cited, for none of these electron transport systems contains all of the essential components of a "typical" electron transport "chain." As we shall see in a later section, none of these organisms contains cytochromes of the "a" type. While practically all contain c-type cytochromes, none of the bacterial "c" cytochromes are identical in physicochemical and biological properties with the mammalian compounds. Whether the relatively slow growth rates of chemosynthetic anaerobes are a reflection of a "rudimentary" electron transport system is at present an open question, and perhaps one of general biological significance.

TABLE I

ELECTROCHEMICAL PROPERTIES OF CYTOCHROMES "c" AND SOME
ACCEPTOR SYSTEMS UTILIZED FOR GROWTH

	Chromatium D	Pseudomonas denitrificans	Desulfovibrio desulfuricans
Cytochrome oxidant	"(OH)," photo-oxidant[a]	NO_3^-	SO_4^-
Estimated potential first step couple, E_0'	(0.0 volt)[a]	+0.5 volt	−0.188 volt
E_0' heme compound	−0.04 volt	+0.32 volt	−0.205 volt

[a] See text.

B. PHOSPHORYLATION SYSTEMS OF ANAEROBES

It is of historical interest that the first demonstration of a phosphorylation reaction in bacteria apparently "coupled" to electron transport was made using an anaerobic system, "chromatophores" from the photosynthetic bacterium *Rhodospirillum rubrum*.[11] Enough data have now been obtained with such systems to warrant some statements about the general characteristics of these anaerobic phosphorylating preparations. Both the *R. rubrum* system[12, 26] and the phosphorylating particles from the obligately anaerobic photoautotroph *Chromatium*[13] have the following properties: (1) they are *inhibited* by oxygen; (2) they are very stable enzyme preparations, particulate in nature; (3) they are relatively insensitive to cyanide and carbon monoxide, but inhibited by certain iron binding agents; (4) catalytic amounts of "poising" reagents stimulate the phosphorylation reaction; (5) all require magnesium ions and are specific for purine nucleotides; The phosphate acceptor is adenosine diphosphate; (6) cytochromes and other electron transport components are tightly bound in the preparations, which contain large amounts of phospholipid.

As mentioned previously, phosphorylation coupled to the reduction of nitrate or sulfate has not yet been demonstrated. However, if past experience with other anaerobic systems serves as a guide, it is probable that such phosphorylations will be found to be inhibited by oxygen. This seems especially probable for the sulfate-reducing system, because its low potential cytochrome is readily autoxidizable. It has been known for some time that oxygen and nitrate can compete with one another as terminal electron acceptor for growth of facultative anaerobes, this being completely analogous to the competition between light and oxygen manifested by photosynthetic heterotrophs. It seems likely therefore that any phosphorylating preparation which will be found coupled to nitrate reduction will also show oxygen competition, or perhaps inhibition, as is characteristic of the photophosphorylating preparations.

All of the bacterial phosphorylating systems studied thus far have been found to be relatively stable, particulate enzyme complexes. Particle size varies, depending on the organism and method of preparation.* In the photosynthetic bacteria the site of ATP synthesis is the bacterial "chromatophore,"[28] a relatively large (400–1000 A.) subcellular macromolecule which contains the photosynthetic pigments of the cell. The phosphorylation system is not very dependent upon particle integrity, because chromatophore fragments prepared by a variety of procedures can carry out light-activated phosphorylation. The bacterial particles appear to be rather rigidly attached to the cell, because they are not immediately released on cell rupture.[16] Chromatophores, as usually prepared by differential centrifugation, contain large amounts of polysaccharide which appears to be derived from the bacterial cell wall. In addition, they contain the bulk of the cellular heme protein and are very rich in an ethanolamine-containing phospholipid. These and other observations all suggest that the site of electron transport and phosphorylation in the purple bacteria is in or near the bacterial cell surface, as it appears to be in aerobic bacteria.[29, 30, 30a]

The bacterial phosphorylating system from the anaerobe *Chromatium* contains very large amounts of nonheme iron, and the phosphorylation reaction is very sensitive to iron-chelating reagents.[16] It resembles in some ways parts of the mammalian electron transport system, especially the succinic dehydrogenase complex, because, for example, it is greatly stimulated by catalytic amounts of phenazine methosulfate.[26, 13] Photophosphorylation is inhibited by 2,4-dinitrophenol, but at relatively high concentrations; the same is true for cyanide.[26, 13]

Since the bacterial myokinase is soluble and can be readily separated from the phosphorylating particles, it has been possible to show that ADP (adenosine diphosphate), and not AMP (adenosine monophosphate), is the primary phosphate acceptor in the coupled phosphorylation reaction.[12] Similar observations have been made with preparations from aerobic bacteria.[31]

Fragments of particulate phosphorylating particles from the anaerobes can be shown to be stimulated by protein fractions and soluble factors from the supernate of cell extracts.[13, 32, 33] Similar results of fractionation studies have been reported using preparations from aerobic bacteria.[34]

One of the more remarkable features of the anaerobic phosphorylating system found in the purple bacteria is its sensitivity to its electrochemical

---

* The reader will find detailed discussions of more recent work on bacterial chromatophores in the report of a symposium entitled "The Photochemical Apparatus, Its Structure and Function," published as ⚡BNL512(C-28) by the Brookhaven National Laboratory, Upton, New York. This document is available from the Office of Technical Services, Department of Commerce, Washington, 25, D. C.

environment. Catalytic amounts of oxidizing and reducing agents can be shown to act synergistically and antagonistically in activating and inhibiting light-activated phosphorylation.[13] These effects are not very specific ones, because a variety of oxidizing and reducing systems can be used to stimulate photophosphorylation. The reagents appear to act as "poising" agents on the electron transport system. That is, they bring it into an optimal electrochemical condition which permits the most efficient electron flow through the presumed series of electron transport components. This effect appears to be analogous, only on a more complex level, to the effect of redox potential on the rate of metalloflavoprotein reactions.[35]

With the bacterial systems there are varying degrees of activation, depending on the redox couple used, but it seems significant that the reagents most effective in activating the phosphorylation reaction are those with redox potentials near zero volts, such as ascorbate and phenazine methosulfate.[13] It is of interest in this connection that the cytochrome which is firmly attached to the phosphorylating particle has an oxidation-reduction potential in this range ($E_0' = -0.040$ volt),[27] which may explain why these reagents can couple so effectively to the redox systems involved in photophosphorylation. It is easy to show by differential spectrophotometry that ascorbate only partially reduces the cytochrome system even when added in great excess.

As was mentioned earlier, the anaerobic photophosphorylation systems are inhibited by molecular oxygen. A clue to the mechanism may lie in an early observation[36] that photosynthetic bacteria, and cell-free "chromatophores" from them, are capable of carrying out a light-activated photooxidation of ferrocytochrome and reduced dyes by molecular oxygen. It is generally thought that oxidants, formed by a combination reaction between the reducing system generated in the light and oxygen, are responsible for at least part of the oxidizing power, and, in addition, the photochemical "(OH)" system is involved.

It is pertinent that of all substrates studied, the one which is photooxidized most rapidly consists of 2,6-dichlorophenolindophenol, reduced with ascorbate. Although the leuco dye can be photooxidized slowly when added alone, the rate of photooxidation is at least seventeen times as fast when an excess of ascorbate is present.[37] Several other reducing agents are effective, but none is as active as ascorbate. It is significant that, when the ascorbate-indophenol couple is added to phosphorylating *Chromatium* particles under anaerobic conditions, an inhibition of phosphorylation is observed, but only under conditions that would permit maximum photooxidation if air were present, namely, an excess of ascorbate with the dye mediator.[13]

All of these data lend support to the suggestion that at least part of the electron transport pathway involved in photophosphorylation is also used for photooxidation when air is present, and can be made to "uncouple" photophosphorylation—even under anaerobic conditions—merely by providing a catalytic amount of a proper oxidation-reduction couple.

It is worth considering further how ascorbate may function in activating both the photooxidase system on one hand, and the photophosphorylation system on the other. We have referred to its "poising" effect on the heme proteins of the electron transport system. However, this property does not entirely explain the possible function of ascorbate, because other mild reducing agents are not as active in promoting photooxidation or phosphorylation activity. A suggestion of an additional function of ascorbate can be taken from studies[38, 39] on the remarkable effect of enediols on heme protein reactions. Using dihydroxymaleic acid it is observed that the enediol permits peroxidase preparations to simulate oxidase action. In addition, it is possible to show oxygen uptake by cytochrome c in the presence of manganous ions and the enediol. Manganous ion forms H_2O_2 from the enediol. In the presence of ferrous ion, which also stimulates oxygen uptake, no peroxide is formed because it is removed by reaction between the enediol and H_2O_2. It seems possible that either ascorbate or an enediol analogous to the latter may be functioning in a similar manner in the bacterial preparation and causing photochemical oxygen uptake catalyzed by photoperoxides and the bacterial heme proteins. The absence of any detectable peroxide formed by the photooxidase can be attributed to the large amounts of iron in the bacterial particles, which should lead to rapid peroxide decomposition and additional ascorbate oxidation. It is of interest that in addition to ascorbate, a variety of enediols, including dihydroxymaleic acid, stimulate photophosphorylation by *Chromatium* particles.[63]

Regardless of what the eventual chemical mechanism may be proven to be for coupling and uncoupling of the photophosphorylation system to terminal oxidant, available evidence supports the view that anaerobic photooxidation of the cytochrome present in the photophosphorylating particles from purple bacteria is a consequence of the photochemical act and probably a necessary requisite for the phosphorylation reaction (see Section IV). That this may be a general phenomenon in photosynthetic organisms is suggested by the finding of photooxidations of cytochromes in green plant cells and extracts.[40-42]

III. Hematin-Protein Components

A. NOMENCLATURE AND VARIATION OF THE HEMOPROTEINS

Current concepts of hemoprotein structure come almost exclusively from studies of mammalian hematin compounds, particularly most recently from elegant work on cytochrome c.[43-45] From these studies it seems very probable that the ferroheme group is surrounded by four peptide spirals and that the iron is bound out of the porphyrin plane to histidine residues contributed by adjacent peptide spirals. The vinyl side chains of the heme are saturated by condensation and formation of thioether linkages to cysteine residues. In a study of the amino acid composition of a highly purified c-type cytochrome from the denitrifying bacterium *Pseudomonas denitrificans*,[46] it was found that the amino acid content differed radically from that of the mammalian compound. However, sufficient histidine was present to account for a structure for the bacterial cytochrome c similar to that postulated for beef heart cytochrome c. Nevertheless, it is apparently not advisable to draw rigorous conclusions about structure of bacterial heme proteins from the studies with mammalian preparations.

Cytochromes have been grouped into three general categories to rationalize spectroscopic observations of respiring mammalian cells. These are cytochromes of the a type with absorption maxima for so-called "alpha" bands in the spectral region around 600 mμ, b type cytochromes characterized by an alpha absorption band at about 560 mμ and a beta band at approximately 525 to 530 mμ, and cytochromes of the c type with alpha and beta band absorption maxima at 550 and 520 mμ. In addition, the so-called Soret absorption in the 400 mμ region, characteristic of the tetrapyrrol structure, is a property of these hemoproteins. Electron flow to oxygen appears, from spectroscopic and other evidence, to take place in the order: b to c to a, the last cytochrome also constituting the terminal part of the electron transport system.

All anaerobic bacteria studied thus far which are capable either of sulfate reduction, nitrate reduction, or photosynthesis contain cytochromes spectroscopically similar to the c type with absorption maxima in the visible near 550 and 520 mμ. Beyond a similarity in absorption spectra, however, the isolated bacterial proteins have very little in common with the mammalian components. They vary not only in enzyme specificity, but also in electrochemical potential, electrophoretic mobility, and a variety of physicochemical properties. The greatest variations in properties are, as might be anticipated, in those associated with the protein moiety.

One of the major problems in the biochemistry of heme proteins, which could probably be attacked fruitfully through study of the bacterial heme proteins, is the manner in which great variation in electrochemical properties is brought about by alterations in protein structures, which in turn are effective through interaction with the extraplanar electrons of the metal chelate. A clue to how some types of structural and functional variation may be accomplished might be taken from early work[47] on redox potentials of simple iron chelates. It was found that a gradual change in redox potential of iron complexes of organic acids occurred as the number of carbon atoms of dicarboxylic acids was increased. In the series from oxalate upward, changes in redox potential were ascribed to increasing molecular dimensions of the iron chelate. The iron atom was assumed to be forming part of a ring system, the redox potential of which changed as the ring increased in size.

Ionization of protons from "heme-linked" acidic amino acid groups to which the prosthetic groups are attached has been known for some time to alter the affinity of the central iron atom for ligands ("Bohr effect"). In addition, however, it has been shown[48] that in the pH range 8.5 to 9.4, where ionization of carboxyl groups linked to the heme group is not likely to be involved, the ionization of other acidic groups on the protein can influence the reactivity of the central iron atom. A more detailed study of the protein constituents of bacterial heme proteins may give some insight into the types of groups responsible for the great array of electrochemical properties found among these compounds.

All of the c type cytochromes have been demonstrated to be oxidized in enzyme extracts and cells by their corresponding terminal oxidants— sulfur compounds, nitrate, and the photooxidant of the purple bacteria. No cytochromes of the a type have been found in any of these bacteria, although some other hemoproteins of varied nature are sometimes detected. Consequently, the nature of any possible hemoprotein mediator between the c cytochromes and their oxidants remains to be clarified. It seems possible from *in vitro* studies that enzymic mediators between the terminal oxidants and cytochrome c, if they exist, either are not hemoproteins, or are functional variants of cytochrome c.

The varied nature of bacterial cytochromes of the c type found in anaerobes makes it increasingly important to formulate nomenclature adequate to describe and identify the various compounds. A suggestion has been made[49] seeking to identify the various heme proteins by specifying isolation source and the position of the reduced alpha band, viz., *Chromatium* cytochrome 552. This has the advantage of readily identifying the heme protein source, and makes no commitment as to function. However, the terminology is apt to become cumbersome. It may be necessary, because of the great variation in properties of hemoproteins derived from closely similar organisms, that the nomenclature adopted retain some reference to cellular origin. It is clear that the present terminology is inadequate for description of these spectroscopic entities from microorganisms.

B. Specific Compounds

1. Cytochromes of the c Type

Some of the heme proteins of anaerobes which have been isolated and investigated in some detail will now be considered. By far the largest group of cytochromes which have been studied are those of the c type. These compounds have been detected in both cells and cell-free extracts. Owing to their stability they can occasionally be extracted using procedures which usually denature most of the other cellular proteins, and consequently they are easily purified. With some organisms, extraction of dried cells with cold dilute acids suffices. The heme protein, being soluble, is readily separated from precipitated cell debris. On the other hand, several of the obligate anaerobes do not yield their cytochromes when extracted directly with aqueous media; a preliminary defatting of the cell is required.[10, 27, 50] Sonic treatment[6, 16] appear to dissociate the cytochromes from their cellular origin, which appears to be near the cell surface. Butanol solubilization has been used[51, 52] as well as detergent treatment or alkaline extraction.[53] Once the heme proteins are brought into solution, they can usually be purified by conventional means.

a. Compounds from Obligate Anaerobes. Table II summarizes some of the properties of the c-type cytochromes which have been isolated from two obligate anaerobes, *Chromatium*, strain D, and *Desulfovibrio desulfuricans. Chromatium* is generally grown as a photoautotroph, e.g., it is grown in light on media containing reduced sulfur compounds as electron donor, and carbon dioxide as carbon source. *Desulfovibrio,* in contrast, is

TABLE II
PROPERTIES OF c-TYPE CYTOCHROMES FROM OBLIGATE ANAEROBES

Properties	Organism	
	Chromatium D[27, 27a]	*Desulfovibrio desulfuricans*[10]
Spectra (mμ)		
Oxidized Soret	410	410
Reduced maxima	416, 523, 552	419, 525, 553
Reduced pyridine hemochromogen	412, 519, 551	408, 517, 546
Reaction with acetone-acetic acid	None	None
Silver salt cleavage of prosthetic group (thiol linkage)	Yes	Yes
Heat stability	Labile	Stable
Autoxidizability	Rapid	Rapid
CO complex	Slight reaction	None
Isoelectric point, pH	5.4	~10.4
Molecular weight	97,000	~12,000
Molecular weight per heme	~32,000	~6,000
Iron content, %	—	0.9
Iron/heme	—	1
Heme/mole	3	2
E_0', pH 7.0	+0.01 volt	−0.205 volt

usually grown on organic media containing sulfate. Direct potential measurements have indicated that the organisms grow in a very reducing environment, a range of -0.100 to -0.300 volt appearing best for growth initiation in cultures of marine sulfate reducing bacteria.[54] Cells do not grow from small inocula unless media are supplemented with reducing agents.[55, 56]

Another cytochrome c has been isolated from the green sulfur bacteria *Chlorobium limicola*[53] and *Chlorobium thiosulfatophilum*.[57] In these bacteria also, low potential c cytochromes are found. The heme proteins make up a large percentage of the total cellular protein of these organisms.

It is of interest that all of these anaerobic bacteria which possess cytochromes of low oxidation potential have also in common the ability to utilize reduced sulfur compounds in one way or another for growth. The terminal oxidants involved appear to be different, sulfate in the sulfate-reducers, and photooxidants in the photosynthetic sulfur bacteria. It is difficult to say at present whether the low values for the electrochemical potentials of cytochromes present in these organisms are simply reflections of their all living in reducing environments. Nor can the question whether the photoxidant acceptor generated in photosynthesis by the anaerobic bacteria is of relatively low potential be answered.

The cytochrome from *Desulfovibrio* has been named cytochrome c_3.[10] It has been brought to a purity of at least 94% by cellulose and ion-exchange chromatography. Degradation studies show it to contain two heme groups per mole protein, which accounts for its high iron content of 0.9%. Both heme groups appear to be attached to the protein by thioether linkages as in mammalian cytochrome c. Thus this remarkable heme protein is another example of a cytochrome c variant, but the changes in properties from that of the mammalian c are accompanied by addition of a second prosthetic group to the protein molecule.

The *Chromatium* cytochrome has recently been brought to a state of high purity by cellulose chromatography.[27a] Studies with intact cells which will be discussed later indicate, however, that *Chromatium* may contain an array of cytochromes of the c type, which may represent functionally different bound forms of the hemoproteins. Precise characterization of the electron transport system of *Chromatium* may require some improvements in isolation methods for the tightly bound cellular hemoproteins.*

* Recent studies[27a] have demonstrated the soluble preparation described in Table II for *Chromatium* heme protein to be a mixture of two heme proteins. One of these, a cytochrome c-type, has a molecular weight of~95,000 and contains three heme groups per mole of protein. The other, a CO-binding protein is similar to the "RHP"-type protein of the faultative photoheterotrophs has a molecular weight of~35,000 and contains two heme groups per mole.

b. Compounds from Facultative Anaerobes. The first cytochrome of the c type isolated from bacteria was obtained from the facultatively anaerobic photoheterotroph *Rhodospirillum rubrum* in 1953.[58] The compound was found to be present in high concentration, and occurred largely in the soluble fraction of the cell.[59] It could be readily extracted from *R. rubrum* cells with warm acid, and had an absorption spectrum almost identical with that of mammalian cytochrome c. In initial investigations on this pigment, it was believed to be indistinguishable from mammalian cytochrome c. More extensive studies showed, however, that its enzymic and electrochemical properties were quite different from mammalian c.[60] These observations provided the first clues leading to the revelation of the great variation in bacterial cytochromes c. Some of the properties of this pigment are listed in Table III.[59]

A distinguishing feature of the *R. rubrum* compound is its relatively high redox potential, some 80 to 100 millivolts more positive than the mammalian compound. This may account for its inability to be oxidized by mammalian cytochrome oxidase preparations,[60, 61] and suggests a role for the pigment in photometabolism analogous to that postulated for green plant cytochrome f.[62]

The *R. rubrum* cytochrome c has now been well characterized.[59] It is a typically small [M.W. (molecular weight) approximately 14,000], heat-stable hemoprotein, contains a prosthetic group apparently identical to that of mammalian c, and is not autoxidizable. Both *in vitro* and *in vivo* spectroscopic observations and enzymic studies suggest an important role for this pigment in the electron transport system of *R. rubrum* (see Section IV).

TABLE III

SOME PROPERTIES OF CYTOCHROME c FROM *Rhodospirillum rubrum*[58]

Absorption maxima (mμ)	
Reduced pigment	550, 521, 416
Pyridine hemochromogen	550, 520, 414
Cyanide hemochromogen	554, 525, 420–21
Oxidized pigment	535, 408–10, 350
% denaturation, 5 min., pH 7.0, 100° C.	None
Autoxidizability	None
CO complex	None
Isoelectric point	7.5–8.0
Molecular weight	∼14,000
Heme/mole	1
E_0', pH 7.0	+0.320
Reaction with mammalian cytochrome oxidase	None

TABLE IV

CYTOCHROMES OF c TYPE FROM NITRATE-REDUCING BACTERIA[6]

Properties	Organism	
	Pseudomonas denitrificans	Micrococcus denitrificans
Absorption maxima (mμ)		
Reduced pigment	552,525,418	550,522,416
Reduced pyridine hemochromogen	551,520,415	550,520,414
Reduced cyanide hemochromogen	556,527,422	554,525,420
Oxidized pigment	412–13	410–11
E_0', pH 7.0	+0.32 volt	+0.25 volt
Oxidized by mammalian cytochrome oxidase	No	Yes

R. rubrum, as well as other photosynthetic bacteria, contain large amounts of heme proteins, especially of the cytochrome c type. It seems rather unlikely, however, that all of this heme protein is functional in the organisms, because the cytochrome content varies considerably with nutritional factors. Cells grown on media low in iron are especially low in cytochrome content, yet are active metabolically.[63]

Cytochromes of the "c" type have been isolated from the denitrifying bacteria *Micrococcus denitrificans* and *Pseudomonas denitrificans.*[6] Some properties of the pigments are given in Table IV. The cytochromes of *M. denitrificans* and *P. denitrificans* are most easily obtained by homogenization of cell pastes with glass beads in a high-speed blendor.[6] Other methods of extraction are relatively ineffective.

It is of interest that the cytochrome c from *M. denitrificans* is the first bacterial cytochrome of the c type which is indistinguishable spectroscopically, electrochemically, and enzymically from mammalian cytochrome c. Recent investigations have shown that a series of soluble cytochromes of the c type can be isolated in high degree of purity from *Pseudomonas aeruginosa,*[63, 64] an aerobic denitrifier. These cytochromes are inactive enzymically when incubated in air with mammalian cytochrome oxidase, but can be oxidized rapidly by a soluble carbon monoxide-binding oxidase which can also be isolated from the organism. However, this bacterial oxidase, while a heme protein with a c-type spectrum, appears to be a mixture of c-type and an a_2-type cytochrome. Many examples of c cytochromes inactive toward cytochrome c oxidase are known in aerobic denitrifiers[51, 52, 65]

2. CYTOCHROMES OF THE b TYPE

Few compounds of the b type have been detected in the bacteria and a very limited number have been observed in the anaerobes. Among the obligate anaerobes, no b cytochromes have been detected thus far. A cytochrome b difference spectrum has been observed[59] in particles obtained from an acetone powder of *R. rubrum* after removal of the cytochrome c, but the component responsible for the absorption bands has not been isolated. More recently[66] cytochromes of the b type have been isolated from several nitrate-reducing bacteria. Both *M. denitrificans* and *P. denitrificans* have been found to contain, in addition to cytochrome c, compounds with absorption maxima in the reduced state at 559, 528, and 426 mμ. The pigments appear to be quite similar, and have been called cytochrome b.[66] The cytochromes are autoxidizable, and chemical evidence indicates protoheme to be the prosthetic group. Both pigments appear to have a low oxidation potential, and are reduced by DPNH rapidly in the presence of cell extracts. In addition, the reduced pigments are rapidly oxidized by nitrate in cell extracts.

3. OTHER PIGMENTED PROTEINS OF ANAEROBES

a. RHP from Rhodospirillum rubrum and Other Photoheterotrophs. During investigations on the hematin compounds of photosynthetic bacteria, a pigmented protein was observed[59] in *R. rubrum* extracts which resembled myoglobin spectroscopically, but which could not be placed wholly in any one of the known categories of hematin compounds. It formed a carbon monoxide complex which, when reduced, had a myoglobin-carbon monoxide type spectrum, but reduced pyridine and cyanide hemochromogens formed by the pigment had spectra which were the same as those prepared from *R. rubrum* cytochrome c. The compound was shown to be reduced by DPNH and a mammalian cytochrome c reductase preparation, and was rapidly autoxidizable. The reduced pigment could be shown to reduce cytochrome c directly, without enzymic mediation. This heme compound has been termed "pseudohemoglobin," "yellow pigment," and, more recently, "RHP," an abbreviation for *Rhodospirillum* heme protein.

In a continuation of these studies[6] the heme compound was found in a number of other photoheterotrophic bacteria. Later studies on the chemical properties of the protein[67] have established some of its more important properties, which are listed in Table V.*

From studies on the reversible binding of various reagents to the pros-

* For more recent information, see R. G. Bartsch and M. D. Kamen, *J. Biol. Chem.* **230**, 41(1958).

TABLE V

SOME PROPERTIES OF *Rhodospirillum rubrum* HEME PROTEIN[67]

Absorption maxima (mμ)	
Oxidized	390–95,640
Reduced	423,550–60
Reduced CO derivative	416,535,565
Reduced cyanide, pyridine derivatives	Same as cytochrome c
Porphyrin,	Same as cytochrome c
Autoxidizability	Rapid, entire physiological pH range
Reaction with CN, F⁻, N₃⁻, etc.	None
Stability to heat, acid	Relatively thermo- and acid-stable
Isoelectric point	5.0–5.1
E_0', pH 7.0	−0.01 volt
Reaction with mammalian cytochrome c oxidase	None
Molecular weight	28,000 ± 2,000
Heme/mole	1
Iron/heme	1

thetic group of the heme protein, it has been inferred[67] that the compound contains the basic features of a cytochrome c type structure in that thioether linkages are involved in prosthetic group attachment, but that one or more of the imidazole bonds to the central iron atom are loosened, broken, or replaced. This compound may represent a widely distributed general group of respiratory catalysts, because its presence, or the presence of closely related compounds, in a number of bacteria has been indicated from spectroscopic data (see review article by Smith, 1954). Its behavior in the presence of oxidants and respiratory inhibitors suggest that it may be the terminal respiratory pigment in these cells.[18]

The soluble oxidase found in *Pseudomonas aeruginosa*,[64] and referred to in a previous section, resembles RHP in having a hematin band at approximately 640 mμ but this band is not affected by reduction, as is the hematin band in RHP. In certain "halotolerant" bacteria carbon monoxide-binding cytochromes combining both "RHP" hematin band-type spectra and c type three-banded spectra have been reported.[68]

b. Desulfoviridin. A soluble, acidic porphyro protein, green in color, has been isolated[69, 70] from the sulfate-reducing bacteria. The compound has absorption maxima at 630, 585, and 411 mμ, and is stable over a limited pH range, decomposing to yield a fluorescent prosthetic group which is very photosensitive and water soluble. It has been suggested[69] that the chromophore may be a highly carboxylated chlorin. Thus far no metabolic function has been ascertained for this compound.

c. The Blue Pigment from Pseudomonads. During the course of purification of a cytochrome c from *Pseudomonas aeruginosa*,[71] it was noted that there was a blue protein in cell extracts. The pigment had a broad absorption band at 630 mμ which disappeared on reduction with hydrosulfite, or by heating. It did not seem to be a hematin compound, or related to desulfoviridin, because it lacked strong Soret absorption. No functional role was ascribed to the pigment. Later, in other studies[64] a similar blue protein was isolated from *Pseudomonas aeruginosa*, purified, and found to be a copper-containing protein. It was shown it could participate in electron transport chains containing cytochromes of the c type and the soluble carbon monoxide-binding heme protein oxidase, discussed previously.

d. Other Compounds. No cytochrome pigments have been detected in the strictly fermentative anaerobes, such as the *Clostridia,* but there are some claims that heme compounds or related material may be present in small amounts in some of these strictly fermentative bacteria.[3, 72] In studies on the hydrogenase system of *Clostridium pasteurianum,* a carbon monoxide-binding pigment with a broad Soret absorption and a slight peak in the 570–580 mμ region has been detected. *C. pasteurianum* is an active nitrogen-fixing organism, and it is of interest that nitrogenase systems are generally found to be inhibited by extremely low concentrations of carbon monoxide. Difference spectra of the *C. pasteurianum* preparation in the presence of nitrogen have indicated an oxidation by molecular nitrogen of the component which absorbs in the Soret region. More recently, evidence has been presented showing that molecular nitrogen can exert an oxidizing effect on the hemoglobin-like pigment from soybean nodules,[73] thus reenforcing the long-suggested role of hemoproteins in nitrogen fixation.

IV. Function of Heme Proteins

A. SPECTROPHOTOMETRIC STUDIES ON PURPLE BACTERIA

Owing primarily to some elegant methods introduced in recent years,[74-77] it has been possible to obtain direct spectrophotometric evidence for the functional role of heme proteins in photometabolism by intact cells of a number of microorganisms. By using double-beam or split-beam recording spectrophotometers, it is possible to eliminate from the recordings any interference which might be caused by nonspecific changes arising from the light-scattering properties of the organisms. By introducing light of the proper wavelength into the sample at right angles to the measuring beam, it has been possible to measure changes in the steady state level of oxidation of the intracellular heme proteins induced by illumination.

In early studies with *Rhodospirillum rubrum* it was found that light and oxygen exerted similar effects on the heme proteins of the cells.[17, 18] It was concluded that the entire cytochrome system of the bacteria became oxidized on illumination under anaerobic conditions.[18] The change in steady state level of oxidation of the cytochromes was toward a more oxidized condition either if oxygen was introduced into the cell suspension in the dark, or if the cells were illuminated anaerobically. The anaerobic light effect was quantitatively less than the effect of molecular oxygen, but the spectral shifts were remarkably similar under both conditions. The anaerobic light oxidation increased in proportion to the extent of reduction of the cellular cytochromes. As the suspension was incubated for longer periods of time in the dark, which caused extensive reduction of the cytochromes, the subsequent effect of illumination became greater in magnitude. The light oxidation of the cytochrome system was not inhibited by either cyanide or carbon monoxide, compounds commonly used as respiratory inhibitors. Consequently, the photooxidant generated in the light which was responsible for oxidation of the cytochrome system was shown to differ from oxygen in the important respect that its reaction with the terminal oxidant was both cyanide- and carbon monoxide-insensitive.

Later, similar spectrophotometric studies were reported on the hemoproteins found in *Chromatium* cells.[15] It appeared, from light-dark and anaerobic-aerobic difference spectra, that an array of four c cytochromes was present. These differed in the peaks of their difference spectra and the rates of these spectral changes under various conditions. They were designated cytochromes c553, c552, c555, and c560, based on the α-band maxima of the difference spectra: c553 was a component which shifted most rapidly to a more oxidized state on illumination, and presumably was closest in the chain to the photooxidant; c555 was also close to the photoactivated pathway; c552 and c560 reacted most rapidly with air, c552 alone binding carbon monoxide. The hemoproteins were reduced at different rates in the dark, the reduction of c555 being accelerated by colloidal sulfur. Three pathways to c553 were suggested as mediated by the other cytochromes, two responsible for transport from organic donors, and the third an "inorganic" pathway from reduced sulfur compounds. It appeared that the inorganic pathway was more intimately connected to the photooxidant in *Chromatium,* because the reaction between c553 and c555 was most rapid.

When the hemoproteins from *Chromatium* acetone powders were extracted, using the techniques of previous studies, only c553 and c552 could be detected, as had been shown earlier,[27] and the residue from the extractions contained no other hemoproteins. Even when the preparations were examined at $-200°$ C. no additional hemoprotein bands could be observed spectroscopically. From this finding it appeared that either the other *Chromatium* hemoproteins were too labile to be isolated using these techniques, or the components responsible for the various spectral changes were hemoprotein complexes with the bacterial phospholipoprotein, the spectral properties of which were altered when extracted.

In addition, the quantum yield for anaerobic photooxidation of the *Chromatium* hemoprotein c553 was estimated.[15] It was found that a maximum of 2 quanta of yellow light was required to remove 1 electron from the cytochrome via light oxidation, permitting computation of the efficiency of energy conversion from bacteriochlorophyll to cytochrome oxidation. The results did not exclude that possibly only 1 quantum of yellow light per electron was required. From the potential of the hydrogen couple (-0.41 volt) and that of the *Chromatium* cytochrome (-0.040 volt), ΔF^0 for cytochrome oxidation was estimated as 8.5 kcal. Since the utilizable energy from 1 einstein of 590 mμ light, corrected for losses in transfer to bacteriochlorophyll[77] would be 32 kcal./einstein, the efficiency of conversion of energy from excited bacteriochlorophyll to oxidation of the cytochrome in a 2-quantum process could be estimated to be about 13%. An even higher efficiency would be expected in the infrared where the energy per quantum is less. The value of 2 quanta per electron removed from the *Chromatium* cytochrome is in reasonable agreement with the quantum yields of about 12 usually found for carbon dioxide reduction by purple bacteria.[78]

It is evident that the major observed effect of light on the metabolism of intact purple bacteria, as revealed by the components of the electron transport system, is to shift the steady state level of the heme proteins present toward a greater degree of oxidation. Recent studies (M. Nishimura and B. Chance, private communication) have shown that anaerobic photochemical cytochrome oxidation can occur at very low temperatures ($-170°$ C.), which indicates close coupling between chlorophyll and cytochromes of the photochemical unit. However, until the photochemistry of the various components involved in electron transport and energy storage is better understood, it will not be possible to discuss with any confidence the mechanisms which are operative.[78a]

The generally accepted postulates of Van Niel[79] ascribed the initial consequences of light absorption in bacterial photosynthesis to generation of photooxidants from water anaerobically, with resultant competition between these photooxidants and oxygen for reducing systems utilized for dark aerobic growth, on the one hand, and light anaerobic growth, on the other. These postulates take on new meaning with the demonstration of the participation of a carrier electron transport system, in particular heme proteins, in light and dark metabolism of the photosynthetic nonsulfur bacteria.

B. Observations on Nitrate-Reducing Bacteria

Much evidence has been obtained that nitrate can serve as ultimate oxidant in the cytochrome systems of *Escherichia coli, Pseudomonas denitrificans,* and *Micrococcus denitrificans.*[80, 81] In *E. coli,* there are data implicating cytochrome b in the major pathway of nitrate reduction. It has been shown by differential spectrophotometry of both intact cells and cell extracts[80, 81] that nitrate causes a rapid anaerobic oxidation of cytochrome b, and further, that addition of the specific inhibitor of cytochrome b oxidation, 2-heptyl-4-hydroxyquinoline-N-oxide, causes a 70% inhibition of nitrate reduction by *E. coli* sonic extracts. That the inhibitor, even at high concentration, never completely inhibits nitrate reduction is taken as evidence for an alternate nitrate-reducing pathway in *E. coli,* perhaps of the flavoprotein type as elaborated in studies with *Neurospora.*[82-84] It seems likely that nitrate, as well as OH in the photosynthetic bacteria, can oxidize the entire electron transport system of organisms capable of reducing nitrate via reactions coupled to the nitrate reductase enzyme, and that eventual identity of the nitrate-reducing enzyme with any specific electron transport component will require extensive purification of the enzyme.

A nitrate reductase has been isolated in relatively pure form[65] from *Achromobacter fisheri,* a luminescent bacterium, which reduces nitrate only to nitrite. The enzyme has been obtained essentially free of several components of the electron transport system and purified 250-fold. The preparation at highest state of purity contains a cytochrome of the c type which is oxidized by nitrate. A specific DPNH-cytochrome reductase can be separated and purified. This enzyme is required for reduction of nitrate by DPNH and the nitrate reductase preparation; neither cytochrome b from yeast or liver can reduce nitrate when added to the enzyme. In the absence of the DPNH-cytochrome reductase, it is possible, however, to reduce nitrate with the nitrate reductase and reduced benzyl viologen, although leucomethylene blue or indophenol is inactive.

The nitrate-reducing systems of *Neurospora* and soybean leaves have been extensively studied and characterized as metalloflavoproteins.[82-84] However, the potential difference between the donor system, TPN-TPNH, and the nitrate-nitrite couple is inordinately large for a single step oxido-reduction, and the possibility of intermediary carrier systems needs consideration. It appears that the nitrate reductase enzyme is rather unspecific for its electron donor and that, when isolated, it can be coupled in a variety of ways to electron donors and mimics the presence of different enzymes from various sources.

TABLE VI

VARIATION IN CYTOCHROME c CONTENT OF DENITRIFIERS
WITH CONDITIONS OF CULTIVATION[71]

Organism	Cultural conditions	Cytochrome c content (μmoles $\times$ 10^{-4}/mg. protein)
Pseudomonas aeruginosa	High-speed shaking	0.74
Pseudomonas aeruginosa	Low-speed shaking	1.03
Pseudomonas aeruginosa	Anaerobic	2.90
Micrococcus denitrificans	High-speed shaking	0.37
Micrococcus denitrificans	Low-speed shaking	0.99
Micrococcus denitrificans	Anaerobic	2.14
Pseudomonas fluorescens, non-denitrifying strain	High-speed shaking	0.19
	Low-speed shaking	0.37

Additional evidence for a functional role of cytochromes in nitrate reduction comes from physiological studies. The cytochrome c content of a number of nitrate-reducing organisms has been studied as a function of varying oxygen tension, including complete anaerobiosis with nitrate as oxidant.[71] Data typical of the results obtained are shown in Table VI. It is seen that by far the largest cytochrome c content is obtained from cells grown under conditions which permit the nitrate-reducing system to function optimally.

It has been shown in earlier work, using P. fluorescens,[85] that the cytochrome content of pseudomonads decreases in response to strong aeration. Similar results are not obtained with certain yeasts, however, which can be shown to synthesize large amounts of cytochrome in response to aeration.[86]

There have been a number of investigations demonstrating great variation in the cytochrome content of bacteria grown under different cultural conditions. No general correlation can be made between degree of anaerobiosis and cytochrome content. The fact that Azotobacter chroococcum can be shown to form large amounts of cytochrome, detected spectroscopically, merely by allowing washed resting cells to stand overnight in the cold (see review by L. Smith, 1954), is suggestive that the heme proteins can be synthesized from endogenous reserves, or alternatively that pathways exist for enzymic interconversion of heme proteins and their prosthetic groups. This latter process might provide a useful regulatory mechanism for a crossover between various types of anaerobic and aerobic electron transport. In this connection, it would be desirable to conduct studies on variation in content or composition of various heme proteins as a function of change from dark aerobic to light anaerobic metabolism in R. rubrum.

C. Sulfate Reduction

A number of studies[10, 87, 88] have implicated a cytochrome c in sulfate reduction by *D. desulfuricans*. If precautions are taken to remove the H_2S formed on reduction of the substrates, it is possible to show that the purified cytochrome can act as a carrier in the reduction of thiosulfate, tetrathionate, and dithionite by molecular hydrogen and either detergent-treated cells or cell-free extracts of *D. desulfuricans*. In addition, these preparations are capable of carrying out a rapid "knallgas" (oxy-hydrogen) reaction mediated by the hydrogenase and cytochrome c_3. Since *D. desulfuricans* is an obligate anaerobe, it is of interest that the rate of this reaction is more rapid than the rate of sulfate reduction. This suggests a mechanism for growth inhibition in these organisms analogous to that which is implicated by results with photoautotrophic bacteria, namely, that a nonphosphorylative oxygen reaction can interfere with the normally used electron transport system.

The low potential dye, benzyl viologen, can replace the cytochrome in the system coupling hydrogenase to reduction of the various sulfur compounds. Hence some caution must be observed in assigning a specific role for the cytochrome in the sulfate-reducing system.

Recently, H. D. Peck, Jr.[90] has obtained a cell-free system from heterotrophically-grown *Desulfovibrio*, which can reduce both sulfates and sulfites, using molecular hydrogen as reductant. ATP is required and evidence is presented implicating adenosine-5'-phosphosulfate as substrate for the sulfate reduction. As with other systems from the anaerobes, the electron transport system from *D. desulfuricans* appears to be both cyanide- and carbon monoxide-insensitive. The cytochrome c in this organism accounts for 0.3% of the weight of dried bacterial cells.

When *D. desulfuricans* is grown in iron-deficient pyruvate media, it contains no detectable cytochrome c_3 and in addition is unable to reduce sulfate. The content of hydrogenase and of the green pigment, desulfoviridin, is reduced five- and twofold, respectively. In sharp contrast to *D. desulfuricans*, no cytochromes are found in *D. thermodesulfuricans*, the thermophilic sulfate reducer. Furthermore, when *D. thermodesulfuricans* strains are selected for growth at 30° C., they still contain no cytochrome. Analogous results are obtained with strains of *D. desulfuricans* selected for growth at 50° C.; under these circumstances the original cytochrome complement of the cells is retained. From these results, then, it appears that although cytochrome deficiency in *D. desulfuricans* is associated with the inability to reduce sulfate, this is not true for the thermophilic strains. The finding that certain strains of *D. desulfuricans* can grow in sulfate-deficient pyruvate media indicates that the sulfate pathway for electron transport is not an obligatory one in these organisms, in contrast to the photosynthetic autotrophs, which so far have never been grown fermentatively in the dark.*

The presence of large amounts of nonheme iron in the photophosphorylating particles from the photosynthetic autotroph *Chromatium* has been mentioned (see Section II, B). It is noteworthy that cells of *D. desulfuricans* have also been found to contain appreciable amounts of nonheme iron. When the uptake of iron by certain strains was studied it was found that although over 90% of the added iron was assimilated, less than 1% of it could be accounted for as cytochrome, and no other hematin compounds could be detected in the cells. This additional iron cannot be ascribed to the presence of metalloflavins, because the flavin content of the *Chromatium* particles[16] or of *D. desulfuricans*[89] is not high enough to bind the very large amounts of iron in the organisms. It seems likely that a search for additional iron-binding compounds in these anaerobes would be rewarding. Some preliminary studies[63] in which growth media for *R. rubrum* were supplemented with Fe[59]-labeled iron have shown the presence of large amounts of nondialyzable, nonheme iron in soluble protein fractions of the cells.

V. Conclusions

So far, there is not enough evidence to justify the conclusion that the electron transport systems of many anaerobic bacteria differ in any major way from those of aerobes, either structurally or functionally. A large number of heme proteins have now been isolated from various anaerobic bacteria, and although none of these compounds has been shown capable of reacting *directly* with its physiological oxidant, the evidence in favor of functional roles for heme protein mediators of electron transport in these organisms is very convincing.

It is worth considering what evidence exists for heme protein catalysis of oxygen reactions of mammalian cells. Generally, "cytochrome oxidase" is regarded as an enzyme capable of reacting with molecular oxygen; however, this reaction has yet to be demonstrated unequivocally. The enzyme of aerobic tissue capable of activating molecular oxygen remains to be identified conclusively as a heme protein, just as do those enzymes which activate nitrate, sulfate, and other anaerobic oxidants.

The photoautotrophic bacteria are extreme obligate anaerobes and will not grow under relatively anaerobic conditions normally used to grow other anaerobic bacteria, such as the clostridia, for example. This leads to the interesting suggestion that the *presence* of a cytochrome system in

* The anomalous status of the thermophilic sulfate-reducers has been clarified by confirmation (J. Postgate, private communication) of findings by Campbell *et al.*[89a] that the so-called thermophilic strains of *Desulfovibrio* are in reality clostridial species.

the former organisms is responsible for their extreme anaerobic character. It is now known that the cytochromes of these bacteria are low potential, extremely autoxidizable heme proteins and that their phosphorylation reactions are inhibited by oxygen. The fermentative clostridia may be able to tolerate lesser degrees of anaerobiosis because their electron transport systems, lacking cytochromes, are relatively oxygen-insensitive.

It has been tacitly assumed throughout this chapter that some sort of an electron transport "chain" may exist in the organisms discussed, through which electron flow occurs in a graded series of reactions leading to reduction of the electron acceptor. However, it should be equally clear that the existence of an array of spectroscopically differentiable cellular heme proteins analogous to that detected in aerobic mammalian cells has not been demonstrated. Instead there are found large concentrations of cytochrome spectroscopically resembling cytochrome c. When some of these compounds are isolated and subjected to extensive purification and analyses, variant cytochrome c types can be found in the preparations which differ in many physicochemical properties, and can be sometimes physically separated into different closely related proteins. It seems a distinct possibility, therefore, that electron flow in these systems may take place through a series of heme proteins which are electrochemically different, but spectroscopically identical, or very similar. If this suggestion is true, the need to search for heme proteins having electrochemical potentials higher or lower than that found in the cytochromes c would be eliminated. The isolated materials would represent an "average potential" of a large number of electrochemically different heme proteins, all of which are spectroscopically indistinguishable. Evidence supporting this suggestion is provided by the studies cited previously, in which it has been possible to identify a number of different reactive species in the cytochrome c in *Chromatium* cells by observing polyphasic effects in the rates of reduction and oxidation of the c cytochrome complex found in this organism.

It should be apparent from the studies recorded in this chapter that many challenging problems await investigation by microbiologists and chemists in the area of electron transport phenomena characteristic of anaerobiosis. It is to be hoped that a great expansion in research in this area of microbiology occurs in the years immediately ahead. It is possible that such activity will yield results which will in addition shed new light on many problems of mammalian respiration. At the least, a better appreciation of the many functional consequences inherent in the structural union of heme and proteins should be attained.

REFERENCES

[1] W. M. Clark, *Bacteriol. Revs.* **19**, 234 (1955).
[2] H. Takahashi, S. Taniguchi, and F. Egami, *J. Biochem. (Tokyo)* **43**, 223 (1956).

[3] A. L. Shug, P. B. Hamilton, and P. W. Wilson, in "Inorganic Nitrogen Metabolism" (W. D. McElroy and B. Glass, eds.), p. 351. Johns Hopkins Press, Baltimore, Maryland, 1956.

[3a] C. W. Shuster and I. C. Gunsalus, Federation Proc. 17, 310 (1958).

[4] L. Anderson and G. W. E. Plaut, in "Respiratory Enzymes" (H. A. Lardy, ed.), Burgess Company, Minneapolis, Minnesota, 1949.

[5] J. O. Nielson and A. L. Lehninger, J. Biol. Chem. 215, 555 (1955).

[6] M. D. Kamen and L. P. Vernon, Biochim. et Biophys. Acta 17, 10 (1955).

[7] R. Hill, Nature 174, 501 (1954).

[8] L. P. Vernon, J. Biol. Chem. 222, 1035 (1956).

[9] P. Strittmatter and S. Velick, J. Biol. Chem. 221, 253 (1956).

[10] J. R. Postgate, J. Gen. Microbiol. 14, 545 (1956); M. Ishimoto, J. Koyama, T. Ohmura, and Y. Nagai, J. Biochem. (Tokyo) 41, 537 (1954).

[11] A. Frenkel, J. Am. Chem. Soc. 76, 5568 (1954).

[12] A. Frenkel, J. Biol. Chem. 222, 823 (1956).

[13] J. W. Newton and M. D. Kamen, Biochim. et Biophys. Acta 25, 463 (1957).

[14] A. M. Williams, Biochim. et Biophys. Acta 19, 570 (1956).

[15] J. M. Olson, Ph.D. Thesis, University of Pennsylvania, Philadelphia, Pennsylvania (1957).

[16] J. W. Newton and G. A. Newton, Arch. Biochem. Biophys. 71, 250 (1957).

[17] L. N. M. Duysens, Science 121, 803 (1955).

[18] B. Chance and L. Smith, Nature 175, 843 (1955).

[19] L. N. M. Duysens, W. J. Huiskamp, J. J. Vos, and J. M. van der Hart, Biochim. et Biophys. Acta 19, 188 (1956).

[20] L. N. M. Duysens, in "Research in Photosynthesis," p. 164. Interscience, New York, 1957.

[21] J. M. Olson, in "Research in Photosynthesis," p. 174. Interscience, New York, 1957.

[22] L. Smith, in "Research in Photosynthesis," p. 179. Interscience, New York, 1957.

[23] B. Chance and L. Smith, in "Research in Photosynthesis," p. 189. Interscience, New York, 1957.

[24] B. Chance, in "Research in Photosynthesis," p. 184. Interscience, New York, 1957.

[25] B. Chance, M. Baltscheffsky, and L. Smith, in "Research in Photosynthesis," p. 192. Interscience, New York, 1957.

[26] D. M. Geller, Ph.D. Dissertation, Harvard University, Cambridge, Massachusetts (1957).

[26a] J. M. Olson, L. N. M. Duysens, and G. H. M. Kronenberg, Biochem. et Biophys. Acta 36, 125 (1959).

[26b] A. W. Frenkel, Brookhaven Symposia in Biol. 11, 276 (1958).

[27] J. W. Newton and M. D. Kamen, Biochim. et Biophys. Acta 21, 71 (1956).

[27a] R. Bartsch and M. D. Kamen, J. Biol. Chem. in press, 1960.

[28] H. K. Schachman, A. B. Pardee, and R. Y. Stanier, Arch. Biochem. Biophys. 38, 245 (1952).

[29] C. Weibull, J. Bacteriol. 66, 688 (1953).

[30] C. Weibull, J. Bacteriol. 66, 696 (1953).

[30a] J. W. Newton and L. Levine, Arch. Biochem. Biophys. 83, 456 (1959).

[31] I. A. Rose and S. Ochoa, J. Biol. Chem. 220, 307 (1956).

[32] J. W. Newton and M. D. Kamen, in "Research in Photosynthesis," p. 311. Interscience, New York, 1957.

[33] I. Anderson and R. C. Fuller, Plant Physiol. 32, Suppl. xvi (1957).

[34] A. Brodie and C. Gray, Biochim. et Biophys. Acta 17, 146 (1955).

[35] H. R. Mahler, A. S. Fairhurst, and B. Mackler, J. Am. Chem. Soc. 77, 1514 (1955).

[36] L. P. Vernon and M. D. Kamen, *Arch Biochem. Biophys.* **44**, 298 (1953).

[37] J. P. Vernon and E. D. Ihnen, *Biochim. et Biophys. Acta* **24**, 115 (1957).

[38] B. Swedin and H. Theorell, *Nature* **145**, 71 (1940).

[39] H. Theorell and B. Swedin, *Naturwissenschaften* **27**, 95 (1939).

[40] H. Lundegardh, *Physiol. Plantarum* **7**, 375 (1954).

[41] R. H. Nieman and B. Vennesland, *Science* **125**, 253 (1957).

[42] R. Hill, *Symposia Soc. Exptl. Biol.* **5**, 222 (1951).

[43] A. Ehrenberg and H. Theorell, *Acta Chem. Scand.* **9**, 1193 (1955).

[44] H. Tuppy and S. Paleus, *Acta Chem. Scand.* **9**, 353 (1955).

[45] S. Paléus, A. Ehrenberg, and H. Tuppy, *Acta Chem. Scand.* **9**, 365 (1955).

[46] M. D. Kamen and Y. Takeda, *Biochim. et Biophys. Acta* **21**, 518 (1956).

[47] L. Michaelis and E. Friedheim, *J. Biol. Chem.* **91**, 343 (1931).

[48] P. George and G. I. H. Hanania, *Nature* **174**, 33 (1954).

[49] R. Scarisbrick, *Ann. Repts. on Progr. Chem. (Chem. Soc. London)* **44**, 226 (1947).

[50] E. Yakushiji and K. Okunuki, *Proc. Imp. Acad. (Tokyo)*, **17**, 38 (1941).

[51] A. Tissières and R. H. Burris, *Biochim. et Biophys. Acta* **20**, 436 (1956).

[52] A. Tissières, *Biochem. J.* **64**, 582 (1956).

[53] M. D. Kamen and L. P. Vernon, *J. Bacteriol.* **67**, 617 (1954).

[54] C. E. ZoBell and S. C. Rittenberg, *J. Med. Research* **7**, 602 (1948).

[55] J. P. Grossman and J. R. Postgate, *Nature* **171**, 600 (1953).

[56] J. P. Grossman and J. R. Postgate, *Proc. Soc. Appl. Bacteriol.* **16**, 1 (1953).

[57] J. Gibson and H. Larsen, *Biochem. J.* **60**, xxvii (1955).

[58] L. P. Vernon, *Arch. Biochem. Biophys.* **43**, 492 (1953).

[59] L. P. Vernon and M. D. Kamen, *J. Biol. Chem.* **211**, 643 (1954).

[60] S. R. Elsden, M. D. Kamen, and L. P. Vernon, *J. Am. Chem. Soc.* **75**, 63 (1953).

[61] M. D. Kamen and L. P. Vernon, *J. Biol. Chem.* **211**, 663 (1954).

[62] H. E. Davenport and R. Hill, *Proc. Roy. Soc.* **B139**, 327 (1952).

[63] T. Horio, *J. Biochem (Tokyo)* **45**, 195 (1958).

[64] T. Horio, T. Higashi, H. Matsubara, K. Kusai, and K. Okunuki, *Biochim. et Biophys. Acta* **29**, 297 (1958).

[65] J. C. Sadana and W. D. McElroy, *Arch. Biochem. Biophys.* **67**, 16 (1957).

[66] L. P. Vernon, *J. Biol. Chem.* **222**, 1035 (1956).

[67] R. G. Bartsch and M. D. Kamen, *J. Biol. Chem.* **230**, 41 (1958).

[68] M. Kono, S. Taniguchi, and F. Egami, *J. Biochem. (Tokyo)* **44**, 615 (1957).

[69] J. Postgate, *Biochem. J.* **56**, xi (1954).

[70] M. Ishimoto, J. Koyama, and Y. Nagai. *Bull. Chem. Soc., Japan* **7**, 565 (1954).

[71] W. Verhoeven and Y. Takeda, *in* "Inorganic Nitrogen Metabolism" (W. D. McElroy and B. Glass, eds.), p. 159. Johns Hopkins Press, Baltimore, Maryland, 1956.

[72] A. L. Shug, personal communication, 1956.

[73] P. B. Hamilton, A. L. Shug, and P. W. Wilson, *Proc. Natl. Acad. Sci. U.S.* **43**, 297 (1957).

[74] B. Chance, *Rev. Sci. Instr.* **22**, 619 (1951).

[75] C. C. Yang and U. Legallais, *Rev. Sci. Instr.* **25**, 801 (1954).

[76] L. N. M. Duysens, *Nature* **173**, 692 (1954).

[77] L. N. M. Duysens, Ph.D. Thesis, Utrecht (1952).

[78] H. Larsen, *in* "Autotrophic Microorganisms" (B. A. Fry and J. L. Peel, eds.), p. 199. Cambridge Univ. Press, London and New York, 1954.

[78a] For more recent examples of functional differentiation between heme components, see L. Smith and M. Baltscheffsky, *J. Biol. Chem.* **234**, 1575 (1959).

[79] C. B. Van Niel, *Advances in Enzymol.* **1**, 263 (1941).

[80] R. Sato, *in* "Inorganic Nitrogen Metabolism" (W. D. McElroy and B. Glass, eds.), p. 163. Johns Hopkins Press, Baltimore, Maryland, 1956.

[81] S. Taniguchi, R. Sato, and F. Egami, *in* "Inorganic Nitrogen Metabolism" (W. D. McElroy and B. Glass, eds.), p. 87. Johns Hopkins Press, Baltimore, Maryland, 1956.

[82] A. Nason and H. J. Evans, *J. Biol. Chem.* **202,** 655 (1953).

[83] H. J. Evans and A. Nason, *Plant Physiol.* **28,** 233 (1953).

[84] D. J. D. Nicholas and A. Nason, *J. Biol. Chem.* **211,** 183 (1954).

[85] H. W. Lenhoff and N. O. Kaplan, *Nature* **172,** 730 (1953).

[86] M. Ycas and D. L. Drabkin, *J. Biol. Chem.* **224,** 921 (1957).

[87] J. R. Postgate, *J. Gen. Microbiol.* **15,** 186 (1956).

[88] J. R. Postgate, *J. Gen. Microbiol.* **15,** 10 (1956).

[89] J. L. Peel, *J. Gen. Microbiol.* **12,** ii (1955).

[89a] L. Campbell, Jr., H. A. Frank, and E. R. Hall, *J. Bacteriol.* **73,** 516 (1957).

[90] H. D. Peck, *Proc. Natl. Acad. Sci. U. S.* **45,** 701 (1959).

GENERAL REFERENCES

Bacterial Cytochromes:

L. Smith, *Bacteriol. Revs.* **18,** 106 (1954).

M. D. Kamen, *Bacteriol. Revs.* **19,** 250 (1955).

M. D. Kamen, *in* "Enzymes: Units of Biological Structure and Function" (O. H. Gaebler, ed.), p. 483, Academic Press, New York, 1956.

Nitrate reduction:

C. C. Delwiche, *in* "Inorganic Nitrogen Metabolism" (W. D. McElroy and B. Glass, eds.), p. 233. Johns Hopkins Press, Baltimore, Maryland, 1956. See also other papers in this volume.

Sulfate reduction:

K. R. Butlin and J. R. Postgate, "Colloque Sur La Biochimie Du Soufre," p. 61. Centre National de la Recherche Scientifique, Paris, 1956.

Heme proteins:

R. Lemberg and J. W. Legge, "Hematin Compounds and Bile Pigments." Interscience, New York, 1949.

P. George, *in* "Currents in Biochemical Research" (D. E. Green, ed.), Interscience, New York, 1956.

CHAPTER 9

Cytochrome-Independent Electron Transport Enzymes of Bacteria

M. I. DOLIN

I. Introduction*

A. ELECTRON TRANSPORT NOT COUPLED TO CYTOCHROME

The known mechanisms of electron transport used by cytochrome-containing bacteria have been discussed in Chapter 6. In addition to the partic-

* Abbreviations used: PN, PNH, oxidized and reduced pyridine nucleotide; DPN, DPNH, oxidized and reduced diphosphopyridine nucleotide; TPN, TPNH, oxidized

ulate oxidases described there, various soluble systems for the reoxidation of reduced pyridine nucleotide are known. These systems, together with some indication of their distribution may be summarized briefly as follows: (a) Flavoproteins (bacteria, yeast): These enzymes may catalyze either two- or four-electron transfer reactions [(equations (1) and (2)]. Thus far,

$$PNH + H^+ + O_2 \xrightarrow{FP} PN^+ + H_2O_2 \tag{1}$$

$$2PNH + 2H^+ + O_2 \xrightarrow{FP} 2PN^+ + 2H_2O \tag{2}$$

four-electron transfer by flavoproteins has been demonstrated only in bacteria.[1] In addition to the flavoproteins that react directly with O_2, bacteria, yeast, animals, and plants contain flavoproteins (diaphorases) which are reoxidized by artificial electron acceptors (Section IV). (b) Hydroperoxidases (plants): Under certain conditions, this enzyme may catalyze four-electron reduction of O_2 to water with reduced diphospho-pyridine nucleotide (DPNH) or reduced triphosphopyridine nucleotide (TPNH) as reductants.[2] (c) Ascorbic acid-dependent enzymes (plants, animal systems, some bacteria): Certain oxidases for reduced pyridine nucleotide require the presence of ascorbic acid plus an ascorbic acid oxi-dase (see Section II, D).

Among the enzymes which catalyze direct substrate oxidation, there are flavoproteins (and the Cu-enzyme, uricase) which catalyze two-elec-tron transfer reactions and copper enzymes such as tyrosinase (polyphenol oxidase) which catalyze four-electron transfer.[3] Although there are early reports in the literature[4, 5] that tyrosinase activity is found in certain bacteria, there is as yet no evidence that tyrosinase or an equivalent enzyme is involved in any main-line respiratory process in bacteria. There is also no evidence that the hydroperoxidase reaction occurs in bacteria. Bacterial pigments such as pyocyanine or toxoflavin are redox systems,[6] but they have not yet been implicated in any physiological electron trans-port mechanism. Available evidence indicates that in cytochrome-free bacteria (e.g., lactic acid bacteria, clostridia) flavoprotein systems are the major link between substrate and oxygen. Such systems may be phys-iologically useful for certain of the cytochrome-free facultative anaerobes (Section IX).

B. Development of Concepts regarding Flavoprotein Respiration

Wieland's dehydrogenation theory[7] called for the activation of substrate by a specific catalyst followed by transfer of the "activated" hydrogen

---

and reduced triphosphopyridine nucleotide; FP, FPH_2, oxidized and reduced flavo-protein; FAD, flavin adenine dinucleotide; FMN, flavin mononucleotide; TPP, co-carboxylase; lip(SS), lip$(SH)_2$, oxidized and reduced lipoic acid; CoA, coenzyme A; ADP, adenosine diphosphate; ATP, adenosine triphosphate; NMNH, reduced nico-tinamide mononucleotide.

to any of a number of unspecific, unactivated oxidants. With O_2 as acceptor, H_2O_2 was considered to be the obligatory reduced product [equation (3)]. Since the formation of stoichiometric amounts of peroxide was con-

$$A \overset{\displaystyle /\ H^*}{\underset{\displaystyle \backslash\ H^*}{}} + O_2 \rightarrow A + H_2O_2 \tag{3}$$

$$H^* = \text{``active'' hydrogen}$$

sidered to be crucial for the validity of the theory, many attempts were made to establish the stoichiometry of reaction (3). Catalase-free bacteria were commonly used as experimental material. Early studies had shown that pneumococci, streptococci,[8, 9] and various anaerobes[10] could form some peroxide in the presence of O_2. However, the first quantitative experiments were reported by Bertho and Gluck,[11] who showed that during glucose oxidation by cell suspensions of *Lactobacillus delbrueckii* or *L. acidophilus* there was a 1:1 equivalence between O_2 uptake and peroxide formation as required by equation (3). These data were thought to confirm the Wieland theory. Similar results were later reported for *L. delbrueckii*,[12] *L. bulgaricus*,[13] and pneumococci.[14] Simultaneous with this work, however, the first flavoprotein, the old yellow enzyme of yeast, was discovered.[15] This enzyme catalyzes CN- and CO-insensitive TPNH oxidation as shown in equations (4a) and (4b). These reactions demonstrated that

$$TPNH + H^+ + FP \rightarrow TPN^+ + FPH_2 \tag{4a}$$

$$FPH_2 + O_2 \rightarrow FP + H_2O_2 \tag{4b}$$

hydrogen peroxide is formed via the two-electron reduction of O_2 by reduced flavoprotein and not by direct reaction between "active" hydrogen and molecular O_2. It was also reported[15] that intact cells of *L. delbrueckii* contained a flavoprotein system that could account for the entire respiration of the organism ($Q_{O_2} = 12$, with glucose-6-phosphate as substrate). The system resembled the old yellow enzyme in turnover, insensitivity to CN and CO, and in formation of H_2O_2 as the reduced product. The turnover of the old yellow enzyme (recent value[16]: 35 min.$^{-1}$) is, however, much too low to account for the respiratory activity of yeast. Furthermore, the old yellow enzyme is unaffected by CN and CO, both of which inhibit yeast respiration. The concept arose, therefore, that the only physiological pathway for flavoprotein reoxidation by O_2 was mediated by CN- and CO-sensitive iron carriers.[15] This belief was strengthened by the finding that in intact yeast cells the rate of cytochrome reduction is equal to the over-all respiratory rate,[17] and by the subsequent isolation of flavoproteins

that catalyzed rapid cytochrome c reduction by reduced pyridine nucleotides (Chapter 6).

Flavins are widely distributed among cytochrome and noncytochrome-
containing organisms.[15, 18]* Since the characteristics of many isolated flavoproteins resemble those of the old yellow enzyme[19] it has been assumed
that the old yellow enzyme is a general model for all flavoprotein systems
that react directly with O_2. The often reiterated properties of flavoprotein
respiration are (a) high O_2 requirement,[20] (b) low turnover, (c) stoichiometric peroxide formation. These characteristics are the basis for calling
flavoprotein respiration "unphysiological." (In cytochrome- and catalase-
free lactic acid bacteria, in which flavoprotein respiration does account
for the observed respiratory rate, toxic concentrations of peroxide were
considered to be the invariable reduced product.)

There have long been indications, however, that this description of
flavoprotein catalysis is not entirely valid. For instance, experiments with
resting cells of Streptococcus faecalis[21] indicated that rapid oxidations could
be achieved and that excessive O_2 concentrations were not required. Table
I shows that the respiratory activity of various cytochrome- and catalase-
free bacteria is equal to or exceeds that of baker's yeast, and that peroxide
need not be the reduced product. Subsequently, these results were confirmed and extended when potent, soluble DPNH oxidases were isolated
from S. faecalis,[29, 30] Clostridium kluyveri,[31] and C. perfringens.[1, 32, 33a,b] In
crude extracts of C. perfringens, DPNH oxidase activity is as great, on
a specific activity basis, as in crude extracts of the strict aerobe Azotobacter
vinelandii.[33a] For the flavoprotein DPNH oxidase system of S. faecalis[30]
for K_s for O_2 has been estimated[34] as $2 \times 10^{-6} M$, a value which is of
the same order of magnitude as that found for various typical cytochrome-
containing respiratory preparations, and some 30 times lower than the
K_s for several classic flavoprotein oxidases.[20]

Although pyruvate can occur as an intermediate during the oxidation
of glucose by lactic acid bacteria, the known spontaneous reaction between
pyruvate and peroxide[35] does not account for the fact that some lactic
acid bacteria, do not form peroxide as a product of glucose or alcohol
oxidation (Table I). However, enzymatic catalysis of peroxide reduction
in the presence of oxidizable substrate has been demonstrated with resting cells of streptococci[26, 36] and lactobacilli.[37, 38] These peroxidase activities were recognized as being atypical since they apparently did not involve heavy metal catalysts. The enzyme responsible for the reaction in

---

* The naturally occurring nucleotides are FAD and FMN. However, L. lactis cells,
grown on lyxoflavin, synthesize lyxoflavin mono- and dinucleotides in place of riboflavin nucleotides. Lyxoflavin nucleotides are less active than FMN and FAD in the
appropriate enzymatic test systems.[18a]

TABLE I

OXIDATIONS CATALYZED BY CELL SUSPENSIONS OF CYTOCHROME AND
CATALASE FREE BACTERIA (COMPARED WITH YEAST)

Organism	Substrate	Reduced product	$Q_{O_2}{}^a$	Reference
Baker's yeast	Glucose	H_2O	40–90	15, 22
Lactobacillus delbrueckii	Glucose	H_2O_2	10–20	12
	Lactate	H_2O_2	30–120	
Lactobacillus casei	Glucose	—	3	23
Streptococcus faecalis (strain 24)	Glycerol	H_2O_2	70–110	21
Streptococcus faecalis, 10C1	Glucose	H_2O	90	24
	Pyruvate	H_2O	80	25
Streptococcus faecalis (strain B 33a)				26
Aerobically grown	Glucose	H_2O	100	
Anaerobically grown	Glucose	H_2O_2	100	
Streptococcus mastitidis	Alcohol	H_2O	60–170	27
Pneumococci	Glucose	H_2O_2	30–100	14
Clostridium saccharobutylicum	Glucose	H_2O_2 doubtful or negative	20–40	28

^{a} $Q_{O_2} = \mu$l. O_2 per hr. per mg. dry wt. of bacterial suspension (based on initial rates). A common feature of the reactions that result in H_2O_2 formation is that the respiratory rate decreases with time and may become negligible within 40 to 60 min. In general, the reactions that do not yield peroxide follow zero-order kinetics.

S. faecalis (and presumably in the other lactic acid bacteria) was later identified as a flavoprotein DPNH peroxidase.[30, 39] The combined action of two enzymes, a flavoprotein DPNH oxidase and the peroxidase, resulted in four-electron reduction of O_2 to water, as shown in equations (5a)–(5c). Another mechanism for catalyzing four-electron reduction of

$$DPNH + H^+ + O_2 \rightarrow DPN^+ + H_2O_2 \tag{5a}$$

$$\underline{DPNH + H^+ + H_2O_2 \rightarrow DPN^+ + 2H_2O} \tag{5b}$$

$$\text{Sum: } 2DPNH + 2H^+ + O_2 \rightarrow 2DPN^+ + 2H_2O \tag{5c}$$

O_2 was discovered in *C. perfringens*.[1, 32, 33a,b] In this organism, reaction (5c) is catalyzed by a single flavoprotein; free peroxide is not an intermediate.

Glycerol oxidation by cells of *S. faecalis*,[21] and pyruvate oxidation by cell-free extracts of *S. faecalis*[40] and *L. delbrueckii*[41] is coupled with the formation of "energy-rich" phosphate bonds (at the substrate level). The utility of some of the oxidations is illustrated by the fact that some strains of *S. faecalis* (and various pediococci) will not utilize glycerol as a growth substrate except under aerobic conditions.[42a,b] Direct growth experiments show that the DPNH oxidation and peroxidation pathway in *S. faecalis* is physiologically useful[26, 30] (see Section IX, A). It appears, therefore, that whereas the classic characteristics of flavoprotein respiration may describe many of the known enzymes, there are, among the cytochrome-free bacteria, flavoprotein systems which do not conform to the "classic" unphysiological pattern. Detailed documentation for these statements is given in the succeeding sections.

C. Nomenclature

A confusing array of terms is currently used to describe enzymes that catalyze the oxidation of reduced pyridine nucleotides. In this chapter, the following system is followed.

DPNH (TPNH) oxidase: These are enzymes that catalyze the oxidation of reduced pyridine nucleotide according to equations (1) or (2). O_2 is the electron acceptor.

Direct flavoprotein oxidases: These enzymes couple the oxidation of "noncoenzyme" substrates to the reduction of O_2. Free coenzymes do not mediate electron transport between the substrate and the oxidized enzyme. (Direct oxidases of this sort are generally less useful than the oxidases for reduced pyridine nucleotides. An organism whose aerobic respiration depends upon the function of one or more direct flavoprotein oxidases is obviously limited in its ability to use oxygen as a terminal electron acceptor. On the other hand, an organism which can transfer electrons from DPNH and TPNH to oxygen can couple any of its pyridine nucleotide-linked dehydrogenases to molecular oxygen.)

Diaphorases: Diaphorase couples the oxidation of reduced pyridine nucleotide to the reduction of artificial electron acceptors. Enzymes that use a physiological oxidant are named after the oxidant (i.e., nitrate reductase, cytochrome c reductase). Enzymes for which a physiological oxidant is known can also show "diaphorase activity" if artificial electron acceptors function as alternative oxidants.

Dehydrogenase: The term diaphorase is usually reserved for enzymes that use reduced pyridine nucleotides as substrates. A dehydrogenase, in general, is an enzyme that couples the oxidation of a substrate to the reduction of an acceptor other than oxygen. Certain of the pyridine nucleotide-linked reactions involving thiol substrates are also best referred to as dehydrogenase activities.

II. Oxidases for Reduced Pyridine Nucleotides

A. Old Yellow Enzyme

The old yellow enzyme of yeast,[15] which catalyzes reaction (4a) and (4b), was the first flavoprotein isolated. The crystalline enzyme[16] has a molecular weight of 100,000–105,000 and contains 2 moles of FMN per mole of enzyme. As mentioned previously, the turnover, 35 min.$^{-1}$, is too low to account for any considerable proportion of yeast respiration. If there is an alternative physiological acceptor, it is as yet undiscovered. It has been reported[43] that at atmospheric O_2 tension and in the presence of cytochrome c, about 50% of the reducing equivalents from reduced old yellow enzyme are transferred to cytochrome c and 50% to O_2. With the discovery of TPNH-cytochrome c reductase (Chapter 6) (turnover, 650 min.$^{-1}$ for a two-electron reaction)[44] it was suggested[45] that the cytochrome c reaction of the old yellow enzyme may have been caused by slight contamination with cytochrome c reductase. The acceptor specificity of crystalline old yellow enzyme has not yet been reported.

When old yellow enzyme is partially reduced by hydrosulfite in the presence of excess TPN,[46a] a red color is formed. The color was originally attributed to the formation of an enzyme-pyridine nucleotide complex, with the flavin stabilized as the red semiquinone. Recent experiments[46b] have shown that a radical is, in fact, detectable (by paramagnetic resonance methods) on reduction of old yellow enzyme by TPNH; however, it appears that the radical is not identical with the red compound. The latter may be a flavoprotein-TPN complex. These spectrophotometric experiments are rather puzzling at present, since the red compound is not always detected.[47]

B. DPNH Oxidase System of S. faecalis

S. faecalis contains at least five separate flavoproteins that catalyze DPNH oxidation[29, 30, 39, 48] (TPNH is not a substrate for any of these reactions). These enzymes are (a) a DPNH oxidase [equation (5a)], (b) a DPNH peroxidase [equation (5b); Section III, B], (c) a cytochrome c reductase (Chapter 6), (d) a diaphorase that uses 2,6-dichlorophenol-indophenol, ferricyanide, and a series of quinones as oxidants (Section IV), and (e) a menadione reductase that is not identical with any of the first four enzymes.

These enzymes may be separated from each other by classic fractionation procedures followed by zone electrophoresis. The enzymes also show different sensitivities to ultraviolet irradiation.[30] These results indicate that the practice, which is sometimes followed, of attributing all DPNH oxidase activities that are observed in crude extracts to the function of a single "DPNH oxidase" is not warranted.

As mentioned in Section I, B, S. faecalis catalyzes the four-electron reduction of O_2 to water via reactions (5a) and (5b), which are catalyzed by DPNH oxidase and peroxidase, respectively. In initial extracts, the activity of the oxidase and peroxidase system ($\sim$0.15 μmoles DPNH oxidized per min. per mg. protein) can account for all the respiration of intact cells (Table I). The cell-free oxidase, unlike the peroxidase, is unstable on storage and has not been purified. However, DPNH oxidase apoenzyme can be prepared either from flavin-deficient cells[30] or by the classic acid resolution procedure.[49] Activity is restored specifically by flavin adenine dinucleotide (FAD). A requirement for Mn^{++} can also be demonstrated. Under conditions in which the peroxidase activity is made limiting, peroxide can be demonstrated as the reduced product.[29]

C. Reduced Pyridine Nucleotide Oxidases of Clostridia

1. Oxygen Uptake by Clostridia

Although clostridia cannot grow aerobically, cell suspensions of many clostridial species are able to catalyze rapid oxygen uptake.[28, 50, 51, 52] Peroxide may or may not be formed in these oxidations, depending upon the nature of the enzymes involved.[1, 32, 33a] The literature dealing with peroxide formation by anaerobes has been reviewed.[53] Since growth studies[53] suggest that peroxide formed through respiratory reactions may account in large measure for the inability of anaerobes to use O_2 as a physiological oxidant, the nature of the oxidative catalysts present in clostridia becomes an important physiological consideration.

2. DPNH Oxidase of *C. perfringens*[1, 32, 33a,b]

a. Isolation, Prosthetic Group. *C. perfringens* extracts catalyze the four-electron reduction of O_2 to water, with DPNH as electron donor [equation (5c)]. Free peroxide is not an intermediate in the reaction, as shown in Fig. 1. The mechanism of the oxidation is thus different both from that of the old yellow enzyme and the oxidase and peroxidase systems of *S. faecalis*. In crude extracts, the specific activity for DPNH oxidation (Table II) equals that shown by extracts of the strict aerobe, *Azotobacter vinelandii*. The clostridial enzyme can be purified by isoelectric precipitation, followed by zone electrophoresis at or near the isoelectric point. With purified fractions, the bound flavin or FAD content is directly proportional to oxidase activity (Fig. 2). On a molar basis, only one-half of the bound flavin is FAD, which suggests that the enzyme contains two flavin prosthetic groups. The turnover of the purified enzyme, unlike that of the old yellow enzyme, compares very favorably with the flavoprotein turnovers of some typical aerobic respiratory preparations (Table II).

b. Inhibitors. The oxidase is not inhibited by 0.01 M CN, but is sensitive to peroxide and *p*-chloromercuribenzoate and is inhibited 50% by 0.01 M azide. Although stoichiometric peroxide concentrations are not formed during DPNH oxidation, traces ($\sim 1 \times 10^{-6} M$) may be detected.

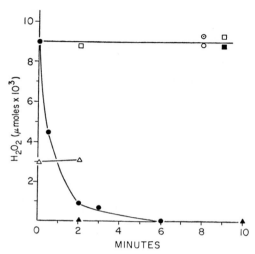

FIG. 1. Difference in role of H_2O_2 in DPNH oxidase systems of *Streptococcus fae-calis* (10C1) and *Clostridium perfringens*. Anaerobic experiment (details in reference 33a). Complete system: 0.066 M potassium phosphate, pH 7.0; DPNH, 0.3 μmoles; H_2O_2, 0.009 μmoles. Final volume 3 ml.; Temp. 23°C. *S. faecalis*: crude extract containing DPNH oxidase and peroxidase, 4 units of DPNH oxidase activity: ●, complete system; ○, without DPNH. *C. perfringens*: crude extract, 11 units of DPNH oxidase activity: □, complete; ■, without DPNH; △, complete, except used 0.003 μmoles H_2O_2; ▲, without H_2O_2. ☉, H_2O_2, 0.009 μmoles in complete system without enzymes. The experiment demonstrates that the DPNH oxidase and peroxidase system of *S. faecalis* utilizes coenzyme levels of H_2O_2 in an enzyme and DPNH dependent reaction, whereas the *C. perfringens* enzyme does not. The free H_2O_2 (approx. 1 × 10^{-6} M) formed during DPNH oxidation by *C. perfringens* extracts is, therefore, not an intermediate in the over-all reaction [equation (5c)]. Reprinted with permission from the *Journal of Bacteriology*.

These small concentrations cause, in the presence of DPNH, a first-order decay of enzyme activity ($k = 0.13$–0.15 min.$^{-1}$), which may be reduced 3-fold in the presence of catalase ($k = 0.049$ min.$^{-1}$).[33a] Concentrations of DPNH in excess of 3 × 10^{-4} M cause immediate inhibitions which are a direct linear function of the DPNH concentration. This type of inhibition, which may reflect the binding of an additional molecule of DPNH to the enzyme, is not prevented by catalase.

c. Specificity. TPNH is not a substrate for the enzyme. Crude extracts contain enzymes which catalyze DPNH-dependent reduction of menadione and free flavins. These reactions are not catalyzed by the four-electron oxidase. Aerobically, the menadione- and FAD-dependent reactions result in peroxide formation (Chapter 6, Section IV, C).

d. Relation to Cytochrome c Reductase. Evidence has been presented[1, 33b]

TABLE II

OXIDASES FOR REDUCED PYRIDINE NUCLEOTIDE: COMPARISON OF PARTICULATE CYTOCHROME CONTAINING ENZYMES AND SOLUBLE FLAVOPROTEIN OXIDASES

Preparation	Source	Composition	TON[a]		Reference
			μmoles PNH oxidized per min. per mg. protein	μmoles PNH oxidized per min. per μmole bound flavin	
"Closed" DPNH oxidase	Beef heart	Flavin and cytochrome-containing particulate oxidase	1.0 (23°C.)	2600	54
Electron transport particle (DPNH oxidase)	Azotobacter vinelandii	Flavin and cytochrome-containing particulate oxidase			55
		(1) crude enzyme	0.8 (35°C.)	—	
		(2) purified particles	6.8 (35°C.)	6800	
Old yellow enzyme (TPNH oxidase)	Bottom yeast	Crystalline flavoprotein (FMN)	0.35 (38°C.)	18	16
DPNH oxidase	Clostridium perfringens	Flavoprotein (FAD + unidentified flavin)			1, 32, 33a,b
		(1) crude enzyme	0.7–0.9	—	
		(2) purified enzyme	14	4500	

[a] The oxidant is air for all preparations except the old yellow enzyme, in which case it is pure O_2.

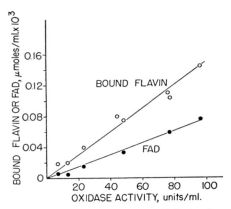

FIG. 2. DPNH oxidase, *Clostridium perfringens*. Relation between DPNH oxidase activity and flavin content of the purified enzyme (text). Bound flavin is the total flavin content, corrected for the amount of flavin that is fluorescent before hydrolysis of the enzyme with trichloracetic acid. FAD was determined enzymically. See reference 33b. Reprinted with permission from the *Journal of Bacteriology*.

which strongly suggests that the native DPNH oxidase is also a cytochrome c reductase. Spontaneous or ultraviolet-induced loss of the four-electron transfer reaction leads to conversion of the oxidase to a cytochrome c reductase devoid of oxidase activity. The altered enzyme has different physical properties from the native oxidase.

    e. Michaelis Constants for the Native Oxidase (pH 7.0, 23° C). With O_2 as acceptor, K_s (DPNH) $= 2.5 \times 10^{-5}\ M$; $V_{max.} = 4500$ moles [2H] transferred per mole bound flavin per minute. With cytochrome c as acceptor, K_s (cyt. c) $= 4.2 \times 10^{-5}\ M$; $V_{max.} = 3700$ moles [2H] transferred per mole bound flavin per minute. The K_s for O_2 was not determined; however, oxygen is an efficient electron acceptor since reaction (5c) proceeds at nearly the same rate at atmospheric O_2 tension or in solutions that have been gassed either with N_2 or O_2 for several minutes.

    f. Summary. Despite the fact that *C. perfringens* contains a very active four-electron DPNH oxidase, O_2 is not a physiological electron acceptor since (*a*) traces of peroxide formed during DPNH oxidation contribute to the decay of oxidase activity, (*b*) other DPNH-oxidizing enzymes of the organism, which use autoxidizable acceptors such as FAD or menadione, cause the rapid formation of growth-inhibitory concentrations of peroxide.

3. DPNH OXIDASE OF *C. kluyveri*

    Extracts of *C. kluyveri* catalyze DPNH[31] and TPNH[56] oxidation with O_2 as electron acceptor. With DPNH as reductant, the extracts also catalyze reduction of cytochrome c[31] and free flavins.[57] The relationship between these various reactions is unknown. By analogy to known systems, the bound prosthetic group of the DPNH oxidase is thought to be a flavin. With extracts from which the free flavins have been removed by dialysis, DPNH oxidation proceeds according to equation (5a) (two-electron reduction of O_2).[33a]

D. Ascorbic Acid-Dependent Reactions

Certain DPNH oxidases of peas,[58] potatoes,[59] suprarenal microsomes,[60] and microorganisms[61] require the presence of ascorbic acid plus some type of ascorbic acid-oxidizing system. The mechanism of these reactions is not completely understood; however, it is thought that ascorbic acid is oxidized to the one-electron intermediate, monodehydroascorbic acid, and that the latter serves as an electron acceptor for DPNH oxidation. Among the microorganisms, ascorbic acid-ascorbic acid oxidase-dependent DPNH oxidase systems have been found in yeast, *E. coli*, and *A. aerogenes*.[61] A DPNH oxidase of *M. denitrificans*[62] is markedly stimulated by ascorbic acid in the absence of an added ascorbic acid oxidase system. In yeast,[61] the DPNH oxidase portion of the over-all system has been purified and shown to be a flavoprotein, which, after acid resolution, can be reactivated either by FAD or FMN. The results with *M. denitrificans* suggest that ascorbic acid-dependent DPNH oxidases may occur normally in bacteria, even though bacteria have not been shown to possess ascorbic acid oxidase. It is possible that other reactions may be able to replace the typical Cu-containing ascorbic acid oxidase. As shown for pea extracts,[58] Cu^{++} or Fe^{+++} or, as suggested for the suprarenal microsome system,[60] cytochrome b_5, may be able to function as the ascorbic acid oxidase portion of the over-all DPNH oxidase system.

The stoichiometry for ascorbic acid-dependent DPNH oxidation has not been reported.

III. Flavoprotein Peroxidase

A. Atypical Peroxidase Activity

Some catalase- and cytochrome-free lactic acid bacteria can catalyze the reduction of peroxide to water with oxidizable substrates as electron donors; therefore O_2 uptake in these organisms does not result in peroxide accumulation (Table I). Such peroxidase reactions have been demonstrated with cell suspensions of the following organisms (substrates indicated in parenthesis): *S. mastitidis* (alcohol);[36] *S. faecalis*, strain B33a (glucose, glycerol, lactate);[26] *S. mitis*, sulfathiazole-resistant strain (glucose);[63] *Lactobacillus brevis* (lactate);[37] *Leuconostoc mesenteroides*, strain 548 (fructose, glucose, gluconate).[38] The reaction is adaptive in *S. faecalis*, strain B33a; peroxidase activity is demonstrable only in cells that have been grown aerobically[26] (cf. Table I). The nature of the organisms which catalyze the peroxidations listed above and the fact that at least two of the reactions are CN-insensitive[36, 37] indicated that the catalysts were not typical iron-protoporphyrin enzymes. Growth studies[64] suggested the function of a flavoprotein in the *S. faecalis* system.

There are indications that nonhematin peroxidases may exist even in organisms containing the usual iron catalysts. In *E. coli*, for instance, there appears to be a CN- and azide-resistant peroxidase activity which can be demonstrated in cell suspensions with H_2, succinate, or glucose as the electron donors.[65]

B. DPNH PEROXIDASE

1. ISOLATION AND PROPERTIES

A flavoprotein DPNH peroxidase, catalyzing reaction (5b), has been isolated from *S. faecalis*, strain 10C1.[29, 30, 39, 66] This enzyme accounts for the peroxidase activity exhibited by cell suspensions of *S. faecalis* and may be a model for the other peroxidase activities described in Section III, A. The enzyme in crude sonic extracts of *S. faecalis* has been purified 2000-fold by conventional fractionation procedures followed by zone electrophoresis on starch. Properties of the purified enzyme[39] are described in the following sections.

a. Prosthetic Group. The enzyme contains 0.66% FAD, which is equivalent to a minimum molecular weight of 120,000. There are no hematin components present and no metals have been found in amounts equivalent to the bound flavin.

b. Substrate Specificity. DPNH is the only physiological reductant known for the peroxidase activity of the enzyme. Molecular oxygen can serve as a weak electron acceptor for the peroxidase. In oxygen saturated solution, DPNH and TPNH are oxidized by molecular oxygen at $\frac{1}{200}$ of the rate at which DPNH is oxidized enzymically by peroxide. A wide variety of compounds including cytochrome c, free flavins, and dyes have been tested as electron acceptors, but the only alternative oxidants found are ferricyanide, menadione, and 1,4-naphthoquinone. The rates of oxidation with the latter three compounds are, respectively, one-half, one-third, and one-fifth of those obtained when H_2O_2 serves as oxidant.

c. pH Optimum. With H_2O_2 as acceptor, the optimum pH is 5.4 in acetate buffer. The rate is still $\frac{2}{3}$ maximal at pH 7, if a mixture of phosphate and acetate is used at the latter pH.

d. Activators and Inhibitors. Enzyme activity is stimulated by anions of the lower fatty acids (C_1–C_4) and by high concentrations of phosphate. The enzyme is not inhibited by 0.01 M CN, or 0.05 M azide, is not appreciably sensitive to —SH reagents, such as p-chloromercuribenzoate, selenite, and arsenite, and shows striking stability towards peroxide. Ag^+, Pb^{++}, and Cu^{++} are effective inhibitors. Incubation of the enzyme with DPNH causes first-order decay of enzyme activity (k = 0.066 min.$^{-1}$). The inhibition is almost completely prevented by the cosubstrate, H_2O_2. Kinetic data suggest that H_2O_2 exerts its protective effect by maintaining the enzyme in the form of a catalytically active ternary complex (composed of flavoprotein, DPNH, and H_2O_2) which does not undergo inactivation.

e. Michaelis Constants and Turnover (pH 5.4, 26° C.): With H_2O_2 as oxidant, K_s (DPNH) = 1.4 × 10^{-5} M; $K_s(H_2O_2)$ = 2 × 10^{-4} M; V_{max} = 6 × 10^3 moles DPNH oxidized per mole bound FAD per minute. With ferricyanide as oxidant, K_s (DPNH) = 6 × 10^{-6} M; K_s (ferricyanide) = 1.1 × 10^{-4} M; V_{max} = 2.96 × 10^3 moles DPNH oxidized per mole bound FAD per minute.

2. Spectrum of Enzyme and Evidence for Enzyme-Substrate Complex Formation[39, 66, 67a, b]

The spectrum of the enzyme is shown in Fig. 3. The oxidized enzyme has a typical flavin spectrum with no anomalies visible. On chemical reduction by hydrosulfite the flavoprotein undergoes typical bleaching; however, reduction of the enzyme by DPNH causes only partial decrease in height of the 450-mμ band and results in the formation of a new band in the long wavelength region (520–600 mμ). Addition of hydrosulfite to DPNH-reduced enzyme causes little further change in absorption. These results indicate that DPNH combines with the flavoprotein to form a complex that cannot be dissociated by reducing equivalents from hydrosulfite. The long wavelength absorption change shown in Fig. 3 is somewhat similar to that seen on substrate reduction of DPNH[68a] or TPNH[44] cytochrome c reductase; substrate reduction of acyl-CoA dehydrogenase[47] causes spectral changes that are strikingly similar to those observed with DPNH peroxidase. In the acyl-CoA dehydrogenase system, the long wavelength absorption band has been attributed to a substrate-stabilized flavin radical.[47] With DPNH peroxidase, it is difficult to reconcile the absorption changes with radical formation, since the addition of fully reduced substrate (DPNH) to chemically reduced enzyme results in immediate reformation of the 450-mμ band and the reappearance of the long wavelength band. (The same spectrum is produced whether hydrosulfite is added before DPNH or DPN or after DPNH.) Present evidence, therefore, suggests a fully reduced structure for the visible complex. The broadness of the 540-mμ band, as well as the lack of detail in the band, suggests that the spec-

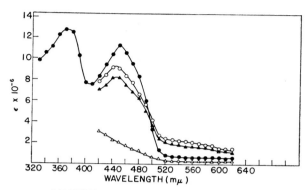

FIG. 3. Spectrum of DPNH peroxidase. Enzyme, specific activity 9000, 3.3 mg. of protein per ml., 0.2 ml. in 0.02 M potassium phosphate buffer, pH 6.5. DPNH, where used, 0.005 ml. of a 30-μmole per ml. solution. Hydrosulfite, where used, 0.01 ml. of a 10% solution in 5% NaHCO₃ . Readings are corrected for dilution. See reference 39.

KEY: ●, peroxidase; ○, peroxidase plus DPNH; △, peroxidase plus hydrosulfite; ▲, peroxidase plus DPNH plus hydrosulfite. Reprinted with permission from the *Journal of Biological Chemistry.*

trum of DPNH-reduced enzyme may be that of a charge-transfer complex.[68b]

The spectral and kinetic properties of the complexes formed between DPNH peroxidase and a series of DPNH analogs (modified in the carboxamide group and in other positions) have been investigated.[67a,b] It has been found that those pyridine nucleotide analogs that are peroxidase substrates are also able to cause the typical absorption changes; those nucleotides that do not cause the typical absorption changes are not substrates. The results may be summarized as follows: (a) Pyridine nucleotides that cause the formation of *both* the 450- and 540-mμ bands are peroxidase substrates. The nucleotides in this group contain an adenylic acid moiety. (b) Those nucleotides (TPNH and NMNH) that cause the formation of only the 450-mμ band are very poor peroxidase substrates, but in common with active nucleotides, they serve as hydrogen donors for the weak oxidase activity of DPNH peroxidase. Apparently the ability to generate the 540-mμ band is characteristic of pyridine nucleotides that contain an adenylic acid moiety that can be bound to the enzyme. Correspondence between the kinetic and spectral properties of the complexes formed between DPNH peroxidase and either TPNH or NMNH suggests that the 2′-phosphate of TPNH prevents the binding of the adenylic acid moiety, thus making TPNH and NMNH identical as substrates. (c) The simplest compound found that can cause the formation of the 450-mμ band is NMNH. On removal of the 5′-phosphate residue, the nucleotide loses most of its ability to complex the enzyme.

Complex formation can be followed by observation of the increase in absorbance at either 450 or 540 mμ on titration of hydrosulfite reduced enzyme with graded levels of pyridine nucleotide analogs.[67a,b] The dissociation constants calculated from these data have been correlated with the Michaelis constants derived from kinetic studies. In all cases there is good correspondence between the two constants, the average ratio of the dissociation constant (K) to the Michaelis constant (K_s) being 4. The physiological substrate of the enzyme, DPNH, shows the lowest dissociation from the enzyme ($K = 1.6 \times 10^{-5}$ M, pH 6.5), whereas TPNH and NMNH show the highest dissociation ($K = 0.97 \times 10^{-3}$ M, pH 6.5). Thus, all the criteria that have been employed lend strong support to the hypothesis that the visible intermediate formed in the DPNH peroxidase system is a kinetically active enzyme-substrate complex.

3. Mechanism and Kinetic Constants

Present kinetic experiments (unpublished experiments of the author) suggest the formation of a ternary complex between enzyme, DPNH and peroxide. One possible reaction sequence is shown in equations (6a), (6b),

$$FP + DPNH \underset{k_2}{\overset{k_1}{\rightleftarrows}} FP \cdot DPNH \tag{6a}$$

$$FP \cdot DPNH + H_2O_2 \underset{k_4}{\overset{k_3}{\rightleftarrows}} FP \cdot DPNH \cdot H_2O_2 \tag{6b}$$

$$FP \cdot H_2O_2 + DPNH \underset{k_6}{\overset{k_5}{\rightleftarrows}} FP \cdot DPNH \cdot H_2O_2 \tag{6c}$$

$$FP \cdot DPNH \cdot H_2O_2 + H^+ \overset{k_7}{\longrightarrow} FP + DPN^+ + 2H_2O \tag{6d}$$

and (6d). A random binding sequence would involve, in addition, the formation of an $FP \cdot H_2O_2$ complex (not shown) and the combination of DPNH with this complex [equation (6c)]. If a fully reduced enzyme-pyridine nucleotide complex is the intermediate, FP may be replaced by FPH_2 in equations (6a) to (6d). The assumption of a random binding sequence for the mechanism shown above leads to Michaelis constants analogous in form to the Briggs-Haldane relation.[68c] The rate constants appropriate to such a mechanism may be estimated by methods similar to those described by Slater.[69] These constants are (26°, pH 5.4):

$$k_3 = 2 \times 10^9 \, 1 \times mole^{-1} \times min.^{-1}$$

$$k_4 = 4 \times 10^5 \, min.^{-1}$$

$$k_5 = 5 \times 10^8 \, 1 \times mole^{-1} \times min.^{-1}$$

$$k_6 = 0.93 \times 10^2 \, min.^{-1}$$

$$k_7 = 6 \times 10^3 \, min.^{-1}$$

$$K_8(\text{DPNH}) = \frac{k_6 + k_7}{k_5} = 1.2 \times 10^{-5}\,M, \text{H}_2\text{O}_2 \text{ present in excess}$$

$$K_8(\text{H}_2\text{O}_2) = \frac{k_4 + k_7}{k_3} = 2 \times 10^{-4}\,M, \text{DPNH present in excess}$$

C. DISTRIBUTION OF FLAVOPROTEIN PEROXIDASES

DPNH peroxidase has, so far, been found in three streptococcal strains which had previously been shown to carry out the atypical peroxidations listed in Section III, A. The organisms are *S. faecalis*, strains 10C1[29, 39] and B33a[34] and *S. mastitidis*.[30] It has been reported that fresh, but not aged extracts of *C. perfringens* exhibit a weak DPNH peroxidase activity.[52] Balances for the DPN-dependent oxidation of acetaldehyde by extracts of *C. kluyveri*[50] indicate a four-electron reduction of O_2. Since the DPNH oxidase of this organism catalyzes a two-electron reduction of oxygen,[33a] a DPNH peroxidase may be part of the over-all oxidase system. DPNH peroxidase is absent in *L. mesenteroides*, strain 39, and *L. delbrueckii* (unpublished experiments of the author).

Extensive surveys for the presence of DPNH peroxidase have not been carried out, since the catalase (and possibly cytochrome c peroxidase) present in cytochrome-containing organisms would offer serious interference. (Mammalian cytochrome c, in the absence of a specific peroxidase, catalyzes a heat-stable peroxidation of DPNH,[70] however, the turnover is very low—2.5 moles DPNH oxidized per min per mole cytochrome c, at pH 5.4.) As mentioned in Section III, A, there are suggestions that non-hematin peroxidases may be present even in organisms which use iron enzymes.

It is possible that there exist flavoprotein peroxidases for "noncoenzyme" substrates. With crude xanthine oxidase preparations, peroxide formed in the initial stages of hypoxanthine oxidation is later used as an oxidant.[71] The properties of xanthine oxidase, however, indicate that peroxide is not a physiological oxidant for the enzyme. It has been suggested[20] that the peroxidase activity of crude xanthine oxidase preparations may be attributable to a contaminating enzyme.

IV. Diaphorases

A. SIGNIFICANCE OF DIAPHORASE ACTIVITY

Diaphorases are enzymes that couple the oxidation of reduced pyridine nucleotide to the reduction of artificial or nonphysiological electron acceptors [equation (7)]. Although many diaphorases have been shown to be

$$\text{PNH} + \text{H}^+ + \text{A} \rightarrow \text{PN}^+ + \text{AH}_2 \tag{7}$$

flavoproteins, it may be premature to conclude that diaphorase activity per se always implies flavoprotein catalysis. Since diaphorases do not use physiological oxidants, the question always arises as to the significance of these enzymes. A diaphorase may represent (a) an enzyme whose physiological oxidant is unknown, or (b) an enzyme which, for various reasons, may have lost its ability to react with the true physiological electron acceptor. With regard to the latter, it has been suggested that the diaphorase of pig heart is derived from cytochrome c reductase.[72] Recent work, however, indicates that heart muscle diaphorase and cytochrome c reductase are, in fact, separate enzymes[73a] which may both have been derived from a common precursor (a lipoflavoprotein).[74]

The question of whether a given oxidant is artificial may, in itself, be difficult to decide. Substrate concentrations of free flavins, for instance, sometimes serve as electron acceptors. It may not always be clear whether these reactions have a special significance or whether the flavins act merely as nonspecific oxidation-reduction dyes. The reduction of menadione (vitamin K_3) is sometimes regarded as of no special interest since (a) quinones are known to be nonspecific oxidants for several flavoproteins (Chapter 6, Section IV, C), and (b) in cytochrome-containing organisms, reduction of exogenous menadione (or quinone) would bypass the cytochrome system and the attendant phosphorylations (Chapter 6, Section VI, A). These arguments lose their force when applied to lactic acid bacteria. In the latter, the establishment of any alternate pathway to oxygen is potentially useful (see Section IX). Menadione (or a physiological equivalent), by virtue of its autoxidizability, may link the oxidation of reduced pyridine nucleotide to O_2 reduction.[48, 75]

B. DIAPHORASES OF MICROORGANISMS

Many diaphorase activities have been reported for crude extracts of bacteria. Since physiologically functional flavoproteins have alternate electron acceptors and since there may be present in extracts several flavoproteins concerned with the oxidation of reduced pyridine nucleotide (e.g., five separate enzymes in *S. faecalis*), systematic examination of a given system is necessary before the relation between various diaphorase activities can be determined. Table III summarizes the properties of the purified diaphorases. On reduction of Straub's soluble diaphorase with DPNH, the enzyme undergoes absorption changes[77] very similar to those described for DPNH peroxidase (Section III, B). The behavior of the *S. faecalis* diaphorase, on its reduction by substrate, is described in Section IV, C.

Table IV lists some of the diaphorase activities that have been described in crude and partially purified systems. Where the information is available, nonidentity between diaphorase activity and other DPNH-oxidizing activities is indicated. For simplicity, the menadione- and flavin-dependent

TABLE III

Purified Diaphorases

Enzyme	Sub-strate	Oxidant	Pros-thetic group	Molec-ular weight[a]	TON[b]	Reference
Straub's soluble diaphorase (pig heart)	DPNH	Methylene blue 2,6-Dichloro-phenol-indo-phenol	FAD	67,000	8500 —	76, 77 76, 77
New yellow en-zyme (yeast)	TPNH	Methylene blue	FAD	60,000	130[c]	78a
Streptococcus faecalis diaphorase	DPNH	Ferricyanide 2,6-Dichloro-phenol-indo-phenol p-Benzoquinone	FMN	53,000	6,000 29,000 88,000	30, 39, 78b 30, 39, 78b 30, 39, 78b

[a] Minimum molecular weight, based on flavin content.
[b] Moles reduced pyridine nucleotide oxidized per mole bound flavin per minute.
[c] Calculated from data given in reference 78a.
The diaphorases do not react with cytochrome c; however, it has been reported[73a] that Straub's soluble diaphorase will catalyze cytochrome c reduction in the presence of lipoic acid. *S. faecalis* diaphorase does not catalyze this reaction nor does it use peroxide or any of the acceptors with which DPNH peroxidase shows no activity.

reactions are listed along with the electron acceptors that are clearly artificial. In the absence of exogenous autoxidizable acceptors, crude extracts of *Leuconostoc mesenteroides*, strain 39, and *Lactobacillus delbrueckii* do not use O_2 as an electron acceptor for DPNH oxidation. TPNH is very slowly oxidized by extracts of these organisms in the presence of menadione or 2,6-dichlorophenol-indophenol (approximately $\frac{1}{50}$ of the rate given by DPNH) (unpublished experiments of the author). Other menadione reductases are listed in Chapter 6, Section III, A.

C. Purified Diaphorase of *S. faecalis*

1. Isolation and Properties

One of the DPNH-oxidizing enzymes of *S. faecalis*, strain 10C1, is a diaphorase that has been obtained in high purity. The enzyme, purified over 600-fold from extracts of *S faecalis*, has the following properties.[78b]

a. *Prosthetic Group.* Firmly bound FMN is the sole prosthetic flavin present. Based on the FMN content, the minimum molecular weight of the enzyme is approximately 53,000.

TABLE IV

CELL FREE DIAPHORASES OF MICROORGANISMS

Organism	Donor	Acceptor	Cofactor	TON[a]	Reference
Escherichia coli	DPNH	Menadione	—	50	75
	DPNH, TPNH	Quinones	—	—	75
	DPNH	Menadione[b]	FMN	—	79
		Furacin[b]	FMN	—	79
		Triphenyltetrazolium, Neotetrazolium	Enzyme preparation contains FAD	—	80
Pseudomonas fluorescens	DPNH	2,6 Dichlorophenol-indophenol	FMN	80	57
Pasteurella tularensis	TPNH	Menadione	—	—	81
Streptococcus faecalis	DPNH	Menadione[c]	FAD, FMN	40–100	48
Leuconostoc mesenteroides, strain 39	DPNH	Menadione	—	80	—[e]
		2,6 Dichlorophenol-indophenol		40	—[e]
		Ferricyanide		5	—[e]
Lactobacillus delbrueckii	DPNH	Menadione	—	30	—[e]
		2,6 Dichlorophenol-indophenol		30	—[e]
		Ferricyanide		20	—[e]
Clostridium kluyveri	DPNH	Menadione	—	—	75
		Free flavins	—	—	57
Clostridium perfringens	DPNH	Menadione[d]	—	—	33a
		Free flavins[d]	—	—	33a
Clostridium sticklandii	DPNH	Triphenyltetrazolium	FMN	—	82
Yeast	DPNH	Furacin	—	—	83a

[a] Moles reduced pyridine nucleotide oxidized per 100,000 g. protein per minute. For comparative purposes, the TON listed is for the crude extract. None of these enzymes has been significantly purified over the crude extract.

[b] Not identical with nitrate, nitrite, or organo-nitrate reductase.

[c] One of the five DPNH-oxidizing enzymes of S. faecalis (Section II, B).

[d] Completely separated from the native DPNH oxidase of C. perfringens (Section II, C, 2).

[e] M. I. Dolin, unpublished.

b. Substrate Specificity. TPNH cannot replace DPNH as the electron donor. Members of all the known classes of flavoprotein oxidant have been tested as potential electron acceptors; however, the only oxidants found were ferricyanide, 2,6-dichlorophenol-indophenol, and a series of quinones and naphthoquinones. Quinones in general are very efficient oxidants of the reduced flavoprotein. With *p*-benzoquinone, for instance, the K_s for quinone is 5×10^{-6} M, the turnover (TON) is 8.8×10^4 moles of DPNH oxidized per min. per mole of enzyme-bound FMN, and k, the second-order rate constant for reoxidation of reduced diaphorase by *p*-quinone is 1.0×10^{10} $M^{-1} \times$ min.$^{-1}$. The latter value exceeds that found for the decomposition of peroxide by catalase. It is of interest that 2,3-dimethoxy-5-methyl-*p*-benzoquinone (coenzyme Q without the isoprenoid side chain) is also an active oxidant (TON, with 10^{-4} M quinone, $= 2.7 \times 10^4$ moles DPNH oxidized per min. per mole bound FMN, and $k = 2.7 \times 10^8$ $M^{-1} \times$ min.$^{-1}$). The values quoted apply at pH 7.0, 24° C., in phosphate buffer. The insoluble quinones, coenzyme Q_{10}, and vitamin K_1 are inactive.

c. pH Optimum. The pH-activity curve is complex, with a peak at pH 4.5, a plateau between pH 7.5 and 8.5, and a minimum between pH 5.0 and 6.5.

d. Inhibition of the Enzyme. Like DPNH peroxidase, the diaphorase is not appreciably affected by hydrogen peroxide or by other —SH inhibitors. These findings are consistent with the fact that *S. faecalis* carries out a physiologically useful flavoprotein respiration.

2. ENZYME-SUBSTRATE COMPLEX FORMATION

The diaphorase has a typical flavoprotein spectrum, with peaks at 270, 370, and 450 mμ. On the addition of DPNH, the yellow color of the enzyme is bleached and there is a 90 % decrease in absorbance of the 450-mμ band. The enzyme does not form the enzyme-substrate complex described for the DPNH peroxidase system (Section III, B); however, the diaphorase does form a complex with DPNH somewhat analogous to the one demonstrated for microsomal cytochrome reductase.[83b] Examination of the ultraviolet difference spectrum of diaphorase reduced with one equivalent of DPNH (absorbance of DPNH-reduced enzyme minus absorbance of oxidized enzyme) reveals the presence of an intermediate (presumably DPN-bound to reduced flavoprotein) which absorbs at approximately 320 mμ. When the alcohol dehydrogenase system is used to generate DPNH, the diaphorase can be reduced in the presence of catalytic concentrations of DPN, without formation of the 320-mμ band. It is difficult therefore to decide whether the kinetically active form of the diaphorase is free, reduced flavoprotein, or reduced flavoprotein complexed with DPN. With quinones as oxidants, kinetic data suggest that the active form of the reduced enzyme is the ternary complex of reduced flavoprotein, DPN, and quinone.

3. Possible Physiological Significance of Quinone-Reductase Activity in Lactic Acid Bacteria

The velocity constants for the reaction between reduced *S. faecalis* diaphorase and various oxidized quinones are extremely high. Very low concentrations of these quinones can, therefore, act as efficient electron acceptors for DPNH oxidation. When the quinones involved are autoxidizable, a direct pathway from DPNH to oxygen is established. As discussed in Sections IV, A and IX, A, such pathways can be useful to lactic acid bacteria, even though the electron transport from DPNH to oxygen is not coupled with phosphorylation. In this respect, the quinone-reductase activity of the *S. faecalis* diaphorase may be physiologically significant, whether or not a quinone is the normal oxidant of the enzyme.

Several pieces of information suggest that quinones may be physiological intermediates in the metabolism of lactic acid bacteria. For instance, certain lactic acid bacteria have been found to contain vitamin K-like compounds (blood clotting assay).[83c] Further, there is a report [83d] that menadione can stimulate the anaerobic growth of *Lactobacillus bifidus*. Preliminary experiments (M. I. Dolin and A. F. Brodie, unpublished) have shown that the particulate, ultraviolet-labile cytochrome c reductase of *S. faecalis*[30] can be stimulated by menadione and also by partially purified lipid extracts of *S. faecalis*. The active lipid extracts have a borohydride difference spectrum similar to that of a quinone or naphthoquinone. Although the cytochrome c reductase activity may be a model reaction (see Chapter 6), the system does demonstrate that the lipid-soluble activator (tentatively identified as a quinone) can interact with a particulate enzyme. The lipid-soluble factor does not function with the soluble, DPNH-oxidizing enzymes of *S. faecalis*.

V. Direct Flavoprotein Oxidases

A. Pyruvate and Lactate Oxidases of *L. delbrueckii*

The absence of oxidases for reduced pyridine nucleotides in extracts of *L. delbrueckii* (Section IV, B) suggests that this organism uses, primarily, direct substrate oxidases in its oxidative metabolism. A portion of the respiratory activity of *L. delbrueckii* (Table I) is accounted for by direct flavoprotein oxidases which use pyruvate or lactate as substrates.[41]

1. Pyruvate Oxidation[41]

Extracts of *L. delbrueckii* catalyze pyruvate oxidation as shown in equations (8a) to (8c).

$$\text{pyruvate} + PO_4 + O_2 \xrightarrow{\text{TPP, FAD}} \text{acetyl-}PO_4 + CO_2 + H_2O_2 \tag{8a}$$

$$\text{pyruvate} + H_2O_2 \longrightarrow \text{acetate} + CO_2 + H_2O \text{ (spontaneous)} \tag{8b}$$

$$2 \text{ pyruvate} + PO_4 + O_2 \longrightarrow \text{acetyl-}PO_4 + \text{acetate} + 2 CO_2 + H_2O \tag{8c}$$

The pyruvate oxidase, purified 30-fold, shows a flavin spectrum. Apo-enzyme can be prepared by the acid ammonium sulfate procedure and then reactivated on the addition of FAD. In common with other pyruvate oxidase systems, cocarboxylase is required. The turnover of the purified enzyme is 85 moles O_2/min./100,000 g. protein. When methylene blue or ferricyanide serve as electron acceptors, the oxidation rate is one-half that obtained with molecular oxygen as oxidant. The rate with neotetrazolium as acceptor is one-tenth that found with oxygen.

An interesting feature of this reaction is the formation of acetyl phosphate with either O_2 or ferricyanide as electron acceptors. The mechanism of acetyl phosphate formation (which is unknown) is different from that of the DPN-linked systems[40] and may have some bearing on the mechanism by which "energy-rich" bonds are generated at the flavoprotein level.

2. LACTATE OXIDATION AND PYRUVATE DISMUTATION

L. delbrueckii also catalyzes the dismutation of pyruvate to lactate, acetate, and CO_2. The over-all reaction requires two enzymes, the flavo-protein pyruvate oxidase and a flavoprotein lactate oxidase.[41] After acid ammonium sulfate treatment, the lactate oxidase requires a mixture of riboflavin and FAD for maximum activity with O_2 as electron acceptor. The mechanism of dismutation is shown in equations (9a) to (9e). (P.O. FAD = pyruvate oxidase flavoprotein; L.O.FAD = lactate oxidase flavo-protein; F = riboflavin.) This reaction sequence, in which high concentra-

$$\text{pyruvate} + PO_4 + \text{P.O.FAD} \rightarrow \text{acetyl-}PO_4 + CO_2 + \text{P.O.FADH}_2 \quad \text{(9a)}$$

$$\text{P.O.FADH}_2 + F \rightarrow \text{P.O.FAD} + FH_2 \quad \text{(9b)}$$

$$FH_2 + \text{L.O.FAD} \rightarrow F + \text{L.O.FADH}_2 \quad \text{(9c)}$$

$$\underline{\text{L.O.FADH}_2 + \text{pyruvate} \rightarrow \text{L.O.FAD} + \text{lactate}} \quad \text{(9d)}$$

$$2 \text{ pyruvate} + PO_4 \rightarrow \text{lactate} + \text{acetyl-}PO_4 + CO_2 \quad \text{(9e)}$$

tions of riboflavin serve to link two flavoprotein oxidases, may be a model for anaerobic electron transport between flavoproteins. Whether free flavin performs this function under physiological conditions is unknown. In the acyl-CoA dehydrogenase system,[84] for instance, a special flavoprotein (ETF) serves as the specific oxidant of reduced acyl-CoA dehydrogenase flavoprotein.

The thermodynamics of pyruvate oxidation and dismutation are considered in Chapter 6.

B. LACTATE OXIDASES OF MYCOBACTERIA

A distinctly different type of lactate oxidase is present in certain myco-bacteria.[85-87] The over-all reaction is shown in equation (10).

$$\text{lactate} + O_2 \rightarrow \text{acetate} + CO_2 + H_2O \quad \text{(10)}$$

A crystalline flavoprotein catalyzing reaction (10) has been isolated from *M. phlei*.[85] The properties of the enzyme may be summarized as follows.

Prosthetic group: FMN (probably 2 moles per mole of enzyme) is the bound flavin.

Molecular weight: 260,000, by ultracentrifugal methods.

TON: 2800 moles O_2 per minute per mole enzyme.

Mechanism of action: The over-all oxidation and decarboxylation of lactate appear to be catalyzed by a single protein. Free pyruvate is not an intermediate, although it is a competitive inhibitor. Evidence has been presented[85] for the occurrence of enzyme-bound pyruvate. Traces of H_2O_2 occur during the oxidation, which implies that bound peroxide may be an intermediate. The stoichiometry of equation (10) suggests a four-electron transfer reaction; however, experiments with O_2^{18} indicate that at least 1 atom of oxygen in acetate is derived directly from molecular O_2 and not from water.[88] The mechanism, then, conforms to that of a mixed function oxidase, in Mason's terminology and resembles the hydroxylations demonstrated for various aromatic compounds.[3] Lactate appears to be the first carbohydrate intermediate implicated in reactions of this type.

It is not yet known whether other mycobacteria[86, 87] that catalyze lactate oxidation with the stoichiometry of equation (10) use a mechanism similar to that described for *M. phlei*.

C. Other Direct Oxidases

Aerobically grown *S. faecalis*[89] (10C1) contains a non-DPN linked oxidase for α-glycerophosphate. With O_2 as acceptor, H_2O_2 is formed. Glucose oxidation, however, is mediated by the DPNH oxidation and peroxidation pathway as shown by the presence of DPN-linked triose phosphate dehydrogenase[89] (and DPNH oxidase and peroxidase)[30] in both aerobically and anaerobically grown cells. It is reported briefly[90] that O_2 uptake by lactobacilli may proceed largely via substrate specific flavoproteins. Glycerophosphate oxidation (organism not specified) requires FAD.

Amino acid oxidases of animal and mold origin have been shown to be flavoproteins.[19] Among the bacteria, L-amino acid oxidase activity has been studied in purified extracts of *Proteus vulgaris*[91] and in cell suspensions of *Clostridium sporogenes* and *C. saccharobutyricum*[92]; however, the nature of the enzymes involved has not been specified.

VI. Dehydrogenase Activities

This section briefly treats several electron transport reactions (not classifiable under previous headings) which can function in the anaerobic phases of electron transport.

A. Coenzyme Level Dehydrogenases

1. Thiol Reactions

a. Glutathione and Cystine Reductases. Plants, animal tissues, and micro-organisms contain an enzyme, glutathione reductase, that catalyzes the irreversible reduction of oxidized glutathione to the monothiol[93] [equation (11)].

$$\text{TPNH} + \text{H}^+ + \text{GSSG} \rightarrow \text{TPN}^+ + 2\,\text{GSH} \qquad (11)$$

Glutathione reductase is said to show specificity for TPNH; however, with purified yeast and liver enzymes[93] high concentrations of DPNH can serve as an electron donor in the presence of phosphate buffer. The high potential of the glutathione couple was thought to account for the virtual irreversibility of reaction (11); however, this explanation cannot be correct if the recently determined potential[94] for the glutathione system ($E_0' = -0.34$ v. at pH 7) is accurate. In plants, glutathione reductase may link pyridine nucleotide dehydrogenases to O_2, in the presence of dehydro-ascorbic acid reductase (GSH as substrate) and ascorbic acid oxidase.[95]

A cystine reductase, catalyzing a reaction analogous to equation (11), except with cystine as substrate, has been isolated from yeast.[96]

On the basis of reactivation experiments, bacterial glutathione reductase, prepared from *E. coli*,[97] is an FAD-containing flavoprotein. Evidence for the nature of other glutathione reductases has not been presented; the *E. coli* enzyme may be a model for the thiol systems described in this section.

b. Lipoic Dehydrogenase. One of the components of the pyruvic dehydrogenase complex[40] is an enzyme that catalyzes the reversible reduction of DPN by lipoic acid[98] [equation (12)]. This reaction is part of the electron

$$\text{lip(SH)}_2 + \text{DPN}^+ \rightleftharpoons \text{lip(SS)} + \text{DPNH} + \text{H}^+ \qquad (12)$$

transfer sequence between keto acids and O_2 both in flavin systems (*S. faecalis*) and cytochrome-containing bacteria (*E. coli*, animal tissues). A lipoic dehydrogenase has also been isolated from *Mycobacterium tuberculosis*.[99] Tentative values[40] for the dehydrogenation potential of reduced lipoic acid indicate an E_0' close to that of the DPNH couple (-0.32 v.).

Leuconostoc mesenteroides, strain 39, contains two types of lipoic dehydrogenase.[100a] One enzyme catalyzes the freely reversible reduction of lipoic acid or lipoamide. The second enzyme is similar to that of *E. coli* in that the reaction is difficult to demonstrate in the direction of lipoic acid reduction. In *L. mesenteroides*, the difficulty is attributable to the inhibitory effect of low concentrations of DPNH.

Lipoic dehydrogenase and various other DPN linked di- and mono-mercaptan dehydrogenases have been demonstrated in extracts of *C. sticklandii*.[82]

The demonstration that the glutathione reductase reaction catalyzed by *E. coli* is flavin-dependent[97] implied that disulfide reductases in general might be flavoprotein enzymes. Direct evidence for the flavoprotein nature of lipoic dehydrogenase has been obtained for the enzymes isolated from pig heart,[73a, b] *E. coli*,[100b] and *L. mesenteroides* (G. W. Notani and I. C. Gunsalus, personal communication).

B. Substrate Dehydrogenases

1. Xanthine Dehydrogenase

A xanthine dehydrogenase has been partially purified from extracts of *Micrococcus lactilyticus*.[101] Ferricyanide or 2,6-dichlorophenol-indophenol serve as oxidants. When ferricyanide is the electron acceptor, the enzyme is inactive in the absence of a mixture of molybdic trioxide and phosphate. This reaction may be similar to the model cytochrome c reductase activity of aldehyde oxidase (Chapter 6). Hydrogen gas, in the presence of hydrogenase, can serve as a reductant for the xanthine dehydrogenase preparation.

2. Pyruvic Dehydrogenase

Several different types of pyruvic acid dehydrogenation have been described. The mechanism and distribution of these reactions has been considered by Gunsalus.[40] A new development in the field is the finding that folic acid may serve as an acceptor for pyruvate dehydrogenation. An enzyme from *C. sticklandii*[102a] catalyzes the following reaction:

$$\text{pyruvate} + \text{teropterin} + \text{CoA} \rightarrow \text{acetyl-CoA} + CO_2 + \text{teropterin} \cdot H_2 \quad (13)$$

The enzyme uses monoglutamyl and triglutamyl pterins as well as their N^{10}-formyl derivatives. It is not yet clear whether folic acid serves a specific function in this reaction, or whether it is one of a series of nonspecific electron acceptors.

An acetate-requiring mutant of *E. coli* contains a pyruvate oxidase system[102b, 102c] consisting of a soluble pyruvic dehydrogenase, which, in the presence of a particulate fraction, can catalyze the oxidation of pyruvate to acetate and CO_2, with either oxygen or ferricyanide as electron acceptors. The soluble enzyme has been identified[102c] as a flavoprotein containing one mole of FAD per 200,000 grams of protein. Trypsin catalyzes the conversion of the soluble flavoprotein to an "activated" form that can use ferricyanide as an oxidant in the absence of the particulate fraction. The soluble flavoprotein, either in its original or "activated" form, requires cocarboxylase for activity. In this requirement, the enzyme resembles the pyruvate oxidase of *L. delbrueckii* (Section V, A). Both flavoproteins seem to be "double-headed" enzymes which contain firmly bound FAD and dissociable cocarboxylase.

3. DIHYDROOROTIC DEHYDROGENASE[102d]

Dihydroorotic dehydrogenase, purified approximately 90-fold from extracts of the anaerobic bacterium *Zymobacterium oroticum*, shows a typical flavoprotein spectrum. Fluorometric analysis suggests the presence of two flavin prosthetic groups, tentatively identified as FAD and FMN. In this respect, the enzyme resembles the DPNH oxidase of *C. perfringens* (Section II, C), which contains two flavin prosthetic groups, only one of which is FAD.

Purified dihydroorotic dehydrogenase catalyzes the reversible reduction of orotic acid to dihydroorotic acid, with DPNH as the electron donor. The enzyme also catalyzes the oxidation of dihydroorotic acid and DPNH, with molecular oxygen or methylene blue as the electron acceptors.

Dihydroorotic acid and DPNH cause only partial bleaching of the 450-$m\mu$ band of the flavoprotein. This behavior is similar to that reported for DPNH peroxidase and acyl-CoA dehydrogenase (see Section III, B). Dihydroorotic acid, however, will not bleach the flavin of the dehydrogenase in the absence of cysteine, although cysteine is not required for the partial bleaching of the enzyme by DPNH. These results are in accord with the finding that dihydroorotic dehydrogenase requires cysteine in order to catalyze the oxidation of dihydroorotic acid with either DPN or oxygen as electron acceptors, whereas catalysis of DPNH oxidation with oxygen as electron acceptor does not require the presence of cysteine. The dehydrogenase shows specificity for the α-H of DPNH;[102e] however, the enzyme does not catalyze direct H transfer from DPNH to orotic acid, presumably because the reduced flavoprotein can exchange protons with water.

4. COUPLED MALIC-LACTIC DEHYDROGENASE

A partially purified enzyme from *Veillonella gazogenes* (*Micrococcus lactilyticus*)[102f] catalyzes the reversible reaction shown in equation (14).

$$\text{malate} + \text{pyruvate} \rightleftarrows \text{lactate} + \text{oxalacetate} \qquad (14)$$

The reaction seems to be catalyzed by a single enzyme; no hydrogen acceptors other than pyruvate or oxalacetate have been found. Oxygen, pyridine nucleotides, ferricyanide, and various dyes do not serve as electron acceptors for malate oxidation. The enzyme may be a malic-lactic transhydrogenase.

VII. Flavoproteins Concerned with Reduction of Nitrate, Nitrite, Hydroxylamine, and Organo-Nitro Compounds

Cytochrome-mediated electron transfer to inorganic nitrogen containing compounds was discussed in Chapter 6. Such reactions apparently account for the "nitrate respiration" which allows certain facultative anaerobes to use nitrate as a physiological electron acceptor. On the other hand, present evidence suggests that the reductive steps of "nitrogen assimilation" are catalyzed by flavoproteins which use nitrogen-containing compounds as the electron acceptors. The reduction of nitrate to ammonia in a series of two electron steps is illustrated in the following scheme:

$$NO_3^- \rightarrow NO_2^- \rightarrow ? \rightarrow NH_2OH \rightarrow NH_3$$

Work with *Neurospora*[103] and with plant and bacterial systems suggests that each step is catalyzed by a pyridine nucleotide-dependent metalloflavoprotein.[104] Table V lists some of the enzymes of microorganisms which catalyze the reduction of NO_3^- to NO_2^-, NO_2^- to NH_3, and NH_2OH to NH_3. (In the *A. vinelandii* system, the product of hydroxylamine reduction has not been identified.) Menadione stimulates the DPNH- or TPNH-dependent reduction of nitrate by *E. coli*[113] and is an absolute requirement for the DPNH-dependent reduction of nitrate by rhizobia.[114]

The mechanism of nitrate reduction to nitrite has been worked out most

TABLE V

PYRIDINE NUCLEOTIDE-DEPENDENT REDUCTION OF NITRATE, NITRITE, HYDROXYLAMINE, AND ORGANO-NITRO COMPOUNDS

Enzyme	Source	Electron donor	Prosthetic group	Metal	Reference
NO_3^- reductase	*Escherichia coli*	DPNH	FAD	Mo	105
	Neurospora	TPNH	FAD	Mo	103
	Hansenula anomala	DPNH, TPNH	FAD	Mo ?	106
NO_2^- reductase	*Azotobacter vinelandii*	DPNH, TPNH	FAD	—	107
	Neurospora	DPNH, TPNH	FAD	Cu, Fe[a]	108, 109
NH_2OH reductase	*Azotobacter vinelandii*	DPNH, TPNH	FAD, FMN	Mn	107
	Bacillus subtilis	DPNH	—	—	110
	Neurospora	DPNH, TPNH	FAD	Mn[a]	109, 111
Organo-nitro reductase	*Escherichia coli*	DPNH	FMN	Mn	112

[a] Based on decrease in enzyme activity in organisms grown in metal-deficient media.

completely for *Neurospora*;[103] the electron transport sequence is shown in the following scheme.

$$TPNH \rightarrow FAD (FMN) \rightarrow Mo \rightarrow NO_3^-$$

To date, this is the only metallo-flavoprotein system in which the metal has been shown to undergo valence change. The enzyme and flavin dependent reduction of molybdenum and the enzyme-dependent reduction of nitrate to nitrite by reduced Mo have been demonstrated. It is not clear whether a single enzyme catalyzes the over-all reaction.

Enzymes which catalyze the reduction of organo-nitro compounds have also been isolated. *E. coli* contains an enzyme that catalyzes the DPNH-dependent reduction of various nitroaryl compounds[112] (e.g., chloramphenicol, *p*-nitrobenzoic acid). The product of two-electron reduction is a nitroso derivative, which is reduced chemically by cysteine to a diazotizable amine.[112] Nitroaryl reductases prepared both from aureomycin-resistant and -sensitive strains of *E. coli* appear to use FMN as the prosthetic group. The enzyme from the sensitive strain is somewhat different in that the flavin is easily dissociable and a Mn^{++} requirement for nitro reduction can be shown. It has been suggested[112] that the acquisition of aureomycin resistance involves the synthesis of an altered enzyme which can compete successfully with aureomycin for free Mn^{++}.

Whether the reductases for organo-nitro compounds or, alternatively, those for inorganic nitrogen compounds are involved in the physiological pathway of nitrogen assimilation appears to be an open question. Evidence obtained with *Neurospora* mutants[115] suggests that the organo-nitro pathway is the physiological route. However, it has also been suggested[104] that the reactions reported for organo-nitro compounds may merely represent examples of nonspecific diaphorase activity.

VIII. Phosphorylation Coupled to Anaerobic Electron Transport

Much, if not most, of the phosphorylation associated with the electron transport reactions of heterotrophic cytochrome-free bacteria takes place at the substrate level. In the lactic acid fermentation of glucose, for instance, all of the phosphorylation is of this type (dehydrogenation of glyceraldehyde phosphate to 1,3-diphosphoglyceric acid and the non-oxidative formation of phosphoenol pyruvate). Other examples of anaerobic substrate-linked phosphorylation are the dehydrogenation of pyruvate to acetyl-CoA and hydrogen gas by various clostridia and the oxidation of acetaldehyde to acetyl-CoA by *C. kluyveri*. (Acetyl-CoA is interconvertible with acetylphosphate in the presence of transacetylase). The thermodynamics of these reactions were considered in Chapter 6. Evidence for a different type of phosphorylation in cytochrome-free bacteria does exist, however. *C. kluyveri* derives energy for growth by fermenting a mixture of ethanol and acetate to butyric acid. Consideration of the mechanism of the butyric fermentation[116] shows that all the acetyl-CoA derived from acetaldehyde oxidation must be used to synthesize the hydrogen acceptor, acetoacetyl-CoA, and is therefore unavailable as an energy source. Several workers postulated that the energy for growth probably came from the reduction of crotonyl-CoA by hydrogen or DPNH.[116] The thermodynamics of this reaction (reduction of olefin to paraffin, Fig. 8, Chapter 6) shows that considerable amounts of energy are made available. Direct evidence for the coupling of the oxidation with the phosphorylation of ADP to ATP has recently been presented by Shuster and Gunsalus,[117] equation (15). Since butyryl-CoA dehydrogenase in *C. kluyveri* is a flavoprotein

$$\text{crotonyl-CoA} + \text{H}_2(\text{DPNH} + \text{H}^+) + \text{ADP} + \text{PO}_4 \rightarrow$$
$$\text{butyryl-CoA} + \text{ATP} + (\text{DPN}^+) \quad (15)$$

(E. Stadtman, personal communication), the over-all reaction conforms to a coupled phosphorylation at the flavoprotein level. Whether a nonspecific oxidant will replace crotonyl-CoA in the ATP-forming reaction is not yet known.

An analogous reaction has been described for *C. sticklandii*.[82] This organism derives energy by coupling the oxidation of one amino acid to the reduction of another.[118] With cell-free enzymes,[82] the reductant can be replaced by various dimercaptans; in such a system, the reduction of glycine is coupled to ATP formation, as shown in equation (16). The DPN-dependent

$$\text{glycine} + \text{R(SH)}_2 + \text{PO}_4 + \text{ADP} \rightarrow \text{acetate} + \text{NH}_3 + \text{R—SS} + \text{ATP} \quad (16)$$

mercaptan dehydrogenase present in the extract does not appear to participate in the ATP-forming reaction.

These reactions are not only of great intrinsic interest but may have a bearing on the general problem of phosphorylation at the flavoprotein level. Such phosphorylation has not yet been directly demonstrated in a complete cytochrome-containing respiratory chain (Chapter 6, Section VIII).

IX. Significance of Flavoprotein Respiration in Anaerobes and Lactic Acid Bacteria

A. Physiological

Electron transfer per se need not be coupled with phosphorylation in order to be useful. Alternative electron transport pathways to oxygen may make available to a fermentative organism a variety of substrates which could not otherwise be used, for lack of hydrogen acceptors. Energy becomes available, in these oxidative reactions, through substrate-linked phosphorylations, just as in the anaerobic fermentations. The lactic acid bacteria offer several examples of such processes. Many lactic acid cocci, for instance, can use glycerol as a growth substrate only under aerobic conditions.[42a,b] Glycerol cannot be used anaerobically, since a balanced fermentation is impossible in the absence of exogenous hydrogen acceptors. The oxidation was studied in detail with *S. faecalis*, strain 24.[21] With this organism, the oxidation of glycerol (O_2 as acceptor) may serve merely to remove a pair of hydrogen atoms so that the subsequent energy-linked fermentation of triosephosphate can take place. This streptococcus may use a direct flavoprotein oxidase for glycerophosphate, since balances suggest that a DPNH oxidase system is absent. With *S. faecalis* strains of more aerobic character, the presence of a DPNH oxidase system permits the coupling between triosephosphate dehydrogenation and O_2 reduction. Even if the reoxidation of DPNH is not energetically coupled (and there is no evidence that it is[30]) the oxidation of glucose with O_2 as electron acceptor furnishes more energy for growth[26, 30] than the lactic acid fermentation, since, aerobically, pyruvate is removed from its role as the obligatory hydrogen acceptor and can then be oxidized to acetyl-CoA,[40] yielding one more "energy-rich" bond per triose.

As a further example, *Lactobacillus brevis*, which lacks the enzyme aldolase, is unable to oxidize glucose in the absence of various organic hydrogen acceptors. These acceptors may be replaced by O_2.[119]

These oxidative reactions become particularly useful if an enzyme, such as DPNH peroxidase, is present to dispose of H_2O_2. A common feature of the peroxide-forming oxidations shown in Table I is that eventually the accumulation of H_2O_2 inhibits the oxidation. Even in lactic acid bacteria which do not contain a peroxidase mechanism, however, a pathway to oxygen appears to be useful, as shown by the glycerol oxidation system of *S. faecalis*, strain 24.[21] Streptococci seem to be more resistant to peroxide than do the strict anaerobes.[120] The finding that various lactic acid bacteria, when grown at low glucose concentrations, display catalase activity (see Chapter 6) offers another possibility for disposing of H_2O_2. In fact, the ability of pediococci to use glycerol as a growth substrate under aerobic conditions is directly correlated with the catalase content of the organisms.[42b] The higher the catalase content, the better the organisms are able to grow on glycerol, with oxygen as the terminal electron acceptor. The prosthetic group of the "catalase" found in lactic acid bacteria has not yet been identified.

Arguments similar to those presented for the lactic acid bacteria would also apply to the anaerobes.[33a] This is illustrated by the requirement for exogenous acceptors in several of the butyric acid fermentations.[116] Oxygen is not a physiological electron acceptor for clostridia however, at least in part because these organisms are much more sensitive to peroxide than are the lactic acid bacteria.[120] With *C. perfringens*, traces of peroxide contribute to the decay of the DPNH oxidase system[33a] and cause the inhibition of several of the dehydrogenases.[65] If this toxicity could be overcome, it is possible that these bacteria might be able to grow aerobically. It has, in fact, been reported that representative strains of clostridia can be grown under aerobic conditions, under a layer of catalase.[53] The "aerotolerance" exhibited by various clostridia[121] may be attributable in part to the presence of electron transport reactions similar to those described for *C. perfringens* and *S. faecalis*, that is mechanisms which result in the reduction of oxygen to water, rather than to peroxide.

B. EVOLUTIONARY

The anaerobic bacteria may represent contemporary examples of early anaerobic forms of life. Among the early bacteria, flavin function was most probably limited to anaerobic electron transport reactions (e.g., the reductive steps of fatty acid synthesis). It may be that flavoprotein oxidase systems, such as those found in *C. perfringens* represent first attempts, in an evolutionary sense, toward adaptation of anaerobes to a developing aerobic environment. For the reasons given in Section IX, A the attempt would be unsuccessful. Lactic acid bacteria appear to be intermediate in physiological characteristics between the strict anaerobes and the cytochrome-containing facultative and obligate aerobes. Streptococci may be related to the more aerobic forms through the pediococci;[122] the rod-shaped lactic acid bacteria show morphological resemblances to the cytochrome-containing propionibacteria and cornynebacteria[123] and may be related to aerobic forms in this way. In this regard it is interesting that certain lactic acid bacteria contain physiologically useful flavoprotein oxidase systems.[30, 39] The transitional nature of these bacteria is also indicated by the fact that the pyruvate oxidase system of *S. faecalis* resembles, in composition and mechanism, the systems of *E. coli* and animal tissue.[40] Furthermore, although *S. faecalis* has no detectable cytochrome components, the organism contains both a soluble and a particulate cytochrome c reductase.[30] In other words, the flavoprotein portion of a cytochrome-linked respiratory chain is present. The sporadic occurrence of catalase activity among the lactic acid bacteria (especially in the genus *Pediococcus*) (Chapter 6) gives further support for an evolutionary relationship. Whatever the validity of such arguments, the enzyme experiments that have been performed to date suggest that the morphologically unrelated clostridia and lactic acid bacteria represent different stages in physiological development (evolution). Although these organisms use similar respiratory mechanisms, the lactic acid bacteria are more successfully adapted to aerobic conditions.

REFERENCES

[1] M. I. Dolin, *Bacteriol. Proc. (Soc. Am. Bacteriologists)* p. 105 (1958).
[2] T. Akazawa and E. E. Conn, *J. Biol. Chem.* **232**, 403 (1958).
[3] H. S. Mason, *Advances in Enzymol.* **19**, 79 (1957).
[4] C. Stapp, *Biochem. Z.* **141**, 42 (1923).
[5] F. C. Happold, *Biochem. J.* **24**, 1737 (1930).
[6] C. Oppenheimer and K. G. Stern, "Biological Oxidation," p. 114. Interscience, New York, 1939.
[7] H. Wieland, *Ergeb. Physiol.* **20**, 477 (1922).
[8] J. W. McLeod and J. Gordon, *Biochem. J.* **16**, 499 (1922).
[9] O. T. Avery and H. J. Morgan, *J. Exptl. Med.* **39**, 275 (1924).
[10] J. W. McLeod and J. Gordon, *J. Pathol. Bacteriol.* **26**, 332 (1923).
[11] A. Bertho and H. Gluck, *Naturwissenschaften* **19**, 88 (1931).
[12] J. G. Davis, *Biochem. Z.* **265**, 90 (1933).
[13] C. Fromageot and J. Roux, *Biochem. Z.* **267**, 202 (1933).
[14] M. G. Sevag, *Biochem. Z.* **267**, 211 (1933).
[15] O. Warburg and W. Christian, *Biochem. Z.* **266**, 377 (1933).
[16] H. Theorell and Å. Åkeson, *Arch. Biochem. Biophys.* **65**, 439 (1956).
[17] E. Haas, *Naturwissenschaften* **22**, 207 (1934).
[18] J. L. Peel, *Biochem. J.* **69**, 403 (1958).
[18a] F. M. Huennekens, S. P. Felton, and E. E. Snell, *J. Am. Chem. Soc.* **79**, 2258 (1957).
[19] T. P. Singer and E. B. Kearney, *in* "The Proteins" (H. Neurath and K. Bailey, eds.), Vol. 2, Part A, p. 123. Academic Press, New York, 1954.
[20] H. Laser, *Proc. Roy. Soc.* **B140**, 230 (1952).
[21] I. C. Gunsalus and W. W. Umbreit, *J. Bacteriol.* **49**, 347 (1945).
[22] F. Lipmann, *Symposium on Respirat. Enzymes (1942)* p. 48. University of Wiscounsin Press.
[23] J. G. Davis, *Biochem. Z.* **267**, 357 (1933).
[24] D. J. O'Kane, *J. Bacteriol.* **60**, 449 (1950).
[25] D. J. O'Kane and I. C. Gunsalus, *J. Bacteriol.* **56**, 499 (1948).
[26] H. W. Seeley and P. J. Vandemark, *J. Bacteriol.* **61**, 27 (1951).
[27] E. C. Greisen and I. C. Gunsalus, *J. Bacteriol.* **48**, 515 (1944).
[28] E. Aubel and J. Houget, *Rev. can. biol.* **4**, 488 (1945).
[29] M. I. Dolin, *Arch. Biochem. Biophys.* **46**, 483 (1953).
[30] M. I. Dolin, *Arch. Biochem. Biophys.* **55**, 415 (1955).
[31] M. M. Weber and N. O. Kaplan, *Bacteriol. Proc. (Soc. Am. Bacteriologists)* p. 96 (1954).
[32] M. I. Dolin, *Bacteriol. Proc. (Soc. Am. Bacteriologists)* p. 110 (1957).
[33a] M. I. Dolin, *J. Bacteriol.* **77**, 383 (1959).
[33b] M. I. Dolin, *J. Bacteriol.* **77**, 393 (1959).
[34] D. J. Niederpruem and D. P. Hackett, *Plant Physiol.* **33**, 113 (1958).
[35] A. F. Holleman, *Rec. trav. chim.* **23**, 169 (1904).
[36] E. C. Greisen and I. C. Gunsalus, *J. Bacteriol.* **45**, 16 (1943).
[37] H. C. Douglas, *J. Bacteriol.* **54**, 272 (1947).
[38] M. K. Johnson and C. S. McCleskey, *J. Bacteriol.* **75**, 98 (1958).
[39] M. I. Dolin, *J. Biol. Chem.* **225**, 557 (1957).
[40] I. C. Gunsalus, *in* "The Mechanism of Enzyme Action" (W. D. McElroy and B. Glass, eds.), p. 545. Johns Hopkins Press, Baltimore, Maryland, 1954.
[41] L. P. Hager, D. M. Geller, and F. Lipmann, *Federation Proc.* **13**, 734 (1954).
[42a] I. C. Gunsalus and J. M. Sherman, *J. Bacteriol.* **45**, 155 (1943).

[42b] W. J. Dobrogosz and R. W. Stone, *Bacteriol. Proc (Soc. Am. Bacteriologists)* p. 111 (1959).

[43] H. Theorell, *Nature* **138**, 687 (1936).

[44] B. L. Horecker, *J. Biol. Chem.* **183**, 593 (1950).

[45] T. R. Hogness, *Symposium on Respirat. Enzymes (1942)* p. 134. University of Wisconsin Press.

[46a] E. Haas, *Biochem. Z.* **290**, 291 (1937).

[46b] A. Ehrenberg and G. D. Ludwig, *Science* **127**, 1177 (1958).

[47] H. Beinert, *J. Biol. Chem.* **225**, 465 (1957).

[48] M. I. Dolin, *Biochim. et Biophys. Acta* **15**, 153 (1954).

[49] O. Warburg and W. Christian, *Biochem. Z.* **298**, 150 (1938).

[50] E. Stadtman and H. A. Barker, *J. Biol. Chem.* **180**, 1095 (1949).

[51] G. M. Frenkel and M. K. Karpenko, *Akad. Nauk. Ukr. R. S. R. Inst. Mikrobiol. i. B. K.* **15**(2), 6 (1953).

[52] M. L. Mallin and H. W. Seeley, *Arch. Biochem. Biophys.* **73**, 306 (1958).

[53] R. A. Holman, *J. Pathol. Bacteriol.* **70**, 195 (1955).

[54] R. W. Estabrook and B. Mackler, *J. Biol. Chem.* **229**, 1091 (1957).

[55] J. H. Bruemmer, P. W. Wilson, J. L. Glenn, and F. L. Crane, *J. Bacteriol.* **73**, 113 (1957).

[56] K. B. Jacobson and L. Astrachan, *Arch. Biochem. Biophys.* **71**, 69 (1954).

[57] M. M. Weber, H. M. Lenhoff, and N. O. Kaplan, *J. Biol. Chem.* **220**, 93 (1956).

[58] A. Nason, W. D. Wosilait, and A. J. Terrell, *Arch. Biochem. Biophys.* **48**, 233 (1954).

[59] D. P. Hackett, *Plant Physiol.* **33**, 8 (1958).

[60] H. Kersten, W. Kersten, and H. Staudinger, *Biochim. et Biophys. Acta* **27**, 598 (1958).

[61] M. Kern and E. Racker, *Arch. Biochem. Biophys.* **48**, 235 (1954).

[62] L. P. Vernon and F. G. White, *Biochim. et Biophys. Acta* **25**, 321 (1957).

[63] G. Haiby and W. E. Clapper, *Bacteriol. Proc. (Soc. Am. Bacteriologists)* p. 84 (1953).

[64] H. W. Seeley and C. del Rio-Estrada, *J. Bacteriol.* **62**, 649 (1951).

[65] M. Grunberg-Manago, J. Szulmajster, and C. Délavier, *Ann. inst. Pasteur* **83**, 102 (1952).

[66] M. I. Dolin, *Bacteriol. Proc. (Soc. Am. Bacteriologists)* p. 115 (1955).

[67a] M. I. Dolin, *Arch. Biochem. Biophys.* **60**, 499 (1956).

[67b] M. I. Dolin, *J. Biol. Chem.* **235**, 544 (1960).

[68a] H. R. Mahler and D. G. Elowe, *J. Biol. Chem.* **210**, 165 (1954).

[68b] L. E. Orgel, *Quart. Revs. (London)* **8**, 422 (1954).

[68c] L. L. Ingraham and B. Makower, *J. Phys. Chem.* **58**, 266 (1954).

[69] E. C. Slater, *Discussions Faraday Soc. No. 20* p. 231 (1955).

[70] M. I. Dolin, *Federation Proc.* **13**, 200 (1954).

[71] S. Thurlow, *Biochem. J.* **19**, 175 (1925).

[72] H. R. Mahler, *Advances in Enzymol.* **17**, 233 (1956).

[73a] V. Massey, *Biochem. J.* **69**, 58 P (1958).

[73b] V. Massey, *Biochim. et Biophys. Acta* **30**, 205 (1958).

[74] D. Ziegler, H. Tisdale, and D. E. Green, *Abstr. 134th Meeting Am. Chem. Soc.* p. 4c (1958).

[75] W. D. Wosilait and A. Nason, *J. Biol. Chem.* **208**, 785 (1954).

[76] H. S. Corran, D. E. Green, and F. B. Straub, *Biochem. J.* **33**, 793 (1939).

[77] N. Savage, *Biochem. J.* **67**, 146 (1957).

[78a] E. Haas, *Biochem. Z.* **298**, 378 (1938).

[78b] M. I. Dolin, and N. P. Wood, *J. Biol. Chem.* **235**, 1809 (1960).

[79] R. E. Asnis, *Arch. Biochem. Biophys.* **66**, 208 (1957).

[80] A. F. Brodie and J. S. Gots, *Science* **116**, 588 (1952).

[81] G. Rendina and R. C. Mills, *J. Bacteriol.* **74**, 572 (1957).

[82] T. C. Stadtman, P. Elliott, and L. Tiemann, *J. Biol. Chem.* **231**, 961 (1958).

[83a] A. F. Brodie and J. S. Gots, *Arch. Biochem. Biophys.* **39**, 165 (1952).

[83b] P. Strittmatter, *J. Biol. Chem.* **233**, 748 (1959).

[83c] W. H. Peterson and M. S. Peterson, *Bacteriol. Revs.* **9**, 49 (1945).

[83d] M. C. Glick, F. Zilliken, and P. György, *J. Bacteriol.* **77**, 230 (1959).

[84] H. Beinert and E. Page, *J. Biol. Chem.* **225**, 479 (1957).

[85] W. B. Sutton, *J. Biol. Chem.* **226**, 395 (1957).

[86] F. B. Cousins, *Biochem. J.* **64**, 297 (1956).

[87] Y. Yamamura, M. Kusunose, and E. Kusunose, *J. Biochem. (Tokyo)* **39**, 227 (1952).

[88] O. Hayaishi and W. B. Sutton, *J. Am. Chem. Soc.* **79**, 4809 (1957).

[89] N. J. Jacobs and P. J. Vandemark, *Bacteriol. Proc. (Soc. Am. Bacteriologists)* p. 104 (1958).

[90] C. F. Strittmatter, *Federation Proc.* **17**, 318 (1958).

[91] P. K. Stumpf and D. E. Green, *J. Biol. Chem.* **153**, 387 (1944).

[92] A. J. Rosenberg and B. Nisman, *Biochim. et Biophys. Acta* **3**, 348 (1949).

[93] E. Racker, *Physiol. Revs.* **35**, 1 (1955).

[94] Cited in K. Burton, appendix to H. A. Krebs and H. L. Kornberg, *Ergeb. Physiol. biol. Chem. u. exptl. Pharmakol.* **49**, 212 (1957).

[95] L. W. Mapson and E. M. Moustafa, *Biochem. J.* **62**, 248 (1956).

[96] W. J. Nickerson and A. H. Romano, *Science* **115**, 676 (1952).

[97] R. E. Asnis, *J. Biol. Chem.* **213**, 77 (1955).

[98] L. P. Hager and I. C. Gunsalus, *J. Am. Chem. Soc.* **75**, 5767 (1953).

[99] D. S. Goldman, *Biochim. et Biophys. Acta* **27**, 513 (1958).

[100a] G. W. Notani and I. C. Gunsalus, *Abstr. 134th Meeting Am. Chem. Soc.* p. 3c (1958).

[100b] L. J. Reed and M. Koike, *Federation Proc.* **18**, 1218 (1959).

[101] H. R. Whiteley and E. J. Ordal, *in* "Inorganic Nitrogen Metabolism" (W. D. McElroy and B. Glass, eds.), p. 521. Johns Hopkins Press, Baltimore, Maryland, 1956.

[102a] B. E. Wright and M. L. Anderson, *Biochim. et Biophys. Acta* **28**, 370 (1958).

[102b] L. P. Hager, *J. Biol. Chem.* **229**, 251 (1957).

[102c] L. P. Hager, *Bacteriol. Proc. (Soc. Am. Bacteriologists)* p. 109 (1959).

[102d] H. C. Friedemann and B. Vennesland, *J. Biol. Chem.* **233**, 1398 (1958).

[102e] J. L. Graves and B. Vennesland, *J. Biol. Chem.* **226**, 307 (1957).

[102f] E. F. Phares and M. V. Long, *Abstr. 130th Meeting Am. Chem. Soc.* p. 62c (1956).

[103] D. J. D. Nicholas and A. Nason, *J. Biol. Chem.* **211**, 183 (1954).

[104] A. Nason, *in* "Inorganic Nitrogen Metabolism" (W. D. McElroy and B. Glass, eds.), p. 109. Johns Hopkins Press, Baltimore, 1956.

[105] D. J. D. Nicholas and A. Nason, *J. Bacteriol.* **69**, 580 (1955).

[106] W. S. Silver, *J. Bacteriol.* **73**, 241 (1957).

[107] D. Spencer, H. Takahashi, and A. Nason, *J. Bacteriol.* **73**, 553 (1957).

[108] A. Nason, R. G. Abraham, and B. C. Averbach, *Biochim. et Biophys. Acta* **15**, 160 (1954).

[109] A. Medina and D. J. D. Nicholas, *Biochim. et Biophys. Acta* **25**, 138 (1957).

[110] R. E. Klausmeier and R. C. Bard, *J. Bacteriol.* **68**, 129 (1954).

[111] M. Zucker and A. Nason, *J. Biol. Chem.* **213**, 463 (1955).

[112] A. K. Saz and L. M. Martinez, *J. Biol. Chem.* **223,** 285 (1956).

[113] S. D. Wainwright, *Biochim. et Biophys. Acta* **18,** 583 (1955).

[114] G. M. Cheniae and H. J. Evans, *Federation Proc.* **17,** 201 (1958).

[115] W. D. McElroy and D. Spencer, *in* "Inorganic Nitrogen Metabolism" (W. D. McElroy and B. Glass, eds.), p. 137, Johns Hopkins Press, Baltimore, Maryland, 1956.

[116] H. A. Barker, "Bacterial Fermentations." Wiley, New York, 1956.

[117] C. W. Shuster and I. C. Gunsalus, *Federation Proc.* **17,** 310 (1958).

[118] L. H. Stickland, *Biochem. J.* **28,** 1746 (1934).

[119] G. Buyze, Ph.D. Thesis, University of Utrecht, Utrecht, 1955.

[120] J. W. McLeod and J. Gordon, *J. Pathol. Bacteriol.* **26,** 326 (1923).

[121] R. S. Breed, E. G. D. Murray, and N. R. Smith, "Bergey's Manual of Determinative Bacteriology," 7th ed. Williams and Wilkins, Baltimore, Maryland, 1957.

[122] H. W. Seeley and E. M. Jensen, *J. Bacteriol.* **67,** 484 (1954).

[123] R. Y. Stanier, M. Doudoroff, and E. A. Adelberg, "The Microbial World." Prentice Hall, Englewood Cliffs, New Jersey, 1957.

Chapter 10

Bacterial Photosynthesis*

David M. Geller

I. Introduction

The problem of the mechanism of bacterial photosynthesis and its relationship to green plant photosynthesis stands today essentially as stated by van Niel in 1941.[1] In green plants and photosynthetic bacteria light energy is presumed to be utilized by chlorophyllous pigment systems by the simultaneous production of reducing and oxidizing powers, so-called "H" and "OH." This primary light reaction is followed by a series of dark reactions. The H is consumed in the reduction of carbon dioxide; OH is converted to oxygen in the green plant or consumed by reducing power supplied by substrate in the bacteria. As stated by van Niel:[1]

Green plant: $2 H_2O + CO_2 \rightarrow (CH_2O) + H_2O + O_2$

Bacteria: $2 H_2A + CO_2 \rightarrow (CH_2O) + H_2O + 2A$

The similarity between the green plant and bacterial systems appears to be so great that the present reviewer cannot avoid comparing one with the other. This is of particular importance at the present time when available information is fragmentary.

---

* This article is not intended as a complete review of the photosynthetic bacteria. It will deal primarily with the relationship of photochemical reactions of extracts to the photosynthetic activity of the intact bacterial cells. A more complete discussion, including the culture and metabolism of photosynthetic bacteria, may be found in H. Gest and M. D. Kamen, Chapter IV, Volume 5 of "Handbuch der Pflanzenphysiologie" (1958). The reader is also referred to S. R. Elsden, Chapter 1 of Volume III of "The Bacteria," for a discussion of carbon dioxide fixation, and to M. D. Kamen and J. W. Newton, Chapter 8 of Volume II of "The Bacteria" for a detailed discussion of the cytochromes in electron transport systems of photosynthetic bacteria.

II. The Chromatophore: Center of Bacterial Photosynthesis

The chromatophore was implicated as the photochemical center of bacterial cells by the finding that the carotenoid and chlorophyll pigments associated with photosynthesis are present only in the chromatophores. Evidence of the photochemical function of the chromatophores emerged from experiments showing photochemical oxidation-reductions involving (a) the oxidation of substances by oxygen, (b) the oxidation of substances by compounds other than oxygen, and (c) the coupled oxidation and reduction of components of the chromatophores themselves. Finally, the chromatophores were demonstrated to carry out the conversion of light energy to "energy-rich" phosphate bonds, a process termed photophosphorylation. An attempt will be made to compare the bacterial chromatophore to the green plant chloroplast, and to formulate a working scheme of bacterial photosynthesis.

A. Size, Structure, and Constitution

The macromolecular organization of the photosynthetic bacterial cell of *Rhodospirillum rubrum* was found by Schachman *et al.*[2] and Pardee *et al.*,[3] to compartmentalize the pigment system in particles having an estimated diameter of 600 A. and a molecular weight of 30,000,000. It was estimated that each cell contained 5000 to 6000 of these chromatophores. Particles of this size were not found in dark-grown *R. rubrum* cells (which did not contain chlorophyll or carotenoid pigments).

Good evidence for the existence of these chromatophores as such in the intact cells has come from electron microscope studies of sectioned cells.[4-6] Similar particles have been found in *Chromatium*.[7-9] The estimated mean diameter of isolated *Chromatium* chromatophores is 320 A.[9] This corresponds to the size of vesicles (200 to 400 A. in diameter) observed in electron micrographs of sectioned *Chromatium* cells by Vatter and Wolfe.[5] In this study similar vesicles were found in *Rhodopseudomonas spheroides* (400 to 800 A. in diameter) and *Chlorobium limicola* (150 to 200 A.).

The most detailed chemical analyses have been made by Newton and Newton[7, 8] on *Chromatium* chromatophores. Large amounts of polysaccharide and phospholipoprotein were found. The phospholipid moiety contained glycerol, ethanolamine, and phosphate in equimolar amounts. The concentration of bacteriochlorophyll was estimated to be 200 molecules per chromatophore. The molar ratio of bacteriochlorophyll, carotenoids, and cytochromes was 10:5:1. Also noteworthy was the presence of large amounts of acid-soluble nonheme ferrous iron.

These chromatophores could be cleaved into "small particle subunits" by sonic oscillation, with subsequent loss of polysaccharide and protein, resulting in a doubling of the chlorophyll, carotenoid, cytochrome, and phospholipid content with respect to protein. Acid-soluble components, including iron, phosphate, pyridine nucleotide, and flavin, were lost during the degradation. It is suggested that the bacterial chromatophores consist of repeating subunits cemented together by polysaccharide. Particles of both types carry out photophosphorylation.[10]

The possibility that *R. rubrum* chromatophores may also be aggregates of small subunits is suggested by the fact that small pigmented particles, about 300 A. in diameter, have been obtained by sonic treatment of cells in viscous media. Photochemically these particles are fully as active as the chromatophores isolated from comparable bacteria in less viscous media.[9, 11, 12]

As noted by Schachman *et al.*,[2] chromatophores are not found in extracts of dark-grown *R. rubrum*.[5] According to Hickman and Frenkel[12] young light-grown cells of *R. rubrum* do not contain chromatophores; instead smaller structures 100 to 150 A. in diameter are found distributed throughout the cells. This would appear to conflict with the work of Vatter and Wolfe.[5] The youth of the cultures is not specified in either case, however; thus it is possible that Hickman and Frenkel's cells may contain developmental forms or subunits of chromatophores.

It should be noted here that members of the photosynthetic bacteria contain large quantities of hematin compounds (as much as 0.1% of the dry weight of the cells).[13] Large amounts of a cytochrome c[14] have been found to be associated with chromatophores of *R. rubrum*[15, 16] and *Chromatium*;[7,8] quantities of the hematin compound RHP (*Rhodospirillum*, or *Rhodopseudomonas*, heme protein)[14, 16, 17] and a cytochrome b[14, 15] have also been found in *R. rubrum* chromatophores. Approximately equimolar quantities of RHP and cytochrome c are present.[16] The concentration of heme pigments has been estimated to be of the order of 0.01 μmole/mg. protein.[15]

B. PHOTOCHEMICAL OXIDATION-REDUCTIONS

1. AEROBIC PHOTOOXIDATIONS

The photooxidation of ascorbic acid by cell-free preparations of *R. rubrum* was first described by French.[18, 19] These experiments were extended by Vernon and Kamen[20] who demonstrated that mammalian cytochrome c and reduced 2,6-dichlorophenol-indophenol (DPIP) were also photooxidized by these preparations. The reaction was heat-labile and relatively insensitive to cyanide, azide, and hydroxylamine. The rate of ascorbate photooxidation was increased by the addition of DPIP. Two moles of ascorbate were oxidized per mole of oxygen consumed. Upon addition of large amounts of catalase and ethanol to the mixture, the final ratio of ascorbate to oxygen consumed was halved; the oxidation of ethanol to acetaldehyde was coupled to the photooxidation of ascorbic acid. Hydrogen peroxide was ruled out as the oxidizing agent of ascorbic acid. Hydrogen peroxide may have been the product of ascorbate photo-oxidation, however, to serve as the oxidant of ethanol. According to the authors, the reaction could be pictured as a bacterial Hill reaction. Water was presumed to be split photochemically to yield an oxidizing agent which reacted with ascorbic acid; the photochemical reductant from water then reacted with molecular oxygen to form the oxidizing agent of ethanol.

Vernon and Kamen[20] also have shown that extracts of *R. rubrum* catalyze the photooxidation of reduced mammalian cytochrome c. One mole of oxygen was consumed for every four moles of reduced cytochrome, in a cyanide-insensitive reaction which was associated with the chromatophores.[21] A cyanide-sensitive "dark" cytochrome oxidase was also found; this was associated with particles smaller than the chromatophores. Furthermore, the photooxidase was found to be more heat-stable (63°C. for 10 minutes) than the "dark" oxidase; a temperature of 80°C. for 10 minutes[20] completely inactivated the photooxidase. The photooxidase of *R. rubrum* catalyzed the oxidation of either *R. rubrum* cytochrome c (cytochrome c_2) or mammalian cytochrome c, whereas *R. rubrum* DPNH-cytochrome c reductase reduced only cytochrome c_2.[21] The mechanism proposed for cytochrome c or DPIP photooxidation was similar [except for equation (3)] to that for ascorbate:

$$2 H_2O \xrightarrow{\text{hv}} 2 (H) + 2 (OH) \tag{1}$$

$$2 (H) + O_2 \longrightarrow \text{``}H_2O_2\text{''} \tag{2}$$

$$\text{``}H_2O_2\text{''} + 2 H^+ + 2 Fe^{++}\text{cyt.} \longrightarrow 2 Fe^{+++}\text{cyt.} + 2 H_2O \tag{3}$$

$$2 (OH) + 2 H^+ + 2 Fe^{++}\text{cyt.} \longrightarrow 2 Fe^{+++}\text{cyt.} + 2 H_2O \tag{4}$$

$$4 Fe^{++}\text{cyt.} + 4 H^+ + O_2 \longrightarrow 4 Fe^{+++}\text{cyt.} + 2 H_2O$$

2. ANAEROBIC LIGHT-INDUCED OXIDATION-REDUCTIONS

The Hill reaction of the chloroplast[22] has not been found in extracts of photosynthetic bacteria; this has been attributed to the absence of the oxygen evolution system in the bacteria.[1] Recently it has been possible to demonstrate the equivalent of the Hill reaction in bacterial systems. Frenkel[11, 23] has described the enzymic photooxidation of reduced flavin mononucleotide (FMN) coupled to photoreduction of oxidized diphosphopyridine nucleotide (DPN) by *R. rubrum* chromatophores under anaerobic conditions. Oxidized triphosphopyridine nucleotide (TPN) would not substitute for DPN in this system. Succinate could be used instead of reduced FMN; the rate of reduced diphosphopyridine nucleotide

(DPNH) formation with succinate was several fold greater than that with FMN as hydrogen donor. This reaction could be visualized as a reaction of the photochemical H with DPN, coupled with oxidation of the hydrogen donor, reduced FMN or succinate, by photochemically generated OH. The general significance of this reaction will be taken up in a later section.

Vernon[24] has described the photoreduction of TPN by *R. rubrum* chromatophores. Unlike Frenkel's system, DPN was not active; reduced triphosphopyridine nucleotide (TPNH) formation [as indicated by reduced glutathione (GSH) formation by glutathione reductase and oxidized glutathione (GSSG)] was inhibited by the addition of various hydrogen donors. The puzzling point concerned the source of reducing power for TPN. According to present concepts, utilization of H alone should result in excess OH and hence inhibition of the system. Therefore, either the present scheme will have to be modified, or the experiments re-examined. The necessary reducing power for TPN reduction (for consumption of OH) may be derived from reducing agents present in the chromatophore preparations. In this case, the effect observed is analogous to Frenkel's observations.

More recently Vernon and Ash[25] have confirmed Frenkel's findings; magnesium ions, cyanide, and a preparation of photosynthetic pyridine nucleotide reductase[26] were required for optimum photoreduction of DPN by *R. rubrum* chromatophores supplemented with succinate. Furthermore, Vernon[27] has noted that these chromatophore preparations carry out the anaerobic photooxidation of a variety of reduced dyes and other substances [reduced 2,6-dichlorophenol-indophenol (DPIP), methylene blue, indigo carmine, and ferrocytochrome c] by fumarate.

The work of Frenkel and Vernon is of particular interest, in that light-induced reduction of pyridine nucleotide has been observed in intact cells. Recently Duysens and Sweep[28] have obtained evidence that irradiation of intact cells of *Chromatium* and *R. rubrum* with infrared light resulted in an increase in concentration of a fluorescent substance similar to reduced pyridine nucleotide. This effect was dependent upon the presence of reducing agents in the medium.

3. COMPARISON OF REACTIONS OF CHROMATOPHORE COMPONENTS WITH INTACT BACTERIAL CELL REACTIONS

a. Light-Induced Oxidation-Reduction: Bacteriochlorophyll and Hemoprotein Components of the Chromatophore and of the Intact Bacterial Cell. A light-induced oxidation-reduction of components of extracts has been observed by Geller and Gregory,[29] Geller,[15, 30] and Smith and Baltscheffsky.[31, 32] Geller studied changes of absorption of *R. rubrum* chromatophore suspensions in the visible portion of the spectrum induced by infrared light. Within one second, infrared light induced an increase in absorption with a maximum at 435 mμ (and smaller peaks at 490, 530, and 565 mμ) and a decrease in absorption at 600 mμ (with a smaller trough at 395 mμ). The 435-mμ peak appeared to be composed of several components. Since the addition of sodium hydrosulfite to chromatophore preparations in the dark induced a maximum increase in absorption at 430 mμ, it was concluded that the peak at 435 mμ induced by light represented photoreduction of one or more components, the most likely being RHP and cytochrome b. The addition of ferricyanide to chromatophores in the dark caused a maximum decrease in absorption at 595–600 mμ. The light-induced change of absorption at 600 mμ therefore represented photooxidation of one or more components (perhaps bacteriochlorophyll, which has a peak at 590 mμ). Thus light induced the simultaneous oxidation of one or more components and the reduction of others.

The significance of the 435-mμ shift has not been established with certainty, however. The effect of infrared light on R. rubrum cells and extracts has been examined in more detail by Smith and Baltscheffsky.[32] In agreement with Geller, it was found that light induced the formation of a broad peak in extracts at 434 mμ. In contrast to this, allowing the extract to become anaerobic in the dark resulted in formation of a peak at 428 mμ. This would probably be the hemoprotein RHP. The same peak appeared if DPNH was added to a preparation in the dark.[33] In the presence of DPNH, however, the light-induced increase in absorption (observed at 430 mμ) persisted. The effects of light on DPNH utilization were irregular and not reproducible. In these experiments the DPNH added was being consumed throughout the experiment, an indication that oxygen was present. Thus the fact that the light-induced increase of absorption at 430 mμ persisted in the presence of DPNH did not rule out the possibility that the light effect represented a photoreduction. However, Duysens[34] has introduced the suggestion that the 430-mμ change may represent bacteriochlorophyll oxidation. He observed the appearance of a broad peak centered at 432 mμ on irradiation of intact cells of R. rubrum in "aerobic distilled water." This was accompanied by shifts in the infrared indicating bacteriochlorophyll photooxidation.[35, 36] The conclusions concerning the significance of the infrared shifts have been supported by the fact that identical spectral changes are induced by ferricyanide and reversed by ferrocyanide.[36-38]

The light-induced change at 432 mμ observed by Duysens does not, however, appear to be related to bacteriochlorophyll (Olson and Kok[39]) since the appearance of the 432-mμ peak is not synchronous with changes in the infrared bands of bacteriochlorophyll. More recently, Smith et al.[40] have concluded that the 435-mμ peak probably does not represent a cyto-

chrome: the absorption band is much broader than that of the usual cytochrome pigment; furthermore, it does not appear to be related to the
spectral changes attributed to the carotenoids. Thus the significance of
the light-induced absorption changes in the region of 430 to 435 mμ and
the nature of the pigment(s) involved are unknown at the present time.

b. Photooxidation of Cytochrome c_2 of the Chromatophore. Two observations of great interest have been made by Smith and co-workers.
The first concerns the effect of phosphate acceptors upon light-induced
absorption changes in extracts of *R. rubrum*.[32] The addition of adenosine
diphosphate (ADP) to an extract resulted in a trough in the light-dark
difference spectrum at 420 mμ. In the absence of ADP a peak at 420 mμ
was induced by light. The difference between the light-induced effects with
and without ADP was thus represented by a trough at 420 mμ. This indicated an increased rate of photooxidation of cytochrome c_2 in the presence
of ADP. Such changes in the steady state of cytochrome c_2 were seen only
in very active extracts. In further work, it was established that the addition of 3-hydroxy-1-heptyl-quinoline-N-oxide to the same extract deep-
ened the trough induced by light at 420 mμ in the presence of ADP and
shifted the broad 434-mμ band to about 430 mμ. These observations were
interpreted as an increased photooxidation of cytochrome c_2 and increased
photoreduction of cytochrome b. Thus this inhibitor, which effectively
blocks photophosphorylation but not respiration by an *R. rubrum* extract,
blocks electron transport between cytochrome b and cytochrome c_2. Thus
cytochromes b and c_2 have been implicated as members of the electron
chain involved in photophosphorylation (discussed below) and phosphorylation is coupled to the oxidation of cytochrome c_2.

c. Light-Induced Changes in the Absorption of the Carotenoid Pigments.
The second observation of Smith and Ramirez[41] may lead to an unraveling
of the complex light-induced absorption changes observed with extracts
of the photosynthetic bacteria. In a study of the possible relationship of
the carotenoid pigments to these absorption changes seen in the intact
cells, Smith and Ramirez have examined a variety of photosynthetic bacteria, varying in kind and quantity of carotenoid pigments. With intact
cells of the carotenoidless blue-green mutant of *R. spheroides* (or dark-
grown photosynthetic bacteria, which are devoid of carotenoids), for example, the difference spectra showed only the oxidation of cytochrome
pigments on oxygenation or illumination. In bacteria containing carotenoids, illumination or oxygenation resulted in the partial loss of absorption bands at wavelengths characteristic of carotenoid pigments of the
organism and the appearance of new absorption bands at longer wavelengths. The similarity between oxygenation and light, taken with the
shift toward longer wavelengths, would be consistent with the view that

these transformations represent oxidation of the carotenoid pigments. More recently, however, Smith and Ramirez[42] have concluded that changes in the absorption spectrum of the carotenoid pigments may represent "structural changes" resulting from the initiation of electron transfer processes rather than oxidation of the carotenoid pigments. The spectral changes attributed to carotenoids have been distinguished from those related to cytochromes by differences in kinetics and differences in inhibition by a variety of agents.

These findings may be related to the experiments of Stanier and coworkers,[43-45] regarding carotenoid synthesis. These workers have reported the increased sensitivity of carotenoidless mutant or diphenylamine-treated (carotenoidless) cells toward oxygen. The carotenoid pigments appear to prevent photooxidation of the photo apparatus; this is manifested by photodestruction of chlorophyll and eventual death of these carotenoidless cells in the light in the presence of oxygen. Particles derived from diphenylamine-treated cells carry out the photophosphorylation reaction in the case of *Chromatium*.[46] The photochemical activity of these particles is (as expected) more sensitive to oxygen than that of the usual carotenoid-containing particles. As suggested by Calvin,[47] this protective effect of carotenoid pigments may be one result of the efficient conversion of excited chlorophyll molecules into reducing and oxidizing agents by a process of conduction in the conjugate chain of the carotenoid molecules associated with chlorophyll.

Thus carotenoid pigments may have functions other than that of the transfer of absorbed light energy to chlorophyll.

d. Photooxidation of Phenazine Methyl Sulfate. In a series of experiments on the activation of photophosphorylation by phenazine methyl sulfate, it was found that partially reduced phenazine dye was photooxidized by suspensions of *R. rubrum* chromatophores.[15, 29] The reaction was unlike the photooxidation of cytochrome c or DPIP in that it was a completely reversible, limited photooxidation which proceeded under rigorously anaerobic conditions. The amount of dye photooxidized was of the order of magnitude of the cytochrome components. When the light was turned off, an equivalent amount of dye was reduced. Absence of oxygen (after thorough flushing with nitrogen or helium) was indicated by the stability of the reduced autoxidizable dye throughout the experiment.

The light-induced absorption changes of the chromatophores were markedly altered by partially reduced phenazine dye. Two effects of the dye were noted. First of all, the trough at 600 mμ induced by light in the absence of reduced dye was abolished or appreciably reduced in size. Secondly, light-induced absorption changes in the 420 to 450 mμ region were markedly altered in the presence of reduced dye. The alteration ap-

peared to depend on the extent of dye reduction. When the ratio of reduced dye to oxidized dye was very low, light induced the formation of a
broad trough centered at 440 mμ; at high ratios of reduced to oxidized
dye, light induced a peak at 440 mμ. When the dye was completely oxidized, the light-dark difference spectra were identical to that observed
in the absence of the dye. On the other hand, completely reduced dye
abolished all light-induced absorption changes.

Photooxidation of partially reduced phenazine dye thus appears to be
caused by direct or indirect oxidation by the "600-mμ" pigment of the
chromatophore. The pigment(s) involved in the 420- to 440-mμ shifts
evidently is unrelated to the 600-mμ pigment. One pigment (such as bacteriochlorophyll) could not be responsible for both absorption changes.

C. PHOTOPHOSPHORYLATION BY CHROMATOPHORES

As noted above, experimental evidence has been obtained for the simultaneous photoproduction of reducing and oxidizing agents in intact cells
and in extracts of photosynthetic bacteria. In addition, high concentrations of hematin compounds are present in even the most obligate anaerobes of the photosynthetic bacteria. These undergo oxidation-reduction
changes in the light. Thus a system analogous to the oxidative phosphorylation system of mitochondria might exist in the photosynthetic
bacteria. This could be a recombination of photochemical H and OH by
electron transport across chains of electron acceptors (including the hematin compounds) coupled with formation of energy-rich phosphate bonds.

Evidence consistent with photophosphorylation was first obtained by
Gest and Kamen's demonstration[48] of a light-accelerated uptake of P[32]
orthophosphate by intact anaerobic cells of R. rubrum.

Photophosphorylation in bacterial extracts was first observed by Frenkel[49] with extracts of R. rubrum at about the time Arnon discovered the
reaction in spinach chloroplasts.[50] The reaction has since been demonstrated in cell-free preparations from R. rubrum, Chromatium,[51-54] and
Chlorobium limicola.[51] The cell-free systems derived from R. rubrum and
Chromatium have been examined in some detail.

Frenkel's[49] first report of photophosphorylation by R. rubrum extracts
was with a particulate fraction corresponding to the chromatophores. The
particles were inactivated by washing; and the activity completely restored
by the original supernate or by a α-ketoglutarate. Geller[15, 29] subsequently
observed reactivation of washed particles by catalytic quantities of succinate, lactate, or DPNH;[15, 55] fumarate, pyruvate, or DPN were ineffective. Both investigators, therefore, concluded that catalytic quantities of
reducing agent were required for photophosphorylation.

The washed particles require ADP or inosine diphosphate (IDP) for photophosphorylation; with added supernate, which contains myokinase, adenosine monophosphate (AMP) will serve as phosphate acceptor. The product, in each case, was characterized as the corresponding triphosphate.[15, 55]

On further investigation the activity of R. rubrum washed particles was found to be markedly increased by the addition of catalytic amounts of phenazine methyl sulfate.[15, 29, 30] Such systems were active in the absence of (and unaffected by) reducing agents, but if the incident light was filtered to remove the wavelengths absorbed by the photosensitive dye, a reducing agent was required for activation by the dye. Excessive reduction of the dye inhibited photophosphorylation; this inhibition was reversed by reoxidation of some of the dye. Thus, partial reduction of the phenazine dye was required for activity. Under optimum conditions the addition of this dye caused as much as an eightfold stimulation of photophosphorylation over that observed with reducing agents alone (DPNH, succinate, or lactate.)[15]

A similar restoration of the photophosphorylation by Chromatium[53] washed particles ("chromatophore fragments") occurred on the addition of such reducing agents as thioethanol, cysteine, or hydrogen sulfide. The highest activity was obtained by adding phenazine methyl sulfate or ascorbate; the system was also activated by DPIP. No filter was used in these studies with the phenazine dye, so it remains to be established whether a reducing agent is required in addition to the phenazine dye. The particles were not activated by preparations of photooxidized phenazine dye.

Photophosphorylation by spinach chloroplasts is activated by phenazine methyl sulfate.[56] When red light was used for photophosphorylation, the phenazine dye had to be exposed to white light and air to activate chloroplast preparations.[57, 58] Pyocyanine, one of the photooxidation products of the phenazine dye, was, however, at one-tenth the concentration, as active as the phenazine dye and required no pretreatment. Pyocyanine, or photooxidized phenazine methyl sulfate does not activate the R. rubrum system. [15]

Photophosphorylation by phenazine methyl sulfate-activated Chromatium particles was inhibited almost completely by the presence of excess reducing agent (ascorbate or thioethanol).[53] The addition of DPIP or thioethanol to ascorbate-activated particles reduced photophosphorylation to that level with DPIP alone.

The effects of various inhibitors upon these photophosphorylation systems have been studied in detail. R. rubrum photophosphorylation is relatively unaffected by cyanide, azide, hydroxylamine, arsenite, and 100% carbon monoxide.[15] The effects of the latter, even though precautions have been taken to remove all visible light at wavelengths below 700 mμ, are in some doubt because of the extreme photosensitivity of the carbon monoxide compound of RHP.[17] Photophosphorylation is inhibited by agents which uncouple phosphorylation from oxidation. *R. rubrum* preparations require rather high concentrations of 2,4-dinitrophenol (10^{-3} M for 50% inhibition).[15, 49] *Chromatium* particles appear to be more sensitive to dinitrophenol.[53] Much lower concentrations ($3 \times 10^{-5} M$) of the butyl ester of 3,5-diiodo-4-hydroxybenzoate[59] inhibit *R. rubrum* photophosphorylation.[15]

In all the inhibition studies with the *R. rubrum* system described above, the effect of inhibitors was the same regardless of the activator used for photophosphorylation. This was not the case in two instances: *R. rubrum* particles were inhibited by low concentrations of antimycin A and compound SN5949;[15, 30] preparations (either crude extracts or particles) supplemented with the phenazine dye were relatively insensitive to either inhibitor. Both inhibitors are known to block electron transport in mitochondrial systems between cytochromes b and c;[60, 61] hence, both may block electron transport in the *R. rubrum* system at the same site at which the phenazine dye provides a bypass. The stimulation by the dye would then be explained by the electron transport step bypassed being the rate-limiting step.

D. CHROMATOPHORE ROLE IN CARBON DIOXIDE FIXATION

Both chloroplast and bacterial chromatophore systems have been shown to catalyze a light-induced incorporation of carbon dioxide into reduced carbon compounds. Intact chloroplasts alone fix carbon dioxide, whereas chloroplast fragments require in addition a soluble extract of chloroplasts.[62] Isolated chromatophores do not catalyze carbon dioxide fixation; they thus correspond to chloroplast fragments.

Fuller and Anderson[63] have observed light-induced incorporation of radioactive carbon dioxide into phosphoglyceric and aspartic acids by cell-free preparations from *Chromatium*. Isolated chromatophores were inactive but could be reactivated by addition of the colorless supernatant fraction obtained by centrifugation of such extracts. Similar observations have been made with *R. rubrum* extracts.[64] The enzymes involved in CO_2 fixation appear to be in the supernatant fraction and the chromatophores to be solely the source of light-derived reducing power. Thus again the chromatophore corresponds to the "chloroplast fragment" rather than the whole chloroplast.

E. CHROMATOPHORE ROLE IN THE PHOTOPRODUCTION OF HYDROGEN

The photoproduction of molecular hydrogen by purple bacteria supplied with certain accessory hydrogen donors, such as pyruvate and C_4-dicarboxylic acids, has been studied in detail by Gest and his colleagues,[65, 66] who find biological H_2 production mediated by a multienzyme electron transport system with hydrogenase the terminal catalyst.

Of interest in this connection are recent experiments of Karunairatnam and Gest[67] which disclose complete localization of *R. rubrum* hydrogenase of extracts in the chromatophores.

III. A General Formulation of Bacterial Photosynthesis

The bacterial chromatophore and the plant chloroplast have much in common. Both contain high concentrations of hematin pigments, aside from the usual photosynthetic pigments. Both catalyze photochemical oxidation-reduction reactions, i.e., Hill reactions or variants thereof. In both photophosphorylation is activated by oxidation-reduction dyes; there still may be some question of the reducing agent requirement for the chloroplast system.

The chief difference between the photochemical activity of the bacterial chromatophore and the plant chloroplast appears to be the ability of the latter to evolve molecular oxygen; the substrate requirement for growth of the photosynthetic bacteria is related to the absence of the oxygen evolution mechanism.[1] One is led to wonder whether the requirement of chromatophore photophosphorylation for reducing agents may be directly related to the substrate requirement of the intact cells.

Indications of this possibility are demonstrated by the catalysis by *R. rubrum* chromatophore suspensions of: (1) the photoreduction of DPN by succinate,[23] (2) carbon dioxide fixation in the presence of acceptor enzymes by the supernatant fraction of a cell-free extract.[64] Succinate is capable of inducing photophosphorylation by washed *R. rubrum* chromatophores;[15] succinic dehydrogenase is localized in the chromatophores.[68] Thus chromatophores should carry out the photoreduction of carbon dioxide by succinate in the presence of pyridine nucleotide and carbon dioxide-fixing enzymes. For photophosphorylation the quantity of succinate required is catalytic, whereas stoichiometric amounts would be required for carbon dioxide fixation. Several schemes relating carbon dioxide fixation, respiration, and photophosphorylation in the photosynthetic bacteria have been advanced.[11, 32]

The requirement of catalytic amounts of reducing agents for photophosphorylation remains unexplained. Newton and Kamen[53] have suggested that, since the photophosphorylation system must consist of a coupled system of electron acceptors, an optimal steady state relationship must exist between the reduced and oxidized forms of the interacting electron carriers. Alteration of this steady state—for example by isolation of the chromatophores—would decrease the activity. The adjustment of the steady states of the carriers toward the "optimal relationship" may be accomplished by "reductants 'driving' the system at low potential level," and by "mild oxidants, e.g., phenazine methyl sulfate and ascorbate, 'pulling' the chain at higher potential levels." Related to this proposal is the possibility that catalytic amounts of reducing agent would effectively remove oxygen, which is an inhibitor of photophosphorylation.[53, 69] One of the functions of the accessory hydrogen donor has been suggested to be prevention of destructive peroxidation resulting in photooxidation of the electron transport chain components.[65]

A second explanation of the reducing agent requirement for photophosphorylation is based on the proposal of Frenkel[55] that the activation effects are due to reduction of one or more of the electron carrier components, enabling the system to react with the "short-lived photochemical oxidant." For example, one may consider the reduction of Y by XH_2 :

$$Y + XH_2 \xrightarrow[b]{a} YH_2 + X$$

The reduction of Y by XH_2 is not a spontaneous process; at equilibrium little or no X or YH_2 may be found. The reaction is, however, driven in direction a by light; and in the dark, proceeds backward spontaneously in direction b. One may then suppose that another pathway for the reduction of X by YH_2 exists, pathway c:

$$Y + XH_2 \xleftarrow[b]{a} YH_2 + X$$
$$\overset{\curvearrowright}{\underset{c}{}}$$

Pathway c consists of a complex of enzymes composed of cytochromes, etc; phosphorylation is coupled to electron transport via pathway c. This pathway is assumed to be such an efficient trap for the reducing power of YH_2 that oxidation of YH_2 by pathway b does not occur.

If one assumes bacteriochlorophyll is XH_2 and the initial component of pathway c is Y, the scheme indicated by Fig. 1 may be formulated. Following the suggestion of Duysens,[70] this scheme depicts the action of light as resulting in a photoreduction of the lowest potential member of the electron transport chain, rather than of photolysis of water. The effect of light is solely to change the potential of (unexcited) bacteriochlorophyll, $Chl \cdot H$, from an estimated 400 to 500 mv.[37, 38] to a potential (of excited bacteriochlorophyll, $Chl \cdot H^*$) sufficiently low to reduce pyridine nucleotide (about -300 mv.). The reduction of A, the lowest potential electron carrier (pyridine nucleotide?), would produce unexcited oxidized bacteriochlorophyll (Chl) which would react either with reduced A or electron carrier C (which has the highest potential in the system, aside from bacteriochlorophyll). Reduced excited and oxidized unexcited bacteriochlorophyll thus correspond to the H and OH of other schemes.

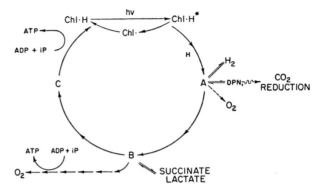

Fig. 1. Scheme of photophosphorylation of bacteriochlorophyll and its associated electron transport system.

Formation of reducing power by light would thus be a function of the concentration of reduced bacteriochlorophyll. In the light bacteriochlorophyll would be oxidized by A. The light excitation and oxidation reactions are assumed not to be rate limiting; the rate-limiting reaction must lie somewhere within the electron transport chain, such as B → C. The light steady states of bacteriochlorophyll and terminal electron acceptor C would thus be more oxidized, and that of electron acceptor A more reduced, with respect to their levels in the dark. Addition of reducing power to the system, to pull the light steady state of C toward reduction would increase the concentration of reduced unexcited bacteriochlorophyll (Chl·H), the substrate of the light reaction, leading to increased electron transport and thus to photophosphorylation.

Bacteriochlorophyll and its associated electron transport system represent, according to Fig. 1, a system which may function either solely as a "closed circuit" or as an "open circuit" for electrons. The first case is represented by photophosphorylation. The phosphorylation is coupled to electron transport; but without loss of electrons from the system. The only over-all change measurable is the accumulation of adenosine triphosphate. The second case is represented by the reduction of pyridine nucleotide and carbon dioxide, or by hydrogen evolution, at the expense of an externally supplied hydrogen donor. Electrons flow into the system at one point and emerge at another. Light energy is utilized to alter the potential of electrons flowing through the system. For example, electrons from the succinate-fumarate couple may enter the system so as to leave it at a lowered potential to reduce pyridine nucleotide or to produce molecular hydrogen. Photophosphorylation may occur simultaneously with these oxidation-reduction processes, as demonstrated by Arnon and his co-workers, who have shown that photophosphorylation may be coupled to TPNH and oxygen production by chloroplast fragments.[71]

Several features favor the scheme just described, as shown in Fig. 1. It is consistent with the activation of photophosphorylation by a catalytic quantity of reducing agent, i.e., with the system operating solely by photophosphorylation, electrons circulating in a closed circuit. The quantity of reducing power to stimulate photophosphorylation would be considerably less than is required for reduction of all of the components of the system; the reducing power furnished to the system would not be consumed.

The scheme is also consistent with inhibition of photophosphorylation by excess reduction or oxidation. For example, excessive reduction of any carrier would slow reduction of that carrier; i.e., the rate of reduction of A would be decreased by "pulling" the steady state level of A to a more reduced level. Complete reduction of pigment A by an external electron donor would block oxidation of bacteriochlorophyll. The system is thus poisoned by excess reducing agent.

Evidence has been obtained implicating bacteriochlorophyll directly in light oxidation-reductions. Duysens[35] and Duysens et al.[36] have demonstrated the photooxidation of bacteriochlorophyll in intact R. rubrum cells deprived of substrates. Goedheer[38] and Duysens[37] have observed identical changes in infrared absorption of intact cells and of extracts on adding ferricyanide. Recently Vishniac and Rose[72] have reported a light-induced incorporation of tritium into chlorophyll from tritium-labeled water by Chromatium chromatophores and acetone powders of spinach chloroplasts. With the latter preparation the experiments indicate a light-induced transfer of tritium from chlorophyll to TPN without loss of tritium to water.

The energy requirement for bacterial photosynthesis has been calculated by Duysens.[70] The maximum efficiency calculated is 68%: on this basis, only 21 kcal. per einstein absorbed by bacteriochlorophyll could be utilized by bacterial systems. Assuming that bacterial pyridine nucleotide is reduced, with the simultaneous oxidation of a substance (presumably bacteriochlorophyll) with an E_0' value of 0.44 volt, Duysens has calculated that 35 kcal. of free energy are required per mole of reduced pyridine nucleotide; or sufficient energy if properly coupled for the production of a maximum of three energy-rich phosphate bonds (assuming a 60 to 70% efficiency for this process). Furthermore, according to Duysens' calculations,[70] two einsteins of quanta would be required per mole of pyridine nucleotide reduced; thus a maximum of three ATP molecules produced per two quanta. The experimental data with Chromatium cells range from three to ten quanta required to reduce one molecule of pyridine nucleotide. Olson and Chance[73] have estimated that two quanta per electron are required for the oxidation of Chromatium cytochrome.

IV. Concluding Remarks

The many gaps in our knowledge reduce the foregoing presentation to but a sketchy picture of the mechanism of bacterial photosynthesis.

The most successful approach to this problem has been through the recognition of reaction steps of the photosynthetic process in intact cells and the demonstration of these reactions in cell-free extracts. By this means, the chromatophore has been recognized as the photochemical center of the bacterial cell, just as the chloroplast is for the plant cell.

ACKNOWLEDGMENTS

The author wishes to express his thanks to Dr. Albert Frenkel for sending him a copy of his review article on this subject, prior to its publication in *Annual Review of Plant Physiology* (1959). He also is indebted greatly to Dr. Lucile Smith for copies of several articles prior to publication.

REFERENCES

[1] C. B. van Niel, *Advances in Enzymol.* **1**, 263 (1941).
[2] H. K. Schachman, A. B. Pardee, and R. Y. Stanier, *Arch. Biochem. Biophys.* **38**, 245 (1952).
[3] A. B. Pardee, H. K. Schachman, and R. Y. Stanier, *Nature* **169**, 282 (1952).
[4] A. E. Vatter and R. S. Wolfe, *Bacteriol. Proc.* (*Soc. Am. Bacteriologists*) p. 30 (1957).
[5] A. E. Vatter and R. S. Wolfe, *J. Bacteriol.* **75**, 480 (1958).
[6] A. Frenkel, D. Hickman, and L. Smith, *Bacteriol. Revs.* **21**, 256 (1957).
[7] J. W. Newton and G. A. Newton, *Arch. Biochem. Biophys.* **71**, 250 (1957).
[8] J. W. Newton, G. A. Newton, and M. D. Kamen, *Intern. Congr. Microbiol., 7th Congr., Stockholm, 1958, Abstr.* p. 75 (1958).
[9] J. A. Bergeron, I. C. Anderson, and R. C. Fuller, *Plant Physiol.* **32**, Suppl. xvi (1957).
[10] J. W. Newton and M. D. Kamen, *Bacteriol. Proc.* (*Soc. Am. Bacteriologists*) p. 115 (1956).
[11] A. W. Frenkel, *Brookhaven Symposia in Biol.* **11**, 276 (1959).
[12] D. D. Hickman and A. W. Frenkel, *J. Biophys. and Biochem. Cytol.* **6**, 277 (1959); A. W. Frenkel and D. D. Hickman, *J. Biophys. and Biochem. Cytol.* **6**, 285 (1959).
[13] M. D. Kamen, *in* "Research in Photosynthesis" (H. Gaffron, A. H. Brown *et al.*, eds.), p. 524. Interscience, New York, 1957.
[14] L. P. Vernon and M. D. Kamen, *J. Biol. Chem.* **211**, 643 (1954).
[15] D. M. Geller, Ph.D. Thesis, Harvard University, Cambridge, Massachusetts, 1957.
[16] R. Hill and M. D. Kamen, Unpublished results (1956).
[17] R. G. Bartsch and M. D. Kamen, *J. Biol. Chem.* **230**, 41 (1958).
[18] C. S. French, *J. Biol. Chem.* **123**, xxxviii (1938).
[19] C. S. French, *J. Gen. Physiol.* **23**, 469 (1940).
[20] L. P. Vernon and M. D. Kamen, *Arch. Biochem. Biophys.* **44**, 298 (1953).
[21] M. D. Kamen and L. P. Vernon, *J. Biol. Chem.* **211**, 663 (1954).
[22] R. Hill, *Proc. Roy. Soc.* **B127**, 192 (1939); *Symposia Soc. Explt. Biol. No. 5*, 222 (1951).
[23] A. W. Frenkel, *J. Am. Chem. Soc.* **80**, 3479 (1958).

[24] L. P. Vernon, *J. Biol. Chem.* **233**, 212 (1958).

[25] L. P. Vernon and O. K. Ash, *J. Biol. Chem.* **234**, 1878 (1959).

[26] A. San Pietro and H. M. Lang, *J. Biol. Chem.* **231**, 211 (1958).

[27] L. P. Vernon, *J. Biol. Chem.* **234**, 1883 (1959).

[28] L. N. M. Duysens and G. Sweep, *Biochim. et Biophys. Acta* **25**, 13 (1957).

[29] D. M. Geller and J. D. Gregory, *Federation Proc.* **15**, 260 (1956).

[30] D. M. Geller, *Intern. Congr. Microbiol. 7th Congr., Stockholm, 1958. Abstr.* p. 73 (1958).

[31] L. Smith and M. Baltscheffsky, *Federation Proc.* **15**, 357 (1956).

[32] L. Smith and M. Baltscheffsky, *J. Biol. Chem.* **234**, 1575 (1959).

[33] B. Chance, M. Baltscheffsky, and L. Smith *in* "Research in Photosynthesis" (H. Gaffron, A. H. Brown *et al.*, eds.), p. 195, 199. Interscience, New York, 1957.

[34] L. N. M. Duysens *in* "Research in Photosynthesis" (H. Gaffron, A. H. Brown, *et al.*, eds.), p. 164. Interscience, New York, 1957.

[35] L. N. M. Duysens, *Nature* **173**, 692 (1954).

[36] L. N. M. Duysens, W. J. Huiskamp, J. J. Vos, and J. M. van der Hart, *Biochim. et Biophys. Acta* **19**, 189 (1956).

[37] L. N. M. Duysens, *Brookhaven Symposia in Biol.* **11**, 10 (1959).

[38] J. C. Goedheer, *Brookhaven Symposia in Biol.* **11**, 325 (1959).

[39] J. M. Olson and B. Kok, *Biochim et Biophys. Acta* **32**, 278 (1959).

[40] L. Smith, M. Baltscheffsky, and J. M. Olson, *J. Biol. Chem.* **235**, 213 (1960).

[41] L. Smith and J. Ramirez, *Arch. Biochem. Biophys.* **79**, 233 (1959).

[42] L. Smith and J. Ramirez, *J. Biol. Chem.* **235**, 219 (1960).

[43] M. Griffiths, W. R. Sistrom, G. Cohen-Bazire, and R. Y. Stanier, *Nature* **176**, 1211 (1955).

[44] G. Cohen-Bazire and R. Y. Stanier, *Nature* **181**, 250 (1958).

[45] R. Y. Stanier and G. Cohen-Bazire, *Intern. Congr. Microbiol., 7th Congr., Stockholm, 1958. Abstr.* p. 76 (1958).

[46] R. C. Fuller and I. C. Anderson, *Nature* **181**, 252 (1958).

[47] M. Calvin, *Nature* **176**, 1215 (1955).

[48] H. Gest and M. D. Kamen, *J. Biol. Chem.* **176**, 299 (1948).

[49] A. W. Frenkel, *J. Am. Chem. Soc.* **76**, 5568 (1954).

[50] D. I. Arnon, M. B. Allen, and F. R. Whatley, *Nature* **174**, 394 (1954).

[51] A. M. Williams, *Biochim. et Biophys. Acta* **19**, 570 (1956).

[52] J. W. Newton and M. D. Kamen, *in* "Research in Photosynthesis" (H. Gaffron, A. H. Brown *et al.*, eds.), p. 311. Interscience, New York, 1957.

[53] J. W. Newton and M. D. Kamen, *Biochim. et Biophys. Acta* **25**, 462 (1957).

[54] I. C. Anderson and R. C. Fuller, *Plant Physiol.* **32**, Suppl. xvi (1957).

[55] A. W. Frenkel, *J. Biol. Chem.* **222**, 823 (1956).

[56] A. T. Jagendorf and M. Avron, *J. Biol. Chem.* **231**, 277 (1958).

[57] D. A. Walker and R. Hill, *Biochem. J.* **69**, 57P (1958).

[58] R. Hill and D. A. Walker, *Plant Physiol.* **34**, 240 (1959).

[59] F. L. Hoch and F. Lipmann, *Proc. Natl. Acad. Sci. U. S.* **40**, 909 (1954).

[60] V. R. Potter and A. E. Reif, *J. Biol. Chem.* **194**, 287 (1952).

[61] E. G. Ball, C. B. Anfinsen, and O. Cooper, *J. Biol. Chem.* **168**, 257 (1947).

[62] F. R. Whatley, M. B. Allen, L. L. Rosenberg, J. B. Capindale, and D. I. Arnon, *Biochim. et Biophys. Acta* **20**, 462 (1956).

[63] R. C. Fuller and I. C. Anderson, *Plant Physiol.* **32**, Suppl. xvi (1957).

[64] A. W. Frenkel, Unpublished observations (1954).

[65] H. Gest and M. D. Kamen *in* "Handbuch der Pflanzenphysiologie" (W. Ruhland, ed.), Vol. V, Chapter IV. Springer, Berlin, 1958.

[66] H. Gest, *in* "Proceedings of the International Symposium on Enzyme Chemistry, Tokyo and Kyoto, 1957, p. 250. Academic Press, New York, 1958.

[67] M. C. Karunairatnam and H. Gest, *Intern. Congr. Microbiol. 7th Congr., Stockholm, 1958. Abstr.* p. 74 (1958).

[68] B. R. Woody and E. S. Lindstrom, *J. Bacteriol.* **69,** 353 (1955).

[69] A. W. Frenkel, *Plant Physiol.* **31,** Suppl. xxx (1956).

[70] L. N. M. Duysens, *Ann. Rev. Plant Physiol.* **7,** 25 (1956).

[71] D. I. Arnon, F. R. Whatley, and M. B. Allen, *Science* **127,** 1026 (1958).

[72] W. Vishniac and I. A. Rose, *Nature* **182,** 1089 (1958).

[73] J. M. Olson and B. Chance, *Biochim. et Biophys. Acta* **28,** 227 (1958).

CHAPTER 11

Bacterial Luminescence

W. D. McELROY

I. Introduction

The first suggestion that the "phosphorescence" of dead fish and flesh might be due to living things was made by Baker in 1742.[1] Aristotle knew of the curious phenomenon of light emission by dead fish, but it was not until later in the history of the development of science that one finds experimental work in this area. Robert Boyle in 1668 was the first to demonstrate the importance of air for light emission by organisms, and Martin in 1761 actually discovered the necessity of a high salt environment for marine luminous bacteria, although he was not aware that he was studying microorganisms at the time. It was not until the late eighteenth and early nineteenth centuries that specific experimental work was done to demonstrate the cause of this light.

Earlier investigators thought that light emission was connected with the decay and decomposition process of the tissues, but it was Heller in 1853 who definitely named an organism, *Sarcina lutea*, as the cause of light emission by meat. Heller demonstrated that new flesh could be inoculated with the luminous material. Several years later, in 1875, Pfluger demonstrated that the bacteria from fish was "filterable" and would grow on complex culture media; in 1878 Cohn proposed the name *Micrococcus phoreus* for this organism. Following the work of Pfluger there were numerous isolations of new forms of luminous bacteria and each isolation was apparently given a new name. The most comprehensive early study of the various species of

479

luminous bacteria was made by Fisher, a ship's medical officer, and an early worker in the field of marine bacteriology. He discovered *Bacterium phosphorescens* from the West Indies and another species from the Baltic Sea. He studied in some detail the cultural characteristics as well as the general properties of these various forms of luminous bacteria. It is clear from the studies by Fisher, as well as those of workers following him, that many of the bacteria previously described were the same or very similar organisms (see Section IV).

The brilliance and intensity of the bacterial light emission has been noted by many investigators. Numerous attempts have been made to measure the light intensity of a single bacterium; the reader is referred to Harvey's book for a review of these observations. Eymers and Van Schouwenburg have made direct measurements in absolute units of the amount of light energy emitted by a suspension of *Photobacterium phosphorium* (2 mg. dry weight). They observed that at $22°$ C. 7.18 ergs per second were emitted and Harvey has indicated in his studies on luminous bacteria that a single organism has an intensity of approximately 2×10^{-14} foot-candle. The colonies of luminous bacteria are so bright that the suggestion was made during the last war that they might be used during blackouts.

Although there were early speculations that the luminescence of the sea is due to luminous bacteria, modern investigations have clearly shown that bacteria emit light only after they have developed in great numbers on dead fish and other organisms. The brilliant luminescence of the sea is usually due to large numbers of dinoflagellates, jellyfish, and other luminous salt water forms.

The emission spectra of luminous bacteria have been studied by a number of workers. The most recent studies by Spruit Van der Berg and by Eymers and Van Schouwenburg indicate that the peak of light emission by luminous bacteria varies only slightly, ranging from approximately 465 to about 495 mμ. Recent observations have also shown that the light emitted in cell-free extracts, as well as in protoplasts, of luminous bacteria, are essentially identical to those obtained in the intact organism.[2] Thus, the broad spectral distribution observed in luminous bacteria is not due to scattering effects of the cell wall or other materials. Although the peak intensity for light emission in the bacteria is in the blue or blue-green region, light is emitted over the range from 400 to 650 mμ. Since, however, the major emission is around 480–490 mμ the light is blue or blue-green in appearance.

II. Chemistry of Bacterial Luminescence

A. The General Problem of Light Emission

Molecules can be made to emit light in a number of ways. The one familiar to most workers is fluorescence, the emission of light from substances during the time they are exposed to radiations of various kinds such as ultraviolet light or X-rays. If the light emission persists after the exciting radiation is cut off, it is called phosphorescence. There are many other examples of luminescence such as electroluminescence, thermoluminescence, and sonoluminescence. Chemiluminescence, light emission accompanying a chemical reaction, is the process of immediate interest to the students of bioluminescence. The chemical reactions in luminous organisms which lead to the excitation of a molecule are oxidative and are catalyzed by an enzyme called luciferase. The immediate electron acceptor is always molecular oxygen. The oxidizable substrate is called luciferin. The nature of the latter compound is different for the various luminous forms. Students of bioluminescence would like to know the exact chemical composition of the components participating in the enzymic reaction leading to light emission. In addition, what is the relationship of this oxidative process to the general electron transport mechanisms that occur in the cell and are necessary for its viability? The fundamental question of the mechanism of excitation is a physical-quantum chemical question difficult for biologists to answer at the present time, but certainly a basic one relating to the general problem of energy transfer. In general, modern chemical theory postulates that a molecule acquires excess energy with the displacement of an electron from a lower to a higher energy level, namely, the excited state of the molecule. In the case of bioluminescence the energy for this displacement comes from a chemical reaction. When the electron in the excited state returns to ground level a quantum of light is emitted. The color of the light depends upon the amount of energy that is liberated in the transition from the excited state to the ground state. In contrast to the very broad spectra of incandescence or high temperature radiation the spectra of light emitted by organisms are usually very narrow bands of light which give them a definite color, as in the case of luminous bacteria (blue-green), the firefly (yellow-green), and the South American railroad worm (red).

One of the important thermodynamic problems that biochemists face in explaining luminescence is the large amount of energy required for the excitation process. For luminous bacteria which have a peak emission spectrum around 490 mμ one can calculate from the general equation, $E = h\gamma$, that the energy requirement is approximately 60 kcal. per mole. Considering the possibility that the initial excitation process may lose approximately 10 kcal. calories before the electron returns to the ground state, it seems likely that an excess of 70 kcal. might be required for the excitation process.

The oxidation-reduction reactions in organisms are coupled in such a way that usually no more than 10 kcal. are liberated in any single step. Therefore, one of the major problems in the bioluminescent reaction is to discover new processes which will liberate large amounts of energy in one single step in order that the basic molecule may be excited to luminescence. Peroxidation of organic moleules often leads to light emission and this has been suggested as a possible explanation for bioluminescent reactions.

B. Purification and Identification of the Compounds Required for Light Emission

1. Historical

DuBois in 1885 reported the first definitive experiments regarding the nature of the chemical components necessary for light production by organisms.[1] He found that the luminous organs of a beetle would cease to emit light if immersed in hot water. He also noted, however, that a cold water extract which had ceased to luminesce could be stimulated to emit light by adding the hot water extract. On the basis of this type of experiment DuBois proposed the theory that there was in the hot water extract a substance stable to heat which was destroyed during its luminescent oxidation through the action of a catalyst present in the cold water extract. He named the heat-stable substance *luciferin* and the heat-labile substance *luciferase*. Numerous studies since that time have confirmed and extended DuBois' observations to include other luminous forms.

The earlier attempts to separate the light-emitting process from the luminous bacterial cells were negative. These observations lead Beijerinck[3] to conclude that luminescence was bound up with living protoplasm. The indispensability of peptones for these bacteria was described by him to be due to the fact that they were converted into a special form of matter, the photoplasm which was the necessary material for light emission.

Judged by present-day knowledge concerning the mechanism of cell free bacterial luminescence, there are two very important historical observations which should have greatly influenced and facilitated the study of light emission in bacteria. The first of these concerns the observations of Gerretsen.[4] Gerretsen reported in 1920 that he was able to obtain a weak luciferin-luciferase reaction from extracts of *Photobacterium javanense*. Gerretsen also observed an increase in luminescence after a short ultraviolet treatment; these observations have been repeated by Harvey and other investigators. As will be discussed later, observations by McElroy and associates have demonstrated that ultraviolet radiation liberates a long chain aldehyde which is one of the essential components for light emission.

Doudoroff[5] in earlier studies found that added riboflavin was essential for maximum luminescence of dim strains during growth. Interestingly, the respiration of the bright and dim strains was the same in the presence and absence of this riboflavin. From these observations Doudoroff concluded, correctly, as we now know, that a flavin was connected with one of the enzymes involved in light production by the bacteria.

In 1951 Shoup and Strehler[6] noted that acetonized powders from

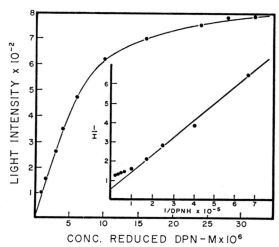

FIG. 1. The relationship between DPNH and light intensity (McElroy and Green[11]).

Achromobacter fischeri would luminesce brightly for 15 minutes after being suspended in water. Following these observations Strehler and Cormier[7] undertook an examination of the luminescence of the acetonized *Achromobacter fischeri* powders. They observed that the duration of luminescence depended upon the concentration of the extracts and that a luciferin-luciferase reaction was obtainable if sufficiently concentrated materials were employed. The factor which first became limiting for luminescence in the crude extract was shown to be reduced diphosphopyridine nucleotide (DPNH). The relationship between DPNH and light intensity is shown in Fig. 1.

2. REQUIREMENTS OF FLAVIN MONONUCLEOTIDE AND ALDEHYDE

Initial attempts to demonstrate other requirements for the luminescence of the crude extracts were inconclusive in that prolonged dialysis of the acetone powder gave preparations which were still capable of responding to added DPNH. By ammonium sulfate fractionation of bacterial extracts which had been lysed with distilled water, McElroy and associates[8] were able to show the requirement of flavin mononucleotide (FMN) as an essential factor for light emission. These preparations would not emit light in the absence of added FMN, thus indicating that a luminescent pathway consisted of a DPN-flavin electron transport system.

McElroy and associates[9] also observed a requirement for an additional factor which they termed bacterial luciferin. This factor was in certain respects analogous to the component in firefly luminescence which has been called firefly luciferin and is used during the course of light emission. This material, which would restore luminescence in crude extracts, was rapidly

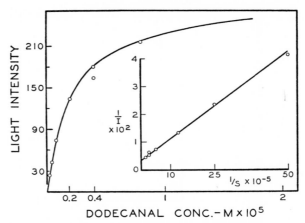

Fɪɢ. 2. The relationship between aldehyde concentration and light intensity (McElroy and Green[11]).

liberated from bound form by irradiating a number of tissues with ultra-violet light. Subsequent work by Cormier and Strehler[10] indicated that this component occurred in high concentrations in hog kidney cortex and they were able to isolate this material and identify it as the long-chain aldehyde, palmital. Subsequent work has indicated that a number of the long-chain aliphatic aldehydes, from C_6 to C_{18}, will support light emission. The relationship of dodecanal concentration to light intensity is shown in Fig. 2 while in Fig. 3 total light production is related to aldehyde. From these

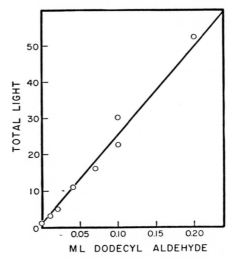

Fɪɢ. 3. The relationship between total light production and aldehyde (McElroy and Green[11]).

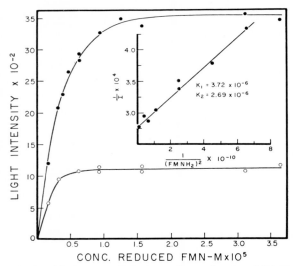

FIG. 4. The relationship between light intensity and reduced FMN concentration (McElroy and Green[11]).

relationships it is clear that a limited amount of light is emitted for a given amount of aldehyde; thus McElroy and Green[11] concluded that the aldehyde was used along with $FMNH_2$ during the process of light emission. Subsequent work by Cormier *et al.*,[12] as well as by McElroy and Green,[11] has indicated that one enzyme is involved in the light-emitting process and that the main components for light emission are reduced FMN, long-chain aldehyde, molecular oxygen, and the bacterial luciferase.

Kinetic analysis of the light emission with varying concentrations of reduced FMN is shown in Fig. 4. The reciprocal plot indicates that two reduced flavins are required for light emission; K_1 and K_2 are the dissociation constants for the reduced FMN-luciferase complex. Similar observations with regard to the aldehyde indicates that one molecule of the latter substance is used. Totter and Cormier[13] have also studied the binding of the flavin to the luciferase molecule and have concluded that there is one tightly bound flavin and one which freely dissociates. From these observations McElroy and Green[11] concluded that during luminescence one molecule of aldehyde combined with one molecule of the reduced flavin to form an FMN-aldehyde compound. Normally this compound would be oxidized directly by molecular oxygen through a catalytic reaction in which peroxide and the corresponding acid are eventually formed. This oxidation would liberate considerable energy but would be approximately 40 kcal. short of that required for light emission. They proposed therefore that the second reduced FMN molecule could react with oxygen to form an unstable organic peroxide similar to that suggested by Drew[14] for aminophthalic hydrazide and that this peroxide would then act as an oxidant for the aldehyde-FMN compound to give a highly excited molecule which would emit light. This proposal therefore is in keeping with the idea that two reduced flavin molecules are necessary for light emission, one for combination with the aldehyde and a second for forming an organic peroxide which acts as the oxidant. The idea that aldehyde can combine with the reduced intermediate prior to oxidation or peroxidation is not fundamentally different from the idea suggested by Racker for triosephosphate dehydrogenase.

The reasons for suggesting that modified flavin is bacterial luciferin are several fold. Flavin fluorescence is a yellow-green in contrast to the blue light of the bacteria which has a peak around 480 mμ. It is possible that modification of the flavin structure by the addition of a long-chain aldehyde would give a conjugated system whose excited state would emit light in the blue region of the spectrum. In addition the energy release by the peroxidation of a long-chain aldehyde to form acid would be adequate to satisfy the requirements for excitation.

3. FACTORS AFFECTING LIGHT EMISSION IN EXTRACTS

Earlier attempts to remove or purify luciferase to the point where it failed to respond to reduced pyridine nucleotides were unsuccessful. Prolonged dialysis against metal-free phosphate buffer and cyanide in the presence and absence of glutathione were ineffective in the further purification of bacterial luciferase. Cormier et al.[12] were able by dialysis at low pH to inactivate the sytem which stimulated the utilization of reduced DPN for light production. Recently Green and McElroy have been able to separate by calcium phosphate gel column the DPNH-FMN oxidase system from the bacterial luciferase system. Under these circumstances the purified luciferase does not respond to reduced pyridine nucleotide. Cormier and Totter demonstrated that their partially inactivated preparation would emit light with DPNH if they added a preparation from *Escherichia coli* which was capable of reducing FMN with reduced DPN. The results indicate, therefore, that the partially purified luciferase contains an enzyme which transfers the electrons from reduced pyridine nucleotides to flavin and a second enzyme, legitimately called bacterial luciferase, which catalyzes light emission.

A number of agents which will reduce FMN will support luminescence. Strehler et al.[15] reported earlier that reduced riboflavin would support luminescence in crude extracts. McElroy and Green[11] were able to show with their purified enzyme, which is essentially free of FMN, that no light is obtained with reduced riboflavin. However, the addition of FMN to these preparations allowed the utilization of a number of reducing agents for light production. Various reduced dyes, such as safarine, indigo trisulfonate, and rosindulin 2 G, support luminescence provided FMN is added. Reduced rosindulin 2 G was approximately 50 % as effective as reduced FMN in supporting light emission, while reduced riboflavin gave only 10 % of maximal flash. From these studies it was apparent that reduced dyes whose oxidation reduction potential were more positive than the indigo trisulfonate (-0.081, pH 7.0) would not initiate light emission.

The partially purified bacterial luciferase which contains the DPNH-flavin oxidase rapidly oxidizes DPNH without light production provided FMN is added. In addition, the enzyme will catalyze the rapid reduction of methylene blue, various quinones, and ferricyanide, but not inorganic iron. If ferricyanide is added to a normal reaction mixture no light is emitted until all of the ferricyanide is reduced. The relationship between ferricyanide concentration and delayed light emission is shown in Fig. 5. The fact that no light is emitted until the ferricyanide is reduced suggests a competition between the latter and FMN for the electrons from DPNH. The oxidation of DPNH by ferricyanide proceeds normally even in the presence of 10^{-3} molar KCN, suggesting that the electron transport process does not require metal as a necessary cofactor. These observations would offer a plausible

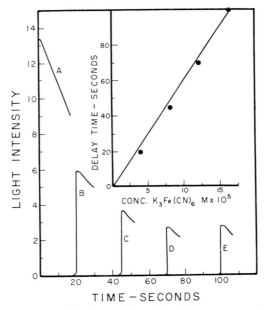

FIG. 5. The inhibition of light by ferricyanide. Various amounts of ferricyanide were added to the reaction mixture and DPNH was added at zero time. Light emission occurred only after the ferricyanide was completely reduced (McElroy and Green[11]).

explanation for the fact that various reduced dyes will support light emission in the presence of FMN. Cormier and Totter[16] have obtained a preparation from luminous bacteria which will catalyze the reduction of cytochrome c by reduced pyridine nucleotide. Their preparation also contains bacterial luciferase and it is presumed that this system is operating in the reduction of the cytochrome system. The crude bacterial luciferase will also reduce various naphthoquinones. The results indicate that the inhibition of light emission by quinones is accomplished by removing reduced pyridine nucleotides. Spruit and Schuiling[17] have made similar observations on whole cells and have concluded that quinone inhibits light emission in the intact bacteria by competing with the light system in the electron transport process. The relationship of the light-emitting oxidative reactions to electron transport in the intact bacteria will be considered in a later section.

In the presence of FMN and aldehyde both DPNH and TPNH will support light emission when a partially purified luciferase is used. The TPNH concentration required for maximum light output is about three times the DPNH concentration. Also the maximum light intensity obtainable with TPNH is only 80 % of that observed with DPNH. The fact that both reduced pyridine nucleotides will function in light emission is of considerable interest with regard to alternate pathways for light emission. Friedman[18] had earlier demonstrated that both pathways of carbohydrate metabolism exist in the luminous bacteria; one leading to the reduction of triphosphopyridine nucleotide via glucose-6-phosphate dehydrogenase, and the usual glycolytic pathway leading to the reduction of DPN. The existence of these two pathways for the formation of reduced pyridine nucleotides is of interest when one attempts to explain earlier observations on the inhibition of light emission in intact bacteria.

In crude enzyme preparations a large amount of the aldehyde is bound to the protein and is slowly made available for luminescence through some unknown reaction. Ultraviolet radiation in some way releases the aldehyde and makes it more available for light production.[9] This seems to explain why ultraviolet radiation stimulates light emission in crude extracts. In the presence of a continuous supply of reduced DPN, the crude enzyme preparations will continue to emit a weak light for hours. With the purified enzyme, however, very little bound aldehyde is present, and under these circumstances light emission is completely dependent upon the addition of aldehyde. A large amount of evidence has been presented which indicates that the aldehyde is used during the luminescent reaction and that in all probability the corresponding acid is produced. The effect of aldehyde chain length on maximum cell-free luminescence, using either DPNH or reduced FMN, is shown in Fig. 6. From experiments by Rogers and McElroy[19, 20] on the effect of aldehyde concentration on light emission, it is clear that the

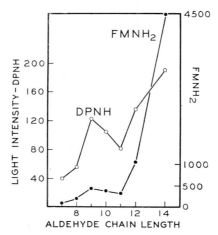

FIG. 6. The effect of aldehyde chain length on cell-free luminescence using either DPNH or FMNH₂ (Rogers and McElroy[20]).

affinity of the luciferase for these substances is greater as the carbon chain length increases. The stimulation of light production by undecanal and nonanal appears to be consistently out of line with respect to that observed by the other aldehydes in the series. There is no apparent explanation for this anomalous behavior. The peculiarity of the series is apparently due to some specificity of the enzyme and probably not to impurities. It may be that the optimal chain length for luminescence for the odd-number aldehydes is approximately C_9 whereas the effectiveness of the even-numbered aldehydes continues to increase even beyond tetradecanal. Unfortunately other aldehydes have not been available for testing.

Terpstra[20a] has studied an enzyme preparation from a dark strain of *Photobacterium splendidum* which appears to be different from other luciferase preparations in that aldehyde and FMNH₂ appear to compete for the same sites on the enzyme.

Strehler and Johnson[21] have studied the effect of pressure on light emission in extracts and in living cells; the results of one such study are shown in Fig. 7. The general relationships observed in the intact bacterium are essentially the same as those observed for the extracts. These observations are of considerable interest when they are compared to the earlier extensive observations of Johnson[22] and Johnson et al.[23] on the effect of temperature and pressure on light emission in the whole cell. Cormier and Strehler[24] have studied the extracts of a number of strains of luminous bacteria and have demonstrated that the temperature optima in the cell-free extracts agree remarkably well with those observed for the intact bacterium, although

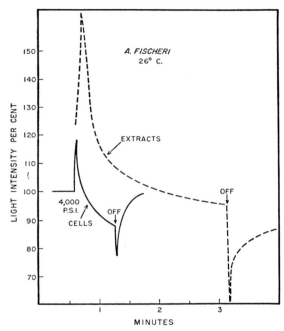

FIG. 7. Effect of pressure on light emission in extracts and in cells. Pressure applied at 30 seconds (Strehler and Johnson[21]).

there was some variation in the activation energies for the different reactions.

It is not possible at the present time to describe in physicochemical terms the exact mechanism of light emission in the bacterial extract. However, apparently the only components required are those discussed in the last section. The best preparations of bacterial luciferase which have been made at the present time apparently contain no other cofactors, and it must be presumed that one of the four components mentioned, or some complex of them, becomes excited during the luminescent reaction.

III. Physiology of Luminous Bacteria

A. The Metabolism of Luminous Bacteria

1. Nutrition

All luminous bacteria which have been studied will grow on ordinary nutrient agar with 0.3 % glycerol. For the salt water bacteria 3 % sodium chloride must be added. Although there was much work on the nutrition of luminous bacteria by earlier investigators, it was not until Doudoroff[25, 26] made an extensive study on the nutritional requirements of several species that a minimum medium was devised. This has been slightly modified by the work of Farghaly and McElroy[27] to ensure greater growth. The minimal medium (as published by Farghaly[28]) to which is added 0.1 % peptone gives vigorous growth and will yield in shake cultures at 23° C. approximately 6 g. wet weight of *Achromobacter fischeri* per liter in an 18-hour period. Studies on the growth requirements of luminous bacteria have been too numerous to report in detail. It is of interest to note that it was Beijerinck in 1889 who introduced the auxanographic method to determine the effects of various substances on growth and light production. He grew the bacteria on a solid medium with insufficient nutrients so that growth and luminescence soon ceased. After this a few drops of various substances were added in order to test their ability to support growth and light production. Beijerinck classified his substances as "light nutrients."

There is a great deal of variation in the carbon sources as well as the nitrogen sources which will support growth and light emission in different strains of luminous bacteria. The one strain of *Achromobacter fischeri* studied by Farghaly is capable of using only glycerol or glucose as the sole carbon source whereas other strains have been reported to grow on lactose, maltose, and a variety of other sugars. Needless to say all of these compounds are adequate in the support of both growth and luminescence. Johnson[29] as well as Harvey have studied in great detail the carbon sources which will support luminescence in resting cell preparations and they have found a number of compounds which will support light emission but which do not necessarily support the growth of the organism. Although *Achromobacter fischeri* appears to be capable of using fructose oxidatively it is not an adequate carbon source for maximum growth unless a number of amino acids are added to the culture medium. From the work of Friedman[18] it would appear that some inhibitory products of fructose metabolism are formed and that amino acids are necessary to prevent the inhibition of growth and luminescence. Anderson[30] has also studied the variation in nutritional requirements at different temperatures. He found when the luminous bacteria failed to grow at a temperature above 26–27° C. on Doudoroff minimal medium the addition of hydrolyzed casein permitted normal growth and luminescence at much higher temperatures. The results suggested that the temperature sensitivity may be related to the synthesis of a particular amino acid. Anderson found that a combination of methionine, glutamic acid, and serine was particularly effective in allowing growth and luminescence at the higher temperatures. The development of luminescence during growth at the higher temperature, 29° C., was critically dependent upon the concentration of these amino acids. It was possible to vary the concentration of glutamic acid to such an extent that the light intensity was almost completely eliminated without greatly affecting growth.

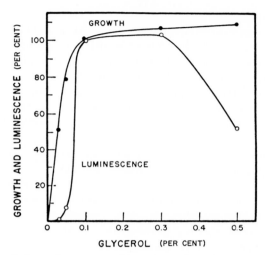

Fig. 8. Effect of glycerol concentration on growth and luminescence of *Achromobacter fischeri* (Farghaly[28]).

2. Environmental Factors Affecting Growth and Luminescence

Farghaly has made a particularly careful analysis of various environmental factors in relation to growth and luminescence. The relationship between growth and luminescence as a function of glycerol concentration for *Achromobacter fischeri* is shown in Fig. 8. The results indicate that 0.3 % glycerol is adequate for maximal growth and luminescence and that the usual 1 % concentration which has been used by other workers for growing these organisms led to considerable inhibition of light emission. It should be noted that the development of luminescence always lags behind growth and that light was not emitted in measurable amounts until 30 to 40 % of maximum growth had taken place. However, following this lag in the luminescence there was a rapid development in light emission. Doudoroff in his nutritional studies of various species of luminous bacteria made the observation that methionine was an essential nutrient. Farghaly has also found for *Achromobacter fischeri* that although methionine is not required it does tend to eliminate the lag in the development of light emission when the organism is grown on the minimal medium. The addition of histidine to the methionine medium greatly stimulated the development of light emission.

It has become a routine procedure among those who work with luminous bacteria to add small amounts of calcium carbonate (0.1 to 1 %) to the medium in order to maintain luminescence for long periods of time. The effect has been assumed to be due to the neutralization of acids produced by the organism. However, a careful study by Farghaly on the effect of calcium carbonate demonstrated that this hypothesis does not provide a complete explanation. In the first place, addition of calcium carbonate to a growing culture not only prolonged the duration of luminescence but increased its intensity over 75 %. In the second place, determination of pH changes during growth with and without calcium carbonate showed that although there was indeed a difference in pH between the two media it was not great enough to account for the increase in luminescence in the presence of $CaCO_3$.

It has been noted by many of the earlier workers that the salt concentration of the medium on which marine bacteria are grown is very important. Following these observations most workers have maintained the correct osmotic environment by the addition of sodium chloride. The work of Johnson and Harvey[31] indicates that the replacement of sodium chloride with other salts has no ill effect on the growth of these organisms provided the correct osmotic pressure is maintained. On the other hand, luminescence appears to be greatly affected by the types as well as the concentration of the salt used. Farghaly has made a careful study of the relationship of the concentration of sodium chloride to the growth and luminescence of *Achrombacter fischeri*. Figure 9 shows the relationship between growth and luminescence as a function of the sodium chloride concentration. Below

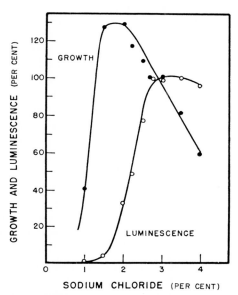

FIG. 9. Effect of sodium chloride concentration on growth and luminescence of *Achromobacter fischeri* (Farghaly[28]).

0.5 % very little growth, if any, occurs. With increasing concentrations growth increased very rapidly until the maximum was reached at around 2.3 % after which growth gradually decreased, reaching zero at 5 % NaCl. At the concentration of sodium chloride which supported maximum growth, luminescence was only 30 to 40 % of maximum and at the concentration where growth declined, light continued to develop reaching its maximum intensity at approximately 3 to 3.3 % sodium chloride. Recent observations on attempts concerned with the isolation of the light-emitting system from bacterial growth at various sodium chloride concentrations indicate that it is the luciferase that fails to be synthesized at the low salt concentration. When cells are grown in 1 % sodium chloride very little luciferase is made. If these cells, however, are immediately transferred to a solution containing 3 % sodium chloride, luciferase synthesis occurs rapidly and the light intensity increases. Thus far only those conditions which foster cell division bring about an increase in the light intensity. It is evident that cells grown under these conditions should be excellent objects for studying protein synthesis, for it is only necessary to place the cells in front of a photocell to note the increase in the luciferase concentration which is directly measured by the light emitted. It is unnecessary to break open the cells in order to analyze for the protein which has been synthesized. Luminous bacteria can be grown on 1 % sodium chloride with adequate luciferase synthesis providing other salts are added to raise the osmotic environment. The addition of 17 % sucrose to such a medium allows the normal development of the luciferase system. Other salts have been tried; these include KCl, KNO_3, K_2SO_4, $NaNO_3$, and Na_2SO_4. All were able to maintain the correct osmotic environment for luciferase synthesis. These observations are of considerable interest because the proteins essential for duplication are made at a normal rate in contrast to the bacterial luciferase. Two explanations appear possible. One, luciferase may be synthesized but is unstable in the low salt environment. This seems most unlikely since the partially purified luciferase is perfectly stable in a solution of low ionic environment. The salt itself could affect a protein-synthesizing particle in the luminous bacteria which is concerned primarily with the synthesis of luciferase.

As noted by earlier workers, when luminous bacteria are suspended in an aqueous solution light emission disappears. It is now known that in such hypotonic solutions the cells rapidly lyse, liberating their cellular contents into the medium. This method has been used extensively by McElroy and Green[11] for obtaining protein extracts from such organisms. In one species of luminous bacteria which has been isolated from a dead flounder it was found that although 3 % sodium chloride was adequate for normal growth and light development these cells would not lyse when suspended in water. A 15-minute incubation period in 6 % sodium chloride so conditioned the cells that rapid lysis occurred when they were resuspended in distilled water. Protein analysis of the lysate as well as the debris has indicated that over 90 % of the cellular protein is extracted by this procedure. It is likely that this same general technique could be used extensively for the lysis of other forms of bacteria.

In connection with his investigations on the penetration of ammonium salts, Hill[32] made the observation that the lysis of marine luminous bacteria led to a decrease in light emission and he has used this technique to study the penetration of a variety of compounds. Johnson and Harvey have made an extensive study of the respiration and luminescence of resting cells of luminous bacteria in different osmotic environments. It would appear from these studies that the luminescence is more sensitive to hypotonic solutions than is the respiration. The reader is referred to Harvey for various other findings of the effect of salts on growth and light emission.

B. OXYGEN REQUIREMENT FOR LUMINESCENCE—ANAEROBIC FLASH

The requirement of oxygen for light emission in luminous bacteria is a well-established fact and was first observed by Boyle in 1667 for light emission associated with luminous fish. Later, as the constituents of air became known, it was acknowledged by all workers that it was oxygen which was the indispensable factor required for light emission. Beijerinck first pointed out that several species of luminous bacteria were facultative anaerobes and would grow without oxygen if adequate nutrients were present. The bacteria failed to emit light, however, when grown under these conditions. On the admission of oxygen to such cultures, light emission occurs. The results indicate that the components necessary for the synthesis of the light-emitting system could be made in the absence of oxygen. Beijerinck was also the first to utilize luminous bacteria as a test for oxygen. In his early paper in 1902 he described the detection of oxygen formed by photosynthesis in an extract of crushed clover leaves to which 3 % salt and luminous bacteria had been added. Harvey[1] and collaborators have made many quantitative studies regarding the minimum amount of oxygen required for light emission and in addition observed the relationship of the oxygen pressure to light intensity. Shapiro[33] observed for *Vibrio phosphorescens* that the light intensity is independent of oxygen pressure until the latter is reduced to about 0.14 % (1.06 mm. mercury). Oxygen concentrations lower than this reduced the light intensity rapidly and no further response was observed at 0.01 %. In more recent studies by Hastings,[34] however, much lower concentrations of oxygen were required to eliminate light emission completely.

When resting cells of luminous bacteria have been placed under anaerobic conditions for a few moments, the addition of oxygen or air gives rise to a very brilliant flash of light which rapidly returns to a normal base-line level.

Harvey and associates were the first to measure carefully this flash response. The total light emitted in the flash appears to be independent of the duration of anoxia, provided these conditions are not prolonged too long and provided adequate time is given for the build-up of a substance which was earlier called luciferin. From the cell-free studies we now know that the component accumulating is undoubtedly reduced FMN. Chance et al.[35] made very rapid recordings of the flash reaction and concluded that the half-time for the development of the maximum light intensity was approximately 0.08 second. The flash has also been extensively studied by Johnson et al.[36] by using well-washed resting cells of luminous bacteria. These workers have been able to study in some detail the effect of various substrates on the build-up of luciferin under anaerobic conditions. Needless to say those compounds which were found to act as excellent hydrogen donors in the respiration of the bacteria were also found to be able to lead to the accumulation of bacterial luciferin. The effect of various inhibitors on this flash process has also been studied and all the results are in keeping with the general observations that light emission following anaerobic conditions depends upon an electron donor. All of these observations, which are discussed in detail by Harvey, are of considerable interest particularly with regard to our present knowledge of the cell-free bacterial light-emitting system.

It would appear that the maximum flash obtained after anaerobic conditions is a direct measure of the concentration of $FMNH_2$ associated with the bacterial enzyme system and that the light intensity observed under aerobic conditions is a measure of the concentration of reduced FMN in the steady state condition. The earlier observations on the stimulation of luminescence by cyanide may now be interpreted as due to the inhibition of electron transport over the cytochrome system, which undoubtedly would lead to an increased concentration of the steady state level of reduced FMN.

C. Relationship of the Light Reaction to Other Electron Transport Processes

The relationship between cell respiration and luminescence has been discussed in great detail by a number of workers and Harvey has summarized most of this information. The earlier investigators considered luminescence simply as a consequence of respiration; this opinion was expressed as early as 1865 by Sachs. However, Beijerinck was quite clear in pointing out the relationship between respiration and light emission, and since that time Harvey and collaborators have done much to clarify this relationship. In a very extensive study involving inhibitors and oxygen tension Van Schouwenburg[37, 38] concluded that the light-emitting system is one which com-

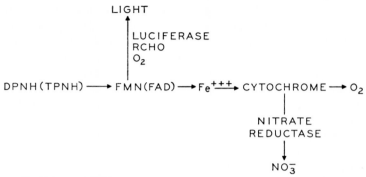

FIG. 10. Relationship of the light reaction to the electron transport process (modified from Sadana and McElroy[39]).

petes with the cytochrome for electrons. In addition, Van Schouwenburg clearly demonstrated that there was electron transport through the light system without actual light emission. The scheme which he presents in his original publication in 1938 is certainly in keeping with the modern knowledge on the nature of bacterial luciferin and luciferase. Friedman has demonstrated the existence of the Embden-Meyerhof pathway as well as the oxidative pathway for carbohydrate metabolism in luminous bacteria. Doudoroff's studies on the nature of the products produced by the anaerobic breakdown of carbohydrates has implicated a number of enzyme systems similar to those found in the Enterobacteriaceae. Sadana and McElroy[39] have isolated a nitrate reductase from luminous bacteria and have demonstrated the importance of a bacterial cytochrome in this reaction. The relationship of the electron transport process in luminous bacteria to the oxygen-consuming reactions and the light-emitting process is illustrated in Fig. 10. With this known relationship it is possible to explain all of the earlier observations on the action of various inhibitors on light emission including the effect of oxygen tension and cyanide. Under low oxygen tensions where the luminescent system would, in effect, be competing with the cytochrome system for oxygen, it is possible to understand now why cyanide should stimulate light emission and why added nitrate might be expected to reverse this stimulation.

D. Use of Luminous Bacteria for Studying Drug Action

Luminous bacteria have been a favorite organism for use in the study of the mechanism of action of drugs and Harvey has reviewed the earlier work from his laboratory.[1] Using dimming time as a simple measure of respiration of luminous bacteria and also by measuring the intensity of light emitted, Taylor[40] was able to study quantitatively the effects of a large number of hormones and narcotics on both respiration and light emission. In general, light emission is very sensitive to low concentrations of all narcotics whereas respiration is relatively unimpaired. From such investigations Taylor and others have concluded that two processes, one involving light emission and a second, respiration, are independent of each other. From recent studies it would appear that there are essentially the two pathways of electron transport which can support light emission. One pathway makes use of the triphosphopyridine nucleotide linked glucose-6-phosphate dehydrogenase system and the other the diphosphopyridine nucleotide requiring triose phosphate dehydrogenase. Apparently, the narcotics affect the glycolytic system and therefore the DPN-linked electron transport processes before affecting the electron transport process involved in the TPN system.

Johnson[22] and Johnson et al.[23] have used the luminous bacteria in order to study quantitatively the effect of various inhibitors, temperature, and pressure on the light-emitting process. They have observed that an increased pressure decreases the light intensity if applied to a suspension maintained at a temperature below the optimum. On the other hand, pressure increases the light intensity if it is applied to a suspension maintained above the optimum temperature. The results were explained on the assumption that there were two reactions which proceed with an increase in volume; one was concerned directly with the light-emitting step and the second was concerned with the reversible inactivation of the enzyme by heat. At low temperatures pressure reduced the luminescent intensity by

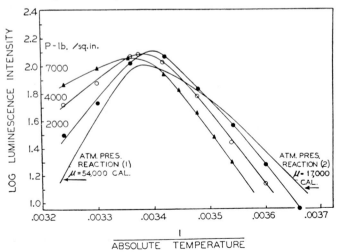

FIG. 11. Effect of pressure and temperature on light emission by *Photobacterium phosphoreum* [F. H. Brown, D. Johnson and D. Marsland, *Science* **95**, 200, (1942)].

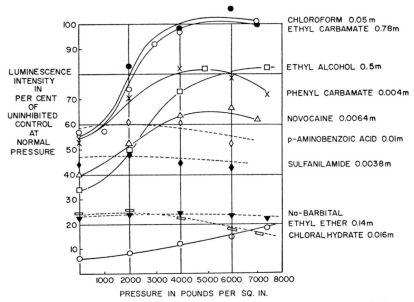

FIG. 12. Effect of pressure on inhibitors of luminescence (Johnson et al.[41])

slowing the dominant light-emitting reaction whereas at elevated temperatures the dominant reaction is the reversible denaturation of the bacterial luciferase and pressure would tend to increase light emission by protecting the unfolding of the enzyme. The results of such a pressure experiment are shown in Fig. 11. In extending these observations to the action of drugs, Johnson et al.[41] were able to demonstrate that certain effects of the narcotics could be reversed by high pressure, leading to the suggestion that the reversible denaturation of luciferase was not only caused by temperature but was also brought about by various narcotic agents (see Fig. 12). Other workers have extended these observations to include a variety of compounds. The action of narcotics on the oxidation of glucose by *Achromobacter fischeri* has been studied by McElroy.[42] In agreement with other studies, the narcotics prevented the assimilation of carbohydrates. The effective concentrations were those which inhibited light emission approximately 50%, while greatly stimulating respiration.

E. MUTATIONS AFFECTING GROWTH AND LIGHT EMISSION

Nonluminous strains or mutants of luminous bacteria have been known for many years. However, it was Beijerinck who first realized the significance of this fact. He wrote in a paper entitled "On Different Forms of Heredity Variation of Microbes" about changes in luminous bacteria which he had observed as early as 1889 and indicated how they were very similar to the observations made by deVries on *Oenothera*. He agreed with deVries that such mutations were responsible for the origin of species. Later, in 1912, Beijerinck[43] pointed out that the most acceptable theory of heredity is the concept that the living part of the protoplasm is built up of a great number of factors or "bearers" which determine the characters of the organism. At this early date he wrote that "the fundamental conception here to be proposed is that every hereditary character of an organism corresponds to one or more 'enzymes' which exert an influence on specific substrates." Beijerinck held that light emission of luminous bacteria was probably the most suitable character for studying the mutation process.

Since Beijerinck's time many workers have noted dim and dark mutants of luminous bacteria. The important observations of Doudoroff on the stimulation of luminescence of dim strains of bacteria by riboflavin have been mentioned previously. Giese[44] has also observed brilliant variants in old cultures of luminous bacteria. This mutant developed a particularly yellow pigment which diffused into the medium and would fluoresce in the ultraviolet light, suggesting the possibility that it was riboflavin. McElroy and Farghaly[27] made an extensive effort to induce mutations in luminous bacteria in order to dissociate growth and light emission. In a strain that requires arginine for growth, the luminescence fails to develop in a growing culture unless the concentration of arginine is high enough to give approximately 30% of the normal growth. With higher concentrations of arginine the luminescent system develops rapidly and finally reaches the wild type level of intensity. In an aspartic acid mutant, luminescence develops only when the concentration of the amino acid is increased to a level where maximum growth is observed. In some cases it is possible to eliminate the lag in the development of the luminescent system by supplementing the medium with other amino acids. The relationship between growth, luminescence, and aspartic acid concentrations is shown in Fig. 13. The effect of an amino acid supplement on the development of the luminescent system is shown in Fig. 14. All of the studies on these nutritional mutants have merely served to emphasize the fact that many physiological functions may not be fully restored with concentrations of growth factors sufficient to give maximum growth. It has been pointed out previously that in the rapid growth of luminous bacteria light emission often lags behind cell division. Recent studies have indicated that this is a failure in the synthesis of the luciferase. A specific effect of aspartic acid on luciferase synthesis has been observed in a mutant requiring arginine, proline, histidine, lysine, tyrosine, and methionine for growth (see Fig. 15).

Miller *et al.*[45] have studied extensively the conditions necessary for the

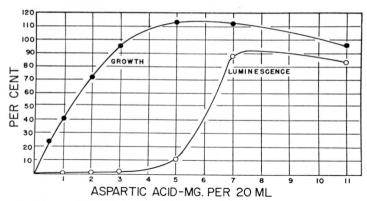

FIG. 13. Relationship between growth, luminescence, and aspartic acid concentration in a mutant of *Achromobacter fischeri* (McElroy and Farghaly[27]).

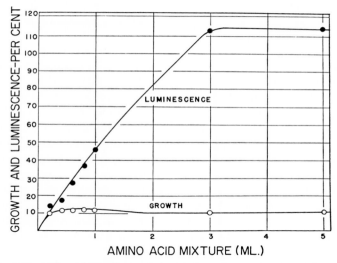

FIG. 14. Stimulation of synthesis of the luminescent system by amino acids. Aspartic acid mutant described in Fig. 13 was used. See text (McElroy and Farghaly[27]).

induction of mutation in *Achromobacter fischeri*. Although a number of mutants have been isolated, there is no evidence to indicate that X-ray, ultraviolet, or nitrogen mustard increased the mutation rate. It was shown during these studies, however, that under nutritional conditions just sufficient to support the normal wild type strain and at temperatures at which metabolic activity is low, there is a selective advantage favoring strains which have more exacting growth requirements. Such selections under

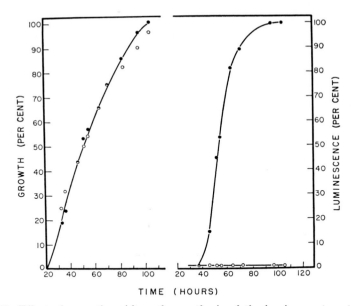

Fig. 15. Effect of aspartic acid on the synthesis of the luminescent system in a multiple mutant of *Achromobacter fischeri*. Open circles refer to light intensity. Graph on the right represents growth and luminescence in the absence of aspartic acid while the graph on the left represents the effect of supplementation with aspartic acid (Friedman[18]).

these conditions were apparently due to a greater loss of essential nutrients from the wild type cells, resulting ultimately in their death. With the cold incubation technique it was possible to increase the apparent mutation rate in luminous bacteria over 20 times. Gene recombination in mutants of luminous bacteria has been described by McElroy and Friedman.[46] Unfortunately, strains of these particular mutants are not available for further investigation and these results have not been confirmed with other strains of luminous bacteria.

Only recently have mutants been obtained which directly affect the light-emitting system without influencing the growth of the bacteria. Rogers and McElroy[19, 20, 47] have described a mutant which requires the long-chain aldehyde for light emission. They found that the addition of minute amounts of dodecyl aldehyde to colonies of this dark mutant immediately restored the light. An analysis of the cells indicated that the mutant contained bacterial luciferase as well as the other components necessary for light emission. Presumably an aldehyde-forming or aldehyde-releasing enzyme is lacking in this particular strain. Other dark strains studied by Rogers and McElroy indicated that the luciferase was lacking. The luminous response of the dark cells to dodecanal is shown in Fig. 16. A log plot

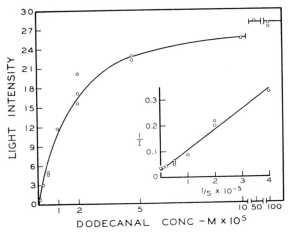

FIG. 16. Luminous response of dark mutant cells to aldehyde (Rogers and Mc-Elroy[20]).

of this data demonstrates that the initial response is first order. When the aldehyde concentration in the cell reaches a level where the enzyme is saturated, it can be shown that the maximum light intensity becomes a measure of the amount of bacteria luciferase plus the steady state concentration of $FMNH_2$ in the cell. However, initially the light intensity is a measure of the aldehyde concentration inside the cell. Therefore, the initial slope of the luminous response in light units per second is a measure of the rate of penetration of the aldehyde into the cell. Additional studies have indicated that the properties of the bacterial light-emitting reaction *in vitro* are identical to those in the cell. Therefore, this system provides a unique one for studying rapidly and quantitatively the penetration of substances which affect light emission. The advantage of this system over others is due to the great accuracy and sensitivity in detecting enzyme activity without disturbing cellular structure. The dark mutant of luminous bacteria is uniquely suited for measuring the penetration of various aldehydes since the latter are required to restore normal light emission. It should be possible to analyze the penetration of other substances, however, provided they affect the light-emitting system. Direct and indirect effects can be determined by studying the response of the isolated enzyme to such agents. The values of maximum light intensity obtained with variation in aldehyde chain length employing intact cells show a close correspondence to those obtained with isolated luciferase when DPNH is used to initiate the reaction. This would support other evidence which indicates that reduced pyridine nucleotides are the most likely source of reducing power for luminescence in the cells.

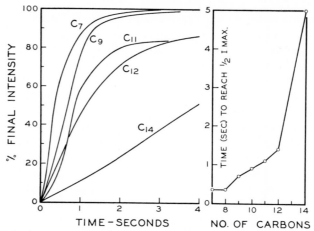

FIG. 17. Relationship between aldehyde chain length and penetration into dark mutant cells (Rogers and McElroy[20]).

Before the bacterial luciferase in the cell is saturated with aldehyde the rate of increase in light intensity with time shows that the penetration of the aldehyde is probably a first-order diffusion process. A comparison of the rates of penetration of the various aldehydes used can be obtained by simply recording the time it takes to reach ½ the maximum light intensity. The relationship between aldehyde chain length and the rate of the penetration is shown in Fig. 17. From these data it is clear that the rate of penetration of these compounds through the membrane decreases with increasing number of carbons in the aliphatic chain. The study of the effect of temperature on the penetration of the aldehyde demonstrated that these compounds in all probability enter the cell by free diffusion and the results clearly indicate that molecular size and steric problems related to the structure of the cell membrane are of prime importance in the permeability process, and that lipoid solubility is relatively unimportant. These results agree with the earlier work on *Beggiatoa mirabilis* in which it was demonstrated that the penetration of nonelectrolytes depended largely upon molecular size.

The rapid penetration of solute molecules into cells will lead to lyses; both Hill[32] and Collander[48] have used this technique with luminous bacteria for permeability studies.

IV. Taxonomy and Evolution

A. Distribution, Isolation, and Classification of Luminous Bacteria

Luminous bacteria may be classified as parasitic, causing infection of various living animals, such as insects, fresh and salt water shrimp, amphipods, etc; saprophytic, living on such dead matter as fish or meat; or symbiotic, those found in the luminous organs of fish or squid. The salt water luminous bacteria have been those most frequently studied and are relatively easy to isolate. Most will grow on ordinary nutrient agar with 3% sodium chloride and a carbon source such as glucose or glycerol. There have been, however, a few fresh water forms isolated, and these have been reported to grow on nutrient agar with 0.9% sodium chloride or none at all. Among the best sources of salt water luminous bacteria are dead fish or squid which have not been washed with fresh water. If such animals are placed in a 15 to 20° C. incubator overnight, one usually observes small luminous colonies developing on the surface of the organism. If one removes a small amount of this material to an agar plate, little difficulty is encountered in obtaining a pure culture of these forms. From such isolations one can obtain luminous bacteria of long or short rods, cocci or vibrios; they may be quite motile or nonmotile. Probably the two forms which have received the greatest attention are those which are the most confused in classification.

Achromobacter fischeri has been used extensively in the laboratory during the past 25 years. It is a motile rod approximately 0.9 by 1.8 microns. It is Gram-negative and requires approximately 2.8% sodium chloride for optimum growth. It is a nitrate reducer and its polar flagella and biochemical characteristics classify it as a *Pseudomonas*. The temperature for optimal luminescence is 25° C. The organism can be grown only aerobically unlike other closely related species. It has been isolated from a number of places but the original was obtained from a dead herring from the sea water at Kiel. The official name for *Achromobacter fischeri* now listed in "Bergey's Manual of Determinative Bacteriology" is *Bacterium phosphorescens indigenus* (Eisenberg). However, most workers in the field have used the earlier and more familiar name.

The second species of luminous bacteria which has been studied in great detail in the laboratory is *Photobacterium phosphoreum*. It will grow either aerobically or anaerobically. However, luminescence occurs only in the presence of oxygen. The temperature optimum for light emission is approximately 15° C. It is readily isolated from dead fish and meat and from time to time has been given the following names: *Micrococcus phosphoreus* (Cohn), *Bacterium phosphorescens* (Fisher), *Photobacterium phosphorescens* (Beijerinck), *Streptococcus phosphoreus* (Trevisan), and *Bacillus phosphoreus* (Mace).

It is evident that much confusion exists in the literature on the naming of these various forms. Some of the confusion in classification has been due in part to the fact that a luminous bacterium isolated from different sources has invariably been given new names. For example, luminous bacteria have been isolated from diseased insect larvae and have been given the

name *Bacterium hemophosphoreum* (Pfeiffer and Stammer), from midges—
Bacterium chironomi (Issatschenko), from marine crustaceans—*Bacterium
giardi* (Kruse), from fresh water fish—*Bacterium hippanici* (Issatschenko),
from luminous clams such as *Pholas dactylis*—*Bacterium pholas* (DuBois),
and from deep sea fish—*Coccobacillus collorhynchus*. In addition, there are
those interesting luminous bacteria which inhabit special glands in the
deep sea fish *Physiculus japonicus*; these have been named *Micrococcus
physiculus*.

Two fresh water species have been studied extensively, *Vibrio albensis*
and *Vibrio phosphorescens*. The optimum sodium chloride concentration for
growth and luminescence is approximately 0.9%. Both species are Gram-
negative and motile. Morphologically they look very much alike, however, Warren's[49] studies on the antigenic properties of these two forms
indicate a definite difference. There are other reasonably well-defined species
of luminous bacteria and the reader is referred to "Bergey's Manual of
Determinative Bacteriology" for this information. However, it is apparent
that despite extensive investigations of the cultural characteristics of these
various forms the separation of luminous bacterial species is in a rather
unsatisfactory state. It is certain that too much attention has been paid
to light emission as a unique and distinguishing characteristic. The earlier
belief that all luminous bacteria must be closely related taxonomically can
no longer be accepted.

B. Evolutionary Significance of the Light-Emitting Reaction

As Harvey[1] has often emphasized, a glance at the evolutionary tree will
reveal luminous species scattered in about half of the phyla with no apparent rhyme or reason. In the course of evolution apparently light production has appeared again and again, and the origin of this light-emitting
process has fascinated a number of workers. The ability to produce light
does not confer a great survival value on the organisms endowed with it
since there are many more nonluminous than luminous forms. Secondarily,
however, this ability may be adapted to uses which do confer a selective
advantage on the luminous organism. In the case of the firefly the light
emission has been restricted to particular organs and the yellow flashing is
used for the identification of the species to ensure sexual reproduction.
One would hardly question the long-range survival advantage of this
unique ability. Luminous bacteria, on the other hand, probably do not
obtain any selective advantage under most conditions from their ability
to luminesce. Rather their light emission has been regarded as an acci-
dental mutation in which the energy liberated by a terminal flavin oxidase
is channeled into an excited state of a molecule which subsequently emits
light. Certainly the ability to emit light in a number of organic oxidations

is not unique. It is very likely that most organisms emit a very weak luminescence. Certainly those luminous bacteria which grow in fish light organs derive an advantage through a symbiotic life.

A mechanism of energy liberation and conservation as phosphate bond energy is reasonably well understood at the present time. However, as Szent-Gyorgyi[50] has recently emphasized, the actual mechanism of utilization of this energy is poorly understood. It may be that, in the transition of oxidation-reduction reactions in which energy is liberated, an excited state does appear with a very short half-life; but it is this excited state which is concerned with the important processes of muscle contraction and other cellular functions that depend upon energy utilization, rather than energy conservation. If in the process of mutation and evolution an organism acquires the ability to trap these excited states it is possible that luminescence will occur. Only because of the extremely low concentration of these excited states in normal oxidation-reduction reactions, and because of their channeling into other processes in the cell, is there a failure to see light emission. Workers have often compared light emission by organisms to the process of light absorption—photosynthesis. In the latter process light quanta are absorbed, exciting the chlorophyll molecule, leading eventually to the formation of a reducing as well as an oxidizing substance. In this excited state the electrons can be passed to a number of acceptors. Light emission is, in essence, a reversal of this process and it is extremely likely that the excited state in the case of bioluminescent organisms is drained off in a wasteful side reaction. In other cases the excitation state may be used in other biosynthetic pathways.

REFERENCES

[1] E. N. Harvey, "Bioluminescence." Academic Press, New York, 1952.
[2] E. N. Harvey, A. Chase, and W. D. McElroy, *J. Cellular Comp. Physiol.* **50,** 499 (1957).
[3] M. W. Beijerinck, *Arch. néerl. sci.* **23,** 401, 416 (1889).
[4] F. C. Gerretsen, *Zenbr. Bakteriol., Parasitenk. Abt. II.* **44,** 660 (1915); **52,** 353 (1920).
[5] M. Doudoroff, *Enzymologia,* **5,** 239 (1938).
[6] See B. L. Strehler, *Luminescence Biol. Systems, Proc. Conf. on Luminescence, Asilomar, Calif. 1954* (1955).
[7] B. L. Strehler and M. J. Cormier, *Arch. Biochem. Biophys.* **47,** 16 (1953); *J. Am. Chem. Soc.* **75,** 1264 (1953).
[8] W. D. McElroy, J. W. Hastings, V. Sonnenfeld, and J. Coulombre, *Science* **118,** 385 (1953).
[9] W. D. McElroy, J. W. Hastings, V. Sonnenfeld, and J. Coulombre, *J. Bacteriol.* **67,** 402 (1954).
[10] M. J. Cormier and B. L. Strehler, *J. Am. Chem. Soc.* **75,** 4864 (1953).
[11] W. D. McElroy and A. Green, *Arch. Biochem. Biophys.* **56,** 240 (1955).
[12] M. J. Cormier, J. R. Totter, and H. H. Rostorfer, *Arch. Biochem. Biophys.* **63,** 414 (1956).
[13] J. R. Totter and M. J. Cormier, *J. Biol. Chem.* **216,** 801 (1955).

[14] H. D. K. Drew, *Trans. Faraday Soc.* **35**, 207 (1939).

[15] B. L. Strehler, E. N. Harvey, J. J. Chang, and M. J. Cormier, *Proc. Natl. Acad. Sci. U. S.* **40**, 10 (1954).

[16] M. J. Cormier and J. R. Totter *J. Am. Chem. Soc.* **76**, 4744 (1954).

[17] C. J. P. Spruit and A. L. Schuiling, *Rec. trav. chim.* **64**, 220 (1945).

[18] S. Friedman, Ph.D. Thesis, Johns Hopkins University, Baltimore, Maryland, 1952.

[19] P. Rogers and W. D. McElroy, *Proc. Natl. Acad. Sci. U. S.* **41**, 67 (1955).

[20] P. Rogers and W. D. McElroy, *Arch. Biochem. Biophys.* **75**, 87 (1958).

[20a] W. Terpstra, *Biochim. et Biophys. Acta* **28**, 159 (1958).

[21] B. L. Strehler and F. H. Johnson, *J. Cellular Comp. Physiol.* (1954).

[22] F. H. Johnson, *Advances in Enzymol.* **7**, 215 (1947); *Luminescence Biol. Systems, Proc. Conf. on Luminescence, Asilomar, Calif. 1954,* p. 265 (1955).

[23] F. H. Johnson, H. Eyring, and M. J. Palissar, "The Kinetic Basis of Molecular Biology." Wiley, New York, 1954.

[24] M. J. Cormier and B. L. Strehler, *J. Cellular Comp. Physiol.* **44**, 277 (1954).

[25] M. Doudoroff, *J. Bacteriol.* **44**, 451 (1942).

[26] M. Doudoroff, *J. Bacteriol.* **44**, 461 (1942).

[27] W. D. McElroy and A. H. Farghaly, *Arch. Biochem.* **17**, 379 (1948).

[28] A. H. Farghaly, *J. Cellular Comp. Physiol.* **36**, 165 (1950).

[29] F. H. Johnson, *J. Cellular Comp. Physiol.* **8**, 439 (1936).

[30] R. E. Anderson, *J. Cellular Comp. Physiol.* **32**, 97 (1948).

[31] F. H. Johnson and E. N. Harvey, *J. Cellular Comp. Physiol.* **11**, 213 (1938).

[32] S. E. Hill, *J. Gen. Physiol.* **12**, 863 (1929); *J. Cellular Comp. Physiol.* **1**, 145 (1932).

[33] H. Shapiro, *J. Cellular Comp. Physiol.* **4**, 313 (1934).

[34] J. W. Hastings, *J. Cellular Comp. Physiol.* **39**, 1 (1952).

[35] B. Chance, E. N. Harvey, F. H. Johnson, and G. Millikan, *J. Cellular Comp. Physiol.* **15**, 195 (1940).

[36] F. H. Johnson, K. L. Van Schouwenburg, and A. Van der Burg, *Enzymologia* **9**, 195 (1939).

[37] K. L. Van Schouwenburg, Ph.D. Thesis. Delft University, Delft, Netherlands, 1938.

[38] K. L. Van Schouwenburg and J. G. Eymers, *Nature* **138**, 245 (1936).

[39] J. C. Sadana and W. D. McElroy, *Arch. Biochem. Biophys.* **67**, 16 (1957).

[40] G. W. Taylor, *J. Cellular Comp. Physiol.* **1**, 297 (1932); **4**, 329 (1934); **7**, 409 (1936).

[41] F. H. Johnson, D. Brown, and D. Marsland, *Science* **95**, 200 (1942); *J. Cellular Comp. Physiol.* **20**, 247, 269 (1942); *Arch. Biochem.* **3**, 1 (1943); *J. Gen. Physiol.* **28**, 463 (1945).

[42] W. D. McElroy. *J. Cellular Comp. Physiol.* **23**, 171 (1944).

[43] M. W. Beijerinck, *Folia Microbiol.* **1**, 1 (1912).

[44] A. C. Giese, *J. Bacteriol.* **46**, 323 (1943); *J. Cellular Comp. Physiol.* **17**, 203 (1941).

[45] H. Miller, A. H. Farghaly, and W. D. McElroy, *J. Bacteriol.* **57**, 595 (1949).

[46] W. D. McElroy and S. Friedman, *J. Bacteriol.* **62**, 129 (1951).

[47] P. Rogers and W. D. McElroy, *Proc. Natl. Acad. Sci. U. S.* **41**, 67 (1955); *Arch. Biochem. Biophys.* **75**, 106 (1958).

[48] R. Collander, *Protoplasma* **46**, 123 (1956).

[49] G. W. Warren, *J. Bacteriol.* **49**, 547 (1945).

[50] A. Szent-Györgyi, "Bioenergetics." Academic Press, New York, 1957.

AUTHOR INDEX

Numbers in parentheses are reference numbers and are included to assist in locating references when the authors' names are not mentioned in the text. Numbers in italics refer to the page on which the reference is listed.

A

Abelson, P. H., 243(66), *255*, *256*

Abood, L. G., 337(104), *361*

Abraham, R. G., 452(108), *459*

Abrams, A., 303(154), *317*

Abrams, R., 339(120), *361*

Adams, G. A., 87(189, 190), 88(189, 190), 114, 115(190), 122(190), 123(190), *143*

Adelberg, E., 8(56), *53*, 456(123), *460*

Adler, J., 167(71), 168(72), *205*

Aisenberg, A. C., 9(67), *53*

Aitken, R. A., 278, 279, *314*

Ajl, S. J., 106, 107(306), 131(396, 397, 398, 399), *146*, *148*, 221(25), 223, 229, 239, 240, 242(63), *254*, *255*, *256*, 379(102), *395*

Akabori, S., 268(33, 34), 281, 282(80), *313*, *315*

Akazawa, T., 426(2), *457*

Åkeson, Å., 427(16), 430(16), 434(16), *457*

Akumatsu, S., 157(42), *204*

Alexander, M., 320(1), 357(1), 358(1), *358*, 375(69, 70), 376(68, 69, 70, 77), 377(68, 77), 378(68, 69, 70), *394*, *395*

Alivisatos, S. G. A., 7(242), *58*

Allen, M. B., 469(50), 471(61), 475(71), *477*, *478*

Allen, M. C., 284(88), *315*

Almasy, F., 343(156), *362*, 368(12), *393*

Altenbern, R. A., 242(61), *255*

Altermatt, H. A., 87, 88(202), 109, 112, 114, 115(344), *143*, *146*, *147*

Altschul, A. M., 339(120), *361*

Anderson, A. A., 75(55), *140*

Anderson, E. H., 48, *57*

Anderson, I. C., 402(33), *421*, 462(9), 463 (9), 468(46), 469(54), 471, *476*, *477*

Anderson, J. A., 111(327), 112(327), *146*

Anderson, L., 349(172c), *362*, 399(4), *421*

Anderson, M. L., 23(143, 144), *55*, 450 (102a), *459*

Anderson, R. E., 491, *508*

Anderson, R. L., 103(313a), 107(313a), *146*

Anderson, W. W., 320(11), 321(11), 356 (11), 357(11), *358*

Ando, Y., 285(91a), *315*

Anfinson, C. B., 471(61), *477*

Appleby, C. A., 322(20), 337(20), *358*

Arnon, D. I., 469(50), 471(61), 474, 475 (71), *477*, *478*

Ash, O. K., 465, *477*

Ashman-Williams, H. G., 325(31a), *359*

Asnis, R. E., 326(36), 337(36), *359*, 370 (33), 376(33), 377(33), 391(33), *394*, 444(79), 449(97), 450(97), *459*

Astrachan, L., 435(56), *458*

Atkinson, D. E., 339(124), 340(124), *361*, 376(181), 378(94), *395*

Aubel, E., 429(28), 432(28), *457*

Aubert, J. P., 87(200), *143*, 339(118), *361*

Averbach, B. C., 452(108), *459*

Avery, O. T., 5(39), *52*, 260(3), 269, 271 (3), 294(3), 295(137), *313*, *314*, *316*, 427(9), *457*

Avron, M., 470(56), *477*

B

Bach, S. J., 375(61), *394*

Baer, H., 296(144a), *316*

Balint, M., 287(99), *315*

Ball, E. G., 321(8), *358*, 471(61), *477*

Ballantine, J., 30(187, 188), *56*

Baltscheffsky, M., 400(25), 415(78a), *421*, *422*, 465, 466(33, 40), 467(32), 472 (32), *477*

Bancroft, W. D., 74(48b), *140*

Barban, S., 106, 107(306), *146*

Bard, R. C., 13(109), 18(109), 20(109), 35(109), 36(109), 37(109), *54*, 80, 89 (215), 90(216), 93(216), 95(216), 96, 97(251), *141*, *143*, *144*, 346(169), *362*, 392(131), *396*, 452(110), *459*

Barer, R., 369, *393*

Barker, H. A., 4(10), 5, 7, 8(17), 10, 15 (94), 21(124, 125), 22(126, 128), 24 (151), 25(17), 26(17, 22), 27(125), 28,

509

SUBJECT INDEX

A

Acetaldehyde, 61
  fermentation and, 68, 71, 73, 80–82, 92,
    96, 98, 100, 118, 134, 210
  oxidation of, 441, 454
  phosphorylation and, 356
  photooxidation and, 464
  threonine and, 177
Acetaldehyde dehydrogenase, fermenta-
    tion and, 97
Acetate, 41
  activation of, 220–222
  allantoin fermentation and, 193
  amino acid synthesis and, 243
  carrier experiments and, 223–225
  condensation of, 218–219, 233–235, 238–
    240
  electrode potential and, 349
  fermentation and 64, 70–73, 76–91, 94–
    98, 101–105, 107, 108, 111–124, 126–
    138, 152, 154–156, 158–163, 167–171,
    173–177, 182–185, 188–190, 454
  formation of, 15, 16, 21, 203
  isotopic experiments and, 222–231, 241–
    242
  lactate oxidase and, 447–448
  lipid synthesis and, 46
  mutants and, 237
  nicotinic acid fermentation and, 194
  oxidation, 218, 220–221, 225, 243
    muscle and, 219
  purine fermentation and, 26
  pyrimidine fermentation and, 190, 192
  pyruvate oxidation and, 24–25
  Stickland reaction and, 196, 199, 201–
    203
  recycling and, 225–227
  sequential induction and, 235–236
Acetoacetate,
  fermentation and, 78, 80–82, 133, 134
  generation of, 50–51
  threonine and, 177
Acetoacetyl coenzyme A, formation of,
    454
Acetobacter,
  difference spectrum of, 383
  pyruvate oxidation by, 338

Acetobacter acetigenum, cellulose and, 48
Acetobacter pasteurianum,
  cytochrome of, 383, 385, 386, 392
  difference spectrum of, 384
  terminal oxidase of, 335, 372, 373
Acetobacter peroxidans,
  cytochrome of, 385
  cytochrome reductase of, 328
  hydrogen peroxide and, 339, 340
  particles of, 387
Acetobacter suboxydans,
  absorption spectrum of, 369
  arabitol degradation and, 109
  cytochrome of, 383, 385, 386
  difference spectrum of, 382, 384
  glucose oxidation by, 251–252, 338
  respiratory chian of, 323
  terminal oxidase of, 373, 374
Acetobacter xylinum,
  cellulose and, 48
  fermentation by, 101
  phosphoketolase of, 15, 16
Acetoin, 61
  fermentation and, 70, 72, 73, 77, 79, 80,
    82, 85, 87–89, 92–93, 115, 119, 121–
    123, 128–131
  reduction of, 51
Acetoin dehydrogenase, fermentation
    and, 93, 97
Acetokinase, 21, 240
  fermentation and, 86
  pyruvate and, 23
α-Acetolactate,
  acetoin and, 92–93
  fermentation and, 82
  racemase and, 76
Acetomycetales, chitin and, 287
Acetone,
  fermentation and, 77–80, 82, 86, 136
  formation of, 50–51
Acetopyruvate, fermentation and, 81
Acetylcoenzyme A, 215, 219, 250
  fermentation and, 74, 81–82, 85, 86,
    108, 129, 133–134, 202
  formation of, 450, 453, 454
  malate and, 240
  mutants and, 237

lysis of, 311
particles of, 377–378
pyridine nucleotides and, 326
Bacillus mesentericus, fermentation by, 89
Bacillus phenologenes, tyrosine and, 180
Bacillus phosphoreus, 505
Bacillus polymyxa, fermentation by, 90, 93
Bacillus proteus vulgaris, fermentation by, 152 158
Bacillus putrificus, fermentation by, 152
Bacillus subtilis, 258, 308
  absorption spectrum of, 369
  acetoin and, 92
  amylase of, 268, 281–282
  cell wall lysis and, 311–312
  cysteine and, 160
  cytochrome of, 335, 346, 383, 385, 386, 391, 392
  difference spectrum of, 381, 384
  fermentation by, 88–90, 93
  growth yield of, 34
  hyaluronidase and, 262, 291
  lysozyme of, 268
  nitrate reduction by, 452
  protease of, 301–303
  ribonuclease of, 311
  terminal oxidase of, 371–373
  tyrosine and, 180
Bacteria,
  acid fast, *see also* Mycobacteria
    electron transport in, 30
  adaptability of, 8
  carbon vs. energy economy of, 8–9
  catalase-free, 427, 429, 436
  cell walls, decomposition of, 311–312
  chemosynthetic, 397
  halotolerant,
    cytochrome of, 389, 390
    heme protein of, 412
  luminescent,
    drug action and, 497–499
    electron transport and, 496–497
    emission spectra of, 480
    environmental factors and, 492–495
    mutations of, 499–504
    nutrition of, 490–492
    oxygen requirements of, 495–496
    taxonomy and evolution of, 504–507

photosynthetic, 397–398
  growth requirements of, 472
  respiratory system of, 375–378
  specificity of, 8
  speed and yield of, 6–7
  variety and specific selection of, 7–8
Bacteriochlorophyll, 415
  carotenoids and, 468
  electron transfer and, 28
  infrared light and, 466
  molar ratio of, 462–463
  photooxidation of, 475
  reducing power and, 473–474
Bacterium, 274
  chitinase of, 287–288
Bacterium chironomi, 506
Bacterium coli phenologenes, tyrosine and, 180
Bacterium giardi, 506
Bacterium hemophosphoreum, 506
Bacterium hippanici, 506
Bacterium pholas, 506
Bacterium phosphorescens, 480
Bacterium phosphorescens indigenus, see *Achromobacter fischeri*
Bacterium tularense, succinic dehydrogenase of, 337
Barbital, luminescence and, 499
Barley, starch of, 281
Beggiatoa mirabilis, solute penetration and, 504
Benzaldehyde dehydrogenases, growth yield and, 42
Benzoate,
  fermentation of, 136
  growth yield and, 41, 42
p-Benzoquinone, diaphorase and, 443, 445
Benzoylarginine amide, hydrolysis of, 299, 306
Benzyl viologen,
  hydrogenase and, 418
  nitrate reduction and, 416
  Stickland reaction and, 195
Betabacterium, fermentation by, 72
Betacoccus, 95
  fermentation by, 72
Biotin, 5, 192
  cycles and, 12
  nitrogen source and, 45